Strategic Inventory Management and Planning

With Tables

Nick T. Thomopoulos

Hitchcock Publishing Co.
Carol Stream, IL 60188

Library of Congress Catalog Number 90-80393

Thomopoulos, Nick T.
    Strategic Inventory Management and Planning: With Tables

First Edition
©1990 by Hitchcock Publishing Co., Carol Stream, IL 60188
A Capital Cities/ABC Inc. company
Loren M. Walsh, President

This publication is designed to provide accurate and authoritative
information in regard to the subject matter covered. It is sold with the
understanding that the publisher is not engaged in rendering legal,
accounting, or other professional service. If legal advice or other expert
assistance is required, the services of a competent professional person should
be sought. *From a Declaration of Principles jointly adopted by a Committee
of the American Bar Association and a Committee of Publishers.*

Printed in the United States of America

10 9 8 7 6 5 4 3 2 1

∞ This book has been printed on high quality, low glare, acid free paper.

ISBN 0-933931-11-5

Ronald Bridenthal: Editor
Jeannette Colfer: Word Processing
Annette Mola: Composing
Arlene Bartolini: Production Coordinator
Charles Doyle, Bev Morris, Lis Schar, Joan Wilder: Production
Jean McNamara: Art Director
Steve Falco: Cover Design
Raymond J. Kimber: Director, Book Publishing
Joseph Campioni: Director, Production

Contents

This book is dedicated to
Elaine, Marie, Melina, Diana and Christopher

Preface

This book has evolved over many years from activities with many persons who have responsibilities in inventory. My experience in inventory began when I was supervisor of operations research at a leading international automotive manufacturer. In this position, I became acquainted with manufacturing plants where various operations pertaining to the fabrication of parts and components and the assembly of vehicles took place. The emphasis at those plants was on developing systems that would ensure smooth and efficient operations. This emphasis included the flow of inventory (material, components and parts) into the plant and throughout the fabrication facilities to meet everchanging production schedules. Without the proper inventory—in terms of quantity, location and timing—the plant could not achieve its production schedules. It thus became eminently clear to me that production management and inventory management must be integrated functions.

After joining a consulting organization with clients worldwide, I worked with major manufacturers in the United States, Europe and Japan. The primary emphasis of my work was to develop scheduling methods for specific production applications as well as computer systems for general use in assembly and job shop operations. How effectively these systems were implemented depended on whether the companies had the proper capacity of people, machines and equipment as well as the supporting flow of inventory to fulfill production needs. Any shortages could cause inefficient scheduling while overages caused waste.

Many companies—in the trucking, construction, agriculture, footwear, food, beauty products, hardware, electronics, parts, components, tools and processing industries—hold millions of dollars worth of inventory on an ongoing basis. This inventory is constantly on the move; new shipments from suppliers are continually being received; and orders to customers are being processed, picked and shipped to their destinations on a daily basis. Because the inventory of equipment and material in stock is costly, it is important to have available only those levels that are needed and economical. The competition confronting these companies is international, and the better they manage their investment in facilities, equipment and inventory, the more profitable they will become. Moreover, those companies that manage poorly may not survive.

Through consulting with these companies in the development of computer systems on forecasting, inventory, production scheduling, assembly sequencing and statistical process control, I learned that a key to a good inventory system is the soundness of the forecasts that drive the system. Thereafter, the main function of the system is to determine the schedule of replenishments from the suppliers to meet the oncoming demands. In some cases, my work centered on determining the distribution system and managing the level and flow of inventory among the locations. For companies that owned retail outlets, I developed forecasting and inventory replenishment systems to control the inventory at each outlet. In developing production scheduling systems, it was important for the proper timing of inventory needed to carry out production and meet promised due dates of customer orders. The sequencing of assembly facilities could not have been accomplished without a smooth inflow of all parts and components used in assembly operations. My experiences further included the development of statistical process control systems for meeting quality specifications and for enhancing the accuracy of a distribution system.

In all of these activities, many persons—in inventory management, scheduling, buying, expediting, operations, customer service and systems—contribute to the profitability of the company. These people require a certain knowledge of inventory to carry out the activities soundly; usually, however, they do not have the need for or the luxury of studying the formulations on a wide range of inventory models as students taking a college course would. A significant number of these people, some with limited college training, have learned the company structure and the related system of inventory within their environment from experience. Over time, they become quite valuable and develop a knowledge of company operations that could not be acquired in the university. This book, along with the tables, is intended to satisfy these persons' desire for further knowledge and to offer guidance in the inventory-related decisions that they face.

I would like to thank the many persons who have made contributions to and suggestions for this book. They include Wayne E. Bancroft, Harry S. Bock, Randy R. Braun, John Cada, Scott L. Haligas, Willard L. Huson, Werner J. Koczian, Nick Z. Malham, Craig M. Marecek, Dolores E. Santucci and Dean H. Walker. Also, thanks to Nick J. Faklis for his assistance in computer programming and to David B. Arai for drafting the figures. I am grateful to Marie E. Thomopoulos for placing the initial draft on the word processor and to Elaine H. Thomopoulos for all her help in editing the many drafts.

Nick T. Thomopoulos

Stuart School of Business

Illinois Institute of Technology

Foreword

Strategic Inventory Management and Planning: With Tables is for anyone who has responsibilities in inventory and also for the student of inventory. The author's goal is to present information that is immediately useful to the inventory practitioner. The book is intended to serve as a handy reference guide in understanding inventory and in making everyday and long range inventory decisions. To achieve this goal, the text is structured around tables that present various solutions to problems which could be anticipated from using the inventory methods presented. Most of the data in these tables was created by the author and has never been published before. Many concepts are presented for the first time, and in many instances this book is unique in showing how these methods may be used in managing inventory.

The book is easy to read and understand. An introduction reviews the various methods of managing inventory—from the standpoint of retailers, distributors and finished goods manufacturers. Also included are some brief commentaries on manufacturing practices. People who wish to familiarize themselves with various aspects of manufacturing and production will find this section informative.

Most of the chapters focus on particular inventory methods. An introduction on the method begins the chapter, followed by a listing of the data and parameters needed to apply the method; the calculations needed to carry out the method are then described. In these discussions of methods, the math steps leading to the table outputs are carefully presented and, generally, tedious mathematical derivations are avoided. Numerous examples that help illustrate how the tables may be used also reinforce the discussions. The tables appear at the end of each chapter. Topics covered in the chapters include forecasting, economic order quantities, probability distributions, normal distributions, safety stock (including an innovative method of setting order point and order level), queueing theory, customer service levels and optimal order quantities. Especially important is discussion on how the concepts of inventory management and Just-in-Time are complementary rather than contradictory. Supplemental chapters present data on loan amortization, learning curves, calendar days and measures frequently used in inventory management.

The tables presented in this book have been especially developed for use in inventory management. Each table contains a wide range of results that facilitate learning and use of the methods presented. The tables also help the reader to clearly understand the sensitive role of each input data or parameter of the method without having to delve into complex mathematical relations.

A glossary is included to clarify terms that may be unfamiliar to the reader. A list of supplementary works that can provide additional information is included at the end of the book.

This is an age when manufacturing practices are undergoing extensive transition, such as the movement towards Just-in-Time manufacturing. This book is intended to serve as a guide for those companies engaged in such transition yet still in need of innovative and practical methods of managing current inventory.

Introduction

In today's highly competitive business environment no firm, large or small, can take lightly the costs associated with inventory. Inventory may well be the highest cost investment in the firm. It is not uncommon to find a 20 percent carrying cost for inventory, which translates to an annual cost of $200,000 for each $1,000,000 in inventory. It is no wonder that top management demands that inventory levels reach the minimum necessary to allow for an efficient and economical operation of the activities of the firm.

For salable products with uncertain demands from customers, too much inventory leads to excess stock and the possibility of obsolescence and deterioration. When inventory is too low, the service level suffers and customers may begin to purchase from competitive firms. A proper balance between inventory investment and service level is necessary. Service level is a measure of the demand filled within a reasonable time period. For the manufacturer of the products, the goal is to have low inventory and high utilization of the production resources. Too much inventory buildup between operations (e.g., work-in-process) is wasteful in investment and storage space needs. Too little inventory may lead to production delays and missed promise dates for customer orders. Again, a proper balance is needed to yield an efficient operating production system.

Inventory can refer to the raw materials, work-in-process, parts, components, finished goods and maintenance service parts. But inventory in a firm may also include the resources needed to carry out the daily activities— regardless of whether the firm is a retailer, distributor or manufacturer. These resources include tools, fixtures, machinery, office equipment, supplies, storage bins, lift trucks and the like. In any event, inventory is more a liability than an asset and has real value only when it is fully utilized to achieve the goals of the firm. A firm should have only the level of inventory that is necessary to meet these goals.

Inventory control is needed by all firms participating in each of the stages that start from procuring of raw materials and end with sale to the consumer. Raw materials—such as iron, wood and oil—are purchased by manufacturers of basic goods such as steel mills, lumber processors and oil refineries. Basic goods are sold to firms that manufacture parts and components; these products in turn are sold to the manufacturers of finished goods. Finished goods are purchased by distributors of finished goods or repair parts. Distributors then sell to retailers, who finally sell to the consumers. Inventory plays a major role in all of the above stages. The common goal is always to stock only the amount of inventory that is efficient and economical. If these goals are carried out over all stages above, then each firm in the chain of events will benefit both themselves and their customers.

Consumers

Consumers of retail goods may be categorized into two broad groups, individuals and businesses. Purchases by individuals for various needs and pleasure may be food, clothes, household items, transportation, television sets, toys, recreation and entertainment. A business mostly purchases products from retailers as the need arises; these purchases may be office furniture and supplies or various products used in conducting the everyday activities.

The need to carry inventory begins with the buying habits of the consumer, who seeks to purchase a product from a retail establishment. The product, which may be directly purchased as a whole (finished) good item such as a radio, a sofa, a pair of shoes or a gallon of milk, may be indirectly purchased when a repair or maintenance service is sought, such as the parts and components needed in servicing an automobile or an airconditioner. In any event, the consumer—whether an individual or a business—seeks the products at irregular time intervals that usually are not known to the retailer in advance and sometimes not known to the consumer himself until just prior to purchase. However, when a consumer wishes to purchase something, he expects to find the product available within a reasonable time frame. If the product is not available at the retailer, the consumer may either not buy from the retailer (causing a loss of sale), choose another like product, choose another retailer, or place with a retailer an order for future delivery in the form of a backorder.

Retailers

Retailers are enterprises that stock products for sale to consumers, either directly or through service. Examples are drug stores, office supply stores, food markets, department stores, service stations and automotive dealers. In most situations, a retailer carries as wide a variety of products as is feasible within space and budget constraints. Faced with the task of providing just the right mix and quantity of stock to produce subsequent sales to consumers, the retailer seeks to maximize sales with minimum inventory investment, thus yielding the highest profit possible. If the stock carried is too low, the result may be lower total sales; for out of stock items, a consumer may possibly place an order for future delivery. In both cases, the retailer risks the possible loss of goodwill on the part of the consumer. When too much stock is carried, the retailer might not be able to sell it all and may be faced with obsolescence and/or deterioration of the products; consequently, he may need to sell the products at a reduced price or return them to his supplier at a loss.

For the purpose of inventory control, retailers generally fall into three categories:
- Those who manage inventory manually
- Those whose inventory management is partially computer supported
- Those who have available a completely computerized inventory system.

Retailers with Manual Inventory Control

Many retailers cannot justify a computerized inventory system. Instead, they control inventory on a manual basis and are directly responsible for placing the replenishment orders to suppliers. The use of tags is one method of indicating out of stock conditions, to help in this process. Detecting that a product is low or out of stock, a retailer estimates his near-future needs (a forecast) and places an order for what he judges is a reasonable amount (an order quantity). Orders often are placed at the end of the week by phone or mail for future delivery. The retailer generally places all his orders with a particular supplier at one time. Many suppliers may receive orders weekly; others, at less frequent time intervals.

Retailers with Partially Computer Controlled Inventory Systems

Some retailers use an inventory system that is partially computer controlled; many levels of partial control are available to the retailer. In some cases the retailer has access to a computer on his site and all decisions are made locally. With some other systems the retailer transmits his sales data to his supplier, and guidance decisions are transmitted back to the retailer. Retailers of this type include chain stores, cooperatives or company owned stores, where a distributor is the main source of supply. For company owned stores, the main distributor is a warehouse operated by the firm. In their retail facilities, such as grocery stores, drug stores, clothing stores and discount stores, each sale is recorded on a computer file usually through the aid of a scanning device at a point of sale register or terminal. The scanner reads a universal product code consisting of a series of computer bars appearing on package labels in order to record the item's purchase price automatically.

When the computer system is fully located at the retailer's site, the sales are recorded on the computer file for periodic review. Sales are compared, usually on a once a week basis, to the inventory position of the products in order to determine the current inventory status. At some previous time, the retailer had manually set for each product an order point as well as a corresponding order quantity. Automatically scanning the file of weekly sales and order points, the computer recommends which products need to be ordered and what is the associated order quantity. The retailer then reviews the order and makes adjustments as may be necessary.

When the computer system is located at the distributor's site, sales data are transmitted nightly to the host computer. The distributor's file monitors the stock status (on-hand and on-order) of each product's inventory at the retailer's site where, after each day, the stock status is reduced by daily sale activities. When an order is initiated, the on-order quantity is increased; and when the order arrives, the on-hand quantity increases and the on-order quantity decreases. The computer system may have a systematic manner of establishing order points and order quantities, or these quantities may be set by some guiding rules as determined by the retailer and the distributor. In any event the host computer determines when the retailer's stock is too low for a product and recommends a replenishment order. Before the order is finalized, the retail manager may adjust the order quantity to account for local conditions.

Retailers (Dealers) with Completely Computerized Inventory Systems

A higher level of computer inventory control is used by dealers that sell whole goods, merchandising goods and repair goods. These dealers usually offer repair and maintenance services; examples are equipment products or automotive products such as car, truck, agriculture, construction, industrial equipment, appliance and computer hardware dealers. The whole goods consist of finished products of manufacturers the dealers represent, such as a line of car models. Merchandising goods—accessories to the whole goods and not sold as a part of the whole goods—might include items such as floor mats, compasses and citizens band radios in a truck dealership. Repair goods are the service parts needed in the repair and maintenance of the equipment.

In many dealers, sale of service parts primarily occurs indirectly from each dealer's service department. Other sales occur through orders from independent service outlets, such as a service facility in the auto industry. In the truck industry, dealers receive a significant portion of their service parts sales from nearby trucking fleets who may order stock and emergency supplies by phone or mail or through computer terminals. Dealers also receive many orders over the counter from individuals who walk in for parts. Some dealers operate rebuild facilities that remanufacture main components of whole goods (such as an engine).

A typical dealer may carry 10,000 to 30,000 part numbers in his service parts storage facility. It is most important to stock the right mix of parts so that a high level of service can be provided in an emergency or to service a unit down (i.e., out of service). At the same time dealers must provide good service to customers who purchase repair parts for their own needs. Dealers must often provide these services with limited storage space and parts inventory budget constraints.

Many computer inventory systems are available for the dealer's use in the control of sales, parts and service. Various systems provide functions such as accounting, payroll, parts order entry and invoicing, parts location, lease management, repair management and invoicing, finance, insurance and parts inventory control. The computer inventory system, generally associated with a particular computer hardware system, is located at the dealer and completely run by dealer personnel.

The inventory system may track the history of demand and options of all whole-good products sold. This history may also include the inquiries of those customers whose sales were lost for some reason. With such a history, the system can generate a suggested order of whole goods to have available.

A big portion of the dealer's profits occurs in the service department, where customers arrive with or without appointments for repair or maintenance services. Parts needed here are usually sought for the current need, and the parts inventory system must provide a high level of service. If a dealer is out of stock for a particular part number, he may contact his distributor or inquire at a nearby dealer or independent distributor to acquire the part on an emergency basis for the purpose of servicing the downed unit as soon as possible. When all work is complete, the computer system invoices all labor and parts used in completing repair or maintenance for the customer.

The parts inventory system generally provides a file that stores the history of 12 to 24 months of sales of the part for all needs (service and other orders). A terminal allows anyone in the dealership, including persons in the service department, countermen or any purchase orders clerks, to inquire on the stock status (on-hand and on-order) of the part. The terminal screen also shows bin location, cost and price matrix. If the part is not in stock or not carried by the dealer, the computer system often has access to the source manufacturer's entire line of part numbers, where the dealer may place an order.

Dealers may have various sources from which to receive stock. One source may be from the service parts distribution center of the manufacturer of the whole goods, commonly called the original equipment manufacturer (OEM). Another source is the part manufacturer, often called the component manufacturer. For emergency orders, a dealer's best source may be from the OEM's service parts distribution center or from independent distributors. When stock orders are needed from a particular supplier, the service parts manager prompts the computer system to generate a suggested replenishment order. All the parts associated with the supplier and which are actively carried by the dealer are scanned. For each part, a forecast is generated (in compliance with certain ordering rules) to determine an order point. If on-hand plus on-order quantity is at or below the order point, another set of calculations and/or rules is followed to determine an appropriate order quantity for the part number. Upon completion of the processing, a stock order is printed for review.

Distributors

The retailers' main suppliers of stock are distributors, sometimes called wholesalers. Serving as a link between manufacturers and retailers, distributors buy large quantities of stock from manufacturers and sell to the retailers from stocking locations often called distribution centers. Distribution centers are operated by various types of companies such as cooperatives, chains, franchises or the manufacturers themselves. In some cases sales personnel take orders from retailers and arrange for shipment directly from the manufacturer. In the repair parts industry, distributors include willfitters, who copy parts of high volume usage and produce them independently of the original manufacturer. Distributors also include rebuild facilities, firms that buy replaced main components (called cores) from service outlets and remanufacture them to original specifications.

Distributors generally have computer systems with higher levels of inventory control sophistication than do retailers. A single distributor may have many stocking locations throughout the country or worldwide, may service many retailers and may stock a large number of products. As orders arrive from retailers for immediate delivery, distributors are faced with providing the proper mix from stock levels that are economic but still yield a high level of customer service. Stock levels are replenished by various manufacturers of products that the distributors carry. Because distributors must provide goods for retail orders that are not known in advance, as orders arrive at irregular time intervals and range from high to low lot sizes, their operations become even more complex.

Service Parts Distribution Centers

Distribution centers of service parts are established according to three basic options. A first type is operated by original equipment manufacturers, such as the maker of a line of cars, trucks, construction equipment, appliances or industrial equipment. A second kind of center is sometimes provided by components manufacturers (such as the manufacturer of transmissions, engines and batteries) who in turn might be a supplier to the OEM. These firms often stock only standard equipment parts on a regular basis and produce the bulk of their parts only when an order is received. All-makes distributors, the third type, house replacement parts over an entire industry and are often in competition with OEM distribution centers. As in any inventory holding enterprise, the goals of all distribution center management are to minimize investment in stock (at proper locations) and to achieve a planned level of customer service. These goals may be obtained only with the use of a sound inventory control system.

Original Equipment Manufacturer Service Parts Distribution Centers
The original equipment manufacturer (OEM) provides one or a multiple of distribution centers that stock service parts and certain merchandising products. In the auto industry, 400,000 individual part numbers on file for

service is not uncommon. Every OEM—the parent company—must have a "smart" inventory control system in order to remain competitive and prosperous. When dealers order on an emergency basis, the distribution center must provide the item in quick response, even if the item is out of stock and the center itself must procure the needed item from the main plant or another dealer. In addition, when a stock order arrives from a dealer, it is important to fill the order in entirety, not just in part, for quick delivery. Distribution centers may also receive orders from specialists in rebuilding certain main components of the whole goods; these firms operate much like the rebuild facilities of the dealers.

A part may be used on a whole good either as an engineering changed part or as an original part. At the outset of the part's use, distribution center management decides whether to stock the part or to order when needed from the supplier. When the choice is to stock the part, an initial quantity of how much to stock must be determined for anticipated future demands. This prediction is a difficult task, as no demand history is yet available. After the initial quantity is stocked, each part is monitored by the inventory control system and replenished as needed. Replenishments can take place for several years after the whole good is dropped from production or after the part is no longer in use on the whole good due to an engineering change. Customers of whole goods expect this parts service from the original manufacturer. For the distribution center, finding a supplier of parts that are not used in volume on the production lines becomes more difficult. In the event a supplier notifies that a part will no longer be produced, a distribution center may determine an *all-time requirement* and order one last time to fill that forecast. After a number of service obligation years is fullfilled or if profit margin on the part is no longer worthwhile, the OEM may then decide to drop the part from further replenishments and may need to scrap stock on hand.

Much information is stored in files of the inventory control system for each part number. A typical system will hold 24 to 36 months of demand history and sometimes the corresponding number of orders. In addition, supplier procurement terms are stored along with procurement lead time. Included also is stock status data of each stocking location.

Generally on a once a month basis the OEM follows a series of steps for all active part numbers. On some systems these steps are carried out in total for the part number; in other systems they occur for each stocking location. A first step may be to filter the data history of demands in seeking any outliers (excessive high or low demands) and adjusting them accordingly. A forecast of future monthly demands is then generated with a corresponding measure of forecast error. Forecasts may span from 12 to 36 future months, and procurement terms and the forecast are combined to determine the economic order quantity. This order size is combined with the service level goals and the lead time to determine the safety stock needs, and all of these results are used to set the order point. Stock status data (on-hand plus on-order) is now used to determine if any replenishment is needed. If so, then appropriate replenishment quantities are calculated. All replenishments needed from a particular supplier are combined and placed on a purchase order that is to be delivered to the supplier.

Many inventory control systems will also carry out two special steps in evaluating a schedule for replenishment of a part:
• First, the replenishment schedule may be partitioned into firm schedules and planning schedules. Firm schedules include all replenishments for the months (or weeks) on or prior to the lead time. These are the schedules that are committed for receipt.
• Second, the planning schedules include those schedules spanning all

months beyond the lead time and not yet committed. An evaluation of the firm schedules could be performed to determine if the scheduled amounts are too low or too high, based on the current forecast and inventory status. If inventory is too low, the distribution center may request a supplier to rush in extra stock or, if inventory is too high, ask the supplier to delay delivery.

Also, sending the planning schedule to suppliers is recommended so that each supplier may plan his future production activities accordingly. By becoming informed about the planning schedule, a supplier will more likely be able to deliver on time and to provide shorter lead times.

When an OEM distribution system contains more than one location, further stocking considerations arise. The first consideration concerns the allocation of a scheduled receipt once new stock is ready to be received. A schedule quantity must be allocated to distribution locations in a manner that is consistent with the distribution center's forecasts and associated stock status positions. An allocation mix is transmitted to the supplier, packager or receiving point, whichever pertains, for appropriate delivery quantities to each distribution center location.

A second consideration concerns maldistribution of stock across individual distribution centers. Periodically, the stocking positions of each distribution center are evaluated to determine if one or more centers are at a dangerously low level. When a low level is identified, a search is made to determine if any of the other distribution centers is at a relatively high inventory level, and if a fit is found, orders are then released to transfer stock accordingly.

Finally a third consideration occurs when an emergency retail order arrives at a distribution center that is out of stock at the moment. A scan of the inventory position of other distribution centers may indicate that another distribution center could fill that order. If such an alternative is possible, the appropriate shipment to the retailer is carried out by the center capable of filling the order.

Component Manufacturers

Original equipment manufacturers have facilities that fabricate many parts used in their whole goods. They also purchase parts from other firms specializing in the manufacture of individual products. These firms, called components manufacturers, usually do not operate distribution centers as the OEM's do, but they receive orders on their line of products directly. The components manufacturer in essence is a supplier of parts for both OEM production lines and OEM distribution centers. Also, he can be a supplier to the all-makes distributors as well as a supplier to retail dealers and rebuild firms. A car dealer, for example, may bypass the distribution center of the OEM if he can receive stock at a lower cost from a components manufacturer. Doing so, however, usually requires a longer lead time and larger replenishment lot sizes.

A component manufacturer receives orders from the dealer and rebuild firms, passes them on to the master scheduler of the production plant, and includes the orders with any other product demands. These other demands may be open orders from OEM's for their production and service needs. All plant demands are combined with available inventory and the plant's already committed production schedule in order to develop the production schedule necessary for the lead time and planning weeks beyond. When units are produced at the plant, they are delivered to each customer.

All-makes Service Parts Distribution Centers

Control of inventory for a service parts distribution center of an all-makes distributor is much the same as that of an OEM. The main exception is that, unlike the OEM, all-makes distributors carry the line of parts from whole goods produced by all manufacturers and thus carry a wider breadth of part numbers than distribution centers of the individual OEM's. All-makes centers might, however, often specialize only in parts with certain functional uses, such as brakes, transmissions and tires. Frequently such centers are aligned with a chain of repair centers that perform repair and maintenance services for customers. An all-makes distributor often operates its own rebuild facility to remanufacture the cores (replaced components from equipment serviced) to levels at, near or beyond original specifications. For these rebuilt items, any associated parts needed may be ordered from the OEM distribution center. Completed rebuilt components are then offered for sale at lowered prices.

To control the large number of parts that are carried, the inventory system of an all-makes distributor generates forecasts, safety stocks and order points for every part and component. This system monitors the stocking position of all parts and components on a frequent basis. When a low stocking position is detected, the system determines the replenishment order size that is economical and which will still provide the desired level of service.

Willfitters

One kind of distributor of service parts to retailers, called willfitters, includes firms that concentrate on the manufacture and sales of high volume service and repair goods for a particular line of product. Willfitters copy (and sometimes improve) the design from the original part or component and produce imitation parts (generally of good quality) that can be substituted for the original part; often they can sell these components at a lower cost. Willfitters do not require the large engineering staff to develop the product from the outset as does the original manufacturer. Typically they manufacture offshore in new industrial countries, usually start out as a small firm and may grow and become the leading supplier of the part. Willfitters generally keep a low amount of inventory and produce products when an order is received. They may send brochures to retailers or advertise in trade journals in order to entice sales. Also their salesmen seek out the retailers to promote their product line and to procure sales orders, as the willfitters are in competition with the OEM's for the retail share of orders.

Finished Goods Distribution Centers

Another major type of distribution center involves only the stocking and shipping of finished goods. These centers, associated with cooperatives, chains, franchises or manufacturers of finished goods, stock finished goods and receive orders from retailers for delivery; often the retailer expects next day or next week delivery. Examples would be drug store goods, grocery goods, hair styling goods, office equipment goods and so forth. This kind of distributor is sometimes faced with providing stock for goods with ever-changing styles and fluctuations of demand due to promotions of various types or due to seasonal needs, for example, Christmas tree lights. He furthermore is confronted with goods that are dated for various reasons, such as deterioration or expiration (food, dry cell batteries, so forth). In general, a high turnover of stock is essential.

At a finished goods distribution center, stock is continually flowing in from manufacturers and out to retailers. Often the goods, arriving to receiving on a 24 hour basis, are stored in bins. At the same time, retailer orders for delivery are given picking labels; order pickers promptly fill those orders for shipment, often using a scanning device to sort the picked goods by retail customer.

Trucks are promptly filled and goods are delivered to the retailers.

With a high turnaround expected by retailers and with a high turnover on a large portion of stocked goods, a finished goods inventory system plays an important role in the control of stock replenishments. The system forecasts demands for individual goods and provides a measure of forecast error. These results are used to calculate the economic order quantity and safety stock; adjustments throughout may be needed for special promotions and for dated goods. Available inventory and the committed replenishments on order are used to determine a replenishment schedule from the lead time out through the planning horizon. Replenishments are sorted by supplier and placed on a purchase order for review by buyers, who may adjust the order to provide for a full truck load of delivered goods.

Manufacturers

Manufacturers receive orders for their products from distributors. They sometimes receive orders directly from retailers for the whole goods, such as autos, trucks and appliances. A government may also place orders, usually on a make-to-order basis. Manufacturers mostly produce goods to meet orders already received from distributors, retailers and governments; also produced are goods for stock to be warehoused in a distribution center, awaiting future orders. Each manufacturer strives to produce products with the maximum level of customer service (meeting due dates), with minimum investment in inventory, and with maximum efficiency of manufacturing resources.

In the production process, manufacturers are confronted with four distinct types of inventory: basic materials, parts and components, work-in-process and finished goods. The basic material goods (chemicals, plastics, castings, rubber goods, steel bar products, so on) are partially purchased from basic materials manufacturers; parts and components are partially supplied from component manufacturers.

Several planning and production steps are followed in the manufacture of products, from beginning to the end of finished products. An overview of several aspects is presented here.

Strategic Planning

An initial step in the manufacturing process is the strategic planning function, where top management gives direction in business, marketing, production and resources. These strategic plans are on a collective basis and may be developed by various divisions of the firm. Business planning pertains to projections of income, funds and expenditures. Market planning concerns the lines of products to produce and the markets to foster. Production planning schedules the level of production, inventories, shipments and backlogs over the future horizon by months. Resource planning sets the level of capacity appropriate to meet production needs, which may be stated in labor hours, machine hours, or other appropriate units.

Distribution Resource Planning

When a manufacturer of make-to-stock products has various locations in the distribution system, the method of distribution resource planning (DRP) is applicable. For each location, a forecast of finished goods demands over the future year (in months, weeks and even days) is generated. This forecast is used—along with the safety stock, current on-hand inventory and schedules due and on-order—to determine when replenishment is needed for that location. The replenishment can first be received at the time period associated with the location's lead time. For the purpose of planning, a replenishment schedule is carried out to the weeks or months beyond the lead time to cover the entire planning period. Location replenishments are summed to give the total demand over the distribution system; this total demand then becomes a part of the input to production requirements on the manufacturing system. Note that DRP also applies to environments outside of manufacturing as well. Any distribution firm that buys and sells products and has multi-locations may benefit from the techniques of DRP.

Master Production Scheduling

A master production schedule (MPS) defines the number of end items to produce over the planning horizon. The sum of end items should equal the amount of production established and/or appropriated in the production plan by time period. An end item is any product with a bill of materials defined. A bill of materials is a list of all parts and components, with quantities that are needed to produce one unit of the end item or one unit of a part or component item. The planning period should cover the time sufficient to meet the lead times of all items needed in the manufacturing process.

To generate the MPS, the following data are gathered for each end item: customer orders, any distribution center requirements, service parts orders, and forecasts of any other demands on the item. In addition, safety stock, lot size and the lead time to procure the bill of material parts and components are needed. Also necessary are the available inventory and production schedule quantities by time period (usually weeks) up to the lead time. All requirements are projected by time period to determine when and how much to produce for the lead time week, up until the end of the planning horizon. Another byproduct result of the MPS is the *available-to-promise* dates for each end item. These dates, used by the sales staff, represent the earliest future date that should be used in promising delivery for new orders.

Final Assembly Schedule

The final assembly schedule (FAS) is a detailed list of the products and components released or to be released for manufacture on each production line. Here, the plans derived from the MPS are executed on the shop floor. In a make-to-stock environment the FAS and MPS are somewhat the same. The MPS states the number of end items to make, and the FAS may specify the number of end items to produce by assembly line. In both, the comprised sum of end items must equal the sum of the production plan. Units produced from the assembly line are used to replenish the finished goods inventory.

In a make-to-order situation, the FAS is the assembly line schedule that is set to satisfy specific customer orders. Customer orders represent end items that may be assembled with a wide variety of options for various features. Consequently, it may be that no unique production model is defined with a common bill of materials; instead, specific customer options are incorporated along with the standard equipment in the assembly process. In any event, the specific product mix and quantities are defined within the FAS. The MPS is the stated production plan for the component mix that makes up the customer orders.

In the make-to-order environments, the production plan is based on the number and mix of models and options to be produced on the assembly line over future time periods. Over the near future, customer orders are available for specific models with feature options and with specific due dates. Over the more distant time periods, forecasts of option mix are needed. These forecasts are passed on to the lower level production and replenishment systems that concern the scheduling of components to meet assembly line needs. Scheduling of these end items is set several weeks in advance; even the sequencing of end items down the assembly line is determined several weeks in advance so that specific components are available when needed. Scheduling and sequencing functions must take into consideration feature options and work loads for every station on the line. Ideally, the daily flow of work down the line should have a level mix of options from day to day. Also, minute by minute assembly station work load should be balanced to allow assembly operators to work at a steady pace, without undue idle and/or congestion time. This latter step is called *line balancing*.

Rough-Cut Capacity Planning

The capacity needed to produce the MPS is measured for each of the weeks over the planning period. Rough-cut capacity planning concerns the labor and machine hours on a broad basis and is usually determined by departments or work centers only. With this projection, management makes intermediate decisions on the capacity to meet production needs. If the capacity is too low, then decisions are made, for example, on procuring new machines, authorizing overtime or subcontracting certain operations, and other strategies.

Materials Requirement Planning

With the MPS situated to accommodate the production plan and to satisfy capacity constraints, the next concern is scheduling the inflow of basic materials and scheduling the fabrication of parts needed to fulfill the MPS. This task is accomplished by use of materials requirement planning (MRP). For each end item on the MPS, the associated bill of material is "exploded" (broken down in detail) to determine timing and quantities of all parts and basic materials needed. The timing is usually associated with weekly or daily buckets (combined orders). In the two above calculations, lead times and routing relationships of parts and basic materials are taken into consideration, when determining the timing needs of each calculated need. Results for parts and basic materials used on more than one end item are now combined. At this time, calculated lot sizes for each component (in units of specified multiple quantities) are used along with currently available inventory to determine a schedule of order releases as well as to order receipts at the next higher stage in production.

Capacity Requirements Planning

The next step in the control of inventory and production is capacity requirements planning (CRP). MRP results and routing information are used to determine the level of capacity requirements, by work centers and weeks over the planning horizon, based on labor hours, machine hours, other critical resources, facilities use and/or warehouse space needs. Required capacities and/or work loads are compared to the corresponding available capacities at individual work centers. When the requirements are uneven, attempts to level the weekly work loads are taken; this function is called *load leveling*. If not enough capacity is available at the work center, decisions on authorizing overtime or alternative sources of production are made. If too much capacity is available, management may act to transfer labor and/or machine assignments to avert inefficient use of resources. When neither of the above adjustments can be accomplished, then adjustments to the MRP and (maybe) the MPS schedules are attempted. CRP attempts to accurately reflect the realities of the shop floor, in its analysis. For example, such aspects as the *learning curve* function may be taken into consideration. This function is often referred to as the *manufacturing progress function* and is used to measure reduced capacity needs as workers become more efficient with carrying out repetitive tasks.

Operation Scheduling

Once MPS, MRP and CRP results are set to the satisfaction of plant management, the process of scheduling the work load to individual operations within each work center is carried out. This process—called operation scheduling—is accomplished depending on the nature of the operations and their functional relationships. Sometimes operations are scheduled by use of single machine scheduling techniques, flow shop scheduling techniques or job shop scheduling techniques. In any event the scheduling process considers the available and due dates of the lots along with lot size quantities, processing times, queues, move time, production batch sizes and any setup times that may pertain.

Manufacturing Resource Planning

Manufacturing resource planning (MRP II), a detailed overall planning system, refers to a combined process beginning with development of the production plan and ending with an acceptable capacity requirement plan. In between and included are the MPS and the MRP. MRP II pertains to all calculations and adjustments needed over these phases to allow the plant to carry out production needs efficiently with the resources available.

In essence, MRP II is the formal manner in which top management is given feedback so the planned versus the actual measures of performance can be assessed and acted on. With this feedback, management has the ability to continually monitor the performance of the products and processes of the plant and to direct resources to those areas needed. The goal is to allow the planned objectives to be achieved. To carry out the process of MRP II, standardized reports with accurate and complete data are needed on the activities of the manufacturing processes and the products. MRP II includes the idea of a "closed-loop" whereby the actual results of shop-floor execution are fed back into the planning process so that the production schedules can be adjusted using the latest information.

Demand Management

Demand management is the function of recognizing and managing all demands for products to ensure that the master scheduler is aware of them. It includes the activities involved in forecasting, order entry, order promising, branch warehouse requirements, interplant orders and service parts requirements. The forecast is the formalized request from sales to have manufacturing capability available to achieve projected demands.

An aggregate of all forecasts is used to produce the production plan. If production ends with the assembly process, then customer orders and stock replenishments are used to determine the final assembly schedule. Forecasts of the individual items are summed with the stock replenishment projections, customer orders, interplant orders and service needs to generate the MPS and

MRP. An output of the MPS is the available-to-promise (by quantities and dates), which in turn is fed back to order entry in order to designate the first future date when a new demand may be delivered.

Just-in-Time

Just-in-time (JIT)* production is based on the concept of adding value and eliminating waste. Value is added only by work performed on the product, and waste is anything—other than a minimal amount of necessary resources like material, manpower, and capital equipment required for production—that does not add value to the finished product. The ideal lot size is one and the ideal output is for each worker to complete his product just before it is required. This philosophy is aimed at reducing all inventory queues of material, work-in-process, and finished goods down to zero. Any excess stock—suspected to hide quality problems—cannot be tolerated under the JIT philosophy, where every piece becomes essential. In the pure sense, safety stock and inventory queues are not allowed.

In real practice, however, inventory queues are sometimes essential because having every manufacturing operation linked to the next one is not always possible. Also, both subassembly operations and outside suppliers usually deliver goods in lot sizes greater than one. Nevertheless, as much as is possible, the concept of JIT is to strive for small lot sizes, smoothed production flow, reduction of setup times, shortened lead times, frequent delivery of parts and materials and so forth.

The following sections are some of the major techniques used to accomplish goals of JIT.

Uniform Plant Loading

To make the JIT production concept a reality (i.e., by eliminating waste) production must flow as smoothly as possible in the plant. Uniform plant loading (UPL) is the starting point. The goal of uniform plant loading is to smooth out the production process by requiring that the same mix of products be built every production day. In this manner, the manufacturing operations become as predictable and repetitive as possible; flow of materials and goods from upstream and downstream work stations or suppliers is level without any wide fluctuations.

Quality at the Source

Quality at the source is needed because in JIT manufacturing environments, safety stock is not allowed, every piece is essential, and defects are (ideally) not permitted. This standard entails that quality must be an integral part of each step along the way so that goods that inflow and outflow are defect free. Conventional quality control methods that consist of after the fact inspection are not acceptable; instead, quality at the source is demanded: each worker inspects his own work. With this type of inspection, production may temporarily be stopped if a quality problem is detected. Mass production of defective goods is thus prevented, and having found and corrected the problem, workers resume manufacturing process. One method of performing these functions is called *statistical process control* which uses graphical

---

*For a definitive discussion of Just-in-Time (and incorporating MRP II with JIT), see Brian H. Maskell, *Just-in-Time: Implementing the New Strategy* (Carol Stream, IL: Hitchcock Publishing Co., 1989).

control charts with a statistical basis to monitor the output quality* at the work stations.

Kanban

Another technique of Just-in-Time is called the *Kanban* system of material management and production control, with the goal of having each operation produce only the necessary quantity of goods at the necessary time. Kanban is the Japanese term for card or ticket; a Kanban system usually consists of production cards, withdrawal cards and standard size traveling containers to house the goods. Each production card gives authority to produce one container of goods, and as production is completed, the card is placed with the container. When the downstream operation uses the components in the container, the production card is then placed in a queue that again authorizes the production of another standard container of the depleted items. Sometimes the container itself serves as the Kanban, with the empty container being used as the signal to control more production.

Each withdrawal card authorizes the withdrawal of one container of goods; thus, every container in the downstream process must have a withdrawal card. When the downstream operation depletes the supply, the empty container is returned to the upstream operation and the withdrawal card (or empty container) "orders" another full container of parts or components.

Work-in-process inventory cannot exceed the supply of items corresponding with the number of cards authorized. When the production rate changes, the number of cards is increased or decreased, depending on the direction of the new rate. Likewise, the number of cards issued can be used to control production flow. For those items to which the Kanban system applies, the need for an MRP system can be eliminated. For other goods that cannot use the Kanban system, the MRP system applies as described earlier.

Minimum Setup Times

Note that JIT, UPL and Kanban require small production lot sizes. Smaller lot sizes in turn call for more frequent setups of the producing operations. This system becomes economically feasible when setup times and costs are held to a minimum. Design and manufacturing engineers have the responsibility to integrate their activities to ensure minimum setup times of all production operations. Holding down setup time becomes necessary to yield small order quantities that are economical when both stocking and ordering costs are considered. When setup times are reduced, lead times to the next work station are reduced accordingly. Even when lot sizes or order quantities cannot be made smaller, reduction in setup time often results in reduction of production costs.

Cellular Manufacturing

Cellular manufacturing is another JIT strategy intended to make manufacturing processes in the complex job shop environment smooth and synchronized. This method applies when there are a large number of items and small order quantities. The concept is to manufacture families of products with the same characteristics from start to finish in one area, using several operations manned in many cases by a single operator or by minimum manpower. A manufacturing work cell may be described as a group of functionally dissimilar operations, located together and dedicated to the

---

*An excellent discussion of this concept is contained in Robert W. Grenier, *Customer Satisfaction through Total Quality Assurance* (Carol Stream, IL: Hitchcock Publishing Co., 1988).

manufacture of similar products called a cell family. The goal is to reduce setup time, lead time, material movement and work-in-process inventory. Included in the goals are a higher level of quality and more flexibility to handle changes in production schedules and changes to product design.

Basic Goods Manufacturing

Basic goods are products such as castings, sheet metal, steel bars, distilled oil and gas and rolls of rubber compounds. Manufacturers of these products are suppliers to manufacturers of whole goods and parts. Their suppliers are producers of raw materials, such as oil, coal, iron ore, rubber, leather, cotton, pulp and lumber. Costs of producing basic goods are high and competition is international; a major challenge is to keep operations costs down and produce quality products. Maintenance and repair of processing machinery and equipment is very costly and is a major concern to basic goods producers.

The primary purpose of basic goods manufacturing is to convert raw materials to homogeneous materials that will have applications in subsequent stages of manufacture. One difficulty is caused by the uncertainty in the raw materials themselves, because their composition is subject to wide variations. Output batches may yield several grades of product, even when they emerge from the same combination of ingredients in the formulation. This unevenness may be caused by any of a number of factors, such as the composition of raw materials, the temperature, pressure, flow rate and the process machinery and equipment in use. Output products may be graded and separated by grade for particular end product uses or may be further processed when necessary. Some items of the output are waste and may have a high disposal cost.

Requirements by distribution centers and direct orders from manufacturers are totaled to determine demands on the basic goods product line. In addition, a forecast of other demands by line of product is used as the basic input to the MPS of the firm. Because of the high level of uncertainty with the yields from various production processes, producing the line of products to meet the exact schedule is a certain difficulty, and thus the role of materials requirement planning is not as straightforward as in other manufacturing industries. Instead, MRP is generally reserved for the preparation of containers and packaging materials to meet the master production schedule.

A Final Word

As this introduction reveals, optimal inventory levels are needed in all stages from basic goods manufacturer to retailer. With local and worldwide competition so fierce, no firm can any longer afford inefficiency in management of inventory. Methods are continually being developed to achieve the goal of optimal inventory and are now being applied by many firms. In the manufacturing industries, MRP II aims at controlling inventory flow at each step in the production process, and concepts of Just-in-Time or zero inventory are aimed at eliminating inventory altogether. The above goals are somewhat achievable since most manufacturing orders are known in advance; much also depends on the integrity of the data base and the proper execution of all stages of progression. In distribution and retail industries, however, where most demands are not known until the moment they occur, an economical balance between inventory levels and customer service is the counterpart aim sought in the control of inventory.

List of Notations

The following notations are used in the chapters throughout the book, unless (as in cases of repetitive use of the same notation symbol) designated as being used in certain chapters only.

a	time to complete first task (as used in learning curves)
a(r)	average task time to complete the first r repetitions of a task
a_t	level of demand at time period t (as used in forecasting)
A	annual demand or annual forecast of demand
b	coefficient associated with the learning rate (Chapter 21 only)
b	ratio of backorder cost per month over cost per unit (Chapter 3 only)
b_t	slope of demand at time t (as used in forecasting)
B	economic backorder quantity
BO	backorders
BO′	expected number of backorders in an order cycle
cov	coefficient of variation (ratio of standard deviation over the mean)
cs	cycle stock in months of demand
C	cost per unit
C′	effective cost per unit
C_b	cost per backorder (Chapter 13 only)
C_b	cost per backorder per unit per month (Chapter 3 only)
C_M	cost per unit after the unit is held in stock M months
Co	cost per order
C_S	cost per shortage
CS	cycle stock
d	average lead time demand
D_L	lead time demand
e	the base of the natural system of logarithms (2.71828)
E(k)	partial expectation of k
E(SL)	expected service level
E(x′)	expected value of x', the demand
f_i	lead time forecast for **SKU** i
f(k)	standard normal probability density of k
f_τ	forecast for future time period τ
F	monthly forecast of demand
F(k)	cumulative standard normal probability of k
F_L	lead time forecast of demand
F_τ	cumulative forecast for future τ months
h	annual holding rate
H(k)	complement of $F(k)$ [i.e., $1 - F(k)$]
i	interest rate per month on the unpaid balance of a loan (Chapter 23 only)
i	annual price change rate (Chapter 6 only)

I	total interest paid over the life of a loan
k	safety factor (used to find the safety stock)
K	annual cost (usually the order plus holding costs)
K(Q)	annual cost when order Q units
K(Q,B)	annual cost when order Q units and have B backorders
L	lead time
L	average number of units in the system (Chapters 15-18 only)
L_q	average number of units in the queue
L_s	average number of units in the service facilities
m	average of a Poisson variable (Chapter 8 only)
m	average demand per month
M	economic order quantity in months of demand
M	number of machines (Chapter 18 only)
M	average number of months a unit is held in stock (Chapter 6 only)
M_b	economic backorder quantity in number of months demand
M_q	economic order quantity in number of months demand
N	number of service facilities (Chapters 15 and 17 only)
N	number of SKU's (Chapter 10 only)
N	number of months to repay a loan (Chapter 23 only)
OH	on-hand inventory
OL	order level
OO	on-order inventory
OP	order point (reorder point)
p	ratio of annual production capacity over annual demand (Chapter 4 only)
P	annual production capacity for an item (Chapter 4 only)
P	selling price per unit (Chapter 6 only)
P	mortgage amount (Chapter 23 only)
P/C	ratio of price per unit over cost per unit
P(loss)	probability an arrival is lost (as a customer) because the system is full
P_M	selling price per unit after the unit is held in stock M months
P(out)	probability of an out of stock condition in an order cycle
Po	probability the queueing (reusable inventory) system is empty
P1	selling price per unit
P2	return price per unit
P3	goodwill loss per unit
q	ratio of order quantity over the average demand
Q	economic order quantity
Qo	economic order quantity from simple lot size model
r	repetition number as used in learning curves (Chapter 21 only)
r	ratio of expected realized profit over cost (Chapter 20 only)
R	annual interest rate on the unpaid balance of a loan (Chapter 23 only)
R	number of repairmen (Chapter 18 only)
R	learning rate (Chapter 21 only)
R	ratio of cost per order over cost per unit
R	ratio of cost per shortage over cost per unit (Chapter 12 and 13)
R1	ratio of selling price per unit over cost per unit
R2	ratio of return price per unit over cost per unit
R3	ratio of goodwill cost per unit over cost per unit
s	stocking rate
s	expected sales over the lead time (Chapter 14 only)
s	standard deviation of the lead time (Chapter 19 only)
sales	expected sales over the order cycle

ss	safety stock in months of demand
SL	service level
SS	safety stock
t_a	average time between arrivals
$t(r)$	time to complete the **rth** repetition of a task
ts	total stock in months of demand
t_s	average time to service a unit
T	total amount paid over the life of a loan (Chapter 23 only)
TO	turnover ratio
$T(r)$	total time to complete **r** repetitions of a task
TS	total stock
w	generic symbol for smoothing coefficient (Chapter 1 only)
w	average time a unit is in a queueing system (Chapters 15-18 only)
w_q	average time a unit is in the queue
w_q'	average time a unit is in the queue given it is delayed
w_s	average time a unit is in the service facility
W	standardized average time a unit is in the queueing system
W_q	standardized average time a unit is in the queue
W_q'	standardized average time a delayed unit is in the queue
W_s	standardized average time a unit is in the service facility
X	lead time demand (Chapter 20 only)
X_b	ratio of the economic backorder quantity over the economic order quantity from the simple lot size model
X_p	ratio of the economic order quantity for the production lot size model over the economic order quantity from the simple lot size model
X_q	ratio of the economic order quantity for the backorder model over the economic order quantity from the simple lot size model
Y	number of years to repay a loan
z	standard normal variate
α	smoothing coefficient used in forecasting to estimate the level
β	smoothing coefficient used in forecasting to estimate the slope
γ	smoothing coefficient used in forecasting to estimate the seasonal ratios
λ	average number of arrivals per unit of time
μ	average number of units serviced per unit of time for a continually busy service facility (Chapters 15-18 only)
μ	average demand per month
μ	average demand for an item over the shelf life (Chapter 20 only)
μ	mean (average) of a variable (Chapter 7 only)
μ_t	the expected level of demand for time period **t**
ρ	the utilization factor for a queueing (reuseable inventory) system
ρ_t	the seasonal ratio of demand for time period **t**
σ	the standard deviation for one month of demand
σ	the standard deviation (standard error) of a variable (Chapter 7 only)
σ_i	the standard deviation of the lead time forecast for **SKU i**
σ_L	the standard deviation of the lead time forecast (or demand)
τ	a future time period (as used in forecasting)
τ_{BO}	the average time a backordered unit is in a backorder condition

Note: Throughout this book mathematical derivations are shown that are necessary for determining results of the models but may not be essential for the general understanding and application of the examples and tables.

CHAPTER 1

Forecasting

One of the key goals in inventory management is to maintain stock levels that meet future demands in a timely and economic manner. When future demands are not known in advance and are subject to unknown fluctuations (such as in retail stores, distribution centers and service parts facilities), estimates of future demands are needed in order to carry out the inventory decision making process. Forecasts provide estimates of future demands and are generally revised at regular time periods, usually monthly. The forecast for an item is developed by fitting a relationship through the flow of demands from past time periods and then projecting the fit throughout future time periods. A wide variety of forecasting methods (or models) has been developed and the method to use generally depends on a particular demand pattern that characterizes the demand flow for the item.

Three demand patterns are most common, the *horizontal, trend* and *trend-seasonal* demand patterns. One forecast method is described in this chapter for each of the three demand patterns. All methods chosen for presentation depend on smoothing the demand. Smoothing entails revising forecasts at the beginning of each new time period with the demand of past time periods. At the same time, smoothing gives relatively higher weights to demands of the more recent past time periods. A full review on various forecasting methods is presented in references 1, 2 and 3.

Consider Figure 1.1 where a plot of the demand history and forecasts is depicted over the time horizon. In the general sense, forecasts are developed from the flow of demands from history. For notation, the history of demands is denoted as:

$$x_1 \cdots \cdots x_t$$

where x_t designates the most current history demand entry. The forecasts are represented by:

$$f_1 \cdots \cdots f_\tau$$

where f_1 identifies the forecast for the first future time period and f_τ is the forecast for the τth future time period. A time period can represent any period of time such as weeks, months or quarters. For most situations, the time period used in forecasting is a month. Using months as an example,

$$x_1 \cdots \cdots x_t / f_1 \cdots \cdots f_\tau$$

represents all demands during months **1** to **t,** respectively, and the forecast projections of demands over each of the future months. Therefore, when a month has just been completed and the sum of demands is known for the month, the forecasts may then be revised with this latest bit of information.

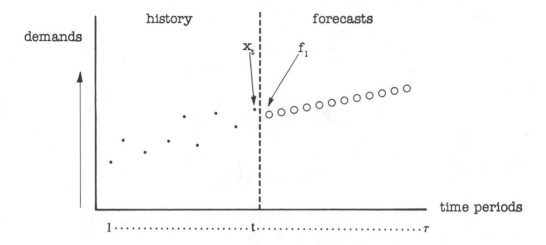

Figure 1.1. Demand history and forecasts

Horizontal Demand Pattern

The horizontal demand pattern applies for an item when the average of the demand remains at a constant value for all time periods; no discernable trend or seasonal influence occurs. Demands per time period fluctuate around this constant mean. In forecasting literature, the average value of the demand is often referred to as the *level of the demand.*

Letting μ_t designate the level of the demand at time **t,** then over any time period the level is a constant value **a** whereby:

$$\mu_t = a$$

as shown in Figure 1.2. As each time period ends, a revised estimate of the level is generated, and at the most current history time period **t,** this estimate is labeled as a'_t. The estimate of the level is subsequently shown to yield the forecasts needed.

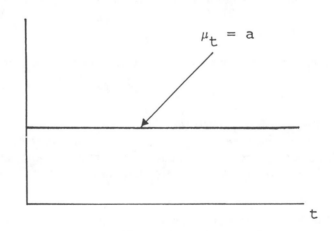

Figure 1.2. Horizontal demand pattern

Using Brown's single exponential smoothing model (reference 4), the parameter and data necessary to revise the forecast at the current time period **t** are the following:

$$\alpha = \text{smoothing coefficient}$$
$$a'_{t-1} = \text{the estimate of the demand level at time period } t - 1$$
$$x_t = \text{the demand at time period t}$$

The smoothing coefficient is a parameter set by management and must lie between 0 and 1. The parameter α directs how much influence the individual demands of the history time periods will have on the forecast. In all situations, smoothing entails that the assignment of weights to monthly demands is relatively smaller as the months become older. When α is set near zero, the assignment of weights to older demand entries tapers off very gradually; and when α is set near one, the assignment of weights to each successively older demand entry then drops very quickly. A common setting of α is 0.10, and for practical considerations α should never exceed a value of 0.50.

Generally α (as previously stated) is set to 0.10 but may be adjusted slightly higher or lower as may be deemed necessary in order to yield appropriate forecasting results. One way to select the value of α to use is to test various candidate values over the history demands for an item and thus determine which candidate value gives the smallest measure of a forecast error for that individual item. Another way is to perform the above analysis over a sample of the items from a single category of items and determine the one value of α that performs the best overall for the sample. This α is then selected as the smoothing coefficient for all items in the category.

With the above data, the revised estimate of the level at time period **t** becomes:

$$a'_t = \alpha \, x_t + (1 - \alpha) \, a'_{t-1}$$

Note from the above that the revised estimate of the level is based on weighing the newest demand entry $\mathbf{x}_t$ by a weight of α and the prior time period's estimate of the level $\mathbf{a}'_{t-1}$ by $(1 - \alpha)$. When $\alpha = 0.10$, for example, $\mathbf{x}_t$ is assigned 10 percent of the weight and $\mathbf{a}'_{t-1}$ is assigned 90 percent of the weight, in determining the current estimate of the level $\mathbf{a}'_t$. Note further that if $\mathbf{x}_t$ is close to $\mathbf{a}'_{t-1}$, the new estimate of the level $\mathbf{a}'_t$ changes slightly from $\mathbf{a}'_{t-1}$. When $\mathbf{x}_t$ is larger than $\mathbf{a}'_{t-1}$, the new level increases above the prior estimate of the level and so on. In this manner, the forecast method is self correcting the estimate of the level as each time period passes.

The forecast for any future time period $t + \tau$ (denoted as $\mathbf{f}_\tau$) is now obtained by use of the most current estimate of the level as shown below:

$$f_\tau = a'_t \qquad \tau = 1, 2, \cdots$$

In this manner the forecasts for future time periods are all set at the same value $\mathbf{a}'_t$ since the level is the same for all time periods when the horizontal demand pattern is used. To determine the cumulative forecast through the future τ time periods (labeled as F_τ), simply multiply the current estimate of the level $(\mathbf{a}'_t)$ by τ, i.e.,

$$F_\tau = f_1 + \cdots + f_\tau = \tau \, a'_t$$

To begin using this system, an initialing stage is carried out to generate the first forecast. When the item is new and only one demand entry x_1 is available, then $t = 1$ and the estimate of the level is set at $a'_1 = x_1$. Thereafter, the smoothing of demands takes over, as shown earlier. With only a few demands available, the forecaster may find it advantageous to use a higher value of α. With a higher value of α, more weight is given to the current demand entry, thus reducing the bias caused from early demands should they begin at a pace that is lower or higher than normal. After a short period, perhaps six months, the regular setting of α takes over.

Example 1.1

Suppose the date is March 31 and the single exponential smoothing model is in use to forecast monthly demands for a storage battery unit that is stocked at an auto distribution center. Assume the smoothing coefficient in use is $\alpha = 0.10$ and the prior month estimate of the level is 50 (i.e., $a'_{t-1} = 50$ is the estimate of the level from the February month end). Also suppose that the total demand for the battery as of the end of the month of March is 60 batteries ($x_t = 60$). Find the revised forecast for the battery and then determine the cumulative six month forecast.

The revised estimate of the level as of month t (March) is now obtained as:

$$a'_t = 0.1\,(60) + 0.9\,(50) = 51.0$$

So the forecast for the future month τ is:

$$f_\tau = 51$$

where in this sample $\tau = 1, \ldots, 6$ represents the months of April through September. Further, the six month cumulative forecast becomes:

$$F_6 = 6\,(51) = 306$$

Trend Demand Pattern

When the level of demands for an item is constantly changing over time at a steady pace and in the same direction (increasing or decreasing), then the flow of demands is shaped like the trend demand pattern. In this situation, the mean of the demand (or the level) at time period t (μ_t) follows the relation:

$$\mu_t = a + bt$$

as shown in Figure 1.3. In the above a is called the intercept (which represents the level at the outset when $t = 0$) and b is the slope. A number of methods have been developed to forecast demand patterns of the trend type. The method described here is called Holt's two parameter method (reference 5), where estimates of the current level a_t and the slope b_t are used. The level a_t represents the mean demand (or level) as of time t, so a_t is the same as μ_t, and thereby the mean for future time period $t + \tau$ becomes:

$$\mu_{t+\tau} = a_t + b\tau$$

Because the true level and slope are not known, estimates are first obtained prior to generating the forecasts.

In order to carry out the method, the following parameters and data are needed as of the just-completed current time period t:

α = smoothing coefficient for the level
β = smoothing coefficient for the slope
a'_{t-1} = estimate of the level as of $t - 1$
b'_{t-1} = estimate of the slope as of $t - 1$
x_t = current demand

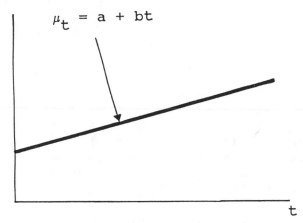

Figure 1.3a. Upward Trend (b > 0)

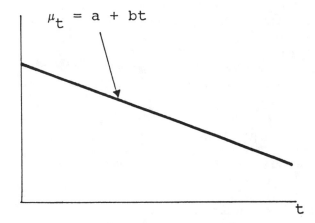

Figure 1.3b. Downward Trend (b < 0)

Figure 1.3. Trend demand patterns

α and β are parameters set by management. The coefficients, along with the accompanying data, are used to revise estimates of the level and slope as shown below:

$$a'_t = \alpha x_t + (1 - \alpha)(a'_{t-1} + b'_{t-1})$$

$$b'_t = \beta(a'_t - a'_{t-1}) + (1 - \beta)b'_{t-1}$$

Note that the above are estimates of the level and slope as of the end of the current time period **t**. The revised estimate of the level a'_t is obtained from weighing the most current demand x_t by α and the prior estimate of the level for time **t** $(a'_{t-1} + b'_{t-1})$ by $(1 - \alpha)$. In the same way the current estimate of the slope b'_t is calculated from weighing the current measure of the slope $(a'_t - a'_{t-1})$ by β and the prior estimate of the slope b'_{t-1} by $(1 - \beta)$.

Once estimates of the level and slope have been revised, the forecast for the τth future time period is found by the relationship:

$$f_\tau = a'_t + b'_t\tau$$

Also, the cumulative forecast for the next τ time periods is generated as:

$$F_\tau = f_1 + \cdots\cdots\cdots + f_\tau$$

Special care is necessary to initialize the system. One such method is described here. When $t = 1$ where only x_1 is available, then the estimate of the level is $a'_1 = x_1$ and the corresponding estimate of the slope is $b'_1 = 0$. When $t = 2$, the forecast model may then be used as described earlier. The forecaster may wish to use higher than normal values of the smoothing parameters (α and β) until some predetermined time period passes, whereby the standard values are then assigned.

Example 1.2

Suppose an electronics distributor of a radio model uses Holt's method to forecast the demands that follow a trend demand pattern. In this situation, assume the smoothing coefficients are $\alpha = 0.10$ for the level and $\beta = 0.20$ for the slope. Also suppose it is the end of June and the prior estimate (or forecast) of the trend relationship is $f_\tau = (40 + 0.5\tau)$ whereby the level from the May month end is $a'_{t-1} = 40$ and the corresponding slope is $b'_{t-1} = 0.50$. Further, if the current demand (for June) is 45 radios, find the cumulative forecast for the future three months (July, August and September).

The revised estimates of the level and slope (as of the end of June) are calculated as:

$$a'_t = 0.1\,(45) + 0.9\,(40 + 0.5) = 40.95$$

$$b'_t = 0.2\,(40.95 - 40.00) + 0.8\,(0.5) = 0.59$$

Now the forecast for future month τ is determined from:

$$f_\tau = 40.95 + 0.59\tau$$

Using $\tau = 1$ to 3, the forecasts needed become:

Future month τ	1	2	3
Forecast f_τ	41.54	42.13	42.72

and the cumulative forecast for the three future months is:

$$F_3 = 41.54 + 42.13 + 42.72 = 126.39$$

Trend Seasonal Demand Pattern

Some items in inventory have demand cycles that repeat from year to year in the same manner. For certain months, the demand shifts upwards and for other months it shifts downwards to form the seasonal cycle of the year. When months are used as the time periods, the mean (or level) for month t can be defined by multiplying the trend $(a + bt)$ by the seasonal ratio for the month ρ_t, as shown below:

$$\mu_t = (a + bt)\,\rho_t$$

Over the 12 months of a year, the average of all seasonal ratios is one. The seasonal ratios never fall below zero, and when $\rho_t < 1$, the seasonal ratio for month t draws the mean below the trend for month t. On the other hand, when $\rho_t > 1$, month t has a mean that is above the trend. The trend in essence may be thought of as a *deseasonalized* average of demands over the time periods, i.e., the mean demand without any seasonal influence. This demand pattern is called the trend seasonal demand pattern (as depicted in Figure 1.4, which shows an example of the trend moving upwards over the months). Although it is assumed here that the time periods are months, the method can be used for other time periods as well, such as weeks or quarters. For clarity, however, the description continues assuming the time periods are the 12 calendar months of a year.

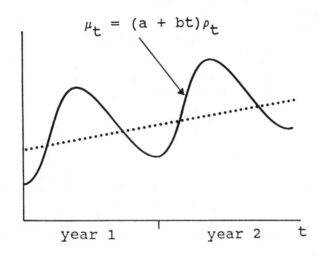

Figure 1.4. Trend seasonal demand pattern

The above demand pattern is also referred to as the *multiplicative trend seasonal demand pattern* because the trend is multiplied by the seasonal ratios to obtain the mean demands for the months. The method to forecast described here is called the Winter's model (reference 6). At the current month **t**, the goal of the forecast method is to estimate the current (deseasonalized) level a_t, the slope b_t and the 12 future seasonal ratios (ρ_{t+1}, ..., ρ_{t+12}). In order to carry out the calculations to revise the estimates, the following parameters and data are needed as of time period **t**:

$$\alpha = \text{smoothing coefficient to estimate the level}$$
$$\beta = \text{smoothing coefficient to estimate the slope}$$
$$\gamma = \text{smoothing coefficient to estimate the seasonal ratios}$$
$$a'_{t-1} = \text{estimate of the level at } t-1$$
$$b'_{t-1} = \text{estimate of the slope at } t-1$$
$$\rho'_t, \cdots, \rho'_{t+11} = \text{estimates of the seasonal ratios}$$
$$x_t = \text{the current demand}$$

The smoothing coefficients α, β, γ are parameters set by company management, and at the startup an initializing phase provides estimates on the level, slope and the seasonal ratios. (See Example 1.8 for a description on initializing the trend seasonal model.) For all subsequent months, the revised estimates are calculated as shown below:

$$a'_t = \alpha \, (x_t / \rho'_t) + (1 - \alpha) \, (a'_{t-1} + b'_{t-1})$$
$$b'_t = \beta \, (a'_t - a'_{t-1}) + (1 - \beta) \, b'_{t-1}$$
$$\rho'_{t+12} = \gamma \, (x_t / a'_t) + (1 - \gamma) \, \rho'_t$$

(The above three equations are also used subsequently in Example 1.8.)

Note that a'_t is an estimate of the (deseasonalized) level as of the current month **t**, and b'_t is the new estimate of the slope. Note further that only the estimate for the twelfth future seasonal ratio ρ'_{t+12} needs to be calculated, as estimates are already available for the other 11 seasonal ratios ($\rho'_{t+1}, \cdots ,$ ρ'_{t+11}).

After the above needed estimate revisions have been obtained, the forecast for future month $t + \tau$ can be generated, by using the relationship:

$$f_\tau = (a'_t + b'_t \tau) \, \rho'_{t+\tau}$$

Also, in the same manner as in the prior demand patterns, the cumulative forecast for the next τ months is obtained by summing the individual forecasts for months $t + 1$ to $t + \tau$, i.e.,

$$F_\tau = f_1 + \cdots\cdots + f_\tau$$

Example 1.3

Suppose the demand for a lawn mower in a wholesale outlet is forecast using the trend seasonal model with smoothing coefficients $\alpha = 0.10$ for the level, $\beta = 0.20$ for the slope and $\gamma = 0.30$ for the seasonal ratios. Assume the date is the end of October and the prior month estimates (from September month end) are:

$$33.05 = \text{estimate of the level}$$
$$1.10 = \text{estimate of the slope}$$

and the estimated future 12 seasonal ratios for months **t** through $t + 11$ (or for October through September, respectively) are:

0.29, 0.43, 0.86, 0.74, 1.07, 1.29, 2.23, 2.36, 1.68, 0.77, 0.25, 0.06

The average of the above 12 seasonal ratios (1.0025) is very near to one, as the average should be. Assume that the most current month's (October) demand for the lawn mower is nine mowers, whereby $x_t = 9$. Find the revised estimates of the level, slope and the twelfth month ahead seasonal ratio; next, generate the forecasts for the future two months.

The revised estimates are the following:

$$a'_t = 0.1 \, (9/0.29) + 0.9 \, (33.05 + 1.10) = 33.84$$
$$b'_t = 0.2 \, (33.84 - 33.05) + 0.8 \, (1.10) = 1.04$$
$$\rho'_{t+12} = 0.3 \, (9/33.84) + 0.7 \, (0.29) = 0.28$$

Note that $\rho'_{t+12} = 0.28$ replaces the prior estimate for the same calendar month (i.e., for October) $\rho'_t = 0.29$ in order to ensure 12 future seasonal ratios.

Now the forecast for future month τ is:

$$f_\tau = (33.84 + 1.04 \, \tau) \, \rho'_{t+\tau}$$

For $\tau = 1$ and 2, the seasonal ratios are .43 and .86, whereby the forecasts become:

$$f_1 = [33.84 + 1.04 \, (1)] \, 0.43 = 15.00$$

$$f_2 = [33.84 + 1.04 \, (2)] \, 0.86 = 30.89$$

Thus the forecasts for November and December are 15.00 and 30.89, respectively. These may be rounded to 15 and 31.

The Lead Time Forecast

For inventory planning decisions, the forecasts covering the lead time period are frequently needed. This section shows how these forecasts are computed. For convenience, the time periods are assumed to be months and the lead time L is then expressed in units of months. The forecasts for the future months are f_1 for future month 1, f_2 for future month 2 and so forth. The forecast for the lead time F_L is computed in the following manner. When L is expressed as an integer (e.g., $L = 3$ months), then:

$$F_L = f_1 + \cdots + f_L$$

which is the sum of the forecasts for each of the future L months. When L is not an integer (e.g., $L = 3.7$ months), then the lead time may be partitioned as $L = Li + Lf$, where Li is the integer portion of L and Lf is the fraction portion of L. The forecast for the lead time becomes:

$$F_L = f_1 + \cdots + f_{Li} + (Lf)\, f_{Li+1}$$

If $L = 3.7$, then $Li = 3$, $Lf = .7$ and:

$$F_L = f_1 + f_2 + f_3 + 0.7\, f_4$$

In the event that the forecast model is horizontal, the forecasts for each future month are the *same* ($f_1 = f_2 = f_3$ and so forth). The lead time forecast now can be computed by multiplying the lead time L by the monthly forecast (expressed by f) as:

$$F_L = L\, f$$

The above formulation is valid whether L is an integer or not.

In the inventory planning models of the subsequent chapters, the lead time forecast F_L is obtained in the same way as the horizontal forecast model. Here F represents the average forecast per month and L is the lead time. So the lead time forecast F_L becomes:

$$F_L = L\, F$$

For example, if $L = 2.8$ months and the average forecast per month for an item is 13.2, the lead time forecast is:

$$F_L = 2.8 \times 13.2 = 36.96$$

Tables

Table 1.1 concerns the weights given to past time periods in smoothing the data to derive the estimates. The tables are developed using generic notation w as the smoothing coefficient. Further, the notation uses j as the age of the past time periods, where $j = 0$ identifies the most current time period, $j = 1$ then identifies the second most current time period and so on. The weight now assigned to past time period j becomes:

$$w\,(1 - w)^j$$

The table lists the above weights along with the cumulative weight for the past j time periods. Also, for each smoothing coefficient, the average age of the data is listed. The age is calculated from the relation:

$$\text{age} = (1 - w)\,/\,w$$

Values of w from 0.05 to 0.50 are reported.

Example 1.4

In forecasting the battery of Example 1.1, show how much weight is given to each of the past 5 monthly demands in determining the forecast. Also list the cumulative weights that correspond.

Table 1.1 is used with a smoothing coefficient of $\alpha = 0.10$ to yield the following weights:

Age of Demands	0	1	2	3	4
Weight	.100	.090	.081	.073	.066
Cumulative Weight	.100	.190	.271	.344	.410

Hence, the past 5 monthly demands have a combined weight of 41 percent in determining the level that is used in the forecasts.

Example 1.5

For the radio forecast in Example 1.2, show how much weight is given for the past five months in determining estimates of the level and slope.

Table 1.1 is used to obtain the following:

Age	0	1	2	3	4	Cumulative Weight
$\alpha = .1$	.100	.090	.081	.073	.066	.410
$\beta = .2$	.200	.160	.128	.102	.082	.672

Example 1.6

For the lawn mower in Example 1.3, find the cumulative weight that is used over the past 12 months in calculating estimates for the level and slope.

Here Table 1.1 is used with $\alpha = 0.10$ and $\beta = 0.20$. The cumulative weights are the following:

$$0.718 \text{ for the level}$$

$$0.931 \text{ for the slope}$$

Example 1.7

Suppose the forecast manager wishes to use a smoothing coefficient that gives 90 percent weight to the most recent 10 demand entries, in calculating the forecasts. What smoothing coefficient should he use?

Table 1.1 shows that when the smoothing coefficient is $w = 0.20$, the cumulative weight then assigned to the closest 10 time periods is 0.893. Further, when $w = 0.25$, the corresponding cumulative weight is 0.944; therefore, a smoothing coefficient of about $w = 0.21$ should be used.

Example 1.8

The steps to initialize the trend seasonal demand pattern are shown in this example. The method applies for a situation where 24 months of demand history are available to carry out the calculations. Assume the parameters to use are $\alpha = .10$, $\beta = .20$ and $\gamma = .30$. For convenience, the months over the history period are denoted as j, where j spans from 1 to 24. The demands are listed in column 2 of the accompanying table in Figure 1.5. The following 7 steps are followed:

- Step 1. The average demand for the first and last year (second year, when 24 months history) of demands are calculated and labeled as x1 and x2, respectively. In the example, x1 = 37.83 and x2 = 40.50. When 3 years of demands are available, then x2 is the average of months 25 to 36.

j (1)	x_j (2)	$\tilde{a}_j$ (3)	r_j (4)	ρ'_j (5)	a'_j (6)	b'_j (7)	ρ'_{j+12} (8)
0		36.38			36.38	0.22	
1	23	36.61	0.63	0.67	36.18	0.14	0.66
2	28	36.83	0.76	0.66	36.81	0.24	0.69
3	32	37.06	0.86	0.80	37.15	0.26	0.82
4	41	37.28	1.10	1.11	37.12	0.20	1.11
5	53	37.50	1.41	1.43	37.11	0.16	1.43
6	48	37.72	1.27	1.44	36.73	0.05	1.40
7	55	37.94	1.45	1.35	37.13	0.12	1.39
8	42	38.17	1.10	1.20	36.92	0.05	1.18
9	39	38.39	1.02	1.01	37.10	0.08	1.02
10	41	38.61	1.06	0.94	37.74	0.19	0.99
11	31	38.83	0.80	0.75	38.10	0.23	0.77
12	21	39.06	0.54	0.64	37.57	0.07	0.62
13	28	39.28	0.71		38.06	0.16	0.68
14	22	39.50	0.56		37.44	0.00	0.66
15	29	39.72	0.73		37.25	−0.04	0.80
16	45	39.94	1.13		37.58	0.04	1.14
17	58	40.17	1.44		37.88	0.09	1.46
18	65	40.39	1.61		38.73	0.24	1.48
19	51	40.61	1.26		38.53	0.15	1.37
20	53	40.83	1.30		39.16	0.25	1.23
21	41	41.06	1.00		39.26	0.22	1.03
22	34	41.28	0.82		38.79	0.08	0.95
23	29	41.50	0.70		38.68	0.04	0.76
24	31	41.72	0.74		39.85	0.27	0.66

Figure 1.5. Worksheet to initialize for the trend seasonal demand pattern

- Step 2. The slope at the outset ($j = 0$) is estimated by:

$$b'_0 = (x2 - x1)/12 = (40.50 - 37.83)/12 = 0.2225$$

When 3 years of demands are available, then divide by 24 instead of 12.

- Step 3. The deseasonalized level at $j = 0$ becomes:

$$a'_0 = x1 - 6.5b'_0 = 37.83 - 6.5\,(0.2225) = 36.3837$$

- Step 4. From the level and slope just found, approximate values for the deseasonalized level for all 24 months are calculated from:

$$\tilde{a}_j = a'_0 + b'_0 j = 36.3837 + 0.2225j$$

The results from these calculations are in column 3 of the table.

● Step 5. Approximate seasonal ratios are now obtained for each of the history months by:

$$r_j = x_j / \tilde{a}_j$$

and the results are listed in column 4.

● Step 6. For each calendar month, the average of the seasonal ratios are now calculated as:

$$\rho'_j = (r_j + r_{j+12}) / 2$$

When 3 years of demands are available, the average of 3 seasonal ratios are used to find the average for each calendar month. For $j = 1$ to 12, the results are listed in column 5 of the table.

● Step 7. For each j (1 to 24), the three equations listed earlier are now used to find estimates for a_j, b_j and ρ_{j+12}. The equations are the same as listed earlier, but the notation j is here used instead of t. Results from this set of calculations are listed in columns 6, 7 and 8 of the table.

The initialization process is now complete. Estimates from the most current time period (now labeled as $t = 24$) are $a'_{24} = 39.85$, $b'_{24} = 0.27$, $\rho'_{25} = 0.68$ and so on until $\rho'_{36} = 0.66$. The forecasts at $t = 24$ are generated from:

$$f_\tau = (39.85 + 0.27\,\tau)\rho'_{24+\tau}$$

Should τ exceed 12, the seasonal ratios then repeat in cyclical form, i.e., $\rho'_{37} = \rho'_{25}$ and so forth.

(Table 1.1 appears on the following pages.)

Table 1.1 Forecast Weights by Age of Data and Smoothing Coefficients

	Smoothing Coefficient									
	— .05 —		— .10 —		— .15 —		— .20 —		— .25 —	
Age	weight	cumulative weight	weight	cumulative weight	weight	cumulative weight	weight	cumulative weight	weight	cumulative weight
0	.050	.050	.100	.100	.150	.150	.200	.200	.250	.250
1	.048	.097	.090	.190	.128	.278	.160	.360	.188	.438
2	.045	.143	.081	.271	.108	.386	.128	.488	.141	.578
3	.043	.185	.073	.344	.092	.478	.102	.590	.105	.684
4	.041	.226	.066	.410	.078	.556	.082	.672	.079	.763
5	.039	.265	.059	.469	.067	.623	.066	.738	.059	.822
6	.037	.302	.053	.522	.057	.679	.052	.790	.044	.867
7	.035	.337	.048	.570	.048	.728	.042	.832	.033	.900
8	.033	.370	.043	.613	.041	.768	.034	.866	.025	.925
9	.032	.401	.039	.651	.035	.803	.027	.893	.019	.944
10	.030	.431	.035	.686	.030	.833	.021	.914	.014	.958
11	.028	.460	.031	.718	.025	.858	.017	.931	.011	.968
12	.027	.487	.028	.746	.021	.879	.014	.945	.008	.976
13	.026	.512	.025	.771	.018	.897	.011	.956	.006	.982
14	.024	.537	.023	.794	.015	.913	.009	.965	.004	.987
15	.023	.560	.021	.815	.013	.926	.007	.972	.003	.990
16	.022	.582	.019	.833	.011	.937	.006	.977	.003	.992
17	.021	.603	.017	.850	.009	.946	.005	.982	.002	.994
18	.020	.623	.015	.865	.008	.954	.004	.986	.001	.996
19	.019	.642	.014	.878	.007	.961	.003	.988	.001	.997
20	.018	.659	.012	.891	.006	.967	.002	.991	.001	.998
21	.017	.676	.011	.902	.005	.972	.002	.993	.001	.998
22	.016	.693	.010	.911	.004	.976	.001	.994	.000	.999
23	.015	.708	.009	.920	.004	.980	.001	.995	.000	.999
24	.015	.723	.008	.928	.003	.983	.001	.996	.000	.999
25	.014	.736	.007	.935	.003	.985	.001	.997	.000	.999
26	.013	.750	.006	.942	.002	.988	.001	.998	.000	1.000
27	.013	.762	.006	.948	.002	.989	.000	.998	.000	1.000
28	.012	.774	.005	.953	.002	.991	.000	.998	.000	1.000
29	.011	.785	.005	.958	.001	.992	.000	.999	.000	1.000
30	.011	.796	.004	.962	.001	.994	.000	.999	.000	1.000
31	.010	.806	.004	.966	.001	.994	.000	.999	.000	1.000
32	.010	.816	.003	.969	.001	.995	.000	.999	.000	1.000
33	.009	.825	.003	.972	.001	.996	.000	.999	.000	1.000
34	.009	.834	.003	.975	.001	.997	.000	1.000	.000	1.000
35	.008	.842	.003	.977	.001	.997	.000	1.000	.000	1.000
Average Age	19.00		9.00		5.67		4.00		3.00	

Table 1.1 Forecast Weights by Age of Data and Smoothing Coefficients (Continued)

Smoothing Coefficient

	—— .30 ——		—— .35 ——		—— .40 ——		—— .45 ——		—— .50 ——	
Age	weight	cumulative weight	weight	cumulative weight	weight	cumulative weight	weight	cumulative weight	weight	cumulative weight
0	.300	.300	.350	.350	.400	.400	.450	.450	.500	.500
1	.210	.510	.228	.578	.240	.640	.248	.698	.250	.750
2	.147	.657	.148	.725	.144	.784	.136	.834	.125	.875
3	.103	.760	.096	.821	.086	.870	.075	.908	.063	.938
4	.072	.832	.062	.884	.052	.922	.041	.950	.031	.969
5	.050	.882	.041	.925	.031	.953	.023	.972	.016	.984
6	.035	.918	.026	.951	.019	.972	.012	.985	.008	.992
7	.025	.942	.017	.968	.011	.983	.007	.992	.004	.996
8	.017	.960	.011	.979	.007	.990	.004	.995	.002	.998
9	.012	.972	.007	.987	.004	.994	.002	.997	.001	.999
10	.008	.980	.005	.991	.002	.996	.001	.999	.000	1.000
11	.006	.986	.003	.994	.001	.998	.001	.999	.000	1.000
12	.004	.990	.002	.996	.001	.999	.000	1.000	.000	1.000
13	.003	.993	.001	.998	.001	.999	.000	1.000	.000	1.000
14	.002	.995	.001	.998	.000	1.000	.000	1.000	.000	1.000
15	.001	.997	.001	.999	.000	1.000	.000	1.000	.000	1.000
16	.001	.998	.000	.999	.000	1.000	.000	1.000	.000	1.000
17	.001	.998	.000	1.000	.000	1.000	.000	1.000	.000	1.000
18	.000	.999	.000	1.000	.000	1.000	.000	1.000	.000	1.000
19	.000	.999	.000	1.000	.000	1.000	.000	1.000	.000	1.000
20	.000	.999	.000	1.000	.000	1.000	.000	1.000	.000	1.000
21	.000	1.000	.000	1.000	.000	1.000	.000	1.000	.000	1.000
22	.000	1.000	.000	1.000	.000	1.000	.000	1.000	.000	1.000
23	.000	1.000	.000	1.000	.000	1.000	.000	1.000	.000	1.000
24	.000	1.000	.000	1.000	.000	1.000	.000	1.000	.000	1.000
25	.000	1.000	.000	1.000	.000	1.000	.000	1.000	.000	1.000
26	.000	1.000	.000	1.000	.000	1.000	.000	1.000	.000	1.000
27	.000	1.000	.000	1.000	.000	1.000	.000	1.000	.000	1.000
28	.000	1.000	.000	1.000	.000	1.000	.000	1.000	.000	1.000
29	.000	1.000	.000	1.000	.000	1.000	.000	1.000	.000	1.000
30	.000	1.000	.000	1.000	.000	1.000	.000	1.000	.000	1.000
31	.000	1.000	.000	1.000	.000	1.000	.000	1.000	.000	1.000
32	.000	1.000	.000	1.000	.000	1.000	.000	1.000	.000	1.000
33	.000	1.000	.000	1.000	.000	1.000	.000	1.000	.000	1.000
34	.000	1.000	.000	1.000	.000	1.000	.000	1.000	.000	1.000
35	.000	1.000	.000	1.000	.000	1.000	.000	1.000	.000	1.000
Average Age	2.33		1.86		1.50		1.22		1.00	

CHAPTER 2

Simple Lot Size Model

The simple lot size model is commonly used in industry to determine order quantities for the items of a stocking facility, such as a warehouse, distribution center or store. The goal is to maintain inventory levels that are economic with respect to holding costs and ordering costs. In the development of the model, demands for each item are assumed to be deterministic and occur evenly throughout the year. Also, the procurement lead time is assumed fixed and replenishments to stock arrive in one lump sum. In the application of the model, shortages are avoided, whereby replenishments are just sufficient to cover the demand needs. This model (references 1 and 2) is perhaps the most common used in industry today, for it is easy to apply and requires item data that are generally available. Although the demands and lead time may not be deterministic for the inventory items, best estimates may readily be available and used accordingly.

As in most order quantity models, the goal of the simple lot size model is to determine the order quantity to use whenever stock is to be replenished for an item. Because the model determines the particular order quantity that yields the minimum combined order and holding costs for the item, the quantity is appropriately called the *economic order quantity.*

Data

The following data are required in order to use the model:

$$L = \text{lead time (in months)}$$
$$A = \text{annual demand for the item}$$
$$C = \text{cost per unit}$$
$$Co = \text{cost per order}$$
$$h = \text{annual holding rate}$$

Note that when the supplier of the item is an outside supplier, the cost per order may include the order processing cost plus the receiving and binning costs. If the supplier is the firm's factory, then the order cost may also include the factory setup cost. Also, for supplier furnished items, the cost per unit may be the procurement cost, and for factory supplied items the cost per unit may be the standard cost.

Model

The goal of the model is to determine the quantity **Q** to order whenever a replenishment of stock is needed. Once **Q** is known, consideration is given as to when to place an order. In this effort, the lead time **L** is used along with the average demand per month **A/12** to derive the demand that is incurred over the lead time. The figure thus derived, known as the *lead time demand,* is the cumulative quantity obtained by multiplying the average demand per month by the number of months. Thus, lead time demand D_L is derived by:

$$D_L = L\,A/12$$

In this model, the order point is equal to D_L, i.e., $OP = D_L$. This formula represents the amount of demand that occurs from when an order is placed until the stock arrives and is available to fill demands (as shown in Figure 2.1). Therefore, when the on-hand plus on-order inventory $(OH + OO)$ reaches the order point, an order of size Q is then placed with the supplier.

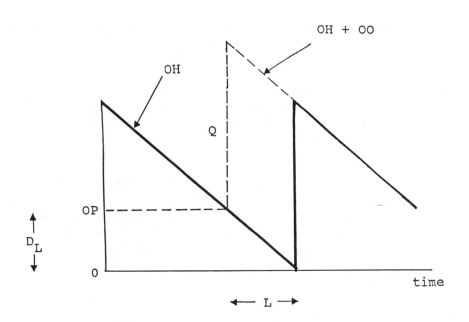

Figure 2.1. Inventory flow for the single lot size model

To determine the size of the order, the following annual cost function is used to relate the combined costs for ordering and holding the stock. If Q' represents an arbitrary order quantity, then the annual cost for an item using Q' is:

that is,
$$K(Q') = \frac{A\,Co}{Q'} + \frac{C\,h\,Q'}{2}$$

$$K(Q') = (\text{order cost}) + (\text{holding cost})$$

The particular value of Q' that yields the minimum annual cost is denoted as Q, the economical order quantity. Q is obtained from the relation:

$$Q = \sqrt{2\,A\,Co/(C\,h)}$$

When Q is used as the order quantity, the associated economic annual order plus holding cost for the item can be determined as:

$$K(Q) = \sqrt{2\,A\,Co\,C\,h}$$

The economic order plus holding cost can be related to the cost per unit C to determine the add-on cost of the unit that is incurred from stocking the unit in inventory. This procedure is here called the stocking rate and is calculated by:

$$s = K(Q)/(AC)$$

Using **s,** it is possible to measure the cost of stocking the unit when the economic order quantity is used to replenish the item. This is merely:

$$\text{stocking cost} = s\,C$$

The effective cost per unit can now be defined. This total is the sum of the procurement cost per unit **C** and the stocking cost per unit. This figure becomes:

$$C' = C\,(1 + s)$$

Tables

For convenience in the adjoining tables of this chapter, two of the above input data are combined to yield a new input parameter **R,** where:

$$R = Co/C = (\text{cost per order} \,/\, \text{cost per unit})$$

Also, it is possible to relate the above economic order quantity **Q** to the monthly demand rate **A/12** and give the results in terms of the month's equivalent to **Q.** This is the economic order quantity in months of demand, denoted as **M,** and becomes:

$$M = 12\,Q/A$$

Tables 2.1 to 2.4 give a calculated value of **M** (economic months of the order quantity) and **s** = stocking rate (or the economic order plus holding cost/cost per unit), for various settings of **A** (annual demand), **R** (cost per order/cost per unit) and **h** (annual holding rate). The only input data difference in the tables is the annual holding rates, as listed below:

Tables	h
2.1	.10
2.2	.20
2.3	.30
2.4	.40

Just-in-Time Applications

The tables of this chapter are particularly useful to those seeking to apply Just-in-Time (JIT) methods. The order quantity in months of supply **M** is listed in the tables with changing values of **R** (the ratio of the cost per order over the cost per unit). The smaller this ratio **R** becomes, the smaller the order quantity in months of supply. Further, the larger the annual demand **A,** the smaller the order quantity in months supply.

In the production facilities of a firm, one goal of JIT is to reduce waste in the storage costs of inventory. To achieve this goal, a steady flow of materials, parts and components is needed. This kind of production flow requires small order quantities. The tables can quickly point out which items are within reach of attaining low order quantities in an economical manner. For those items that are not economical, other arrangements of replenishments and storage may be necessary to maintain economy in the overall operations.

In the distribution facilities of a firm, the usual goal is to hold the minimum inventory to achieve the level of customer service desired by the management. Although it is sometimes difficult to apply JIT methods here, the spirit persists and management seeks to receive replenishment stock in small and steady quantities. Oftentimes management will negotiate with suppliers to replenish stock in this manner. Management must identify items with sufficient volume and make arrangements with the supplier to provide a steady inflow of replenishments in small quantities, at the same time assuring the supplier that replenishment orders will be continual over the planning horizon. With this arrangement, the supplier can steadily produce the items and apply JIT methods on his operations of the items as well and thus provide the distribution center with reduced lead times and sometimes with reduced procurement costs. This arrangement becomes economically worthwhile to both parties. By use of the tables, management may determine which of the items they stock are economically compatible to JIT replenishments.

Example 2.1

Consider a home center that stocks a flashlight costing $5 and selling for $8, and which has an annual demand of 500 units. Suppose that the lead time is one half month and a cost of $15 occurs each time a replenishment order is made. Also assume that the company policy is to charge a rate of 30 percent of the procurement cost for a unit held in stock for one year. Find the economic order quantity, the associated profit margin on the flashlight and the corresponding order point.

First note the following:

$$L = .5 \text{ (of a month)}$$
$$A = 500$$
$$R = 15/5 = 3$$
$$h = .30$$

With $h = .30$, Table 2.3 is used to seek the corresponding results. With $A = 500$ and $R = 3$, then:

$$M = 2.4$$
$$s = .06$$

Now, because the average monthly demand is $500/12 = 41.67$, the economic order quantity becomes:

$$Q = 2.4 \times 41.67 = 100$$

The effective cost of the item is determined from the relation:

$$C' = C (1 + .06)$$

that is,

$$C' = 5 (1 + .06) = \$5.30$$

and the profit for each item sold is ($8.00 − $5.30) = $2.70.

With $L = .5$, then the order point is $OP = .5 (41.67) = 20.83$ units.

Example 2.2

For the flashlight in Example 2.1 suppose that, in an effort to reduce on-hand inventory, the materials manager wishes to use an order quantity equal to one month of demand, but at the same time desires that the quantity be an economical order quantity. In this situation, suppose the manager can refine the ordering procedure and thereby reduce the cost per order. How low must the order cost become in order to fulfill the desire?

Table 2.3 is again used ($h = .30$) with $A = 500$, and the goal is to search for a value of **R** which yields $M = 1$. Examination of the table shows that $R \approx .5$. Since $R = Co/C$, then $Co = .5 \times \$5 = \$2.50$ is the order cost required for the flashlight. Note also that the corresponding order plus holding cost per unit is approximately $.025 \times \$5 = \$0.12$.

Example 2.3

Suppose for the flashlight in Example 2.1 that the manager can only lower the order cost to $5 (from $15); what now is the economical order quantity?

In this situation, Table 2.3 is used along with $R = 5/5 = 1$, whereby the table yields $M = 1.4$ months. As a result, $Q = 1.4 \times 41.67 = 58.3$ (or about 58).

Example 2.4

Assume that an office supply company stocks a particular notebook with an annual demand of 1000 units, with a per unit cost of $2. Also assume the cost per order is $20 and the annual holding rate is 30 percent. If management wishes to set the selling price for the notebook at a value that will give a 50 percent markup, what should be the selling price?

Table 2.3 ($h = .30$) is used along with $A = 1000$ and $R = 20/2 = 10$ to give $s = .08$. The effective unit cost becomes:

$$\$2\,(1 + .08) = \$2.16.$$

The selling price should then be 50 percent higher, or:

$$1.5 \times \$2.16 = \$3.24.$$

Example 2.5

Suppose a department store stocks a radio model with a procurement cost of $100 per unit and incurs a cost of $50 each time an order is placed. Assume also that the annual holding rate is 30 percent and the annual demand is 100 units. Note from Table 2.3 that for this item $M = 2.2$ and thereby $Q = 2.2 \times 100/12 = 18.3$.

Suppose the radio's unit cost is increased to $125, and all else remains the same. How does this increase in cost affect the economic order quantity?

Using Table 2.3 along with $A = 100$ and $R = 50/125 = .40$, then $M = 2.0$; and now $Q = 2.0 \times 100/12 = 16.7$. Note in this situation that a 25 percent increase in the cost gives a 9 percent decrease in the economic order quantity.

Example 2.6

Consider a hand calculator with a unit cost of $10, selling for $12 and with an annual demand of 1000 units. Also, the order cost is $1000 (which includes the factory setup cost) and the annual holding rate is 30 percent. For this item, find the expected annual profit.

Using Table 2.3 with $A = 1000$, $R = 1000/10 = 100$, the effective cost per calculator becomes:

$$C' = \$10\,(1 + .24) = \$12.40$$

and so the profit for the year is:

$$1000\,(12.00 - 12.40) = -\$400$$

or a loss of $400.

Example 2.7

Consider a windshield wiper with an annual demand of 1000 units, a cost per unit of $5, a cost per order of $50, and with an annual stock holding rate of 40 percent. Note for this situation $R = 50/5 = 10$ and Table 2.4 yields $M = 2.7$ and $s = .09$. Show how the results are obtained.

First the economic order quantity is calculated by:

$$Q = \sqrt{[2\,(1000)\,50/(5 \times .40)]} = 223.6$$

Since the average demand per month is $1000/12 = 83.3$, then the months of demand in the order quantity is:

$$M = 223.6/83.3 = 2.68$$

which corresponds to the results from Table 2.4.

With $M = 2.68$, the windshield wiper is ordered $12/2.68 = 4.48$ times per year, whereby the:

$$\text{annual order cost} = 4.48 \times 50 = \$224$$

Because $Q = 223.6$, then the:

$$\text{annual holding cost} = 223.6 \,(5)\, .40/2 = \$223.60$$

The sum from the above gives the annual order cost plus holding cost:

$$224.00 + 223.60 = \$447.60$$

Note that the order plus holding cost per unit is now:

$$447.60/1000 = \$0.448$$

and so the stocking rate is:

$$s = 0.448/5 = .0896$$

which agrees with the corresponding result in Table 2.4.

Table 2.1 Order Quantities and Stocking Costs for the Simple Lot Size Model

h = 10% (Annual Holding Rate)

M = Economic Order Quantity in Months of Demand

R A	1000	750	500	250	100	75	50	25	10	5
10	536.7	464.8	379.5	268.3	169.7	147.0	120.0	84.9	53.7	37.9
25	339.4	293.9	240.0	169.7	107.3	93.0	75.9	53.7	33.9	24.0
50	240.0	207.8	169.7	120.0	75.9	65.7	53.7	37.9	24.0	17.0
75	196.0	169.7	138.6	98.0	62.0	53.7	43.8	31.0	19.6	13.9
100	169.7	147.0	120.0	84.9	53.7	46.5	37.9	26.8	17.0	12.0
250	107.3	93.0	75.9	53.7	33.9	29.4	24.0	17.0	10.7	7.6
500	75.9	65.7	53.7	37.9	24.0	20.8	17.0	12.0	7.6	5.4
750	62.0	53.7	43.8	31.0	19.6	17.0	13.9	9.8	6.2	4.4
1,000	53.7	46.5	37.9	26.8	17.0	14.7	12.0	8.5	5.4	3.8
2,500	33.9	29.4	24.0	17.0	10.7	9.3	7.6	5.4	3.4	2.4
5,000	24.0	20.8	17.0	12.0	7.6	6.6	5.4	3.8	2.4	1.7
7,500	19.6	17.0	13.9	9.8	6.2	5.4	4.4	3.1	2.0	1.4
10,000	17.0	14.7	12.0	8.5	5.4	4.6	3.8	2.7	1.7	1.2
25,000	10.7	9.3	7.6	5.4	3.4	2.9	2.4	1.7	1.1	.8
50,000	7.6	6.6	5.4	3.8	2.4	2.1	1.7	1.2	.8	.5
75,000	6.2	5.4	4.4	3.1	2.0	1.7	1.4	1.0	.6	.4
100,000	5.4	4.6	3.8	2.7	1.7	1.5	1.2	.8	.5	.4
250,000	3.4	2.9	2.4	1.7	1.1	.9	.8	.5	.3	.2
500,000	2.4	2.1	1.7	1.2	.8	.7	.5	.4	.2	.2
1,000,000	1.7	1.5	1.2	.8	.5	.5	.4	.3	.2	.1

s = Economic Order plus Hold Cost / Cost per Unit

R A	1000	750	500	250	100	75	50	25	10	5
10	4.47	3.87	3.16	2.24	1.41	1.22	1.00	.71	.45	.32
25	2.83	2.45	2.00	1.41	.89	.77	.63	.45	.28	.20
50	2.00	1.73	1.41	1.00	.63	.55	.45	.32	.20	.14
75	1.63	1.41	1.15	.82	.52	.45	.37	.26	.16	.12
100	1.41	1.22	1.00	.71	.45	.39	.32	.22	.14	.10
250	.89	.77	.63	.45	.28	.24	.20	.14	.09	.06
500	.63	.55	.45	.32	.20	.17	.14	.10	.06	.04
750	.52	.45	.37	.26	.16	.14	.12	.08	.05	.04
1,000	.45	.39	.32	.22	.14	.12	.10	.07	.04	.03
2,500	.28	.24	.20	.14	.09	.08	.06	.04	.03	.02
5,000	.20	.17	.14	.10	.06	.05	.04	.03	.02	.01
7,500	.16	.14	.12	.08	.05	.04	.04	.03	.02	.01
10,000	.14	.12	.10	.07	.04	.04	.03	.02	.01	.01
25,000	.09	.08	.06	.04	.03	.02	.02	.01	.01	.01
50,000	.06	.05	.04	.03	.02	.02	.01	.01	.01	.00
75,000	.05	.04	.04	.03	.02	.01	.01	.01	.01	.00
100,000	.04	.04	.03	.02	.01	.01	.01	.01	.00	.00
250,000	.03	.02	.02	.01	.01	.01	.01	.00	.00	.00
500,000	.02	.02	.01	.01	.01	.01	.00	.00	.00	.00
1,000,000	.01	.01	.01	.01	.00	.00	.00	.00	.00	.00

A = Annual Demand

R = Cost to Order/Cost per Unit

Table 2.1 Order Quantities and Stocking Costs for the Simple Lot Size Model (Continued)

h = 10% (Annual Holding Rate)

M = Economic Order Quantity in Months of Demand

A \ R	3	1	.8	.6	.4	.2	.1	.07	.03	.01
10	29.4	17.0	15.2	13.1	10.7	7.6	5.4	4.5	2.9	1.7
25	18.6	10.7	9.6	8.3	6.8	4.8	3.4	2.8	1.9	1.1
50	13.1	7.6	6.8	5.9	4.8	3.4	2.4	2.0	1.3	.8
75	10.7	6.2	5.5	4.8	3.9	2.8	2.0	1.6	1.1	.6
100	9.3	5.4	4.8	4.2	3.4	2.4	1.7	1.4	.9	.5
250	5.9	3.4	3.0	2.6	2.1	1.5	1.1	.9	.6	.3
500	4.2	2.4	2.1	1.9	1.5	1.1	.8	.6	.4	.2
750	3.4	2.0	1.8	1.5	1.2	.9	.6	.5	.3	.2
1,000	2.9	1.7	1.5	1.3	1.1	.8	.5	.4	.3	.2
2,500	1.9	1.1	1.0	.8	.7	.5	.3	.3	.2	.1
5,000	1.3	.8	.7	.6	.5	.3	.2	.2	.1	.1
7,500	1.1	.6	.6	.5	.4	.3	.2	.2	.1	.1
10,000	.9	.5	.5	.4	.3	.2	.2	.1	.1	.1
25,000	.6	.3	.3	.3	.2	.2	.1	.1	.1	.0
50,000	.4	.2	.2	.2	.2	.1	.1	.1	.0	.0
75,000	.3	.2	.2	.2	.1	.1	.1	.1	.0	.0
100,000	.3	.2	.2	.1	.1	.1	.1	.0	.0	.0
250,000	.2	.1	.1	.1	.1	.0	.0	.0	.0	.0
500,000	.1	.1	.1	.1	.0	.0	.0	.0	.0	.0
1,000,000	.1	.1	.0	.0	.0	.0	.0	.0	.0	.0

s = Economic Order plus Hold Cost / Cost per Unit

A \ R	3	1	.8	.6	.4	.2	.1	.07	.03	.01
10	.24	.14	.13	.11	.09	.06	.04	.04	.02	.01
25	.15	.09	.08	.07	.06	.04	.03	.02	.02	.01
50	.11	.06	.06	.05	.04	.03	.02	.02	.01	.01
75	.09	.05	.05	.04	.03	.02	.02	.01	.01	.01
100	.08	.04	.04	.03	.03	.02	.01	.01	.01	.00
250	.05	.03	.03	.02	.02	.01	.01	.01	.00	.00
500	.03	.02	.02	.02	.01	.01	.01	.01	.00	.00
750	.03	.02	.01	.01	.01	.01	.01	.00	.00	.00
1,000	.02	.01	.01	.01	.01	.01	.00	.00	.00	.00
2,500	.02	.01	.01	.01	.01	.00	.00	.00	.00	.00
5,000	.01	.01	.01	.00	.00	.00	.00	.00	.00	.00
7,500	.01	.01	.00	.00	.00	.00	.00	.00	.00	.00
10,000	.01	.00	.00	.00	.00	.00	.00	.00	.00	.00
25,000	.00	.00	.00	.00	.00	.00	.00	.00	.00	.00
50,000	.00	.00	.00	.00	.00	.00	.00	.00	.00	.00
75,000	.00	.00	.00	.00	.00	.00	.00	.00	.00	.00
100,000	.00	.00	.00	.00	.00	.00	.00	.00	.00	.00
250,000	.00	.00	.00	.00	.00	.00	.00	.00	.00	.00
500,000	.00	.00	.00	.00	.00	.00	.00	.00	.00	.00
1,000,000	.00	.00	.00	.00	.00	.00	.00	.00	.00	.00

A = Annual Demand

R = Cost to Order/Cost per Unit

Table 2.2 Order Quantities and Stocking Costs for the Simple Lot Size Model

h = 20% (Annual Holding Rate)

M = Economic Order Quantity in Months of Demand

R \ A	1000	750	500	250	100	75	50	25	10	5
10	379.5	328.6	268.3	189.7	120.0	103.9	84.9	60.0	37.9	26.8
25	240.0	207.8	169.7	120.0	75.9	65.7	53.7	37.9	24.0	17.0
50	169.7	147.0	120.0	84.9	53.7	46.5	37.9	26.8	17.0	12.0
75	138.6	120.0	98.0	69.3	43.8	37.9	31.0	21.9	13.9	9.8
100	120.0	103.9	84.9	60.0	37.9	32.9	26.8	19.0	12.0	8.5
250	75.9	65.7	53.7	37.9	24.0	20.8	17.0	12.0	7.6	5.4
500	53.7	46.5	37.9	26.8	17.0	14.7	12.0	8.5	5.4	3.8
750	43.8	37.9	31.0	21.9	13.9	12.0	9.8	6.9	4.4	3.1
1,000	37.9	32.9	26.8	19.0	12.0	10.4	8.5	6.0	3.8	2.7
2,500	24.0	20.8	17.0	12.0	7.6	6.6	5.4	3.8	2.4	1.7
5,000	17.0	14.7	12.0	8.5	5.4	4.6	3.8	2.7	1.7	1.2
7,500	13.9	12.0	9.8	6.9	4.4	3.8	3.1	2.2	1.4	1.0
10,000	12.0	10.4	8.5	6.0	3.8	3.3	2.7	1.9	1.2	.8
25,000	7.6	6.6	5.4	3.8	2.4	2.1	1.7	1.2	.8	.5
50,000	5.4	4.6	3.8	2.7	1.7	1.5	1.2	.8	.5	.4
75,000	4.4	3.8	3.1	2.2	1.4	1.2	1.0	.7	.4	.3
100,000	3.8	3.3	2.7	1.9	1.2	1.0	.8	.6	.4	.3
250,000	2.4	2.1	1.7	1.2	.8	.7	.5	.4	.2	.2
500,000	1.7	1.5	1.2	.8	.5	.5	.4	.3	.2	.1
1,000,000	1.2	1.0	.8	.6	.4	.3	.3	.2	.1	.1

s = Economic Order plus Hold Cost / Cost per Unit

R \ A	1000	750	500	250	100	75	50	25	10	5
10	6.32	5.48	4.47	3.16	2.00	1.73	1.41	1.00	.63	.45
25	4.00	3.46	2.83	2.00	1.26	1.10	.89	.63	.40	.28
50	2.83	2.45	2.00	1.41	.89	.77	.63	.45	.28	.20
75	2.31	2.00	1.63	1.15	.73	.63	.52	.37	.23	.16
100	2.00	1.73	1.41	1.00	.63	.55	.45	.32	.20	.14
250	1.26	1.10	.89	.63	.40	.35	.28	.20	.13	.09
500	.89	.77	.63	.45	.28	.24	.20	.14	.09	.06
750	.73	.63	.52	.37	.23	.20	.16	.12	.07	.05
1,000	.63	.55	.45	.32	.20	.17	.14	.10	.06	.04
2,500	.40	.35	.28	.20	.13	.11	.09	.06	.04	.03
5,000	.28	.24	.20	.14	.09	.08	.06	.04	.03	.02
7,500	.23	.20	.16	.12	.07	.06	.05	.04	.02	.02
10,000	.20	.17	.14	.10	.06	.05	.04	.03	.02	.01
25,000	.13	.11	.09	.06	.04	.03	.03	.02	.01	.01
50,000	.09	.08	.06	.04	.03	.02	.02	.01	.01	.01
75,000	.07	.06	.05	.04	.02	.02	.02	.01	.01	.01
100,000	.06	.05	.04	.03	.02	.02	.01	.01	.01	.00
250,000	.04	.03	.03	.02	.01	.01	.01	.01	.00	.00
500,000	.03	.02	.02	.01	.01	.01	.01	.00	.00	.00
1,000,000	.02	.02	.01	.01	.01	.01	.00	.00	.00	.00

A = Annual Demand

R = Cost to Order/Cost per Unit

Table 2.2 Order Quantities and Stocking Costs for the Simple Lot Size Model
(Continued)

h = 20% (Annual Holding Rate)

M = Economic Order Quantity in Months of Demand

R \ A	3	1	.8	.6	.4	.2	.1	.07	.03	.01
10	20.8	12.0	10.7	9.3	7.6	5.4	3.8	3.2	2.1	1.2
25	13.1	7.6	6.8	5.9	4.8	3.4	2.4	2.0	1.3	.8
50	9.3	5.4	4.8	4.2	3.4	2.4	1.7	1.4	.9	.5
75	7.6	4.4	3.9	3.4	2.8	2.0	1.4	1.2	.8	.4
100	6.6	3.8	3.4	2.9	2.4	1.7	1.2	1.0	.7	.4
250	4.2	2.4	2.1	1.9	1.5	1.1	.8	.6	.4	.2
500	2.9	1.7	1.5	1.3	1.1	.8	.5	.4	.3	.2
750	2.4	1.4	1.2	1.1	.9	.6	.4	.4	.2	.1
1,000	2.1	1.2	1.1	.9	.8	.5	.4	.3	.2	.1
2,500	1.3	.8	.7	.6	.5	.3	.2	.2	.1	.1
5,000	.9	.5	.5	.4	.3	.2	.2	.1	.1	.1
7,500	.8	.4	.4	.3	.3	.2	.1	.1	.1	.0
10,000	.7	.4	.3	.3	.2	.2	.1	.1	.1	.0
25,000	.4	.2	.2	.2	.2	.1	.1	.1	.0	.0
50,000	.3	.2	.2	.1	.1	.1	.1	.0	.0	.0
75,000	.2	.1	.1	.1	.1	.1	.0	.0	.0	.0
100,000	.2	.1	.1	.1	.1	.1	.0	.0	.0	.0
250,000	.1	.1	.1	.1	.0	.0	.0	.0	.0	.0
500,000	.1	.1	.0	.0	.0	.0	.0	.0	.0	.0
1,000,000	.1	.0	.0	.0	.0	.0	.0	.0	.0	.0

s = Economic Order plus Hold Cost / Cost per Unit

R \ A	3	1	.8	.6	.4	.2	.1	.07	.03	.01
10	.35	.20	.18	.15	.13	.09	.06	.05	.03	.02
25	.22	.13	.11	.10	.08	.06	.04	.03	.02	.01
50	.15	.09	.08	.07	.06	.04	.03	.02	.02	.01
75	.13	.07	.07	.06	.05	.03	.02	.02	.01	.01
100	.11	.06	.06	.05	.04	.03	.02	.02	.01	.01
250	.07	.04	.04	.03	.03	.02	.01	.01	.01	.00
500	.05	.03	.03	.02	.02	.01	.01	.01	.00	.00
750	.04	.02	.02	.02	.01	.01	.01	.01	.00	.00
1,000	.03	.02	.02	.02	.01	.01	.01	.01	.00	.00
2,500	.02	.01	.01	.01	.01	.01	.00	.00	.00	.00
5,000	.02	.01	.01	.01	.01	.00	.00	.00	.00	.00
7,500	.01	.01	.01	.01	.00	.00	.00	.00	.00	.00
10,000	.01	.01	.01	.00	.00	.00	.00	.00	.00	.00
25,000	.01	.00	.00	.00	.00	.00	.00	.00	.00	.00
50,000	.00	.00	.00	.00	.00	.00	.00	.00	.00	.00
75,000	.00	.00	.00	.00	.00	.00	.00	.00	.00	.00
100,000	.00	.00	.00	.00	.00	.00	.00	.00	.00	.00
250,000	.00	.00	.00	.00	.00	.00	.00	.00	.00	.00
500,000	.00	.00	.00	.00	.00	.00	.00	.00	.00	.00
1,000,000	.00	.00	.00	.00	.00	.00	.00	.00	.00	.00

A = Annual Demand

R = Cost to Order/Cost per Unit

Table 2.3 Order Quantities and Stocking Costs for the Simple Lot Size Model

h = 30% (Annual Holding Rate)

M = Economic Order Quantity in Months of Demand

R \ A	1000	750	500	250	100	75	50	25	10	5
10	309.8	268.3	219.1	154.9	98.0	84.9	69.3	49.0	31.0	21.9
25	196.0	169.7	138.6	98.0	62.0	53.7	43.8	31.0	19.6	13.9
50	138.6	120.0	98.0	69.3	43.8	37.9	31.0	21.9	13.9	9.8
75	113.1	98.0	80.0	56.6	35.8	31.0	25.3	17.9	11.3	8.0
100	98.0	84.9	69.3	49.0	31.0	26.8	21.9	15.5	9.8	6.9
250	62.0	53.7	43.8	31.0	19.6	17.0	13.9	9.8	6.2	4.4
500	43.8	37.9	31.0	21.9	13.9	12.0	9.8	6.9	4.4	3.1
750	35.8	31.0	25.3	17.9	11.3	9.8	8.0	5.7	3.6	2.5
1,000	31.0	26.8	21.9	15.5	9.8	8.5	6.9	4.9	3.1	2.2
2,500	19.6	17.0	13.9	9.8	6.2	5.4	4.4	3.1	2.0	1.4
5,000	13.9	12.0	9.8	6.9	4.4	3.8	3.1	2.2	1.4	1.0
7,500	11.3	9.8	8.0	5.7	3.6	3.1	2.5	1.8	1.1	.8
10,000	9.8	8.5	6.9	4.9	3.1	2.7	2.2	1.5	1.0	.7
25,000	6.2	5.4	4.4	3.1	2.0	1.7	1.4	1.0	.6	.4
50,000	4.4	3.8	3.1	2.2	1.4	1.2	1.0	.7	.4	.3
75,000	3.6	3.1	2.5	1.8	1.1	1.0	.8	.6	.4	.3
100,000	3.1	2.7	2.2	1.5	1.0	.8	.7	.5	.3	.2
250,000	2.0	1.7	1.4	1.0	.6	.5	.4	.3	.2	.1
500,000	1.4	1.2	1.0	.7	.4	.4	.3	.2	.1	.1
1,000,000	1.0	.8	.7	.5	.3	.3	.2	.2	.1	.1

s = Economic Order plus Hold Cost / Cost per Unit

R \ A	1000	750	500	250	100	75	50	25	10	5
10	7.75	6.71	5.48	3.87	2.45	2.12	1.73	1.22	.77	.55
25	4.90	4.24	3.46	2.45	1.55	1.34	1.10	.77	.49	.35
50	3.46	3.00	2.45	1.73	1.10	.95	.77	.55	.35	.24
75	2.83	2.45	2.00	1.41	.89	.77	.63	.45	.28	.20
100	2.45	2.12	1.73	1.22	.77	.67	.55	.39	.24	.17
250	1.55	1.34	1.10	.77	.49	.42	.35	.24	.15	.11
500	1.10	.95	.77	.55	.35	.30	.24	.17	.11	.08
750	.89	.77	.63	.45	.28	.24	.20	.14	.09	.06
1,000	.77	.67	.55	.39	.24	.21	.17	.12	.08	.05
2,500	.49	.42	.35	.24	.15	.13	.11	.08	.05	.03
5,000	.35	.30	.24	.17	.11	.09	.08	.05	.03	.02
7,500	.28	.24	.20	.14	.09	.08	.06	.04	.03	.02
10,000	.24	.21	.17	.12	.08	.07	.05	.04	.02	.02
25,000	.15	.13	.11	.08	.05	.04	.03	.02	.02	.01
50,000	.11	.09	.08	.05	.03	.03	.02	.02	.01	.01
75,000	.09	.08	.06	.04	.03	.02	.02	.01	.01	.01
100,000	.08	.07	.05	.04	.02	.02	.02	.01	.01	.01
250,000	.05	.04	.03	.02	.02	.01	.01	.01	.00	.00
500,000	.03	.03	.02	.02	.01	.01	.01	.01	.00	.00
1,000,000	.02	.02	.02	.01	.01	.01	.01	.00	.00	.00

A = Annual Demand

R = Cost to Order/Cost per Unit

Table 2.3 Order Quantities and Stocking Costs for the Simple Lot Size Model
(Continued)

h = 30% (Annual Holding Rate)

M = Economic Order Quantity in Months of Demand

R A	3	1	.8	.6	.4	.2	.1	.07	.03	.01
10	17.0	9.8	8.8	7.6	6.2	4.4	3.1	2.6	1.7	1.0
25	10.7	6.2	5.5	4.8	3.9	2.8	2.0	1.6	1.1	.6
50	7.6	4.4	3.9	3.4	2.8	2.0	1.4	1.2	.8	.4
75	6.2	3.6	3.2	2.8	2.3	1.6	1.1	.9	.6	.4
100	5.4	3.1	2.8	2.4	2.0	1.4	1.0	.8	.5	.3
250	3.4	2.0	1.8	1.5	1.2	.9	.6	.5	.3	.2
500	2.4	1.4	1.2	1.1	.9	.6	.4	.4	.2	.1
750	2.0	1.1	1.0	.9	.7	.5	.4	.3	.2	.1
1,000	1.7	1.0	.9	.8	.6	.4	.3	.3	.2	.1
2,500	1.1	.6	.6	.5	.4	.3	.2	.2	.1	.1
5,000	.8	.4	.4	.3	.3	.2	.1	.1	.1	.0
7,500	.6	.4	.3	.3	.2	.2	.1	.1	.1	.0
10,000	.5	.3	.3	.2	.2	.1	.1	.1	.1	.0
25,000	.3	.2	.2	.2	.1	.1	.1	.1	.0	.0
50,000	.2	.1	.1	.1	.1	.1	.0	.0	.0	.0
75,000	.2	.1	.1	.1	.1	.1	.0	.0	.0	.0
100,000	.2	.1	.1	.1	.1	.0	.0	.0	.0	.0
250,000	.1	.1	.1	.0	.0	.0	.0	.0	.0	.0
500,000	.1	.0	.0	.0	.0	.0	.0	.0	.0	.0
1,000,000	.1	.0	.0	.0	.0	.0	.0	.0	.0	.0

s = Economic Order plus Hold Cost / Cost per Unit

R A	3	1	.8	.6	.4	.2	.1	.07	.03	.01
10	.42	.24	.22	.19	.15	.11	.08	.06	.04	.02
25	.27	.15	.14	.12	.10	.07	.05	.04	.03	.02
50	.19	.11	.10	.08	.07	.05	.03	.03	.02	.01
75	.15	.09	.08	.07	.06	.04	.03	.02	.02	.01
100	.13	.08	.07	.06	.05	.03	.02	.02	.01	.01
250	.08	.05	.04	.04	.03	.02	.02	.01	.01	.00
500	.06	.03	.03	.03	.02	.02	.01	.01	.01	.00
750	.05	.03	.03	.02	.02	.01	.01	.01	.00	.00
1,000	.04	.02	.02	.02	.02	.01	.01	.01	.00	.00
2,500	.03	.02	.01	.01	.01	.01	.00	.00	.00	.00
5,000	.02	.01	.01	.01	.01	.00	.00	.00	.00	.00
7,500	.02	.01	.01	.01	.01	.00	.00	.00	.00	.00
10,000	.01	.01	.01	.01	.00	.00	.00	.00	.00	.00
25,000	.01	.00	.00	.00	.00	.00	.00	.00	.00	.00
50,000	.01	.00	.00	.00	.00	.00	.00	.00	.00	.00
75,000	.00	.00	.00	.00	.00	.00	.00	.00	.00	.00
100,000	.00	.00	.00	.00	.00	.00	.00	.00	.00	.00
250,000	.00	.00	.00	.00	.00	.00	.00	.00	.00	.00
500,000	.00	.00	.00	.00	.00	.00	.00	.00	.00	.00
1,000,000	.00	.00	.00	.00	.00	.00	.00	.00	.00	.00

A = Annual Demand

R = Cost to Order/Cost per Unit

Table 2.4 Order Quantities and Stocking Costs for the Simple Lot Size Model

h = 40% (Annual Holding Rate)

M = Economic Order Quantity in Months of Demand

R \ A	1000	750	500	250	100	75	50	25	10	5
10	268.3	232.4	189.7	134.2	84.9	73.5	60.0	42.4	26.8	19.0
25	169.7	147.0	120.0	84.9	53.7	46.5	37.9	26.8	17.0	12.0
50	120.0	103.9	84.9	60.0	37.9	32.9	26.8	19.0	12.0	8.5
75	98.0	84.9	69.3	49.0	31.0	26.8	21.9	15.5	9.8	6.9
100	84.9	73.5	60.0	42.4	26.8	23.2	19.0	13.4	8.5	6.0
250	53.7	46.5	37.9	26.8	17.0	14.7	12.0	8.5	5.4	3.8
500	37.9	32.9	26.8	19.0	12.0	10.4	8.5	6.0	3.8	2.7
750	31.0	26.8	21.9	15.5	9.8	8.5	6.9	4.9	3.1	2.2
1,000	26.8	23.2	19.0	13.4	8.5	7.3	6.0	4.2	2.7	1.9
2,500	17.0	14.7	12.0	8.5	5.4	4.6	3.8	2.7	1.7	1.2
5,000	12.0	10.4	8.5	6.0	3.8	3.3	2.7	1.9	1.2	.8
7,500	9.8	8.5	6.9	4.9	3.1	2.7	2.2	1.5	1.0	.7
10,000	8.5	7.3	6.0	4.2	2.7	2.3	1.9	1.3	.8	.6
25,000	5.4	4.6	3.8	2.7	1.7	1.5	1.2	.8	.5	.4
50,000	3.8	3.3	2.7	1.9	1.2	1.0	.8	.6	.4	.3
75,000	3.1	2.7	2.2	1.5	1.0	.8	.7	.5	.3	.2
100,000	2.7	2.3	1.9	1.3	.8	.7	.6	.4	.3	.2
250,000	1.7	1.5	1.2	.8	.5	.5	.4	.3	.2	.1
500,000	1.2	1.0	.8	.6	.4	.3	.3	.2	.1	.1
1,000,000	.8	.7	.6	.4	.3	.2	.2	.1	.1	.1

s = Economic Order plus Hold Cost / Cost per Unit

R \ A	1000	750	500	250	100	75	50	25	10	5
10	8.94	7.75	6.32	4.47	2.83	2.45	2.00	1.41	.89	.63
25	5.66	4.90	4.00	2.83	1.79	1.55	1.26	.89	.57	.40
50	4.00	3.46	2.83	2.00	1.26	1.10	.89	.63	.40	.28
75	3.27	2.83	2.31	1.63	1.03	.89	.73	.52	.33	.23
100	2.83	2.45	2.00	1.41	.89	.77	.63	.45	.28	.20
250	1.79	1.55	1.26	.89	.57	.49	.40	.28	.18	.13
500	1.26	1.10	.89	.63	.40	.35	.28	.20	.13	.09
750	1.03	.89	.73	.52	.33	.28	.23	.16	.10	.07
1,000	.89	.77	.63	.45	.28	.24	.20	.14	.09	.06
2,500	.57	.49	.40	.28	.18	.15	.13	.09	.06	.04
5,000	.40	.35	.28	.20	.13	.11	.09	.06	.04	.03
7,500	.33	.28	.23	.16	.10	.09	.07	.05	.03	.02
10,000	.28	.24	.20	.14	.09	.08	.06	.04	.03	.02
25,000	.18	.15	.13	.09	.06	.05	.04	.03	.02	.01
50,000	.13	.11	.09	.06	.04	.03	.03	.02	.01	.01
75,000	.10	.09	.07	.05	.03	.03	.02	.02	.01	.01
100,000	.09	.08	.06	.04	.03	.02	.02	.01	.01	.01
250,000	.06	.05	.04	.03	.02	.02	.01	.01	.01	.00
500,000	.04	.03	.03	.02	.01	.01	.01	.01	.00	.00
1,000,000	.03	.02	.02	.01	.01	.01	.01	.00	.00	.00

A = Annual Demand

R = Cost to Order/Cost per Unit

Table 2.4 Order Quantities and Stocking Costs for the Simple Lot Size Model
(Continued)

h = 40% (Annual Holding Rate)

M = Economic Order Quantity in Months of Demand

A \ R	3	1	.8	.6	.4	.2	.1	.07	.03	.01
10	14.7	8.5	7.6	6.6	5.4	3.8	2.7	2.2	1.5	.8
25	9.3	5.4	4.8	4.2	3.4	2.4	1.7	1.4	.9	.5
50	6.6	3.8	3.4	2.9	2.4	1.7	1.2	1.0	.7	.4
75	5.4	3.1	2.8	2.4	2.0	1.4	1.0	.8	.5	.3
100	4.6	2.7	2.4	2.1	1.7	1.2	.8	.7	.5	.3
250	2.9	1.7	1.5	1.3	1.1	.8	.5	.4	.3	.2
500	2.1	1.2	1.1	.9	.8	.5	.4	.3	.2	.1
750	1.7	1.0	.9	.8	.6	.4	.3	.3	.2	.1
1,000	1.5	.8	.8	.7	.5	.4	.3	.2	.1	.1
2,500	.9	.5	.5	.4	.3	.2	.2	.1	.1	.1
5,000	.7	.4	.3	.3	.2	.2	.1	.1	.1	.0
7,500	.5	.3	.3	.2	.2	.1	.1	.1	.1	.0
10,000	.5	.3	.2	.2	.2	.1	.1	.1	.0	.0
25,000	.3	.2	.2	.1	.1	.1	.1	.0	.0	.0
50,000	.2	.1	.1	.1	.1	.1	.0	.0	.0	.0
75,000	.2	.1	.1	.1	.1	.0	.0	.0	.0	.0
100,000	.1	.1	.1	.1	.1	.0	.0	.0	.0	.0
250,000	.1	.1	.0	.0	.0	.0	.0	.0	.0	.0
500,000	.1	.0	.0	.0	.0	.0	.0	.0	.0	.0
1,000,000	.0	.0	.0	.0	.0	.0	.0	.0	.0	.0

s = Economic Order plus Hold Cost / Cost per Unit

A \ R	3	1	.8	.6	.4	.2	.1	.07	.03	.01
10	.49	.28	.25	.22	.18	.13	.09	.07	.05	.03
25	.31	.18	.16	.14	.11	.08	.06	.05	.03	.02
50	.22	.13	.11	.10	.08	.06	.04	.03	.02	.01
75	.18	.10	.09	.08	.07	.05	.03	.03	.02	.01
100	.15	.09	.08	.07	.06	.04	.03	.02	.02	.01
250	.10	.06	.05	.04	.04	.03	.02	.01	.01	.01
500	.07	.04	.04	.03	.03	.02	.01	.01	.01	.00
750	.06	.03	.03	.03	.02	.01	.01	.01	.01	.00
1,000	.05	.03	.03	.02	.02	.01	.01	.01	.00	.00
2,500	.03	.02	.02	.01	.01	.01	.01	.00	.00	.00
5,000	.02	.01	.01	.01	.01	.01	.00	.00	.00	.00
7,500	.02	.01	.01	.01	.01	.00	.00	.00	.00	.00
10,000	.02	.01	.01	.01	.01	.00	.00	.00	.00	.00
25,000	.01	.01	.01	.00	.00	.00	.00	.00	.00	.00
50,000	.01	.00	.00	.00	.00	.00	.00	.00	.00	.00
75,000	.01	.00	.00	.00	.00	.00	.00	.00	.00	.00
100,000	.00	.00	.00	.00	.00	.00	.00	.00	.00	.00
250,000	.00	.00	.00	.00	.00	.00	.00	.00	.00	.00
500,000	.00	.00	.00	.00	.00	.00	.00	.00	.00	.00
1,000,000	.00	.00	.00	.00	.00	.00	.00	.00	.00	.00

A = Annual Demand

R = Cost to Order/Cost per Unit

CHAPTER 3

Backorder Model

The simple lot size model can be modified to account for situations where it may be economical to allow shortages to occur (reference 1). An item may be out of stock for some demands; these unfilled demands, however, must be filled as soon as a sufficient replenishment quantity arrives. Unfilled demands, called backorders, may occur when the customer's need for the item cannot readily be substituted by another item or cannot be filled by another stocking outlet. If the stocking facility is out of stock, the customer may have little choice other than to wait until the next replenishment of stock arrives.

The model presented here seeks two corresponding quantities, the economic order quantity **Q** and the economic backorder quantity **B,** which in combination yield the minimum stocking cost. Here the stocking cost consists of the order cost plus holding cost plus backorder cost. The costs corresponding with the backorder are based on the length of time a unit is in a backorder position.

Data

The following data are needed in order to apply the model:

$$L = \text{lead time (in months)}$$
$$A = \text{annual demand}$$
$$C = \text{cost per unit}$$
$$Co = \text{cost per order}$$
$$Cb = \text{cost per backordered unit per month}$$
$$h = \text{annual holding rate}$$

Model

In this model, the economic order quantity **Q** and the economic backorder quantity **B** are determined for an item with a particular set of input data. These quantities **Q** and **B** are used along with the lead time **L** to carry out the reordering policy for the item. Note that the demand per month is **A/12** and the corresponding lead time demand is derived from the relation:

$$D_L = A \, L/12$$

D_L and **B** are now used to set the order point quantity **OP**:

$$OP = D_L - B$$

Therefore, when the on-hand plus on-order (OH + OO) inventory reaches the order point, a replenishment of size **Q** is ordered. This replenishment is received one lead time after placing the order (as shown in Figure 3.1).

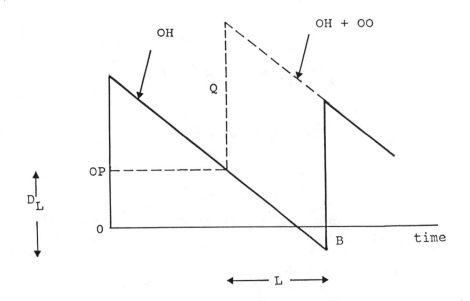

Figure 3.1. Inventory flow for the backorder model

In seeking the optimum sizes of **Q** and **B** for an item, a cost relation including the order, holding and backorder cost is developed. In a general situation, if **Q′** represents an arbitrary order quantity and **B′** the associated backorder when the replacement quantity is received, then the annual stocking cost is derived from the relation:

$$K(Q', B') = A\,Co/Q' + Ch\,(Q' - B')^2/2Q' + 12\,Cb\,(B')^2/2Q'$$

that is,

$$K(Q', B') = (\text{order cost}) + (\text{holding cost}) + (\text{backorder cost})$$

By using the cost relation above, optimizing methods are now applied to determine the values of **Q′** and **B′** that yield the minimum overall cost for an item. The economic order quantity **Q** becomes:

$$Q = \sqrt{\left(\frac{12\,Cb + hC}{12\,Cb}\right)\left(\frac{2\,A\,Co}{C\,h}\right)} = \sqrt{\frac{12\,Cb + hC}{12\,Cb}} \quad (Qo)$$

where **Qo** denotes the economic order quantity when the simple lot size model is used.

The corresponding economic backorder quantity **B** is obtained by the relation:

$$B = \sqrt{\frac{h\,C\ \ 2\,A\,Co}{12\,Cb\,(12\,Cb + h\,C)}}$$

In order to calculate the annual cost associated with the economic quantities **Q** and **B**, the cost function **K(Q, B)** given earlier is used. For a particular item, **Q** and **B** are used along with the pertaining input data.

As in the simple lot size model, the stocking cost represents the add-on cost for an item that is caused from stocking the item in the inventory. In this backorder model this sum is the combined costs for ordering, holding and backorders. The stocking rate **s** measures the percent of the stocking cost in relation to the procurement cost. This rate is obtained from the relation:

$$s = K\,(Q, B)/A\,C$$

The effective cost **C′** for the item can now be determined. This is the sum of the procurement cost plus the stocking cost and is derived from:

$$C' = C\,(1 + s)$$

Tables

For convenience in using the tables of this chapter, three of the above input data are combined to yield the following input parameters:

$$R = Co/C \text{ (cost per order/cost per unit)}$$
$$b = Cb/C \text{ (backorder cost per month/cost per unit)}$$

Also for later use in the tables, the following coefficients **Xq** and **Xb** are here defined:

$$Xq = \sqrt{\frac{12\,b + h}{12\,b}}$$

$$Xb = \sqrt{\frac{h^2}{12\,b\,(12\,b + h)}}$$

These coefficients are used to express **Q** and **B** for this backorder model in relation to the economic order quantity **Qo** from the simple lot size model, i.e.:

$$Q = Xq\,Qo$$
$$B = Xb\,Qo$$

The adjoining tables give results for **Q** and **B** in terms of their months of demand. These monthly values are derived by dividing **Q** and **B** by the average demand per month, **A/12**. These results give, first, the economic months of the order quantity **Mq** where:

$$Mq = 12\,Q/A$$

and second, the economic months of the backorder quantity **Mb** where:

$$Mb = 12\,B/A$$

Moreover, the values of **Mq** and **Mb** are also related to **M** (the economic months of demand in the order quantity from the simple lot size model). These relations are as follows:

$$Mq = Xq\,M$$
$$Mb = Xb\,M$$

Table 3.9 lists the calculated values of **Xq** and **Xb** for selected combinations of **h** and **b**. These tables may be used along with Tables 2.1 to 2.4 (from the simple lot size model) to find the corresponding values for the backorder model. Using the values of **Mq** and **Mb**, the counterpart quantities, **Q** and **B,** respectively are easily found. These are:

$$Q = A\,Mq/12$$
$$B = A\,Mb/12$$

The tables of this chapter are arranged as follows. Tables 3.1 to 3.4 give values of **Mq** and **Mb** for selected values of **R, A, h** and **b**. Tables 3.5 to 3.8 list the corresponding values of **s** (the stocking rate). The coefficients **Xq** and **Xb** are listed in Table 3.9 for selected values of **b** and **h**.

Table	Contents
3.1	Mq and Mb with h = .2 and b = .2
3.2	Mq and Mb with h = .2 and b = .4
3.3	Mq and Mb with h = .3 and b = .2
3.4	Mq and Mb with h = .3 and b = .4
3.5	s with h = .2 and b = .2
3.6	s with h = .2 and b = .4
3.7	s with h = .3 and b = .2
3.8	s with h = .3 and b = .4
3.9	Xq and Xb

Just-in-Time Applications

As was the case in Chapter 2, the above tables are useful to management seeking to apply Just-in-Time (JIT) methods. In JIT, cost is not always considered as the primary factor (as waste is) but is a significant ancillary consideration. The ratio R = cost per order over cost per unit and A = annual demand are related to the month's supply in the order quantity. One goal of Just-in-Time is to reduce the order quantity to attain lower inventory investments. With use of the tables, management may quickly sort out those items (according to item demands) that are not compatible to JIT methods. Furthermore, management may determine the magnitude of the decrease in cost per order that must be attained in order to provide an order quantity that would make processing on a JIT basis profitable and feasible.

Example 3.1

Consider a parts distribution center that stocks an automobile engine hose with annual demand of 1000 units. The procurement cost per unit is $2 and the cost per order is $100. Suppose also the holding rate is 30 percent per year and the backorder cost for a unit is $0.80 per month. Find the economic order quantity **Q** and backorder quantity **B** for the engine hose along with the effective cost for the item.

First note that A = 1000, R = 100/2 = 50, h = .30 and b = 0.80/2 = 0.40. Table 3.4 is used, where the values Mq = 7.1 and Mb = 0.4 are obtained. Since the average monthly demand is 1000/12 = 83.33,

$$Q = 7.1\,(83.33) = 592$$
$$B = 0.4\,(83.33) = 33$$

Second, the associated stocking rate is now found from Table 3.8, where s = 0.17. Now the effective cost **C'** becomes:

$$C' = 2\,(1 + .17) = \$2.34$$

Example 3.2

For the engine hose in Example 3.1, suppose management wishes to determine the annual cost associated with ordering, holding and backordering. The economic order quantity and backorder quantity will be Q = 592 and B = 33, respectively.

For this computation, the cost relation **K (Q, B)** is used, where the costs associated with ordering, holding and backordering are partitioned as shown below.

First, the annual ordering cost becomes:

$$A\,C_o/Q = 1000\,(100)/592 = \$168.92$$

Second, the annual holding cost becomes:

$$\frac{C\,h\,(Q-B)^2}{2Q} = \frac{2\,(.3)\,(592-33)^2}{2\,(592)} = 158.35$$

and third, the annual backorder cost is:

$$\frac{12\,C_b\,B^2}{2\,Q} = \frac{12\,(0.80)\,33^2}{2\,(592)} = 8.83$$

Now the total annual cost of stocking the item is:

$$\$168.92 + \$158.35 + \$8.83 = \$336.10$$

Finally, the stocking rate is:

$$s = K\,(Q,\,B)/C\,A = 336.10/2\,(1000) = .17$$

Example 3.3

For the engine hose in Example 3.1, find the order point assuming the lead time is five months.

Since $L = 5$ months and the monthly demand is 83.33, the lead time demand D_L is:

$$D_L = 5\,(83.33) = 416.7 = 417$$

The order point now becomes:

$$OP = D_L - B = 417 - 33 = 384$$

When the on-hand plus on-order inventory quantity reaches 384, an order point replenishment for $Q = 592$ units is placed with the supplier.

Example 3.4

For the engine hose in Example 3.1, find the average on-hand inventory and the average backorder quantity over the order cycle.

For this purpose, recall $M_q = 7.1$, $M_b = 0.4$, $Q = 592$ and $B = 33$. Note Figure 3.2, where the order cycle covers 7.1 months and the average on hand becomes $(Q - B)/2 = (592 - 33)/2 = 559/2 = 279.5$ for $(7.1 - 0.4) = 6.7$ months and zero for 0.40 months. The average stock on hand over the order cycle is:

$$[279.5\,(6.7) + 0\,(0.4)]\,/\,7.1 = 263.8$$

The maximum backorder for the order cycle is 33 units, and the backorders build up to this value for 0.4 months. The average number of backorders during the order cycle is thus $33/2 = 16.5$ for 0.40 months and zero for 6.7 months. The average backorders for the 7.1 months of the order cycle is:

$$[0\,(6.7) + 16.5\,(0.4)]\,/\,7.1 = 0.9$$

Notice, also, that the net on-hand inventory over the order cycle is $(263.8 - 0.9) = 262.9$.

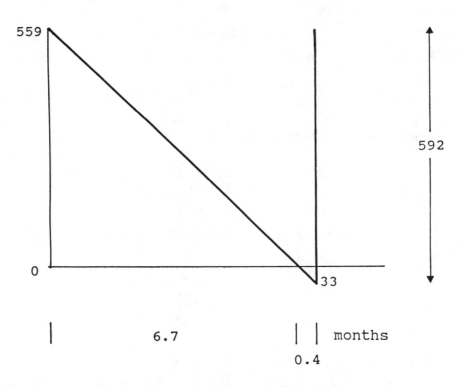

Figure 3.2. Flow of inventory for Example 3.4

Example 3.5

Compare the results from Examples 3.1 to 3.4 with the counterpart findings from the simple lot size model (b = 0). In order to perform the above calculation for the simple lot size model, Table 2.3 (h = .3) is used along with A = 1000, R = 50, C = 2 and Co = 100. The comparison results are summarized below:

	Simple Lot Size Model	Backorder Model
Mq	6.9	7.1
Mb	0	0.4
Q	575	592
B	0	33
s	0.17	0.17
C′	$2.34	$2.34
order cost	$173.91	$168.92
holding cost	$172.50	$158.35
backorder cost	$0	$8.83
total cost	$346.41	$336.10
order point	417	384
net on-hand	287.5	262.9

Example 3.6

Consider an item where the simple lot size model is used with an annual holding rate of .25 and where the economic order quantity becomes

Qo = 200. Find the economic order quantity for this item using the backorder model with b = .50 and with h = .25.

Table 3.9, used here, indicates Xq = 1.02 and Xb = 0.04. So,

$$Q = 1.02 \, (200) = 204$$
$$B = 0.04 \, (200) = 8$$

Table 3.1 Order and Backorder Quantities for the Backorder Model

h = 20% (Annual Holding Rate)

b = 20% (Monthly Cost per Backorder / Cost per Unit)

Mq = Economic Order Quantity in Months of Demand

A \ R	1000	750	500	250	100	75	50	25	10	5
10	395.0	342.1	279.3	197.5	124.9	108.2	88.3	62.4	39.5	27.9
25	249.8	216.3	176.6	124.9	79.0	68.4	55.9	39.5	25.0	17.7
50	176.6	153.0	124.9	88.3	55.9	48.4	39.5	27.9	17.7	12.5
75	144.2	124.9	102.0	72.1	45.6	39.5	32.2	22.8	14.4	10.2
100	124.9	108.2	88.3	62.4	39.5	34.2	27.9	19.7	12.5	8.8
250	79.0	68.4	55.9	39.5	25.0	21.6	17.7	12.5	7.9	5.6
500	55.9	48.4	39.5	27.9	17.7	15.3	12.5	8.8	5.6	3.9
750	45.6	39.5	32.2	22.8	14.4	12.5	10.2	7.2	4.6	3.2
1,000	39.5	34.2	27.9	19.7	12.5	10.8	8.8	6.2	3.9	2.8
2,500	25.0	21.6	17.7	12.5	7.9	6.8	5.6	3.9	2.5	1.8
5,000	17.7	15.3	12.5	8.8	5.6	4.8	3.9	2.8	1.8	1.2
7,500	14.4	12.5	10.2	7.2	4.6	3.9	3.2	2.3	1.4	1.0
10,000	12.5	10.8	8.8	6.2	3.9	3.4	2.8	2.0	1.2	.9
25,000	7.9	6.8	5.6	3.9	2.5	2.2	1.8	1.2	.8	.6
50,000	5.6	4.8	3.9	2.8	1.8	1.5	1.2	.9	.6	.4
75,000	4.6	3.9	3.2	2.3	1.4	1.2	1.0	.7	.5	.3
100,000	3.9	3.4	2.8	2.0	1.2	1.1	.9	.6	.4	.3
250,000	2.5	2.2	1.8	1.2	.8	.7	.6	.4	.2	.2
500,000	1.8	1.5	1.2	.9	.6	.5	.4	.3	.2	.1
1,000,000	1.2	1.1	.9	.6	.4	.3	.3	.2	.1	.1

Mb = Economic Backorder Quantity in Months of Demand

A \ R	1000	750	500	250	100	75	50	25	10	5
10	30.4	26.3	21.5	15.2	9.6	8.3	6.8	4.8	3.0	2.1
25	19.2	16.6	13.6	9.6	6.1	5.3	4.3	3.0	1.9	1.4
50	13.6	11.8	9.6	6.8	4.3	3.7	3.0	2.1	1.4	1.0
75	11.1	9.6	7.8	5.5	3.5	3.0	2.5	1.8	1.1	.8
100	9.6	8.3	6.8	4.8	3.0	2.6	2.1	1.5	1.0	.7
250	6.1	5.3	4.3	3.0	1.9	1.7	1.4	1.0	.6	.4
500	4.3	3.7	3.0	2.1	1.4	1.2	1.0	.7	.4	.3
750	3.5	3.0	2.5	1.8	1.1	1.0	.8	.6	.4	.2
1,000	3.0	2.6	2.1	1.5	1.0	.8	.7	.5	.3	.2
2,500	1.9	1.7	1.4	1.0	.6	.5	.4	.3	.2	.1
5,000	1.4	1.2	1.0	.7	.4	.4	.3	.2	.1	.1
7,500	1.1	1.0	.8	.6	.4	.3	.2	.2	.1	.1
10,000	1.0	.8	.7	.5	.3	.3	.2	.2	.1	.1
25,000	.6	.5	.4	.3	.2	.2	.1	.1	.1	.0
50,000	.4	.4	.3	.2	.1	.1	.1	.1	.0	.0
75,000	.4	.3	.2	.2	.1	.1	.1	.1	.0	.0
100,000	.3	.3	.2	.2	.1	.1	.1	.0	.0	.0
250,000	.2	.2	.1	.1	.1	.1	.0	.0	.0	.0
500,000	.1	.1	.1	.1	.0	.0	.0	.0	.0	.0
1,000,000	.1	.1	.1	.0	.0	.0	.0	.0	.0	.0

A = Annual Demand

R = Cost to Order / Cost per Unit

Table 3.1 Order and Backorder Quantities for the Backorder Model
(Continued)

h = 20% (Annual Holding Rate)

b = 20% (Monthly Cost per Backorder / Cost per Unit)

Mq = Economic Order Quantity in Months of Demand

A \ R	3	1	.8	.6	.4	.2	.1	.07	.03	.01
10	21.6	12.5	11.2	9.7	7.9	5.6	3.9	3.3	2.2	1.2
25	13.7	7.9	7.1	6.1	5.0	3.5	2.5	2.1	1.4	.8
50	9.7	5.6	5.0	4.3	3.5	2.5	1.8	1.5	1.0	.6
75	7.9	4.6	4.1	3.5	2.9	2.0	1.4	1.2	.8	.5
100	6.8	3.9	3.5	3.1	2.5	1.8	1.2	1.0	.7	.4
250	4.3	2.5	2.2	1.9	1.6	1.1	.8	.7	.4	.2
500	3.1	1.8	1.6	1.4	1.1	.8	.6	.5	.3	.2
750	2.5	1.4	1.3	1.1	.9	.6	.5	.4	.2	.1
1,000	2.2	1.2	1.1	1.0	.8	.6	.4	.3	.2	.1
2,500	1.4	.8	.7	.6	.5	.4	.2	.2	.1	.1
5,000	1.0	.6	.5	.4	.4	.2	.2	.1	.1	.1
7,500	.8	.5	.4	.4	.3	.2	.1	.1	.1	.0
10,000	.7	.4	.4	.3	.2	.2	.1	.1	.1	.0
25,000	.4	.2	.2	.2	.2	.1	.1	.1	.0	.0
50,000	.3	.2	.2	.1	.1	.1	.1	.0	.0	.0
75,000	.2	.1	.1	.1	.1	.1	.0	.0	.0	.0
100,000	.2	.1	.1	.1	.1	.1	.0	.0	.0	.0
250,000	.1	.1	.1	.1	.0	.0	.0	.0	.0	.0
500,000	.1	.1	.0	.0	.0	.0	.0	.0	.0	.0
1,000,000	.1	.0	.0	.0	.0	.0	.0	.0	.0	.0

Mb = Economic Backorder Quantity in Months of Demand

A \ R	3	1	.8	.6	.4	.2	.1	.07	.03	.01
10	1.7	1.0	.9	.7	.6	.4	.3	.3	.2	.1
25	1.1	.6	.5	.5	.4	.3	.2	.2	.1	.1
50	.7	.4	.4	.3	.3	.2	.1	.1	.1	.0
75	.6	.4	.3	.3	.2	.2	.1	.1	.1	.0
100	.5	.3	.3	.2	.2	.1	.1	.1	.1	.0
250	.3	.2	.2	.1	.1	.1	.1	.1	.0	.0
500	.2	.1	.1	.1	.1	.1	.0	.0	.0	.0
750	.2	.1	.1	.1	.1	.0	.0	.0	.0	.0
1,000	.2	.1	.1	.1	.1	.0	.0	.0	.0	.0
2,500	.1	.1	.1	.0	.0	.0	.0	.0	.0	.0
5,000	.1	.0	.0	.0	.0	.0	.0	.0	.0	.0
7,500	.1	.0	.0	.0	.0	.0	.0	.0	.0	.0
10,000	.1	.0	.0	.0	.0	.0	.0	.0	.0	.0
25,000	.0	.0	.0	.0	.0	.0	.0	.0	.0	.0
50,000	.0	.0	.0	.0	.0	.0	.0	.0	.0	.0
75,000	.0	.0	.0	.0	.0	.0	.0	.0	.0	.0
100,000	.0	.0	.0	.0	.0	.0	.0	.0	.0	.0
250,000	.0	.0	.0	.0	.0	.0	.0	.0	.0	.0
500,000	.0	.0	.0	.0	.0	.0	.0	.0	.0	.0
1,000,000	.0	.0	.0	.0	.0	.0	.0	.0	.0	.0

A = Annual Demand

R = Cost to Order / Cost per Unit

Table 3.2 Order and Backorder Quantities for the Backorder Model

h = 20% (Annual Holding Rate)
b = 40% (Monthly Cost per Backorder / Cost per Unit)

Mq = Economic Order Quantity in Months of Demand

A \ R	1000	750	500	250	100	75	50	25	10	5
10	387.3	335.4	273.9	193.6	122.5	106.1	86.6	61.2	38.7	27.4
25	244.9	212.1	173.2	122.5	77.5	67.1	54.8	38.7	24.5	17.3
50	173.2	150.0	122.5	86.6	54.8	47.4	38.7	27.4	17.3	12.2
75	141.4	122.5	100.0	70.7	44.7	38.7	31.6	22.4	14.1	10.0
100	122.5	106.1	86.6	61.2	38.7	33.5	27.4	19.4	12.2	8.7
250	77.5	67.1	54.8	38.7	24.5	21.2	17.3	12.2	7.7	5.5
500	54.8	47.4	38.7	27.4	17.3	15.0	12.2	8.7	5.5	3.9
750	44.7	38.7	31.6	22.4	14.1	12.2	10.0	7.1	4.5	3.2
1,000	38.7	33.5	27.4	19.4	12.2	10.6	8.7	6.1	3.9	2.7
2,500	24.5	21.2	17.3	12.2	7.7	6.7	5.5	3.9	2.4	1.7
5,000	17.3	15.0	12.2	8.7	5.5	4.7	3.9	2.7	1.7	1.2
7,500	14.1	12.2	10.0	7.1	4.5	3.9	3.2	2.2	1.4	1.0
10,000	12.2	10.6	8.7	6.1	3.9	3.4	2.7	1.9	1.2	.9
25,000	7.7	6.7	5.5	3.9	2.4	2.1	1.7	1.2	.8	.5
50,000	5.5	4.7	3.9	2.7	1.7	1.5	1.2	.9	.5	.4
75,000	4.5	3.9	3.2	2.2	1.4	1.2	1.0	.7	.4	.3
100,000	3.9	3.4	2.7	1.9	1.2	1.1	.9	.6	.4	.3
250,000	2.4	2.1	1.7	1.2	.8	.7	.5	.4	.2	.2
500,000	1.7	1.5	1.2	.9	.5	.5	.4	.3	.2	.1
1,000,000	1.2	1.1	.9	.6	.4	.3	.3	.2	.1	.1

Mb = Economic Backorder Quantity in Months of Demand

A \ R	1000	750	500	250	100	75	50	25	10	5
10	15.5	13.4	11.0	7.7	4.9	4.2	3.5	2.4	1.5	1.1
25	9.8	8.5	6.9	4.9	3.1	2.7	2.2	1.5	1.0	.7
50	6.9	6.0	4.9	3.5	2.2	1.9	1.5	1.1	.7	.5
75	5.7	4.9	4.0	2.8	1.8	1.5	1.3	.9	.6	.4
100	4.9	4.2	3.5	2.4	1.5	1.3	1.1	.8	.5	.3
250	3.1	2.7	2.2	1.5	1.0	.8	.7	.5	.3	.2
500	2.2	1.9	1.5	1.1	.7	.6	.5	.3	.2	.2
750	1.8	1.5	1.3	.9	.6	.5	.4	.3	.2	.1
1,000	1.5	1.3	1.1	.8	.5	.4	.3	.2	.2	.1
2,500	1.0	.8	.7	.5	.3	.3	.2	.2	.1	.1
5,000	.7	.6	.5	.3	.2	.2	.2	.1	.1	.0
7,500	.6	.5	.4	.3	.2	.2	.1	.1	.1	.0
10,000	.5	.4	.3	.2	.2	.1	.1	.1	.0	.0
25,000	.3	.3	.2	.2	.1	.1	.1	.0	.0	.0
50,000	.2	.2	.2	.1	.1	.1	.0	.0	.0	.0
75,000	.2	.2	.1	.1	.1	.0	.0	.0	.0	.0
100,000	.2	.1	.1	.1	.0	.0	.0	.0	.0	.0
250,000	.1	.1	.1	.0	.0	.0	.0	.0	.0	.0
500,000	.1	.1	.0	.0	.0	.0	.0	.0	.0	.0
1,000,000	.0	.0	.0	.0	.0	.0	.0	.0	.0	.0

A = Annual Demand
R = Cost to Order / Cost per Unit

Table 3.2 Order and Backorder Quantities for the Backorder Model (Continued)

h = 20% (Annual Holding Rate)

b = 40% (Monthly Cost per Backorder / Cost per Unit)

Mq = Economic Order Quantity in Months of Demand

A \ R	3	1	.8	.6	.4	.2	.1	.07	.03	.01
10	21.2	12.2	11.0	9.5	7.7	5.5	3.9	3.2	2.1	1.2
25	13.4	7.7	6.9	6.0	4.9	3.5	2.4	2.0	1.3	.8
50	9.5	5.5	4.9	4.2	3.5	2.4	1.7	1.4	.9	.5
75	7.7	4.5	4.0	3.5	2.8	2.0	1.4	1.2	.8	.4
100	6.7	3.9	3.5	3.0	2.4	1.7	1.2	1.0	.7	.4
250	4.2	2.4	2.2	1.9	1.5	1.1	.8	.6	.4	.2
500	3.0	1.7	1.5	1.3	1.1	.8	.5	.5	.3	.2
750	2.4	1.4	1.3	1.1	.9	.6	.4	.4	.2	.1
1,000	2.1	1.2	1.1	.9	.8	.5	.4	.3	.2	.1
2,500	1.3	.8	.7	.6	.5	.3	.2	.2	.1	.1
5,000	.9	.5	.5	.4	.3	.2	.2	.1	.1	.1
7,500	.8	.4	.4	.3	.3	.2	.1	.1	.1	.0
10,000	.7	.4	.3	.3	.2	.2	.1	.1	.1	.0
25,000	.4	.2	.2	.2	.2	.1	.1	.1	.0	.0
50,000	.3	.2	.2	.1	.1	.1	.1	.0	.0	.0
75,000	.2	.1	.1	.1	.1	.1	.0	.0	.0	.0
100,000	.2	.1	.1	.1	.1	.1	.0	.0	.0	.0
250,000	.1	.1	.1	.1	.0	.0	.0	.0	.0	.0
500,000	.1	.1	.0	.0	.0	.0	.0	.0	.0	.0
1,000,000	.1	.0	.0	.0	.0	.0	.0	.0	.0	.0

Mb = Economic Backorder Quantity in Months of Demand

A \ R	3	1	.8	.6	.4	.2	.1	.07	.03	.01
10	.8	.5	.4	.4	.3	.2	.2	.1	.1	.0
25	.5	.3	.3	.2	.2	.1	.1	.1	.1	.0
50	.4	.2	.2	.2	.1	.1	.1	.1	.0	.0
75	.3	.2	.2	.1	.1	.1	.1	.0	.0	.0
100	.3	.2	.1	.1	.1	.1	.0	.0	.0	.0
250	.2	.1	.1	.1	.1	.0	.0	.0	.0	.0
500	.1	.1	.1	.1	.0	.0	.0	.0	.0	.0
750	.1	.1	.1	.0	.0	.0	.0	.0	.0	.0
1,000	.1	.0	.0	.0	.0	.0	.0	.0	.0	.0
2,500	.1	.0	.0	.0	.0	.0	.0	.0	.0	.0
5,000	.0	.0	.0	.0	.0	.0	.0	.0	.0	.0
7,500	.0	.0	.0	.0	.0	.0	.0	.0	.0	.0
10,000	.0	.0	.0	.0	.0	.0	.0	.0	.0	.0
25,000	.0	.0	.0	.0	.0	.0	.0	.0	.0	.0
50,000	.0	.0	.0	.0	.0	.0	.0	.0	.0	.0
75,000	.0	.0	.0	.0	.0	.0	.0	.0	.0	.0
100,000	.0	.0	.0	.0	.0	.0	.0	.0	.0	.0
250,000	.0	.0	.0	.0	.0	.0	.0	.0	.0	.0
500,000	.0	.0	.0	.0	.0	.0	.0	.0	.0	.0
1,000,000	.0	.0	.0	.0	.0	.0	.0	.0	.0	.0

A = Annual Demand

R = Cost to Order / Cost per Unit

Table 3.3 Order and Backorder Quantities for the Backorder Model

h = 30% (Annual Holding Rate)
b = 20% (Monthly Cost per Backorder / Cost per Unit)

Mq = Economic Order Quantity in Months of Demand

A \ R	1000	750	500	250	100	75	50	25	10	5
10	328.6	284.6	232.4	164.3	103.9	90.0	73.5	52.0	32.9	23.2
25	207.8	180.0	147.0	103.9	65.7	56.9	46.5	32.9	20.8	14.7
50	147.0	127.3	103.9	73.5	46.5	40.2	32.9	23.2	14.7	10.4
75	120.0	103.9	84.9	60.0	37.9	32.9	26.8	19.0	12.0	8.5
100	103.9	90.0	73.5	52.0	32.9	28.5	23.2	16.4	10.4	7.3
250	65.7	56.9	46.5	32.9	20.8	18.0	14.7	10.4	6.6	4.6
500	46.5	40.2	32.9	23.2	14.7	12.7	10.4	7.3	4.6	3.3
750	37.9	32.9	26.8	19.0	12.0	10.4	8.5	6.0	3.8	2.7
1,000	32.9	28.5	23.2	16.4	10.4	9.0	7.3	5.2	3.3	2.3
2,500	20.8	18.0	14.7	10.4	6.6	5.7	4.6	3.3	2.1	1.5
5,000	14.7	12.7	10.4	7.3	4.6	4.0	3.3	2.3	1.5	1.0
7,500	12.0	10.4	8.5	6.0	3.8	3.3	2.7	1.9	1.2	.8
10,000	10.4	9.0	7.3	5.2	3.3	2.8	2.3	1.6	1.0	.7
25,000	6.6	5.7	4.6	3.3	2.1	1.8	1.5	1.0	.7	.5
50,000	4.6	4.0	3.3	2.3	1.5	1.3	1.0	.7	.5	.3
75,000	3.8	3.3	2.7	1.9	1.2	1.0	.8	.6	.4	.3
100,000	3.3	2.8	2.3	1.6	1.0	.9	.7	.5	.3	.2
250,000	2.1	1.8	1.5	1.0	.7	.6	.5	.3	.2	.1
500,000	1.5	1.3	1.0	.7	.5	.4	.3	.2	.1	.1
1,000,000	1.0	.9	.7	.5	.3	.3	.2	.2	.1	.1

Mb = Economic Backorder Quantity in Months of Demand

A \ R	1000	750	500	250	100	75	50	25	10	5
10	36.5	31.6	25.8	18.3	11.5	10.0	8.2	5.8	3.7	2.6
25	23.1	20.0	16.3	11.5	7.3	6.3	5.2	3.7	2.3	1.6
50	16.3	14.1	11.5	8.2	5.2	4.5	3.7	2.6	1.6	1.2
75	13.3	11.5	9.4	6.7	4.2	3.7	3.0	2.1	1.3	.9
100	11.5	10.0	8.2	5.8	3.7	3.2	2.6	1.8	1.2	.8
250	7.3	6.3	5.2	3.7	2.3	2.0	1.6	1.2	.7	.5
500	5.2	4.5	3.7	2.6	1.6	1.4	1.2	.8	.5	.4
750	4.2	3.7	3.0	2.1	1.3	1.2	.9	.7	.4	.3
1,000	3.7	3.2	2.6	1.8	1.2	1.0	.8	.6	.4	.3
2,500	2.3	2.0	1.6	1.2	.7	.6	.5	.4	.2	.2
5,000	1.6	1.4	1.2	.8	.5	.4	.4	.3	.2	.1
7,500	1.3	1.2	.9	.7	.4	.4	.3	.2	.1	.1
10,000	1.2	1.0	.8	.6	.4	.3	.3	.2	.1	.1
25,000	.7	.6	.5	.4	.2	.2	.2	.1	.1	.1
50,000	.5	.4	.4	.3	.2	.1	.1	.1	.1	.0
75,000	.4	.4	.3	.2	.1	.1	.1	.1	.0	.0
100,000	.4	.3	.3	.2	.1	.1	.1	.1	.0	.0
250,000	.2	.2	.2	.1	.1	.1	.1	.0	.0	.0
500,000	.2	.1	.1	.1	.1	.0	.0	.0	.0	.0
1,000,000	.1	.1	.1	.1	.0	.0	.0	.0	.0	.0

A = Annual Demand
R = Cost to Order / Cost per Unit

Table 3.3 Order and Backorder Quantities for the Backorder Model
(Continued)

h = 30% (Annual Holding Rate)

b = 20% (Monthly Cost per Backorder / Cost per Unit)

Mq = Economic Order Quantity in Months of Demand

A \ R	3	1	.8	.6	.4	.2	.1	.07	.03	.01
10	18.0	10.4	9.3	8.0	6.6	4.6	3.3	2.7	1.8	1.0
25	11.4	6.6	5.9	5.1	4.2	2.9	2.1	1.7	1.1	.7
50	8.0	4.6	4.2	3.6	2.9	2.1	1.5	1.2	.8	.5
75	6.6	3.8	3.4	2.9	2.4	1.7	1.2	1.0	.7	.4
100	5.7	3.3	2.9	2.5	2.1	1.5	1.0	.9	.6	.3
250	3.6	2.1	1.9	1.6	1.3	.9	.7	.5	.4	.2
500	2.5	1.5	1.3	1.1	.9	.7	.5	.4	.3	.1
750	2.1	1.2	1.1	.9	.8	.5	.4	.3	.2	.1
1,000	1.8	1.0	.9	.8	.7	.5	.3	.3	.2	.1
2,500	1.1	.7	.6	.5	.4	.3	.2	.2	.1	.1
5,000	.8	.5	.4	.4	.3	.2	.1	.1	.1	.0
7,500	.7	.4	.3	.3	.2	.2	.1	.1	.1	.0
10,000	.6	.3	.3	.3	.2	.1	.1	.1	.1	.0
25,000	.4	.2	.2	.2	.1	.1	.1	.1	.0	.0
50,000	.3	.1	.1	.1	.1	.1	.0	.0	.0	.0
75,000	.2	.1	.1	.1	.1	.1	.0	.0	.0	.0
100,000	.2	.1	.1	.1	.1	.0	.0	.0	.0	.0
250,000	.1	.1	.1	.1	.0	.0	.0	.0	.0	.0
500,000	.1	.0	.0	.0	.0	.0	.0	.0	.0	.0
1,000,000	.1	.0	.0	.0	.0	.0	.0	.0	.0	.0

Mb = Economic Backorder Quantity in Months of Demand

A \ R	3	1	.8	.6	.4	.2	.1	.07	.03	.01
10	2.0	1.2	1.0	.9	.7	.5	.4	.3	.2	.1
25	1.3	.7	.7	.6	.5	.3	.2	.2	.1	.1
50	.9	.5	.5	.4	.3	.2	.2	.1	.1	.1
75	.7	.4	.4	.3	.3	.2	.1	.1	.1	.0
100	.6	.4	.3	.3	.2	.2	.1	.1	.1	.0
250	.4	.2	.2	.2	.1	.1	.1	.1	.0	.0
500	.3	.2	.1	.1	.1	.1	.1	.0	.0	.0
750	.2	.1	.1	.1	.1	.1	.0	.0	.0	.0
1,000	.2	.1	.1	.1	.1	.1	.0	.0	.0	.0
2,500	.1	.1	.1	.1	.0	.0	.0	.0	.0	.0
5,000	.1	.1	.0	.0	.0	.0	.0	.0	.0	.0
7,500	.1	.0	.0	.0	.0	.0	.0	.0	.0	.0
10,000	.1	.0	.0	.0	.0	.0	.0	.0	.0	.0
25,000	.0	.0	.0	.0	.0	.0	.0	.0	.0	.0
50,000	.0	.0	.0	.0	.0	.0	.0	.0	.0	.0
75,000	.0	.0	.0	.0	.0	.0	.0	.0	.0	.0
100,000	.0	.0	.0	.0	.0	.0	.0	.0	.0	.0
250,000	.0	.0	.0	.0	.0	.0	.0	.0	.0	.0
500,000	.0	.0	.0	.0	.0	.0	.0	.0	.0	.0
1,000,000	.0	.0	.0	.0	.0	.0	.0	.0	.0	.0

A = Annual Demand

R = Cost to Order / Cost per Unit

Table 3.4 Order and Backorder Quantities for the Backorder Model

h = 30%   (Annual Holding Rate)
b = 40%   (Monthly Cost per Backorder / Cost per Unit)

Mq = Economic Order Quantity in Months of Demand

A \ R	1000	750	500	250	100	75	50	25	10	5
10	319.4	276.6	225.8	159.7	101.0	87.5	71.4	50.5	31.9	22.6
25	202.0	174.9	142.8	101.0	63.9	55.3	45.2	31.9	20.2	14.3
50	142.8	123.7	101.0	71.4	45.2	39.1	31.9	22.6	14.3	10.1
75	116.6	101.0	82.5	58.3	36.9	31.9	26.1	18.4	11.7	8.2
100	101.0	87.5	71.4	50.5	31.9	27.7	22.6	16.0	10.1	7.1
250	63.9	55.3	45.2	31.9	20.2	17.5	14.3	10.1	6.4	4.5
500	45.2	39.1	31.9	22.6	14.3	12.4	10.1	7.1	4.5	3.2
750	36.9	31.9	26.1	18.4	11.7	10.1	8.2	5.8	3.7	2.6
1,000	31.9	27.7	22.6	16.0	10.1	8.7	7.1	5.0	3.2	2.3
2,500	20.2	17.5	14.3	10.1	6.4	5.5	4.5	3.2	2.0	1.4
5,000	14.3	12.4	10.1	7.1	4.5	3.9	3.2	2.3	1.4	1.0
7,500	11.7	10.1	8.2	5.8	3.7	3.2	2.6	1.8	1.2	.8
10,000	10.1	8.7	7.1	5.0	3.2	2.8	2.3	1.6	1.0	.7
25,000	6.4	5.5	4.5	3.2	2.0	1.7	1.4	1.0	.6	.5
50,000	4.5	3.9	3.2	2.3	1.4	1.2	1.0	.7	.5	.3
75,000	3.7	3.2	2.6	1.8	1.2	1.0	.8	.6	.4	.3
100,000	3.2	2.8	2.3	1.6	1.0	.9	.7	.5	.3	.2
250,000	2.0	1.7	1.4	1.0	.6	.6	.5	.3	.2	.1
500,000	1.4	1.2	1.0	.7	.5	.4	.3	.2	.1	.1
1,000,000	1.0	.9	.7	.5	.3	.3	.2	.2	.1	.1

Mb = Economic Backorder Quantity in Months of Demand

A \ R	1000	750	500	250	100	75	50	25	10	5
10	18.8	16.3	13.3	9.4	5.9	5.1	4.2	3.0	1.9	1.3
25	11.9	10.3	8.4	5.9	3.8	3.3	2.7	1.9	1.2	.8
50	8.4	7.3	5.9	4.2	2.7	2.3	1.9	1.3	.8	.6
75	6.9	5.9	4.9	3.4	2.2	1.9	1.5	1.1	.7	.5
100	5.9	5.1	4.2	3.0	1.9	1.6	1.3	.9	.6	.4
250	3.8	3.3	2.7	1.9	1.2	1.0	.8	.6	.4	.3
500	2.7	2.3	1.9	1.3	.8	.7	.6	.4	.3	.2
750	2.2	1.9	1.5	1.1	.7	.6	.5	.3	.2	.2
1,000	1.9	1.6	1.3	.9	.6	.5	.4	.3	.2	.1
2,500	1.2	1.0	.8	.6	.4	.3	.3	.2	.1	.1
5,000	.8	.7	.6	.4	.3	.2	.2	.1	.1	.1
7,500	.7	.6	.5	.3	.2	.2	.2	.1	.1	.0
10,000	.6	.5	.4	.3	.2	.2	.1	.1	.1	.0
25,000	.4	.3	.3	.2	.1	.1	.1	.1	.0	.0
50,000	.3	.2	.2	.1	.1	.1	.1	.0	.0	.0
75,000	.2	.2	.2	.1	.1	.1	.0	.0	.0	.0
100,000	.2	.2	.1	.1	.1	.1	.0	.0	.0	.0
250,000	.1	.1	.1	.1	.0	.0	.0	.0	.0	.0
500,000	.1	.1	.1	.0	.0	.0	.0	.0	.0	.0
1,000,000	.1	.1	.0	.0	.0	.0	.0	.0	.0	.0

A = Annual Demand
R = Cost to Order / Cost per Unit

Table 3.4 Order and Backorder Quantities for the Backorder Model
(Continued)

h = 30% (Annual Holding Rate)

b = 40% (Monthly Cost per Backorder / Cost per Unit)

Mq = Economic Order Quantity in Months of Demand

A \ R	3	1	.8	.6	.4	.2	.1	.07	.03	.01
10	17.5	10.1	9.0	7.8	6.4	4.5	3.2	2.7	1.7	1.0
25	11.1	6.4	5.7	4.9	4.0	2.9	2.0	1.7	1.1	.6
50	7.8	4.5	4.0	3.5	2.9	2.0	1.4	1.2	.8	.5
75	6.4	3.7	3.3	2.9	2.3	1.6	1.2	1.0	.6	.4
100	5.5	3.2	2.9	2.5	2.0	1.4	1.0	.8	.6	.3
250	3.5	2.0	1.8	1.6	1.3	.9	.6	.5	.3	.2
500	2.5	1.4	1.3	1.1	.9	.6	.5	.4	.2	.1
750	2.0	1.2	1.0	.9	.7	.5	.4	.3	.2	.1
1,000	1.7	1.0	.9	.8	.6	.5	.3	.3	.2	.1
2,500	1.1	.6	.6	.5	.4	.3	.2	.2	.1	.1
5,000	.8	.5	.4	.3	.3	.2	.1	.1	.1	.0
7,500	.6	.4	.3	.3	.2	.2	.1	.1	.1	.0
10,000	.6	.3	.3	.2	.2	.1	.1	.1	.1	.0
25,000	.3	.2	.2	.2	.1	.1	.1	.1	.0	.0
50,000	.2	.1	.1	.1	.1	.1	.0	.0	.0	.0
75,000	.2	.1	.1	.1	.1	.1	.0	.0	.0	.0
100,000	.2	.1	.1	.1	.1	.0	.0	.0	.0	.0
250,000	.1	.1	.1	.0	.0	.0	.0	.0	.0	.0
500,000	.1	.0	.0	.0	.0	.0	.0	.0	.0	.0
1,000,000	.1	.0	.0	.0	.0	.0	.0	.0	.0	.0

Mb = Economic Backorder Quantity in Months of Demand

A \ R	3	1	.8	.6	.4	.2	.1	.07	.03	.01
10	1.0	.6	.5	.5	.4	.3	.2	.2	.1	.1
25	.7	.4	.3	.3	.2	.2	.1	.1	.1	.0
50	.5	.3	.2	.2	.2	.1	.1	.1	.0	.0
75	.4	.2	.2	.2	.1	.1	.1	.1	.0	.0
100	.3	.2	.2	.1	.1	.1	.1	.0	.0	.0
250	.2	.1	.1	.1	.1	.1	.0	.0	.0	.0
500	.1	.1	.1	.1	.1	.0	.0	.0	.0	.0
750	.1	.1	.1	.1	.0	.0	.0	.0	.0	.0
1,000	.1	.1	.1	.0	.0	.0	.0	.0	.0	.0
2,500	.1	.0	.0	.0	.0	.0	.0	.0	.0	.0
5,000	.0	.0	.0	.0	.0	.0	.0	.0	.0	.0
7,500	.0	.0	.0	.0	.0	.0	.0	.0	.0	.0
10,000	.0	.0	.0	.0	.0	.0	.0	.0	.0	.0
25,000	.0	.0	.0	.0	.0	.0	.0	.0	.0	.0
50,000	.0	.0	.0	.0	.0	.0	.0	.0	.0	.0
75,000	.0	.0	.0	.0	.0	.0	.0	.0	.0	.0
100,000	.0	.0	.0	.0	.0	.0	.0	.0	.0	.0
250,000	.0	.0	.0	.0	.0	.0	.0	.0	.0	.0
500,000	.0	.0	.0	.0	.0	.0	.0	.0	.0	.0
1,000,000	.0	.0	.0	.0	.0	.0	.0	.0	.0	.0

A = Annual Demand

R = Cost to Order / Cost per Unit

Table 3.5 Stocking Costs for the Backorder Model

h = 20% (Annual Holding Rate)

b = 20% (Monthly Cost per Backorder / Cost per Unit)

s = Stocking Cost / Cost per Unit

A \ R	1000	750	500	250	100	75	50	25	10	5
10	6.08	5.26	4.30	3.04	1.92	1.66	1.36	.96	.61	.43
25	3.84	3.33	2.72	1.92	1.22	1.05	.86	.61	.38	.27
50	2.72	2.35	1.92	1.36	.86	.74	.61	.43	.27	.19
75	2.22	1.92	1.57	1.11	.70	.61	.50	.35	.22	.16
100	1.92	1.66	1.36	.96	.61	.53	.43	.30	.19	.14
250	1.22	1.05	.86	.61	.38	.33	.27	.19	.12	.09
500	.86	.74	.61	.43	.27	.24	.19	.14	.09	.06
750	.70	.61	.50	.35	.22	.19	.16	.11	.07	.05
1,000	.61	.53	.43	.30	.19	.17	.14	.10	.06	.04
2,500	.38	.33	.27	.19	.12	.11	.09	.06	.04	.03
5,000	.27	.24	.19	.14	.09	.07	.06	.04	.03	.02
7,500	.22	.19	.16	.11	.07	.06	.05	.04	.02	.02
10,000	.19	.17	.14	.10	.06	.05	.04	.03	.02	.01
25,000	.12	.11	.09	.06	.04	.03	.03	.02	.01	.01
50,000	.09	.07	.06	.04	.03	.02	.02	.01	.01	.01
75,000	.07	.06	.05	.04	.02	.02	.02	.01	.01	.00
100,000	.06	.05	.04	.03	.02	.02	.01	.01	.01	.00
250,000	.04	.03	.03	.02	.01	.01	.01	.01	.00	.00
500,000	.03	.02	.02	.01	.01	.01	.01	.00	.00	.00
1,000,000	.02	.02	.01	.01	.01	.01	.00	.00	.00	.00

A \ R	3	1	.8	.6	.4	.2	.1	.07	.03	.01
10	.33	.19	.17	.15	.12	.09	.06	.05	.03	.02
25	.21	.12	.11	.09	.08	.05	.04	.03	.02	.01
50	.15	.09	.08	.07	.05	.04	.03	.02	.01	.01
75	.12	.07	.06	.05	.04	.03	.02	.02	.01	.01
100	.11	.06	.05	.05	.04	.03	.02	.02	.01	.01
250	.07	.04	.03	.03	.02	.02	.01	.01	.01	.00
500	.05	.03	.02	.02	.02	.01	.01	.01	.00	.00
750	.04	.02	.02	.02	.01	.01	.01	.01	.00	.00
1,000	.03	.02	.02	.01	.01	.01	.01	.01	.00	.00
2,500	.02	.01	.01	.01	.01	.01	.00	.00	.00	.00
5,000	.01	.01	.01	.01	.01	.00	.00	.00	.00	.00
7,500	.01	.01	.01	.01	.00	.00	.00	.00	.00	.00
10,000	.01	.01	.01	.00	.00	.00	.00	.00	.00	.00
25,000	.01	.00	.00	.00	.00	.00	.00	.00	.00	.00
50,000	.00	.00	.00	.00	.00	.00	.00	.00	.00	.00
75,000	.00	.00	.00	.00	.00	.00	.00	.00	.00	.00
100,000	.00	.00	.00	.00	.00	.00	.00	.00	.00	.00
250,000	.00	.00	.00	.00	.00	.00	.00	.00	.00	.00
500,000	.00	.00	.00	.00	.00	.00	.00	.00	.00	.00
1,000,000	.00	.00	.00	.00	.00	.00	.00	.00	.00	.00

A = Annual Demand

R = Cost to Order / Cost per Unit

Stocking Cost = Economic Order plus Holding plus Backorder Costs

Table 3.6 Stocking Costs for the Backorder Model

h = 20% (Annual Holding Rate)

b = 40% (Monthly Cost per Backorder / Cost per Unit)

s = Stocking Cost / Cost per Unit

A \ R	1000	750	500	250	100	75	50	25	10	5
10	6.20	5.37	4.38	3.10	1.96	1.70	1.39	.98	.62	.44
25	3.92	3.39	2.77	1.96	1.24	1.07	.88	.62	.39	.28
50	2.77	2.40	1.96	1.39	.88	.76	.62	.44	.28	.20
75	2.26	1.96	1.60	1.13	.72	.62	.51	.36	.23	.16
100	1.96	1.70	1.39	.98	.62	.54	.44	.31	.20	.14
250	1.24	1.07	.88	.62	.39	.34	.28	.20	.12	.09
500	.88	.76	.62	.44	.28	.24	.20	.14	.09	.06
750	.72	.62	.51	.36	.23	.20	.16	.11	.07	.05
1,000	.62	.54	.44	.31	.20	.17	.14	.10	.06	.04
2,500	.39	.34	.28	.20	.12	.11	.09	.06	.04	.03
5,000	.28	.24	.20	.14	.09	.08	.06	.04	.03	.02
7,500	.23	.20	.16	.11	.07	.06	.05	.04	.02	.02
10,000	.20	.17	.14	.10	.06	.05	.04	.03	.02	.01
25,000	.12	.11	.09	.06	.04	.03	.03	.02	.01	.01
50,000	.09	.08	.06	.04	.03	.02	.02	.01	.01	.01
75,000	.07	.06	.05	.04	.02	.02	.02	.01	.01	.01
100,000	.06	.05	.04	.03	.02	.02	.01	.01	.01	.00
250,000	.04	.03	.03	.02	.01	.01	.01	.01	.00	.00
500,000	.03	.02	.02	.01	.01	.01	.01	.00	.00	.00
1,000,000	.02	.02	.01	.01	.01	.01	.00	.00	.00	.00

A \ R	3	1	.8	.6	.4	.2	.1	.07	.03	.01
10	.34	.20	.18	.15	.12	.09	.06	.05	.03	.02
25	.21	.12	.11	.10	.08	.06	.04	.03	.02	.01
50	.15	.09	.08	.07	.06	.04	.03	.02	.02	.01
75	.12	.07	.06	.06	.05	.03	.02	.02	.01	.01
100	.11	.06	.06	.05	.04	.03	.02	.02	.01	.01
250	.07	.04	.04	.03	.02	.02	.01	.01	.01	.00
500	.05	.03	.02	.02	.02	.01	.01	.01	.00	.00
750	.04	.02	.02	.02	.01	.01	.01	.01	.00	.00
1,000	.03	.02	.02	.02	.01	.01	.01	.01	.00	.00
2,500	.02	.01	.01	.01	.01	.01	.00	.00	.00	.00
5,000	.02	.01	.01	.01	.01	.00	.00	.00	.00	.00
7,500	.01	.01	.01	.01	.00	.00	.00	.00	.00	.00
10,000	.01	.01	.01	.00	.00	.00	.00	.00	.00	.00
25,000	.01	.00	.00	.00	.00	.00	.00	.00	.00	.00
50,000	.00	.00	.00	.00	.00	.00	.00	.00	.00	.00
75,000	.00	.00	.00	.00	.00	.00	.00	.00	.00	.00
100,000	.00	.00	.00	.00	.00	.00	.00	.00	.00	.00
250,000	.00	.00	.00	.00	.00	.00	.00	.00	.00	.00
500,000	.00	.00	.00	.00	.00	.00	.00	.00	.00	.00
1,000,000	.00	.00	.00	.00	.00	.00	.00	.00	.00	.00

A = Annual Demand

R = Cost to Order / Cost per Unit

Stocking Cost = Economic Order plus Holding plus Backorder Costs

Table 3.7 Stocking Costs for the Backorder Model

h = 30% (Annual Holding Rate)
b = 20% (Monthly Cost per Backorder / Cost per Unit)

s = Stocking Cost / Cost per Unit

A \ R	1000	750	500	250	100	75	50	25	10	5
10	7.30	6.32	5.16	3.65	2.31	2.00	1.63	1.15	.73	.52
25	4.62	4.00	3.27	2.31	1.46	1.26	1.03	.73	.46	.33
50	3.27	2.83	2.31	1.63	1.03	.89	.73	.52	.33	.23
75	2.67	2.31	1.89	1.33	.84	.73	.60	.42	.27	.19
100	2.31	2.00	1.63	1.15	.73	.63	.52	.37	.23	.16
250	1.46	1.26	1.03	.73	.46	.40	.33	.23	.15	.10
500	1.03	.89	.73	.52	.33	.28	.23	.16	.10	.07
750	.84	.73	.60	.42	.27	.23	.19	.13	.08	.06
1,000	.73	.63	.52	.37	.23	.20	.16	.12	.07	.05
2,500	.46	.40	.33	.23	.15	.13	.10	.07	.05	.03
5,000	.33	.28	.23	.16	.10	.09	.07	.05	.03	.02
7,500	.27	.23	.19	.13	.08	.07	.06	.04	.03	.02
10,000	.23	.20	.16	.12	.07	.06	.05	.04	.02	.02
25,000	.15	.13	.10	.07	.05	.04	.03	.02	.01	.01
50,000	.10	.09	.07	.05	.03	.03	.02	.02	.01	.01
75,000	.08	.07	.06	.04	.03	.02	.02	.01	.01	.01
100,000	.07	.06	.05	.04	.02	.02	.02	.01	.01	.01
250,000	.05	.04	.03	.02	.01	.01	.01	.01	.00	.00
500,000	.03	.03	.02	.02	.01	.01	.01	.01	.00	.00
1,000,000	.02	.02	.02	.01	.01	.01	.01	.00	.00	.00

A \ R	3	1	.8	.6	.4	.2	.1	.07	.03	.01
10	.40	.23	.21	.18	.15	.10	.07	.06	.04	.02
25	.25	.15	.13	.11	.09	.07	.05	.04	.03	.01
50	.18	.10	.09	.08	.07	.05	.03	.03	.02	.01
75	.15	.08	.08	.07	.05	.04	.03	.02	.01	.01
100	.13	.07	.07	.06	.05	.03	.02	.02	.01	.01
250	.08	.05	.04	.04	.03	.02	.01	.01	.01	.00
500	.06	.03	.03	.03	.02	.01	.01	.01	.01	.00
750	.05	.03	.02	.02	.02	.01	.01	.01	.00	.00
1,000	.04	.02	.02	.02	.01	.01	.01	.01	.00	.00
2,500	.03	.01	.01	.01	.01	.01	.00	.00	.00	.00
5,000	.02	.01	.01	.01	.01	.00	.00	.00	.00	.00
7,500	.01	.01	.01	.01	.01	.00	.00	.00	.00	.00
10,000	.01	.01	.01	.01	.00	.00	.00	.00	.00	.00
25,000	.01	.00	.00	.00	.00	.00	.00	.00	.00	.00
50,000	.01	.00	.00	.00	.00	.00	.00	.00	.00	.00
75,000	.00	.00	.00	.00	.00	.00	.00	.00	.00	.00
100,000	.00	.00	.00	.00	.00	.00	.00	.00	.00	.00
250,000	.00	.00	.00	.00	.00	.00	.00	.00	.00	.00
500,000	.00	.00	.00	.00	.00	.00	.00	.00	.00	.00
1,000,000	.00	.00	.00	.00	.00	.00	.00	.00	.00	.00

A = Annual Demand

R = Cost to Order / Cost per Unit

Stocking Cost = Economic Order plus Holding plus Backorder Costs

Table 3.8 Stocking Costs for the Backorder Model

h = 30% (Annual Holding Rate)

b = 40% (Monthly Cost per Backorder / Cost per Unit)

s = Stocking Cost / Cost per Unit

A \ R	1000	750	500	250	100	75	50	25	10	5
10	7.51	6.51	5.31	3.76	2.38	2.06	1.68	1.19	.75	.53
25	4.75	4.12	3.36	2.38	1.50	1.30	1.06	.75	.48	.34
50	3.36	2.91	2.38	1.68	1.06	.92	.75	.53	.34	.24
75	2.74	2.38	1.94	1.37	.87	.75	.61	.43	.27	.19
100	2.38	2.06	1.68	1.19	.75	.65	.53	.38	.24	.17
250	1.50	1.30	1.06	.75	.48	.41	.34	.24	.15	.11
500	1.06	.92	.75	.53	.34	.29	.24	.17	.11	.08
750	.87	.75	.61	.43	.27	.24	.19	.14	.09	.06
1,000	.75	.65	.53	.38	.24	.21	.17	.12	.08	.05
2,500	.48	.41	.34	.24	.15	.13	.11	.08	.05	.03
5,000	.34	.29	.24	.17	.11	.09	.08	.05	.03	.02
7,500	.27	.24	.19	.14	.09	.08	.06	.04	.03	.02
10,000	.24	.21	.17	.12	.08	.07	.05	.04	.02	.02
25,000	.15	.13	.11	.08	.05	.04	.03	.02	.02	.01
50,000	.11	.09	.08	.05	.03	.03	.02	.02	.01	.01
75,000	.09	.08	.06	.04	.03	.02	.02	.01	.01	.01
100,000	.08	.07	.05	.04	.02	.02	.02	.01	.01	.01
250,000	.05	.04	.03	.02	.02	.01	.01	.01	.00	.00
500,000	.03	.03	.02	.02	.01	.01	.01	.01	.00	.00
1,000,000	.02	.02	.02	.01	.01	.01	.01	.00	.00	.00

A \ R	3	1	.8	.6	.4	.2	.1	.07	.03	.01
10	.41	.24	.21	.18	.15	.11	.08	.06	.04	.02
25	.26	.15	.13	.12	.10	.07	.05	.04	.03	.02
50	.18	.11	.10	.08	.07	.05	.03	.03	.02	.01
75	.15	.09	.08	.07	.05	.04	.03	.02	.02	.01
100	.13	.08	.07	.06	.05	.03	.02	.02	.01	.01
250	.08	.05	.04	.04	.03	.02	.02	.01	.01	.00
500	.06	.03	.03	.03	.02	.02	.01	.01	.01	.00
750	.05	.03	.02	.02	.02	.01	.01	.01	.00	.00
1,000	.04	.02	.02	.02	.02	.01	.01	.01	.00	.00
2,500	.03	.02	.01	.01	.01	.01	.00	.00	.00	.00
5,000	.02	.01	.01	.01	.01	.00	.00	.00	.00	.00
7,500	.02	.01	.01	.01	.01	.00	.00	.00	.00	.00
10,000	.01	.01	.01	.01	.00	.00	.00	.00	.00	.00
25,000	.01	.00	.00	.00	.00	.00	.00	.00	.00	.00
50,000	.01	.00	.00	.00	.00	.00	.00	.00	.00	.00
75,000	.00	.00	.00	.00	.00	.00	.00	.00	.00	.00
100,000	.00	.00	.00	.00	.00	.00	.00	.00	.00	.00
250,000	.00	.00	.00	.00	.00	.00	.00	.00	.00	.00
500,000	.00	.00	.00	.00	.00	.00	.00	.00	.00	.00
1,000,000	.00	.00	.00	.00	.00	.00	.00	.00	.00	.00

A = Annual Demand

R = Cost to Order / Cost per Unit

Stocking Cost = Economic Order plus Holding plus Backorder Costs

Table 3.9 Xq and Xb for the Backorder Model

Qo = EOQ for Simple Lot Size Model
Q = EOQ for Backorder Model
B = Backorders for Backorder Model
Xq = Q/Qo
Xb = B/Qo

Xq

b	.10	.20	.30	.40	.50	.60	.70	.80	.90	1.00
h										
.05	1.02	1.01	1.01	1.01	1.00	1.00	1.00	1.00	1.00	1.00
.10	1.04	1.02	1.01	1.01	1.01	1.01	1.01	1.01	1.00	1.00
.15	1.06	1.03	1.02	1.02	1.01	1.01	1.01	1.01	1.01	1.01
.20	1.08	1.04	1.03	1.02	1.02	1.01	1.01	1.01	1.01	1.01
.25	1.10	1.05	1.03	1.03	1.02	1.02	1.01	1.01	1.01	1.01
.30	1.12	1.06	1.04	1.03	1.02	1.02	1.02	1.02	1.01	1.01
.35	1.14	1.07	1.05	1.04	1.03	1.02	1.02	1.02	1.02	1.01
.40	1.15	1.08	1.05	1.04	1.03	1.03	1.02	1.02	1.02	1.02
.45	1.17	1.09	1.06	1.05	1.04	1.03	1.03	1.02	1.02	1.02
.50	1.19	1.10	1.07	1.05	1.04	1.03	1.03	1.03	1.02	1.02
.55	1.21	1.11	1.07	1.06	1.04	1.04	1.03	1.03	1.03	1.02
.60	1.22	1.12	1.08	1.06	1.05	1.04	1.04	1.03	1.03	1.02
.65	1.24	1.13	1.09	1.07	1.05	1.04	1.04	1.03	1.03	1.03
.70	1.26	1.14	1.09	1.07	1.06	1.05	1.04	1.04	1.03	1.03
.75	1.27	1.15	1.10	1.08	1.06	1.05	1.04	1.04	1.03	1.03
.80	1.29	1.15	1.11	1.08	1.06	1.05	1.05	1.04	1.04	1.03
.85	1.31	1.16	1.11	1.08	1.07	1.06	1.05	1.04	1.04	1.03
.90	1.32	1.17	1.12	1.09	1.07	1.06	1.05	1.05	1.04	1.04
.95	1.34	1.18	1.12	1.09	1.08	1.06	1.06	1.05	1.04	1.04
1.00	1.35	1.19	1.13	1.10	1.08	1.07	1.06	1.05	1.05	1.04

Xb

b	.10	.20	.30	.40	.50	.60	.70	.80	.90	1.00
h										
.05	.04	.02	.01	.01	.01	.01	.01	.01	.00	.00
.10	.08	.04	.03	.02	.02	.01	.01	.01	.01	.01
.15	.12	.06	.04	.03	.02	.02	.02	.02	.01	.01
.20	.15	.08	.05	.04	.03	.03	.02	.02	.02	.02
.25	.19	.10	.07	.05	.04	.03	.03	.03	.02	.02
.30	.22	.12	.08	.06	.05	.04	.04	.03	.03	.02
.35	.26	.14	.09	.07	.06	.05	.04	.04	.03	.03
.40	.29	.15	.11	.08	.06	.05	.05	.04	.04	.03
.45	.32	.17	.12	.09	.07	.06	.05	.05	.04	.04
.50	.35	.19	.13	.10	.08	.07	.06	.05	.05	.04
.55	.38	.21	.14	.11	.09	.07	.06	.06	.05	.04
.60	.41	.22	.15	.12	.10	.08	.07	.06	.05	.05
.65	.44	.24	.17	.13	.10	.09	.07	.07	.06	.05
.70	.46	.26	.18	.14	.11	.09	.08	.07	.06	.06
.75	.49	.27	.19	.15	.12	.10	.09	.08	.07	.06
.80	.52	.29	.20	.15	.13	.11	.09	.08	.07	.06
.85	.54	.30	.21	.16	.13	.11	.10	.08	.08	.07
.90	.57	.32	.22	.17	.14	.12	.10	.09	.08	.07
.95	.59	.34	.23	.18	.15	.12	.11	.09	.08	.08
1.00	.62	.35	.25	.19	.15	.13	.11	.10	.09	.08

h = Annual Holding Rate
b = Monthly Backorder Cost per Unit / Cost per Unit

CHAPTER 4

Production Lot Size Model

The production lot size model is applicable when the supplier to a stocking location of a firm is one of the firm's nearby production facilities. When a replenishment lot is ordered by the stocking location and production begins, the replenishment units arrive to the stocking location as they are being produced—not in one lump sum. These units are immediately available to fill oncoming demands. The demands are assumed to be deterministic, and shortages are avoided as the replenishment sizes are planned to fill all of the demand needs. In the development of the inventory model, it is assumed that the production facility has a production capacity that is larger than the annual demand on the item.

The costs associated with the model are the order and holding costs. In this production lot size model, order cost is comprised of the sum of the procurement ordering cost for the item at the stocking location plus the setup cost for the item at the production facility. Holding cost is the cost of stocking the units at the stocking location. The goal of the model is to determine the size of the order quantity Q that yields the minimum of the sum of the order plus holding costs (references 1, 2 and 3).

Data

The input data required to use this model are the following:

$$L = \text{lead time}$$
$$A = \text{annual demand}$$
$$C = \text{cost per unit}$$
$$Co = \text{cost per order}$$
$$h = \text{annual holding rate}$$
$$P = \text{annual production capacity for the item}$$

The above capacity represents the number of units of the item that can be produced in one year.

Model

The role of the lot size model is to determine the economic order quantity Q. This quantity is used along with the lead time L (in months) to establish when the item should be reordered. Since the average demand per month is $A/12$, the lead time demand is:

$$D_L = L\,A/12$$

The order point OP is the same as the lead time demand, whereas:

$$OP = D_L$$

So, when the on-hand plus on-order (OH + OO) inventory reaches the order point quantity, a replenishment order of size **Q** is then placed with the production facility. The production facility will begin to produce the units at lead time **L** in the future, as shown in Figure 4.1. As the units are being completed, they arrive to the stocking facility for immediate use in filling demands.

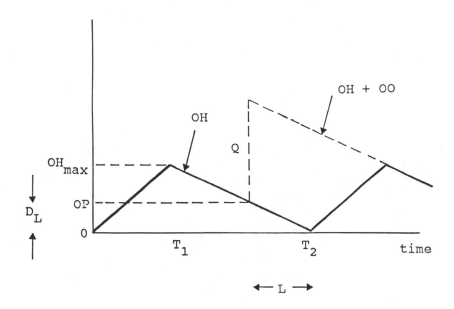

Figure 4.1. Inventory flow for the production lot size model

The production time T_1 represents the time needed by the production facility to produce **Q** units. As the facility can produce **P** units in a year, it then has a capacity to produce **P/12** units per month. To complete **Q** units, the number of months is determined by the relation:

$$T_1 = Q\ 12/P$$

The on-hand stock is depleted at month T_2. Because the lot size of **Q** covers the demands from months **0** to T_2 and the demands are **A/12** per month, then:

$$T_2 = 12\ Q/A$$

The maximum on-hand inventory OH_{max} at the stocking facility can also be determined. As the demand rate is **A/12** per month and the production facility requires T_1 months to complete the lot of size **Q**, the maximum on-hand becomes:

$$OH_{max} = Q - (A\ T_1/12) = Q\ (1 - A/P)$$

The cost function is used to calculate the annual costs associated with ordering and holding the item in the inventory. In general, if **Q′** designates an arbitrary order quantity, the annual cost is:

$$K(Q') = A \, Co/Q' + h \, C \, Q' \, (P - A)/2P$$

that is,

$$K(Q') = (\text{order cost}) + (\text{holding cost})$$

When the above cost function is used, optimization methods are used to determine the value of Q' that minimizes the combined order plus holding cost. This computation yields the economic order quantity Q and is determined as:

$$Q = \sqrt{\left(\frac{P}{P - A}\right)\left(\frac{2 \, A \, Co}{h \, C}\right)}$$

that is,

$$Q = \sqrt{\frac{P}{P - A}} \quad Qo$$

Note that Q above is related to Qo, the economic order quantity from the simple lot size model.

By using the above Q as the order quantity, the economic annual order plus holding cost for the item can be determined. This is the relation:

$$K(Q) = \sqrt{\frac{P}{P - A}} \, (2 \, A \, Co \, h \, C)$$

The stocking rate s is obtained from the ratio of the cost to stock the item over the procurement cost for the item. Since $K(Q)$ is the annual order plus holding cost and AC is the annual procurement cost, this measure is calculated as:

$$s = K(Q)/A \, C$$

The order plus holding cost that is incurred to stock the item can be determined from multiplying s by C, and so the associated effective cost for the item is:

$$C' = C \, (1 + s)$$

As in the previous order quantity models, C' represents the combined cost to procure and stock one unit of the item.

Tables

For use in the adjoining tables, two new input parameters are introduced, R and p, where:

$$R = Co/C = \text{cost per order/cost per unit}$$
$$p = P/A = \text{annual production capacity/annual demand}$$

Notice that when $p = 2$, for example, the production facility has the capacity to produce twice the annual demand for the item. When $p = 100$, for example, the capacity is then 100 times the annual demand and so forth.

The adjoining tables list the economic order quantity in months of demand M for selected values of h, p, R and A. Because $A/12$ gives the average demands per month, M is found from:

$$M = 12\,Q/A$$

Table 4.7 gives values for the coefficient X_p that is obtained from the relation:

$$X_p = \sqrt{p/(p-1)}$$

X_p is useful in relating the economic order quantity Q from the production lot size model to the economic order quantity Q_o from the simple lot size model, i.e.:

$$Q = X_p\,Q_o$$

The above relation holds as long as the holding rate h is the same for both models. In the same way, the order quantity in months of demand M for the production lot size model is related to the corresponding months for the simple lot size model M_o by the relation:

$$M = X_p\,M_o$$

The tables of this chapter are arranged as follows:

Tables	Contents
4.1	M and s for h = .2 and p = 2
4.2	M and s for h = .2 and p = 5
4.3	M and s for h = .2 and p = 10
4.4	M and s for h = .3 and p = 2
4.5	M and s for h = .3 and p = 5
4.6	M and s for h = .3 and p = 10
4.7	Xp

Just-in-Time Applications

The above tables may be used by management in determining which items are most compatable to Just-in-Time (JIT) methods, as was the case in Chapters 2 and 3. The tables show that the months of order quantity is smaller as the ratio of R = (cost per order) over (cost per unit) decreases. The cost per order in this model is the combined cost of setup (in the production facility) and the order processing cost (in the distribution center). A scan of the tables quickly shows how much decrease in the combined cost would be necessary to enable the item to be processed in a JIT manner. The tables also reveal how the size of the annual demand for an item (A) is related to the order quantity, where the larger the annual demand, the smaller the months of order quantity. As a result management may realize that the items with low demands may not be economical to run with JIT methods. The tables also reveal that the months of the order quantity is smaller as the production capacity P for the item increases. Management may thus determine the benefits involved in providing ample production capacity for the individual items.

Example 4.1

Consider a firm that stocks a tool kit in its central warehouse and produces the kit at the firm's nearby factory. Assume the kit has an annual demand of 5,000 units. Suppose the cost per unit is $10 and the cost per order is $50. Further assume the holding rate is 30 percent of the unit cost per year, and the production facility can produce up to 25,000 units per year. Find the economic order quantity and the effective cost per unit.

Since h = .30 and p = 25,000/5,000 = 5, Table 4.5 is used for this situation. With A = 5,000 and R = 50/10 = 5, the table entries give M = 1.1 and s = .02. Now, the monthly demand is 5,000/12 = 416.7 and the economic order quantity Q then becomes:

$$Q = 1.1 \ (416.7) = 458$$

Also, the effective cost per unit is:

$$C' = 10 \ (1 + .02) = \$10.20$$

Example 4.2

For the tool kit in Example 4.1, how long does it take to produce the order quantity of 458? Furthermore, what is the maximum level of stock for the item at the central warehouse?

The factory capacity allows production of 25,000/12 = 2083.3 units per month. Thus, the order quantity of Q = 458 is produced in:

$$T_1 = 458 \ / \ 2083.3 = 0.22 \text{ months}$$

Further, the maximum stock on hand over the order cycle is determined as:

$$458 \ (1\text{-}5000/25,000) = 366.4$$

Example 4.3

Suppose, for the tool kit of Example 4.1, that the management wishes to reduce the order quantity to a one-half month demand. What change in the order cost is needed, when all else remains the same, and when management still desires an economic order quantity to be used?

In this situation, with h = .30 and p = 5, Table 4.5 is used to search for a value of M = 0.50 representing one half of a month when A = 5000. The table shows that this point occurs when R = 1. Because R = Co/C = 1 and C = \$10, Co = C = \$10 is the order cost needed.

Example 4.4

Suppose an extra-firm mattress is produced in a factory and stocked in an adjoining warehouse, to meet oncoming demands. Assume the mattress has an annual demand of 500 units and that the cost per unit is \$100 and the cost per order is \$5000. Further assume the annual holding rate is 30 percent and the production facility can produce 1000 units a year. Find the order quantity and the effective cost per unit.

Because h = .30 and p = 1000 / 500 = 2, Table 4.4 is used with A = 500 and R = 5000 / 100 = 50. The table shows the economic months in the order quantity is M = 13.9 and the associated stocking rate is s = 0.17. As the monthly demand is 500 / 12 = 41.67, the economic order quantity becomes:

$$Q = 13.9 \ (41.67) = 579$$

Further, the effective cost per unit C' is:

$$C' = 100 \ (1 + .17) = \$117$$

Example 4.5

Consider the mattress in Example 4.4 and suppose it is possible to increase the capacity of the production facility for the item from 1000 to 2500 per year. If all else remains the same, how will this change affect the economic order quantity and the effective cost per unit?

By using h = .30 as before and p = 2500/500 = 5 for the upgraded capacity, Table 4.5 is now used along with A = 500 and R = 50. The table entries give M = 11.0 and s = .22. Hence, with an average monthly demand of 500 / 12 = 41.67, the economic order quantity now becomes:

$$Q = 11.0 \, (41.67) = 458$$

which is a decrease from the earlier value of Q = 579.

Because the stocking rate is s = .22, the effective stocking cost C' becomes:

$$C' = 100 \, (1.22) = \$122$$

Example 4.6

Suppose a firm makes engineering rulers in a local factory and stocks the rulers in an adjoining warehouse for distribution as demands occur. Assume the demand rate is 10,000 rulers a year. Suppose further the cost per ruler is $0.50 and the cost per order is $50. Assume h = 40 percent per year and the production facility can produce 80,000 units per year if necessary. Find the economic order quantity for the ruler.

First note that h = .40 and p = 80,000/10,000 = 8. Because no tables for these values are available for the production lot size model, Table 2.4 from the simple lot size model with h = .40 can be used. Here, A = 10,000 and R = 50/0.50 = 100 are used to give the economic order quantity in months of demand Mo = 2.7 for the simple lot size model. Note that the economic order quantity here becomes Qo = 2.7 (10,000/12) = 2250.

Second, Table 4.7 is used to find **Xp** for the value p = 8. After finding that Xp = 1.069, the economic order quantity in months of demand is then:

$$M = 1.069 \, (2.7) = 2.89$$

and thus the economic order quantity for the ruler becomes:

$$Q = 2.89 \, (10,000) \, / \, 12 = 2,408$$

Table 4.1 Order Quantities and Stocking Costs for the Production Lot Size Model

h = 20% (Annual Holding Rate)

p = 2 (Annual Production Capacity / Annual Demand)

M = Economic Order Quantity in Months of Demand

A \ R	1000	750	500	250	100	75	50	25	10	5
10	536.7	464.8	379.5	268.3	169.7	147.0	120.0	84.9	53.7	37.9
25	339.4	293.9	240.0	169.7	107.3	93.0	75.9	53.7	33.9	24.0
50	240.0	207.8	169.7	120.0	75.9	65.7	53.7	37.9	24.0	17.0
75	196.0	169.7	138.6	98.0	62.0	53.7	43.8	31.0	19.6	13.9
100	169.7	147.0	120.0	84.9	53.7	46.5	37.9	26.8	17.0	12.0
250	107.3	93.0	75.9	53.7	33.9	29.4	24.0	17.0	10.7	7.6
500	75.9	65.7	53.7	37.9	24.0	20.8	17.0	12.0	7.6	5.4
750	62.0	53.7	43.8	31.0	19.6	17.0	13.9	9.8	6.2	4.4
1,000	53.7	46.5	37.9	26.8	17.0	14.7	12.0	8.5	5.4	3.8
2,500	33.9	29.4	24.0	17.0	10.7	9.3	7.6	5.4	3.4	2.4
5,000	24.0	20.8	17.0	12.0	7.6	6.6	5.4	3.8	2.4	1.7
7,500	19.6	17.0	13.9	9.8	6.2	5.4	4.4	3.1	2.0	1.4
10,000	17.0	14.7	12.0	8.5	5.4	4.6	3.8	2.7	1.7	1.2
25,000	10.7	9.3	7.6	5.4	3.4	2.9	2.4	1.7	1.1	.8
50,000	7.6	6.6	5.4	3.8	2.4	2.1	1.7	1.2	.8	.5
75,000	6.2	5.4	4.4	3.1	2.0	1.7	1.4	1.0	.6	.4
100,000	5.4	4.6	3.8	2.7	1.7	1.5	1.2	.8	.5	.4
250,000	3.4	2.9	2.4	1.7	1.1	.9	.8	.5	.3	.2
500,000	2.4	2.1	1.7	1.2	.8	.7	.5	.4	.2	.2
1,000,000	1.7	1.5	1.2	.8	.5	.5	.4	.3	.2	.1

s = Stocking Cost / Cost per Unit

A \ R	1000	750	500	250	100	75	50	25	10	5
10	4.47	3.87	3.16	2.24	1.41	1.22	1.00	.71	.45	.32
25	2.83	2.45	2.00	1.41	.89	.77	.63	.45	.28	.20
50	2.00	1.73	1.41	1.00	.63	.55	.45	.32	.20	.14
75	1.63	1.41	1.15	.82	.52	.45	.37	.26	.16	.12
100	1.41	1.22	1.00	.71	.45	.39	.32	.22	.14	.10
250	.89	.77	.63	.45	.28	.24	.20	.14	.09	.06
500	.63	.55	.45	.32	.20	.17	.14	.10	.06	.04
750	.52	.45	.37	.26	.16	.14	.12	.08	.05	.04
1,000	.45	.39	.32	.22	.14	.12	.10	.07	.04	.03
2,500	.28	.24	.20	.14	.09	.08	.06	.04	.03	.02
5,000	.20	.17	.14	.10	.06	.05	.04	.03	.02	.01
7,500	.16	.14	.12	.08	.05	.04	.04	.03	.02	.01
10,000	.14	.12	.10	.07	.04	.04	.03	.02	.01	.01
25,000	.09	.08	.06	.04	.03	.02	.02	.01	.01	.01
50,000	.06	.05	.04	.03	.02	.02	.01	.01	.01	.00
75,000	.05	.04	.04	.03	.02	.01	.01	.01	.01	.00
100,000	.04	.04	.03	.02	.01	.01	.01	.01	.00	.00
250,000	.03	.02	.02	.01	.01	.01	.01	.00	.00	.00
500,000	.02	.02	.01	.01	.01	.01	.00	.00	.00	.00
1,000,000	.01	.01	.01	.01	.00	.00	.00	.00	.00	.00

A = Annual Demand

R = Cost to Order / Cost per Unit

Stocking Cost = Economic Order plus Holding Costs

Table 4.1 Order Quantities and Stocking Costs for the Production Lot Size Model
(Continued)

h = 20% (Annual Holding Rate)

p = 2 (Annual Production Capacity / Annual Demand)

M = Economic Order Quantity in Months of Demand

A \ R	3	1	.8	.6	.4	.2	.1	.07	.03	.01
10	29.4	17.0	15.2	13.1	10.7	7.6	5.4	4.5	2.9	1.7
25	18.6	10.7	9.6	8.3	6.8	4.8	3.4	2.8	1.9	1.1
50	13.1	7.6	6.8	5.9	4.8	3.4	2.4	2.0	1.3	.8
75	10.7	6.2	5.5	4.8	3.9	2.8	2.0	1.6	1.1	.6
100	9.3	5.4	4.8	4.2	3.4	2.4	1.7	1.4	.9	.5
250	5.9	3.4	3.0	2.6	2.1	1.5	1.1	.9	.6	.3
500	4.2	2.4	2.1	1.9	1.5	1.1	.8	.6	.4	.2
750	3.4	2.0	1.8	1.5	1.2	.9	.6	.5	.3	.2
1,000	2.9	1.7	1.5	1.3	1.1	.8	.5	.4	.3	.2
2,500	1.9	1.1	1.0	.8	.7	.5	.3	.3	.2	.1
5,000	1.3	.8	.7	.6	.5	.3	.2	.2	.1	.1
7,500	1.1	.6	.6	.5	.4	.3	.2	.2	.1	.1
10,000	.9	.5	.5	.4	.3	.2	.2	.1	.1	.1
25,000	.6	.3	.3	.3	.2	.2	.1	.1	.1	.0
50,000	.4	.2	.2	.2	.2	.1	.1	.1	.0	.0
75,000	.3	.2	.2	.2	.1	.1	.1	.1	.0	.0
100,000	.3	.2	.2	.1	.1	.1	.1	.0	.0	.0
250,000	.2	.1	.1	.1	.1	.0	.0	.0	.0	.0
500,000	.1	.1	.1	.1	.0	.0	.0	.0	.0	.0
1,000,000	.1	.1	.0	.0	.0	.0	.0	.0	.0	.0

s = Stocking Cost / Cost per Unit

A \ R	3	1	.8	.6	.4	.2	.1	.07	.03	.01
10	.24	.14	.13	.11	.09	.06	.04	.04	.02	.01
25	.15	.09	.08	.07	.06	.04	.03	.02	.02	.01
50	.11	.06	.06	.05	.04	.03	.02	.02	.01	.01
75	.09	.05	.05	.04	.03	.02	.02	.01	.01	.01
100	.08	.04	.04	.03	.03	.02	.01	.01	.01	.00
250	.05	.03	.03	.02	.02	.01	.01	.01	.00	.00
500	.03	.02	.02	.02	.01	.01	.01	.01	.00	.00
750	.03	.02	.01	.01	.01	.01	.01	.00	.00	.00
1,000	.02	.01	.01	.01	.01	.01	.00	.00	.00	.00
2,500	.02	.01	.01	.01	.01	.00	.00	.00	.00	.00
5,000	.01	.01	.01	.00	.00	.00	.00	.00	.00	.00
7,500	.01	.01	.00	.00	.00	.00	.00	.00	.00	.00
10,000	.01	.00	.00	.00	.00	.00	.00	.00	.00	.00
25,000	.00	.00	.00	.00	.00	.00	.00	.00	.00	.00
50,000	.00	.00	.00	.00	.00	.00	.00	.00	.00	.00
75,000	.00	.00	.00	.00	.00	.00	.00	.00	.00	.00
100,000	.00	.00	.00	.00	.00	.00	.00	.00	.00	.00
250,000	.00	.00	.00	.00	.00	.00	.00	.00	.00	.00
500,000	.00	.00	.00	.00	.00	.00	.00	.00	.00	.00
1,000,000	.00	.00	.00	.00	.00	.00	.00	.00	.00	.00

A = Annual Demand

R = Cost to Order / Cost per Unit

Stocking Cost = Economic Order plus Holding Costs

Table 4.2 Order Quantities and Stocking Costs for the Production Lot Size Model

h = 20% (Annual Holding Rate)

p = 5 (Annual Production Capacity / Annual Demand)

M = Economic Order Quantity in Months of Demand

A \ R	1000	750	500	250	100	75	50	25	10	5
10	424.3	367.4	300.0	212.1	134.2	116.2	94.9	67.1	42.4	30.0
25	268.3	232.4	189.7	134.2	84.9	73.5	60.0	42.4	26.8	19.0
50	189.7	164.3	134.2	94.9	60.0	52.0	42.4	30.0	19.0	13.4
75	154.9	134.2	109.5	77.5	49.0	42.4	34.6	24.5	15.5	11.0
100	134.2	116.2	94.9	67.1	42.4	36.7	30.0	21.2	13.4	9.5
250	84.9	73.5	60.0	42.4	26.8	23.2	19.0	13.4	8.5	6.0
500	60.0	52.0	42.4	30.0	19.0	16.4	13.4	9.5	6.0	4.2
750	49.0	42.4	34.6	24.5	15.5	13.4	11.0	7.7	4.9	3.5
1,000	42.4	36.7	30.0	21.2	13.4	11.6	9.5	6.7	4.2	3.0
2,500	26.8	23.2	19.0	13.4	8.5	7.3	6.0	4.2	2.7	1.9
5,000	19.0	16.4	13.4	9.5	6.0	5.2	4.2	3.0	1.9	1.3
7,500	15.5	13.4	11.0	7.7	4.9	4.2	3.5	2.4	1.5	1.1
10,000	13.4	11.6	9.5	6.7	4.2	3.7	3.0	2.1	1.3	.9
25,000	8.5	7.3	6.0	4.2	2.7	2.3	1.9	1.3	.8	.6
50,000	6.0	5.2	4.2	3.0	1.9	1.6	1.3	.9	.6	.4
75,000	4.9	4.2	3.5	2.4	1.5	1.3	1.1	.8	.5	.3
100,000	4.2	3.7	3.0	2.1	1.3	1.2	.9	.7	.4	.3
250,000	2.7	2.3	1.9	1.3	.8	.7	.6	.4	.3	.2
500,000	1.9	1.6	1.3	.9	.6	.5	.4	.3	.2	.1
1,000,000	1.3	1.2	.9	.7	.4	.4	.3	.2	.1	.1

s = Stocking Cost / Cost per Unit

A \ R	1000	750	500	250	100	75	50	25	10	5
10	5.66	4.90	4.00	2.83	1.79	1.55	1.26	.89	.57	.40
25	3.58	3.10	2.53	1.79	1.13	.98	.80	.57	.36	.25
50	2.53	2.19	1.79	1.26	.80	.69	.57	.40	.25	.18
75	2.07	1.79	1.46	1.03	.65	.57	.46	.33	.21	.15
100	1.79	1.55	1.26	.89	.57	.49	.40	.28	.18	.13
250	1.13	.98	.80	.57	.36	.31	.25	.18	.11	.08
500	.80	.69	.57	.40	.25	.22	.18	.13	.08	.06
750	.65	.57	.46	.33	.21	.18	.15	.10	.07	.05
1,000	.57	.49	.40	.28	.18	.15	.13	.09	.06	.04
2,500	.36	.31	.25	.18	.11	.10	.08	.06	.04	.03
5,000	.25	.22	.18	.13	.08	.07	.06	.04	.03	.02
7,500	.21	.18	.15	.10	.07	.06	.05	.03	.02	.01
10,000	.18	.15	.13	.09	.06	.05	.04	.03	.02	.01
25,000	.11	.10	.08	.06	.04	.03	.03	.02	.01	.01
50,000	.08	.07	.06	.04	.03	.02	.02	.01	.01	.01
75,000	.07	.06	.05	.03	.02	.02	.01	.01	.01	.00
100,000	.06	.05	.04	.03	.02	.02	.01	.01	.01	.00
250,000	.04	.03	.03	.02	.01	.01	.01	.01	.00	.00
500,000	.03	.02	.02	.01	.01	.01	.01	.00	.00	.00
1,000,000	.02	.02	.01	.01	.01	.00	.00	.00	.00	.00

A = Annual Demand

R = Cost to Order / Cost per Unit

Stocking Cost = Economic Order plus Holding Costs

Table 4.2 Order Quantities and Stocking Costs for the Production Lot Size Model

h = 20% (Annual Holding Rate)   (Continued)

p = 5 (Annual Production Capacity / Annual Demand)

M = Economic Order Quantity in Months of Demand

A \ R	3	1	.8	.6	.4	.2	.1	.07	.03	.01
10	23.2	13.4	12.0	10.4	8.5	6.0	4.2	3.5	2.3	1.3
25	14.7	8.5	7.6	6.6	5.4	3.8	2.7	2.2	1.5	.8
50	10.4	6.0	5.4	4.6	3.8	2.7	1.9	1.6	1.0	.6
75	8.5	4.9	4.4	3.8	3.1	2.2	1.5	1.3	.8	.5
100	7.3	4.2	3.8	3.3	2.7	1.9	1.3	1.1	.7	.4
250	4.6	2.7	2.4	2.1	1.7	1.2	.8	.7	.5	.3
500	3.3	1.9	1.7	1.5	1.2	.8	.6	.5	.3	.2
750	2.7	1.5	1.4	1.2	1.0	.7	.5	.4	.3	.2
1,000	2.3	1.3	1.2	1.0	.8	.6	.4	.4	.2	.1
2,500	1.5	.8	.8	.7	.5	.4	.3	.2	.1	.1
5,000	1.0	.6	.5	.5	.4	.3	.2	.2	.1	.1
7,500	.8	.5	.4	.4	.3	.2	.2	.1	.1	.0
10,000	.7	.4	.4	.3	.3	.2	.1	.1	.1	.0
25,000	.5	.3	.2	.2	.2	.1	.1	.1	.0	.0
50,000	.3	.2	.2	.1	.1	.1	.1	.1	.0	.0
75,000	.3	.2	.1	.1	.1	.1	.0	.0	.0	.0
100,000	.2	.1	.1	.1	.1	.1	.0	.0	.0	.0
250,000	.1	.1	.1	.1	.1	.0	.0	.0	.0	.0
500,000	.1	.1	.1	.0	.0	.0	.0	.0	.0	.0
1,000,000	.1	.0	.0	.0	.0	.0	.0	.0	.0	.0

s = Stocking Cost / Cost per Unit

A \ R	3	1	.8	.6	.4	.2	.1	.07	.03	.01
10	.31	.18	.16	.14	.11	.08	.06	.05	.03	.02
25	.20	.11	.10	.09	.07	.05	.04	.03	.02	.01
50	.14	.08	.07	.06	.05	.04	.03	.02	.01	.01
75	.11	.07	.06	.05	.04	.03	.02	.02	.01	.01
100	.10	.06	.05	.04	.04	.03	.02	.01	.01	.01
250	.06	.04	.03	.03	.02	.02	.01	.01	.01	.00
500	.04	.03	.02	.02	.02	.01	.01	.01	.00	.00
750	.04	.02	.02	.02	.01	.01	.01	.01	.00	.00
1,000	.03	.02	.02	.01	.01	.01	.01	.00	.00	.00
2,500	.02	.01	.01	.01	.01	.01	.00	.00	.00	.00
5,000	.01	.01	.01	.01	.01	.00	.00	.00	.00	.00
7,500	.01	.01	.01	.01	.00	.00	.00	.00	.00	.00
10,000	.01	.01	.01	.00	.00	.00	.00	.00	.00	.00
25,000	.01	.00	.00	.00	.00	.00	.00	.00	.00	.00
50,000	.00	.00	.00	.00	.00	.00	.00	.00	.00	.00
75,000	.00	.00	.00	.00	.00	.00	.00	.00	.00	.00
100,000	.00	.00	.00	.00	.00	.00	.00	.00	.00	.00
250,000	.00	.00	.00	.00	.00	.00	.00	.00	.00	.00
500,000	.00	.00	.00	.00	.00	.00	.00	.00	.00	.00
1,000,000	.00	.00	.00	.00	.00	.00	.00	.00	.00	.00

A = Annual Demand

R = Cost to Order / Cost per Unit

Stocking Cost = Economic Order plus Holding Costs

Table 4.3 Order Quantities and Stocking Costs for the Production Lot Size Model

h = 20% (Annual Holding Rate)

p = 10 (Annual Production Capacity / Annual Demand)

M = Economic Order Quantity in Months of Demand

A \ R	1000	750	500	250	100	75	50	25	10	5
10	400.0	346.4	282.8	200.0	126.5	109.5	89.4	63.2	40.0	28.3
25	253.0	219.1	178.9	126.5	80.0	69.3	56.6	40.0	25.3	17.9
50	178.9	154.9	126.5	89.4	56.6	49.0	40.0	28.3	17.9	12.6
75	146.1	126.5	103.3	73.0	46.2	40.0	32.7	23.1	14.6	10.3
100	126.5	109.5	89.4	63.2	40.0	34.6	28.3	20.0	12.6	8.9
250	80.0	69.3	56.6	40.0	25.3	21.9	17.9	12.6	8.0	5.7
500	56.6	49.0	40.0	28.3	17.9	15.5	12.6	8.9	5.7	4.0
750	46.2	40.0	32.7	23.1	14.6	12.6	10.3	7.3	4.6	3.3
1,000	40.0	34.6	28.3	20.0	12.6	11.0	8.9	6.3	4.0	2.8
2,500	25.3	21.9	17.9	12.6	8.0	6.9	5.7	4.0	2.5	1.8
5,000	17.9	15.5	12.6	8.9	5.7	4.9	4.0	2.8	1.8	1.3
7,500	14.6	12.6	10.3	7.3	4.6	4.0	3.3	2.3	1.5	1.0
10,000	12.6	11.0	8.9	6.3	4.0	3.5	2.8	2.0	1.3	.9
25,000	8.0	6.9	5.7	4.0	2.5	2.2	1.8	1.3	.8	.6
50,000	5.7	4.9	4.0	2.8	1.8	1.5	1.3	.9	.6	.4
75,000	4.6	4.0	3.3	2.3	1.5	1.3	1.0	.7	.5	.3
100,000	4.0	3.5	2.8	2.0	1.3	1.1	.9	.6	.4	.3
250,000	2.5	2.2	1.8	1.3	.8	.7	.6	.4	.3	.2
500,000	1.8	1.5	1.3	.9	.6	.5	.4	.3	.2	.1
1,000,000	1.3	1.1	.9	.6	.4	.3	.3	.2	.1	.1

s = Stocking Cost / Cost per Unit

A \ R	1000	750	500	250	100	75	50	25	10	5
10	6.00	5.20	4.24	3.00	1.90	1.64	1.34	.95	.60	.42
25	3.79	3.29	2.68	1.90	1.20	1.04	.85	.60	.38	.27
50	2.68	2.32	1.90	1.34	.85	.73	.60	.42	.27	.19
75	2.19	1.90	1.55	1.10	.69	.60	.49	.35	.22	.15
100	1.90	1.64	1.34	.95	.60	.52	.42	.30	.19	.13
250	1.20	1.04	.85	.60	.38	.33	.27	.19	.12	.08
500	.85	.73	.60	.42	.27	.23	.19	.13	.08	.06
750	.69	.60	.49	.35	.22	.19	.15	.11	.07	.05
1,000	.60	.52	.42	.30	.19	.16	.13	.09	.06	.04
2,500	.38	.33	.27	.19	.12	.10	.08	.06	.04	.03
5,000	.27	.23	.19	.13	.08	.07	.06	.04	.03	.02
7,500	.22	.19	.15	.11	.07	.06	.05	.03	.02	.02
10,000	.19	.16	.13	.09	.06	.05	.04	.03	.02	.01
25,000	.12	.10	.08	.06	.04	.03	.03	.02	.01	.01
50,000	.08	.07	.06	.04	.03	.02	.02	.01	.01	.01
75,000	.07	.06	.05	.03	.02	.02	.02	.01	.01	.00
100,000	.06	.05	.04	.03	.02	.02	.01	.01	.01	.00
250,000	.04	.03	.03	.02	.01	.01	.01	.01	.00	.00
500,000	.03	.02	.02	.01	.01	.01	.01	.00	.00	.00
1,000,000	.02	.02	.01	.01	.01	.01	.00	.00	.00	.00

A = Annual Demand

R = Cost to Order / Cost per Unit

Stocking Cost = Economic Order plus Holding Costs

Table 4.3 Order Quantities and Stocking Costs for the Production Lot Size Model (Continued)

h = 20% (Annual Holding Rate)

p = 10 (Annual Production Capacity / Annual Demand)

M = Economic Order Quantity in Months of Demand

A \ R	3	1	.8	.6	.4	.2	.1	.07	.03	.01
10	21.9	12.6	11.3	9.8	8.0	5.7	4.0	3.3	2.2	1.3
25	13.9	8.0	7.2	6.2	5.1	3.6	2.5	2.1	1.4	.8
50	9.8	5.7	5.1	4.4	3.6	2.5	1.8	1.5	1.0	.6
75	8.0	4.6	4.1	3.6	2.9	2.1	1.5	1.2	.8	.5
100	6.9	4.0	3.6	3.1	2.5	1.8	1.3	1.1	.7	.4
250	4.4	2.5	2.3	2.0	1.6	1.1	.8	.7	.4	.3
500	3.1	1.8	1.6	1.4	1.1	.8	.6	.5	.3	.2
750	2.5	1.5	1.3	1.1	.9	.7	.5	.4	.3	.1
1,000	2.2	1.3	1.1	1.0	.8	.6	.4	.3	.2	.1
2,500	1.4	.8	.7	.6	.5	.4	.3	.2	.1	.1
5,000	1.0	.6	.5	.4	.4	.3	.2	.1	.1	.1
7,500	.8	.5	.4	.4	.3	.2	.1	.1	.1	.0
10,000	.7	.4	.4	.3	.3	.2	.1	.1	.1	.0
25,000	.4	.3	.2	.2	.2	.1	.1	.1	.0	.0
50,000	.3	.2	.2	.1	.1	.1	.1	.0	.0	.0
75,000	.3	.1	.1	.1	.1	.1	.0	.0	.0	.0
100,000	.2	.1	.1	.1	.1	.1	.0	.0	.0	.0
250,000	.1	.1	.1	.1	.1	.0	.0	.0	.0	.0
500,000	.1	.1	.1	.0	.0	.0	.0	.0	.0	.0
1,000,000	.1	.0	.0	.0	.0	.0	.0	.0	.0	.0

s = Stocking Cost / Cost per Unit

A \ R	3	1	.8	.6	.4	.2	.1	.07	.03	.01
10	.33	.19	.17	.15	.12	.08	.06	.05	.03	.02
25	.21	.12	.11	.09	.08	.05	.04	.03	.02	.01
50	.15	.08	.08	.07	.05	.04	.03	.02	.01	.01
75	.12	.07	.06	.05	.04	.03	.02	.02	.01	.01
100	.10	.06	.05	.05	.04	.03	.02	.02	.01	.01
250	.07	.04	.03	.03	.02	.02	.01	.01	.01	.00
500	.05	.03	.02	.02	.02	.01	.01	.01	.00	.00
750	.04	.02	.02	.02	.01	.01	.01	.01	.00	.00
1,000	.03	.02	.02	.01	.01	.01	.01	.01	.00	.00
2,500	.02	.01	.01	.01	.01	.01	.00	.00	.00	.00
5,000	.01	.01	.01	.01	.01	.00	.00	.00	.00	.00
7,500	.01	.01	.01	.01	.00	.00	.00	.00	.00	.00
10,000	.01	.01	.01	.00	.00	.00	.00	.00	.00	.00
25,000	.01	.00	.00	.00	.00	.00	.00	.00	.00	.00
50,000	.00	.00	.00	.00	.00	.00	.00	.00	.00	.00
75,000	.00	.00	.00	.00	.00	.00	.00	.00	.00	.00
100,000	.00	.00	.00	.00	.00	.00	.00	.00	.00	.00
250,000	.00	.00	.00	.00	.00	.00	.00	.00	.00	.00
500,000	.00	.00	.00	.00	.00	.00	.00	.00	.00	.00
1,000,000	.00	.00	.00	.00	.00	.00	.00	.00	.00	.00

A = Annual Demand

R = Cost to Order / Cost per Unit

Stocking Cost = Economic Order plus Holding Costs

Table 4.4 Order Quantities and Stocking Costs for the Production Lot Size Model

h = 30% (Annual Holding Rate)

p = 2 (Annual Production Capacity / Annual Demand)

M = Economic Order Quantity in Months of Demand

A \ R	1000	750	500	250	100	75	50	25	10	5
10	438.2	379.5	309.8	219.1	138.6	120.0	98.0	69.3	43.8	31.0
25	277.1	240.0	196.0	138.6	87.6	75.9	62.0	43.8	27.7	19.6
50	196.0	169.7	138.6	98.0	62.0	53.7	43.8	31.0	19.6	13.9
75	160.0	138.6	113.1	80.0	50.6	43.8	35.8	25.3	16.0	11.3
100	138.6	120.0	98.0	69.3	43.8	37.9	31.0	21.9	13.9	9.8
250	87.6	75.9	62.0	43.8	27.7	24.0	19.6	13.9	8.8	6.2
500	62.0	53.7	43.8	31.0	19.6	17.0	13.9	9.8	6.2	4.4
750	50.6	43.8	35.8	25.3	16.0	13.9	11.3	8.0	5.1	3.6
1,000	43.8	37.9	31.0	21.9	13.9	12.0	9.8	6.9	4.4	3.1
2,500	27.7	24.0	19.6	13.9	8.8	7.6	6.2	4.4	2.8	2.0
5,000	19.6	17.0	13.9	9.8	6.2	5.4	4.4	3.1	2.0	1.4
7,500	16.0	13.9	11.3	8.0	5.1	4.4	3.6	2.5	1.6	1.1
10,000	13.9	12.0	9.8	6.9	4.4	3.8	3.1	2.2	1.4	1.0
25,000	8.8	7.6	6.2	4.4	2.8	2.4	2.0	1.4	.9	.6
50,000	6.2	5.4	4.4	3.1	2.0	1.7	1.4	1.0	.6	.4
75,000	5.1	4.4	3.6	2.5	1.6	1.4	1.1	.8	.5	.4
100,000	4.4	3.8	3.1	2.2	1.4	1.2	1.0	.7	.4	.3
250,000	2.8	2.4	2.0	1.4	.9	.8	.6	.4	.3	.2
500,000	2.0	1.7	1.4	1.0	.6	.5	.4	.3	.2	.1
1,000,000	1.4	1.2	1.0	.7	.4	.4	.3	.2	.1	.1

s = Stocking Cost / Cost per Unit

A \ R	1000	750	500	250	100	75	50	25	10	5
10	5.48	4.74	3.87	2.74	1.73	1.50	1.22	.87	.55	.39
25	3.46	3.00	2.45	1.73	1.10	.95	.77	.55	.35	.24
50	2.45	2.12	1.73	1.22	.77	.67	.55	.39	.24	.17
75	2.00	1.73	1.41	1.00	.63	.55	.45	.32	.20	.14
100	1.73	1.50	1.22	.87	.55	.47	.39	.27	.17	.12
250	1.10	.95	.77	.55	.35	.30	.24	.17	.11	.08
500	.77	.67	.55	.39	.24	.21	.17	.12	.08	.05
750	.63	.55	.45	.32	.20	.17	.14	.10	.06	.04
1,000	.55	.47	.39	.27	.17	.15	.12	.09	.05	.04
2,500	.35	.30	.24	.17	.11	.09	.08	.05	.03	.02
5,000	.24	.21	.17	.12	.08	.07	.05	.04	.02	.02
7,500	.20	.17	.14	.10	.06	.05	.04	.03	.02	.01
10,000	.17	.15	.12	.09	.05	.05	.04	.03	.02	.01
25,000	.11	.09	.08	.05	.03	.03	.02	.02	.01	.01
50,000	.08	.07	.05	.04	.02	.02	.02	.01	.01	.01
75,000	.06	.05	.04	.03	.02	.02	.01	.01	.01	.00
100,000	.05	.05	.04	.03	.02	.02	.01	.01	.01	.00
250,000	.03	.03	.02	.02	.01	.01	.01	.01	.00	.00
500,000	.02	.02	.02	.01	.01	.01	.01	.00	.00	.00
1,000,000	.02	.02	.01	.01	.01	.00	.00	.00	.00	.00

A = Annual Demand

R = Cost to Order / Cost per Unit

Stocking Cost = Economic Order plus Holding Costs

Table 4.4 Order Quantities and Stocking Costs for the Production Lot Size Model

h = 30% (Annual Holding Rate)   **(Continued)**

p = 2 (Annual Production Capacity / Annual Demand)

M = Economic Order Quantity in Months of Demand

A \ R	3	1	.8	.6	.4	.2	.1	.07	.03	.01
10	24.0	13.9	12.4	10.7	8.8	6.2	4.4	3.7	2.4	1.4
25	15.2	8.8	7.8	6.8	5.5	3.9	2.8	2.3	1.5	.9
50	10.7	6.2	5.5	4.8	3.9	2.8	2.0	1.6	1.1	.6
75	8.8	5.1	4.5	3.9	3.2	2.3	1.6	1.3	.9	.5
100	7.6	4.4	3.9	3.4	2.8	2.0	1.4	1.2	.8	.4
250	4.8	2.8	2.5	2.1	1.8	1.2	.9	.7	.5	.3
500	3.4	2.0	1.8	1.5	1.2	.9	.6	.5	.3	.2
750	2.8	1.6	1.4	1.2	1.0	.7	.5	.4	.3	.2
1,000	2.4	1.4	1.2	1.1	.9	.6	.4	.4	.2	.1
2,500	1.5	.9	.8	.7	.6	.4	.3	.2	.2	.1
5,000	1.1	.6	.6	.5	.4	.3	.2	.2	.1	.1
7,500	.9	.5	.5	.4	.3	.2	.2	.1	.1	.1
10,000	.8	.4	.4	.3	.3	.2	.1	.1	.1	.0
25,000	.5	.3	.2	.2	.2	.1	.1	.1	.0	.0
50,000	.3	.2	.2	.2	.1	.1	.1	.1	.0	.0
75,000	.3	.2	.1	.1	.1	.1	.1	.0	.0	.0
100,000	.2	.1	.1	.1	.1	.1	.0	.0	.0	.0
250,000	.2	.1	.1	.1	.1	.0	.0	.0	.0	.0
500,000	.1	.1	.1	.0	.0	.0	.0	.0	.0	.0
1,000,000	.1	.0	.0	.0	.0	.0	.0	.0	.0	.0

s = Stocking Cost / Cost per Unit

A \ R	3	1	.8	.6	.4	.2	.1	.07	.03	.01
10	.30	.17	.15	.13	.11	.08	.05	.05	.03	.02
25	.19	.11	.10	.08	.07	.05	.03	.03	.02	.01
50	.13	.08	.07	.06	.05	.03	.02	.02	.01	.01
75	.11	.06	.06	.05	.04	.03	.02	.02	.01	.01
100	.09	.05	.05	.04	.03	.02	.02	.01	.01	.01
250	.06	.03	.03	.03	.02	.02	.01	.01	.01	.00
500	.04	.02	.02	.02	.02	.01	.01	.01	.00	.00
750	.03	.02	.02	.02	.01	.01	.01	.01	.00	.00
1,000	.03	.02	.02	.01	.01	.01	.01	.00	.00	.00
2,500	.02	.01	.01	.01	.01	.00	.00	.00	.00	.00
5,000	.01	.01	.01	.01	.00	.00	.00	.00	.00	.00
7,500	.01	.01	.01	.00	.00	.00	.00	.00	.00	.00
10,000	.01	.01	.00	.00	.00	.00	.00	.00	.00	.00
25,000	.01	.00	.00	.00	.00	.00	.00	.00	.00	.00
50,000	.00	.00	.00	.00	.00	.00	.00	.00	.00	.00
75,000	.00	.00	.00	.00	.00	.00	.00	.00	.00	.00
100,000	.00	.00	.00	.00	.00	.00	.00	.00	.00	.00
250,000	.00	.00	.00	.00	.00	.00	.00	.00	.00	.00
500,000	.00	.00	.00	.00	.00	.00	.00	.00	.00	.00
1,000,000	.00	.00	.00	.00	.00	.00	.00	.00	.00	.00

A = Annual Demand

R = Cost to Order / Cost per Unit

Stocking Cost = Economic Order plus Holding Costs

Table 4.5 Order Quantities and Stocking Costs for the Production Lot Size Model

h = 30% (Annual Holding Rate)

p = 5 (Annual Production Capacity / Annual Demand)

M = Economic Order Quantity in Months of Demand

A \ R	1000	750	500	250	100	75	50	25	10	5
10	346.4	300.0	244.9	173.2	109.5	94.9	77.5	54.8	34.6	24.5
25	219.1	189.7	154.9	109.5	69.3	60.0	49.0	34.6	21.9	15.5
50	154.9	134.2	109.5	77.5	49.0	42.4	34.6	24.5	15.5	11.0
75	126.5	109.5	89.4	63.2	40.0	34.6	28.3	20.0	12.6	8.9
100	109.5	94.9	77.5	54.8	34.6	30.0	24.5	17.3	11.0	7.7
250	69.3	60.0	49.0	34.6	21.9	19.0	15.5	11.0	6.9	4.9
500	49.0	42.4	34.6	24.5	15.5	13.4	11.0	7.7	4.9	3.5
750	40.0	34.6	28.3	20.0	12.6	11.0	8.9	6.3	4.0	2.8
1,000	34.6	30.0	24.5	17.3	11.0	9.5	7.7	5.5	3.5	2.4
2,500	21.9	19.0	15.5	11.0	6.9	6.0	4.9	3.5	2.2	1.5
5,000	15.5	13.4	11.0	7.7	4.9	4.2	3.5	2.4	1.5	1.1
7,500	12.6	11.0	8.9	6.3	4.0	3.5	2.8	2.0	1.3	.9
10,000	11.0	9.5	7.7	5.5	3.5	3.0	2.4	1.7	1.1	.8
25,000	6.9	6.0	4.9	3.5	2.2	1.9	1.5	1.1	.7	.5
50,000	4.9	4.2	3.5	2.4	1.5	1.3	1.1	.8	.5	.3
75,000	4.0	3.5	2.8	2.0	1.3	1.1	.9	.6	.4	.3
100,000	3.5	3.0	2.4	1.7	1.1	.9	.8	.5	.3	.2
250,000	2.2	1.9	1.5	1.1	.7	.6	.5	.3	.2	.2
500,000	1.5	1.3	1.1	.8	.5	.4	.3	.2	.2	.1
1,000,000	1.1	.9	.8	.5	.3	.3	.2	.2	.1	.1

s = Stocking Cost / Cost per Unit

A \ R	1000	750	500	250	100	75	50	25	10	5
10	6.93	6.00	4.90	3.46	2.19	1.90	1.55	1.10	.69	.49
25	4.38	3.79	3.10	2.19	1.39	1.20	.98	.69	.44	.31
50	3.10	2.68	2.19	1.55	.98	.85	.69	.49	.31	.22
75	2.53	2.19	1.79	1.26	.80	.69	.57	.40	.25	.18
100	2.19	1.90	1.55	1.10	.69	.60	.49	.35	.22	.15
250	1.39	1.20	.98	.69	.44	.38	.31	.22	.14	.10
500	.98	.85	.69	.49	.31	.27	.22	.15	.10	.07
750	.80	.69	.57	.40	.25	.22	.18	.13	.08	.06
1,000	.69	.60	.49	.35	.22	.19	.15	.11	.07	.05
2,500	.44	.38	.31	.22	.14	.12	.10	.07	.04	.03
5,000	.31	.27	.22	.15	.10	.08	.07	.05	.03	.02
7,500	.25	.22	.18	.13	.08	.07	.06	.04	.03	.02
10,000	.22	.19	.15	.11	.07	.06	.05	.03	.02	.02
25,000	.14	.12	.10	.07	.04	.04	.03	.02	.01	.01
50,000	.10	.08	.07	.05	.03	.03	.02	.02	.01	.01
75,000	.08	.07	.06	.04	.03	.02	.02	.01	.01	.01
100,000	.07	.06	.05	.03	.02	.02	.02	.01	.01	.00
250,000	.04	.04	.03	.02	.01	.01	.01	.01	.00	.00
500,000	.03	.03	.02	.02	.01	.01	.01	.00	.00	.00
1,000,000	.02	.02	.02	.01	.01	.01	.00	.00	.00	.00

A = Annual Demand

R = Cost to Order / Cost per Unit

Stocking Cost = Economic Order plus Holding Costs

Table 4.5 Order Quantities and Stocking Costs for the Production Lot Size Model

(Continued)

h = 30% (Annual Holding Rate)

p = 5 (Annual Production Capacity / Annual Demand)

M = Economic Order Quantity in Months of Demand

A \ R	3	1	.8	.6	.4	.2	.1	.07	.03	.01
10	19.0	11.0	9.8	8.5	6.9	4.9	3.5	2.9	1.9	1.1
25	12.0	6.9	6.2	5.4	4.4	3.1	2.2	1.8	1.2	.7
50	8.5	4.9	4.4	3.8	3.1	2.2	1.5	1.3	.8	.5
75	6.9	4.0	3.6	3.1	2.5	1.8	1.3	1.1	.7	.4
100	6.0	3.5	3.1	2.7	2.2	1.5	1.1	.9	.6	.3
250	3.8	2.2	2.0	1.7	1.4	1.0	.7	.6	.4	.2
500	2.7	1.5	1.4	1.2	1.0	.7	.5	.4	.3	.2
750	2.2	1.3	1.1	1.0	.8	.6	.4	.3	.2	.1
1,000	1.9	1.1	1.0	.8	.7	.5	.3	.3	.2	.1
2,500	1.2	.7	.6	.5	.4	.3	.2	.2	.1	.1
5,000	.8	.5	.4	.4	.3	.2	.2	.1	.1	.0
7,500	.7	.4	.4	.3	.3	.2	.1	.1	.1	.0
10,000	.6	.3	.3	.3	.2	.2	.1	.1	.1	.0
25,000	.4	.2	.2	.2	.1	.1	.1	.1	.0	.0
50,000	.3	.2	.1	.1	.1	.1	.0	.0	.0	.0
75,000	.2	.1	.1	.1	.1	.1	.0	.0	.0	.0
100,000	.2	.1	.1	.1	.1	.0	.0	.0	.0	.0
250,000	.1	.1	.1	.1	.0	.0	.0	.0	.0	.0
500,000	.1	.0	.0	.0	.0	.0	.0	.0	.0	.0
1,000,000	.1	.0	.0	.0	.0	.0	.0	.0	.0	.0

s = Stocking Cost / Cost per Unit

A \ R	3	1	.8	.6	.4	.2	.1	.07	.03	.01
10	.38	.22	.20	.17	.14	.10	.07	.06	.04	.02
25	.24	.14	.12	.11	.09	.06	.04	.04	.02	.01
50	.17	.10	.09	.08	.06	.04	.03	.03	.02	.01
75	.14	.08	.07	.06	.05	.04	.03	.02	.01	.01
100	.12	.07	.06	.05	.04	.03	.02	.02	.01	.01
250	.08	.04	.04	.03	.03	.02	.01	.01	.01	.00
500	.05	.03	.03	.02	.02	.01	.01	.01	.01	.00
750	.04	.03	.02	.02	.02	.01	.01	.01	.00	.00
1,000	.04	.02	.02	.02	.01	.01	.01	.01	.00	.00
2,500	.02	.01	.01	.01	.01	.01	.00	.00	.00	.00
5,000	.02	.01	.01	.01	.01	.00	.00	.00	.00	.00
7,500	.01	.01	.01	.01	.01	.00	.00	.00	.00	.00
10,000	.01	.01	.01	.01	.00	.00	.00	.00	.00	.00
25,000	.01	.00	.00	.00	.00	.00	.00	.00	.00	.00
50,000	.01	.00	.00	.00	.00	.00	.00	.00	.00	.00
75,000	.00	.00	.00	.00	.00	.00	.00	.00	.00	.00
100,000	.00	.00	.00	.00	.00	.00	.00	.00	.00	.00
250,000	.00	.00	.00	.00	.00	.00	.00	.00	.00	.00
500,000	.00	.00	.00	.00	.00	.00	.00	.00	.00	.00
1,000,000	.00	.00	.00	.00	.00	.00	.00	.00	.00	.00

A = Annual Demand

R = Cost to Order / Cost per Unit

Stocking Cost = Economic Order plus Holding Costs

Table 4.6 Order Quantities and Stocking Costs for the Production Lot Size Model

h = 30% (Annual Holding Rate)

p = 10 (Annual Production Capacity / Annual Demand)

M = Economic Order Quantity in Months of Demand

A \ R	1000	750	500	250	100	75	50	25	10	5
10	326.6	282.8	230.9	163.3	103.3	89.4	73.0	51.6	32.7	23.1
25	206.6	178.9	146.1	103.3	65.3	56.6	46.2	32.7	20.7	14.6
50	146.1	126.5	103.3	73.0	46.2	40.0	32.7	23.1	14.6	10.3
75	119.3	103.3	84.3	59.6	37.7	32.7	26.7	18.9	11.9	8.4
100	103.3	89.4	73.0	51.6	32.7	28.3	23.1	16.3	10.3	7.3
250	65.3	56.6	46.2	32.7	20.7	17.9	14.6	10.3	6.5	4.6
500	46.2	40.0	32.7	23.1	14.6	12.6	10.3	7.3	4.6	3.3
750	37.7	32.7	26.7	18.9	11.9	10.3	8.4	6.0	3.8	2.7
1,000	32.7	28.3	23.1	16.3	10.3	8.9	7.3	5.2	3.3	2.3
2,500	20.7	17.9	14.6	10.3	6.5	5.7	4.6	3.3	2.1	1.5
5,000	14.6	12.6	10.3	7.3	4.6	4.0	3.3	2.3	1.5	1.0
7,500	11.9	10.3	8.4	6.0	3.8	3.3	2.7	1.9	1.2	.8
10,000	10.3	8.9	7.3	5.2	3.3	2.8	2.3	1.6	1.0	.7
25,000	6.5	5.7	4.6	3.3	2.1	1.8	1.5	1.0	.7	.5
50,000	4.6	4.0	3.3	2.3	1.5	1.3	1.0	.7	.5	.3
75,000	3.8	3.3	2.7	1.9	1.2	1.0	.8	.6	.4	.3
100,000	3.3	2.8	2.3	1.6	1.0	.9	.7	.5	.3	.2
250,000	2.1	1.8	1.5	1.0	.7	.6	.5	.3	.2	.1
500,000	1.5	1.3	1.0	.7	.5	.4	.3	.2	.1	.1
1,000,000	1.0	.9	.7	.5	.3	.3	.2	.2	.1	.1

s = Stocking Cost / Cost per Unit

A \ R	1000	750	500	250	100	75	50	25	10	5
10	7.35	6.36	5.20	3.67	2.32	2.01	1.64	1.16	.73	.52
25	4.65	4.02	3.29	2.32	1.47	1.27	1.04	.73	.46	.33
50	3.29	2.85	2.32	1.64	1.04	.90	.73	.52	.33	.23
75	2.68	2.32	1.90	1.34	.85	.73	.60	.42	.27	.19
100	2.32	2.01	1.64	1.16	.73	.64	.52	.37	.23	.16
250	1.47	1.27	1.04	.73	.46	.40	.33	.23	.15	.10
500	1.04	.90	.73	.52	.33	.28	.23	.16	.10	.07
750	.85	.73	.60	.42	.27	.23	.19	.13	.08	.06
1,000	.73	.64	.52	.37	.23	.20	.16	.12	.07	.05
2,500	.46	.40	.33	.23	.15	.13	.10	.07	.05	.03
5,000	.33	.28	.23	.16	.10	.09	.07	.05	.03	.02
7,500	.27	.23	.19	.13	.08	.07	.06	.04	.03	.02
10,000	.23	.20	.16	.12	.07	.06	.05	.04	.02	.02
25,000	.15	.13	.10	.07	.05	.04	.03	.02	.01	.01
50,000	.10	.09	.07	.05	.03	.03	.02	.02	.01	.01
75,000	.08	.07	.06	.04	.03	.02	.02	.01	.01	.01
100,000	.07	.06	.05	.04	.02	.02	.02	.01	.01	.01
250,000	.05	.04	.03	.02	.01	.01	.01	.01	.00	.00
500,000	.03	.03	.02	.02	.01	.01	.01	.01	.00	.00
1,000,000	.02	.02	.02	.01	.01	.01	.01	.00	.00	.00

A = Annual Demand

R = Cost to Order / Cost per Unit

Stocking Cost = Economic Order plus Holding Costs

Table 4.6 Order Quantities and Stocking Costs for the Production Lot Size Model

h = 30% (Annual Holding Rate)   **(Continued)**

p = 10 (Annual Production Capacity / Annual Demand)

M = Economic Order Quantity in Months of Demand

A \ R	3	1	.8	.6	.4	.2	.1	.07	.03	.01
10	17.9	10.3	9.2	8.0	6.5	4.6	3.3	2.7	1.8	1.0
25	11.3	6.5	5.8	5.1	4.1	2.9	2.1	1.7	1.1	.7
50	8.0	4.6	4.1	3.6	2.9	2.1	1.5	1.2	.8	.5
75	6.5	3.8	3.4	2.9	2.4	1.7	1.2	1.0	.7	.4
100	5.7	3.3	2.9	2.5	2.1	1.5	1.0	.9	.6	.3
250	3.6	2.1	1.8	1.6	1.3	.9	.7	.5	.4	.2
500	2.5	1.5	1.3	1.1	.9	.7	.5	.4	.3	.1
750	2.1	1.2	1.1	.9	.8	.5	.4	.3	.2	.1
1,000	1.8	1.0	.9	.8	.7	.5	.3	.3	.2	.1
2,500	1.1	.7	.6	.5	.4	.3	.2	.2	.1	.1
5,000	.8	.5	.4	.4	.3	.2	.1	.1	.1	.0
7,500	.7	.4	.3	.3	.2	.2	.1	.1	.1	.0
10,000	.6	.3	.3	.3	.2	.1	.1	.1	.1	.0
25,000	.4	.2	.2	.2	.1	.1	.1	.1	.0	.0
50,000	.3	.1	.1	.1	.1	.1	.0	.0	.0	.0
75,000	.2	.1	.1	.1	.1	.1	.0	.0	.0	.0
100,000	.2	.1	.1	.1	.1	.0	.0	.0	.0	.0
250,000	.1	.1	.1	.1	.0	.0	.0	.0	.0	.0
500,000	.1	.0	.0	.0	.0	.0	.0	.0	.0	.0
1,000,000	.1	.0	.0	.0	.0	.0	.0	.0	.0	.0

s = Stocking Cost / Cost per Unit

A \ R	3	1	.8	.6	.4	.2	.1	.07	.03	.01
10	.40	.23	.21	.18	.15	.10	.07	.06	.04	.02
25	.25	.15	.13	.11	.09	.07	.05	.04	.03	.01
50	.18	.10	.09	.08	.07	.05	.03	.03	.02	.01
75	.15	.08	.08	.07	.05	.04	.03	.02	.01	.01
100	.13	.07	.07	.06	.05	.03	.02	.02	.01	.01
250	.08	.05	.04	.04	.03	.02	.01	.01	.01	.00
500	.06	.03	.03	.03	.02	.01	.01	.01	.01	.00
750	.05	.03	.02	.02	.02	.01	.01	.01	.00	.00
1,000	.04	.02	.02	.02	.01	.01	.01	.01	.00	.00
2,500	.03	.01	.01	.01	.01	.01	.00	.00	.00	.00
5,000	.02	.01	.01	.01	.01	.00	.00	.00	.00	.00
7,500	.01	.01	.01	.01	.01	.00	.00	.00	.00	.00
10,000	.01	.01	.01	.01	.00	.00	.00	.00	.00	.00
25,000	.01	.00	.00	.00	.00	.00	.00	.00	.00	.00
50,000	.01	.00	.00	.00	.00	.00	.00	.00	.00	.00
75,000	.00	.00	.00	.00	.00	.00	.00	.00	.00	.00
100,000	.00	.00	.00	.00	.00	.00	.00	.00	.00	.00
250,000	.00	.00	.00	.00	.00	.00	.00	.00	.00	.00
500,000	.00	.00	.00	.00	.00	.00	.00	.00	.00	.00
1,000,000	.00	.00	.00	.00	.00	.00	.00	.00	.00	.00

A = Annual Demand

R = Cost to Order / Cost per Unit

Stocking Cost = Economic Order plus Holding Costs

Table 4.7   Xp for the Production Lot Size Model

Qo = EOQ for the Simple Lot Size Model
Q = EOQ for the Production Lot Size Model
Xp = Q/Qo
p = annual production capacity / annual demand

p	Xp	p	Xp	p	Xp
2	1.414	35	1.015	68	1.007
3	1.225	36	1.014	69	1.007
4	1.155	37	1.014	70	1.007
5	1.118	38	1.013	71	1.007
6	1.095	39	1.013	72	1.007
7	1.080	40	1.013	73	1.007
8	1.069	41	1.012	74	1.007
9	1.061	42	1.012	75	1.007
10	1.054	43	1.012	76	1.007
11	1.049	44	1.012	77	1.007
12	1.044	45	1.011	78	1.006
13	1.041	46	1.011	79	1.006
14	1.038	47	1.011	80	1.006
15	1.035	48	1.011	81	1.006
16	1.033	49	1.010	82	1.006
17	1.031	50	1.010	83	1.006
18	1.029	51	1.010	84	1.006
19	1.027	52	1.010	85	1.006
20	1.026	53	1.010	86	1.006
21	1.025	54	1.009	87	1.006
22	1.024	55	1.009	88	1.006
23	1.022	56	1.009	89	1.006
24	1.022	57	1.009	90	1.006
25	1.021	58	1.009	91	1.006
26	1.020	59	1.009	92	1.005
27	1.019	60	1.008	93	1.005
28	1.018	61	1.008	94	1.005
29	1.018	62	1.008	95	1.005
30	1.017	63	1.008	96	1.005
31	1.017	64	1.008	97	1.005
32	1.016	65	1.008	98	1.005
33	1.016	66	1.008	99	1.005
34	1.015	67	1.008		

CHAPTER 5

Sensitivity Relations For The Simple Lot Size Model

The inventory model of Chapter 2 (Simple Lot Size Model) is developed to yield the economic order quantity **Q** for a given set of input data, and the adjoining tables of the chapter show how the results vary with the input data. This chapter gives relations on the sensitivity of those results with respect to the input data (reference 1). Two situations often occur where the application of these relations are useful.

The first situation occurs when the precise values of input data are not really known for certain, such as **A** (the annual demand), **Co** (the cost per order), **C** (the cost per unit) or **h** (the annual holding rate). In these events, the inventory model may nevertheless be run using the best estimates possible. The sensitivity relations show how the order quantity changes as input data varies according to the values used. The obtained results give the materials management a sense of how truly urgent it is to seek precise input data.

A second application occurs when management seeks to determine the inventory effects when input data are varied for some strategic purpose. For example, management may question how order quantities will be affected should the order cost be decreased or if the holding rates are increased and so forth. Thus, the materials manager can study the replenishment effects on the inventory system when he/she desires to alter the input data to achieve certain goals. In essence, since replenishments to the system are completely determined by input data, how may the input data be varied to steer replenishments in the direction desired by management?

The chapter also shows how costs may vary when an order quantity other than the economic order quantity is used in its place. These results again give management a sense of how costly using an order quantity other than the economic order quantity really is. (This situation may be caused by certain limitations set by the supplier and/or the stocking facility.)

Notation
The following notation are used to study the various sensitivity relations of the simple lot size model (Confer also data and model of Chapter 2):

$$A = \text{annual demand}$$
$$Co = \text{cost per order}$$
$$C = \text{cost per unit}$$
$$h = \text{annual holding rate}$$
$$Q = \text{economic order quantity}$$
$$K = \text{order plus holding cost using } Q$$

Sensitivity of the Annual Demand

Suppose **A** is the actual demand for an item, but assume **A** is not really known for certain and a value **A′** must be used in its place. If **A** were known, then the true economic order quantity would be **Q**; but since **A′** is used instead of **A**, another order quantity **Q′** is calculated in its place. Assuming all other input data are known and used appropriately, the relation between **Q′** and **Q** with respect to **A′** and **A** is then:

$$Q'/Q = \sqrt{A'/A}$$

Figure 5.1 shows the shape of the above relationship.

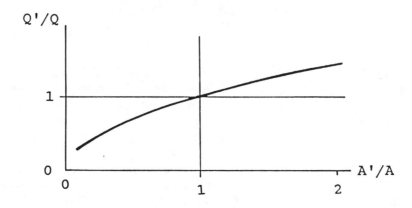

Figure 5.1. Q′/Q versus A′/A

Sensitivity of the Cost per Order

Suppose **Co** (cost per order) is used in the simple lot size model along with the other input data to yield the economic order quantity **Q**. Further assume **Co** is replaced by a value **Co′** and all other input data are used as before. The results will now give another order quantity **Q′**, and the relation between **Q** and **Q′** with respect to **Co′** and **Co** becomes:

$$Q'/Q = \sqrt{Co'/Co}$$

The above relation is as described in Figure 5.2.

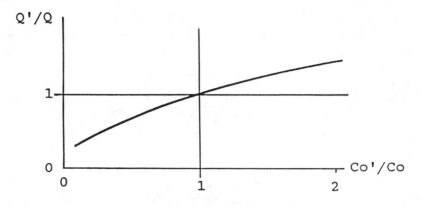

Figure 5.2. Q′/Q versus Co′/Co

Sensitivity of the Cost per Unit

Assume now that **C** (the cost per unit) is used along with all the other input data to yield the economic order quantity **Q**. **C**′(any other cost per unit) will be used in place of **C** and all else remains the same. The results will be a new order quantity **Q**′, and the relation between **Q**′ and **Q** with respect to **C**′ and **C** is now:

$$Q'/Q = \sqrt{C/C'}$$

Figure 5.3 shows the shape of the above relation.

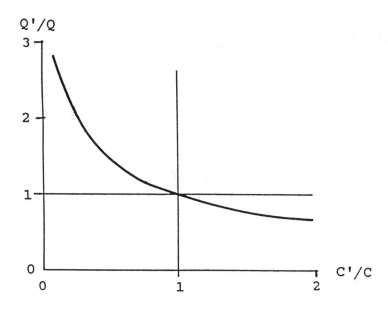

Figure 5.3. Q′/Q versus C′/C

Sensitivity of the Annual Holding Rate

Suppose that **h** (the annual holding rate) is used along with the other input data to yield an economic order quantity **Q**. **h**′, another holding rate, yields the order quantity **Q**′. The relation between **Q**′ and **Q** with **h**′ and **h** is given as:

$$Q'/Q = \sqrt{h/h'}$$

The above relation is described in Figure 5.4.

Sensitivity of the Order Quantity

All the sensitivity relations given above demonstrate how **Q**′ varies from **Q** whenever one of the input data for the item is changed from its current value. The relation given here shows how the annual order plus holding cost changes whenever **Q**′ is used instead of **Q** (the current economic order quantity). Letting **K** represent the economic order plus holding cost when **Q** is used and **K**′ the corresponding cost when **Q**′ is used, the relation between **K** and **K**′, following the relationships in Chapter 2, becomes:

$$K'/K = .5\,(Q'/Q + Q/Q')$$

The above relation applies for both the simple lot size model and the production lot size model, as depicted in Figure 5.5.

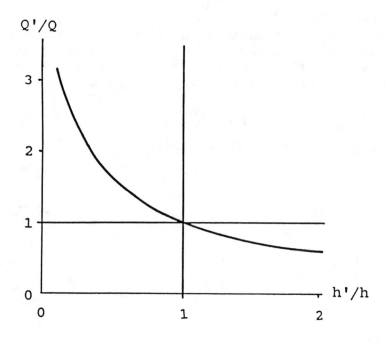

Figure 5.4. Q′/Q versus h′/h

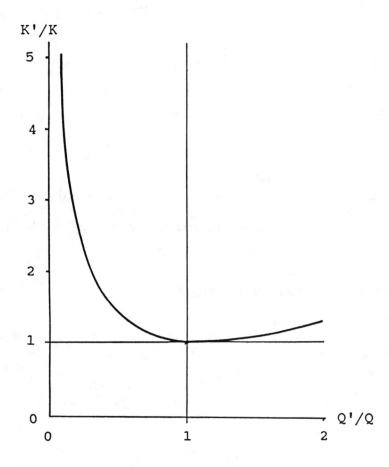

Figure 5.5. K′/K versus Q′/Q

Tables

The results from the five sensitivity relations of this chapter are listed in Tables 5.1 to 5.5. Tables 5.1 to 5.4 give relations concerning Q'/Q with respect to varying values of A'/A, Co'/Co, C'/C and h'/h. Table 5.5 shows how K'/K changes with varying values of Q'/Q.

Example 5.1

Suppose the annual forecast of an item calls for 1000 units and, using the related input data, the resulting economic order quantity becomes 100 units. Show how the economic order quantity will change should the forecast increase to 1200 units.

With $A = 1000$ and $A' = 1200$, then $A'/A = 1.20$. Table 5.1 now yields the ratio of $Q'/Q = 1.10$, and thereby the economic order quantity will become $Q' = 1.10\,(100) = 110$.

Example 5.2

Suppose a factory item has an annual demand of 12,000 units and an economic order quantity of 1,500 units (a one and a half month supply). Assume that the plant scheduler, wishing to reduce the order quantity to a two week supply, plans to accomplish this reduction by reducing the cost per order. How much reduction in the cost per order is needed to accomplish this goal and yet allow the resulting order quantity to remain an economic order quantity?

Since Q is currently 1.5 months of demand and the desired order quantity is 0.50 months of demand, then $Q'/Q = 0.5/1.5 = .33$ is sought. Table 5.1 yields the value of Co'/Co that corresponds to $Q'/Q = .33$. This value is closely obtained when $Co'/Co = 0.10$, which implies the order cost will need to be reduced to 10 percent of its current value.

Example 5.3

Consider a product line where the procurement cost per unit will be raised by 10 percent across all items and where all else remains the same. What will be the corresponding effect on the order quantities?

Table 5.1 shows that, when $C'/C = 1.10$, $Q'/Q = .95$, and thus all economic order quantities will decrease by 5 percent.

Example 5.4

Suppose a company is using $h = 0.30$ as the annual holding rate for its warehouse items. Assume further that the materials manager wishes to reduce all order quantities by 15 percent and will implement this strategy by changing the annual holding rate parameter. What value of h should be used to accomplish the goal?

Table 5.1 reveals that the value of h'/h when $Q'/Q = .85$ (a 15 percent reduction) occurs when $h'/h = 1.40$; consequently, the holding rate should be increased to $1.40\,(.30) = .42$.

Example 5.5

In an effort to reduce stocked inventory, suppose the management of a firm gives a directive to reduce all order quantities to 50 percent of the calculated economic order quantities. Show what the effect will be on the sum of the order cost plus holding cost.

Table 5.1 shows that when $Q'/Q = .50$, then $K'/K = 1.25$. Using the above reduction strategy, the firm will incur an increase of 25 percent in the sum of the order cost plus holding cost.

Table 5.1 Relation between A'/A and Q'/Q

A'/A	.10	.20	.30	.40	.50	.60	.70	.80	.90	1.00
Q'/Q	.32	.45	.55	.63	.71	.77	.84	.89	.95	1.00

A'/A	1.10	1.20	1.30	1.40	1.50	1.60	1.70	1.80	1.90	2.00
Q'/Q	1.05	1.10	1.14	1.18	1.22	1.26	1.30	1.34	1.38	1.41

A = 12 Month Demand   A' = Any Other 12 Month Demand
Q = Economic Order Quantity using A   Q' = Economic Order Quantity using A'

Table 5.2 Relation between Co'/Co and Q'/Q

Co'/Co	.10	.20	.30	.40	.50	.60	.70	.80	.90	1.00
Q'/Q	.32	.45	.55	.63	.71	.77	.84	.89	.95	1.00

Co'/Co	1.10	1.20	1.30	1.40	1.50	1.60	1.70	1.80	1.90	2.00
Q'/Q	1.05	1.10	1.14	1.18	1.22	1.26	1.30	1.34	1.38	1.41

Co = Cost per Order   Co' = Any Other Cost per Order
Q = Economic Order Quantity using Co   Q' = Economic Order Quantity using Co'

Table 5.3 Relation between C'/C and Q'/Q

C'/C	.10	.20	.30	.40	.50	.60	.70	.80	.90	1.00
Q'/Q	3.16	2.24	1.83	1.58	1.41	1.29	1.20	1.12	1.05	1.00

C'/C	1.10	1.20	1.30	1.40	1.50	1.60	1.70	1.80	1.90	2.00
Q'/Q	.95	.91	.88	.85	.82	.79	.77	.75	.73	.71

C = Cost per Unit   C' = Any Other Cost per Unit
Q = Economic Order Quantity using C   Q' = Economic Order Quantity using C'

Table 5.4   Relation between h'/h and Q'/Q

h'/h	.10	.20	.30	.40	.50	.60	.70	.80	.90	1.00
Q'/Q	3.16	2.24	1.83	1.58	1.41	1.29	1.20	1.12	1.05	1.00

h'/h	1.10	1.20	1.30	1.40	1.50	1.60	1.70	1.80	1.90	2.00
Q'/Q	.95	.91	.88	.85	.82	.79	.77	.75	.73	.71

h = 12 Month Holding Rate   h' = Any Other 12 Month Holding Rate

Q = Economic Order Quantity using h   Q' = Economic Order Quantity using h'

Table 5.5   Relation between Q'/Q and K'/K

Q'/Q	.10	.20	.30	.40	.50	.60	.70	.80	.90	1.00
K'/K	5.05	2.60	1.82	1.45	1.25	1.13	1.06	1.03	1.01	1.00

Q'/Q	1.10	1.20	1.30	1.40	1.50	1.60	1.70	1.80	1.90	2.00
K'/K	1.00	1.02	1.03	1.06	1.08	1.11	1.14	1.18	1.21	1.25

Q = Economic Order Quantity   Q' = Any Other Order Quantity

K = Order + Hold Cost using Q   K' = Order + Hold Cost using Q'

CHAPTER 6

Profit Ratio And Turnover

Generally, the main purpose of carrying inventory in stock is to subsequently sell the stock and achieve as high a profit as possible. Profit is merely the difference between the sales price and the associated cost. Another measure of profit is the ratio of price over cost. This ratio, used in this chapter, is called the *profit ratio*. Profit ratio may vary as time moves on due to two basic considerations. One consideration is the cost of the unit wherein the cost increases in time due to the need for holding the item in inventory, where the longer the unit is held in stock, the higher the effective cost of the unit becomes. The second consideration concerns the selling price of the unit. For some items the selling price is not likely to change, while for others the price may either increase or decrease as time passes.

Because the profit ratio varies with the length of stay for a unit in inventory, this ratio is consequently related to the *turnover ratio*, which is a common measure of how long a unit is held in stock. Although the turnover ratio may be defined and calculated in various ways, one common definition is the following:

$$\text{turnover ratio} = \frac{\text{annual sales}}{\text{average on-hand inventory}}$$

The above relation is the one used in developing the adjoining tables of this chapter.

Notation

The following notation are used in this chapter:

$$TO = \text{turnover ratio}$$
$$P/C = \text{current profit ratio (price per unit/cost per unit)}$$
$$h = \text{annual holding rate}$$
$$i = \text{annual price change rate}$$

For the annual price change rate, if $i = 0$, there is no price change. If $i > 0$, the price is expected to increase as time passes; and if $i < 0$, a price decrease is then expected.

Model

As stated earlier, turnover ratio is herein defined as the ratio of annual sales over the average on-hand inventory. The larger the ratio, the faster the inventory is sold from the time it is available in stock. A firm with a higher turnover ratio has the advantage of carrying a smaller inventory investment to attain its sales. In many firms, the turnover ratio is a common measure of the amount of on-hand inventory investment. This measure is often used to compare the stocking profitability of one line of items against another line or to compare one item against another.

In the calculation of turnover for a line of items, a common measure of both annual sales and average on-hand inventory must be used. For example, if the annual sales are stated in standard cost dollars, then the average on-hand inventory must also be stated in standard cost dollars. In the same manner, the turnover ratio could be derived using other common units, such as pieces or the selling price.

Note that the turnover ratio for an item is also related to the average number of months an item is held in stock before it is sold. To show this relation, let:

A = annual sales
M = average number of months a unit is held in stock

The average sales per month and the average on-hand inventory are now determined by the relations:

$A/12$ = average sales per month
$M(A/12)$ = average on-hand inventory

The turnover ratio becomes:

$$TO = \frac{A}{M(A/12)} = \frac{12}{M}$$

which is merely related to M. Reversing the relation gives:

$$M = \frac{12}{TO}$$

The above relation between TO and M is included in the adjoining tables of this chapter.

The profit ratio is calculated in the following way. For an item in inventory, let:

C = cost per unit
P = selling price per unit

The ratio of the price over the cost is the profit ratio, i.e.,

P/C = price per unit / cost per unit

Note that the profit ratio P/C is not a constant value and may vary as time passes.

Consider first the cost per unit. For a given item, if C_o is the current cost per unit and h is the annual holding rate, then after M months the cost of the unit C_M (current cost plus the add-on holding cost) is:

$$C_M = C_o (1 + h M/12)$$

Second, the price per unit may also vary with time. If P_o is the current price per unit and if i is the annual rate at which the price changes, after M months the price per unit P_M then becomes:

$$P_M = P_o (1 + i M/12)$$

Thus, the profit ratio P/C varies in relation to h, i and M. At the current time period, the profit ratio is $(P/C)_o = P_o/C_o$, and after M months, it is:

$$P/C = (P/C)_0 \frac{(1 + i\,M/12)}{(1 + h\,M/12)}$$

This latter value is here called the *effective profit ratio.*

Tables

The tables of this chapter list the values of the profit ratio for selected values of the current profit ratio, the turnover ratio, the annual holding rate and the annual price change rate. The tables are arranged in the following manner:

Table	h	i
6.1	.20	−.10
6.2	.20	.00
6.3	.20	.10
6.4	.30	−.10
6.5	.30	.00
6.6	.30	.10
6.7	.40	−.10
6.8	.40	.00
6.9	.40	.10

Example 6.1

Assume in one firm that a particular line of items experiences a turnover ratio of 2.0 on the average. The procurement cost for the line is $2,000,000 and the inventory value at the current selling price is $3,000,000; hence, the current profit ratio is $P/C = 1.50$. Assume further that the annual holding rate is $h = .40$ and the average annual price change rate is $i = 0.10$ (or a 10 percent increase in selling price is expected during a year). (Notice that if all the items in the line could be sold immediately, profit would be 50 percent of the cost.) Find the corresponding profit percent for this line of items with the turnover of 2.0.

With $h = .40$ and $i = .10$, Table 6.9 is used to show a profit ratio of $P/C = 1.31$, and thus the profit over the cost is 31 percent. Further note that the turnover ratio of 2.0 yields 6.0 months as the average length of time the stock is in the inventory.

Example 6.2

Assuming the line from Example 6.1, what would be the profit ratio if the turnover ratio is increased to $TO = 3$ and all else remains the same?

Table 6.9 is used again with $TO = 3$ to yield $M = 4$ months and $P/C = 1.37$. Now the ratio of profit over cost is 37 percent. Note also that the new profit of 37 percent over the old profit of 31 percent represents a profit increase of $37/31 = 1.19$, or a 19 percent increase.

Example 6.3

Suppose that a line in a firm is stocked with an annual holding rate of $h = .30$ and has an annual price change of $i = -.10$ (or a decrease of 10 percent). Suppose further that the turnover ratio for this item is traditionally an average $TO = 12$. If management desires an effective profit ratio of 1.40, what should the current profit ratio P/C be in order to achieve the goal?

Table 6.4 is used with $TO = 12$ ($M = 1$) to search for an effective profit ratio of about $P/C = 1.40$. This point occurs when the current profit ratio is

P/C = 1.45; therefore, the current price per unit should be set at 1.45 times the current cost per unit.

Example 6.4

Suppose an auto dealer's cost for a new car is $10,000 and the sales price is $12,000. Assume the annual holding rate is h = .30 and the price increase rate is i = 0 (i.e., no price increase). Assume each car in the lot will remain stock (at the current price of $12,000) on the average 6 months before it is sold. Find the effective profit per sale.

Using Table 6.5 with P/C = 12,000/10,000 = 1.2 and M = 6 (turnover = 2), the effective profit ratio becomes P/C = 1.04. Because the car sells for $12,000, the effective cost is $12,000/1.04 = $11,538 and yields a corresponding effective profit of $12,000 − $11,538 = $462.

Example 6.5

For the auto dealer in Example 6.4, assume the dealer estimates he can reduce selling time in half if he discounts the sales price by $500 (to $11,500). How would this strategy affect the effective profit per sale?

Table 6.5 is again used with M = 6/2 = 3 months and P/C = 11,500/10,000 = 1.15. In this situation, the effective profit ratio becomes P/C = 1.07. Because the adjusted car sales price is $11,500, the cost per car is determined by $11,500/1.07 = $10,748. The effective profit per sale now becomes $11,500 − $10,748 = $752.

Table 6.1 Effective Ratio of (Unit Price)/(Unit Cost) by Turnover Rate

h = 20% (Annual Holding Rate)

i = -10% (Annual Price Change Rate)

TO	50.00	40.00	30.00	20.00	12.00	10.00	8.00	7.50	7.00	6.50	6.00
M	.24	.30	.40	.60	1.00	1.20	1.50	1.60	1.71	1.85	2.00
P/C											
.80	.80	.79	.79	.79	.78	.78	.77	.77	.77	.76	.76
.85	.84	.84	.84	.84	.83	.83	.82	.82	.81	.81	.81
.90	.89	.89	.89	.89	.88	.87	.87	.86	.86	.86	.86
.95	.94	.94	.94	.94	.93	.92	.92	.91	.91	.91	.90
1.00	.99	.99	.99	.99	.98	.97	.96	.96	.96	.96	.95
1.05	1.04	1.04	1.04	1.03	1.02	1.02	1.01	1.01	1.01	1.00	1.00
1.10	1.09	1.09	1.09	1.08	1.07	1.07	1.06	1.06	1.05	1.05	1.05
1.15	1.14	1.14	1.14	1.13	1.12	1.12	1.11	1.11	1.10	1.10	1.09
1.20	1.19	1.19	1.19	1.18	1.17	1.16	1.16	1.15	1.15	1.15	1.14
1.25	1.24	1.24	1.24	1.23	1.22	1.21	1.20	1.20	1.20	1.19	1.19
1.30	1.29	1.29	1.29	1.28	1.27	1.26	1.25	1.25	1.25	1.24	1.24
1.35	1.34	1.34	1.34	1.33	1.32	1.31	1.30	1.30	1.29	1.29	1.28
1.40	1.39	1.39	1.39	1.38	1.37	1.36	1.35	1.35	1.34	1.34	1.33
1.45	1.44	1.44	1.44	1.43	1.41	1.41	1.40	1.39	1.39	1.39	1.38
1.50	1.49	1.49	1.49	1.48	1.46	1.46	1.45	1.44	1.44	1.43	1.43
1.55	1.54	1.54	1.53	1.53	1.51	1.50	1.49	1.49	1.49	1.48	1.47
1.60	1.59	1.59	1.58	1.58	1.56	1.55	1.54	1.54	1.53	1.53	1.52
1.65	1.64	1.64	1.63	1.63	1.61	1.60	1.59	1.59	1.58	1.58	1.57
1.70	1.69	1.69	1.68	1.67	1.66	1.65	1.64	1.63	1.63	1.62	1.62
1.75	1.74	1.74	1.73	1.72	1.71	1.70	1.69	1.68	1.68	1.67	1.67
1.80	1.79	1.79	1.78	1.77	1.76	1.75	1.73	1.73	1.72	1.72	1.71
1.85	1.84	1.84	1.83	1.82	1.80	1.80	1.78	1.78	1.77	1.77	1.76
1.90	1.89	1.89	1.88	1.87	1.85	1.84	1.83	1.83	1.82	1.81	1.81
1.95	1.94	1.94	1.93	1.92	1.90	1.89	1.88	1.87	1.87	1.86	1.86
2.00	1.99	1.99	1.98	1.97	1.95	1.94	1.93	1.92	1.92	1.91	1.90
2.05	2.04	2.03	2.03	2.02	2.00	1.99	1.97	1.97	1.96	1.96	1.95
2.10	2.09	2.08	2.08	2.07	2.05	2.04	2.02	2.02	2.01	2.01	2.00
2.15	2.14	2.13	2.13	2.12	2.10	2.09	2.07	2.07	2.06	2.05	2.05
2.20	2.19	2.18	2.18	2.17	2.15	2.14	2.12	2.11	2.11	2.10	2.09
2.25	2.24	2.23	2.23	2.22	2.19	2.18	2.17	2.16	2.16	2.15	2.14
2.30	2.29	2.28	2.28	2.27	2.24	2.23	2.22	2.21	2.20	2.20	2.19
2.35	2.34	2.33	2.33	2.32	2.29	2.28	2.26	2.26	2.25	2.24	2.24
2.40	2.39	2.38	2.38	2.36	2.34	2.33	2.31	2.31	2.30	2.29	2.28
2.45	2.44	2.43	2.43	2.41	2.39	2.38	2.36	2.35	2.35	2.34	2.33
2.50	2.49	2.48	2.48	2.46	2.44	2.43	2.41	2.40	2.40	2.39	2.38
2.55	2.53	2.53	2.52	2.51	2.49	2.47	2.46	2.45	2.44	2.44	2.43
2.60	2.58	2.58	2.57	2.56	2.54	2.52	2.50	2.50	2.49	2.48	2.47
2.65	2.63	2.63	2.62	2.61	2.58	2.57	2.55	2.55	2.54	2.53	2.52
2.70	2.68	2.68	2.67	2.66	2.63	2.62	2.60	2.59	2.59	2.58	2.57
2.75	2.73	2.73	2.72	2.71	2.68	2.67	2.65	2.64	2.64	2.63	2.62
2.80	2.78	2.78	2.77	2.76	2.73	2.72	2.70	2.69	2.68	2.67	2.66
2.85	2.83	2.83	2.82	2.81	2.78	2.77	2.75	2.74	2.73	2.72	2.71
2.90	2.88	2.88	2.87	2.86	2.83	2.81	2.79	2.79	2.78	2.77	2.76
2.95	2.93	2.93	2.92	2.91	2.88	2.86	2.84	2.84	2.83	2.82	2.81
3.00	2.98	2.98	2.97	2.96	2.93	2.91	2.89	2.88	2.87	2.87	2.85

TO = Turnover Rate

M = Average Number of Months Unit is Held in Stock

P/C = Current Ratio of (Unit Price)/(Unit Cost)

h = 20% (Annual Holding Rate)
i = -10% (Annual Price Change Rate)

TO	5.50	5.00	4.50	4.00	3.50	3.00	2.50	2.00	1.50	1.00	.50
M	2.18	2.40	2.67	3.00	3.43	4.00	4.80	6.00	8.00	12.00	24.00
P/C											
.80	.76	.75	.75	.74	.74	.72	.71	.69	.66	.60	.46
.85	.81	.80	.80	.79	.78	.77	.76	.73	.70	.64	.49
.90	.85	.85	.84	.84	.83	.82	.80	.78	.74	.67	.51
.95	.90	.90	.89	.88	.87	.86	.84	.82	.78	.71	.54
1.00	.95	.94	.94	.93	.92	.91	.89	.86	.82	.75	.57
1.05	.99	.99	.98	.98	.96	.95	.93	.91	.86	.79	.60
1.10	1.04	1.04	1.03	1.02	1.01	1.00	.98	.95	.91	.82	.63
1.15	1.09	1.08	1.08	1.07	1.06	1.04	1.02	.99	.95	.86	.66
1.20	1.14	1.13	1.12	1.11	1.10	1.09	1.07	1.04	.99	.90	.69
1.25	1.18	1.18	1.17	1.16	1.15	1.13	1.11	1.08	1.03	.94	.71
1.30	1.23	1.22	1.22	1.21	1.19	1.18	1.16	1.12	1.07	.97	.74
1.35	1.28	1.27	1.26	1.25	1.24	1.22	1.20	1.17	1.11	1.01	.77
1.40	1.33	1.32	1.31	1.30	1.29	1.27	1.24	1.21	1.15	1.05	.80
1.45	1.37	1.37	1.36	1.35	1.33	1.31	1.29	1.25	1.19	1.09	.83
1.50	1.42	1.41	1.40	1.39	1.38	1.36	1.33	1.30	1.24	1.12	.86
1.55	1.47	1.46	1.45	1.44	1.42	1.40	1.38	1.34	1.28	1.16	.89
1.60	1.52	1.51	1.50	1.49	1.47	1.45	1.42	1.38	1.32	1.20	.91
1.65	1.56	1.55	1.54	1.53	1.52	1.50	1.47	1.42	1.36	1.24	.94
1.70	1.61	1.60	1.59	1.58	1.56	1.54	1.51	1.47	1.40	1.27	.97
1.75	1.66	1.65	1.64	1.62	1.61	1.59	1.56	1.51	1.44	1.31	1.00
1.80	1.71	1.70	1.69	1.67	1.65	1.63	1.60	1.55	1.48	1.35	1.03
1.85	1.75	1.74	1.73	1.72	1.70	1.68	1.64	1.60	1.52	1.39	1.06
1.90	1.80	1.79	1.78	1.76	1.75	1.72	1.69	1.64	1.56	1.42	1.09
1.95	1.85	1.84	1.83	1.81	1.79	1.77	1.73	1.68	1.61	1.46	1.11
2.00	1.89	1.88	1.87	1.86	1.84	1.81	1.78	1.73	1.65	1.50	1.14
2.05	1.94	1.93	1.92	1.90	1.88	1.86	1.82	1.77	1.69	1.54	1.17
2.10	1.99	1.98	1.97	1.95	1.93	1.90	1.87	1.81	1.73	1.57	1.20
2.15	2.04	2.03	2.01	2.00	1.98	1.95	1.91	1.86	1.77	1.61	1.23
2.20	2.08	2.07	2.06	2.04	2.02	1.99	1.96	1.90	1.81	1.65	1.26
2.25	2.13	2.12	2.11	2.09	2.07	2.04	2.00	1.94	1.85	1.69	1.29
2.30	2.18	2.17	2.15	2.14	2.11	2.08	2.04	1.99	1.89	1.72	1.31
2.35	2.23	2.21	2.20	2.18	2.16	2.13	2.09	2.03	1.94	1.76	1.34
2.40	2.27	2.26	2.25	2.23	2.21	2.17	2.13	2.07	1.98	1.80	1.37
2.45	2.32	2.31	2.29	2.27	2.25	2.22	2.18	2.12	2.02	1.84	1.40
2.50	2.37	2.36	2.34	2.32	2.30	2.27	2.22	2.16	2.06	1.87	1.43
2.55	2.42	2.40	2.39	2.37	2.34	2.31	2.27	2.20	2.10	1.91	1.46
2.60	2.46	2.45	2.43	2.41	2.39	2.36	2.31	2.25	2.14	1.95	1.49
2.65	2.51	2.50	2.48	2.46	2.44	2.40	2.36	2.29	2.18	1.99	1.51
2.70	2.56	2.54	2.53	2.51	2.48	2.45	2.40	2.33	2.22	2.02	1.54
2.75	2.61	2.59	2.57	2.55	2.53	2.49	2.44	2.37	2.26	2.06	1.57
2.80	2.65	2.64	2.62	2.60	2.57	2.54	2.49	2.42	2.31	2.10	1.60
2.85	2.70	2.69	2.67	2.65	2.62	2.58	2.53	2.46	2.35	2.14	1.63
2.90	2.75	2.73	2.71	2.69	2.66	2.63	2.58	2.50	2.39	2.17	1.66
2.95	2.79	2.78	2.76	2.74	2.71	2.67	2.62	2.55	2.43	2.21	1.69
3.00	2.84	2.83	2.81	2.79	2.76	2.72	2.67	2.59	2.47	2.25	1.71

TO = Turnover Rate

M   = Average Number of Months Unit is Held in Stock

P/C = Current Ratio of (Unit Price)/(Unit Cost)

Table 6.2 Effective Ratio of (Unit Price)/(Unit Cost) by Turnover Rate

h = 20% (Annual Holding Rate)

i = 0% (Annual Price Change Rate)

TO	50.00	40.00	30.00	20.00	12.00	10.00	8.00	7.50	7.00	6.50	6.00
M	.24	.30	.40	.60	1.00	1.20	1.50	1.60	1.71	1.85	2.00
P/C											
.80	.80	.80	.79	.79	.79	.78	.78	.78	.78	.78	.77
.85	.85	.85	.84	.84	.84	.83	.83	.83	.83	.82	.82
.90	.90	.90	.89	.89	.89	.88	.88	.88	.88	.87	.87
.95	.95	.95	.94	.94	.93	.93	.93	.93	.92	.92	.92
1.00	1.00	1.00	.99	.99	.98	.98	.98	.97	.97	.97	.97
1.05	1.05	1.04	1.04	1.04	1.03	1.03	1.02	1.02	1.02	1.02	1.02
1.10	1.10	1.09	1.09	1.09	1.08	1.08	1.07	1.07	1.07	1.07	1.06
1.15	1.15	1.14	1.14	1.14	1.13	1.13	1.12	1.12	1.12	1.12	1.11
1.20	1.20	1.19	1.19	1.19	1.18	1.18	1.17	1.17	1.17	1.16	1.16
1.25	1.25	1.24	1.24	1.24	1.23	1.23	1.22	1.22	1.22	1.21	1.21
1.30	1.29	1.29	1.29	1.29	1.28	1.27	1.27	1.27	1.26	1.26	1.26
1.35	1.34	1.34	1.34	1.34	1.33	1.32	1.32	1.31	1.31	1.31	1.31
1.40	1.39	1.39	1.39	1.39	1.38	1.37	1.37	1.36	1.36	1.36	1.35
1.45	1.44	1.44	1.44	1.44	1.43	1.42	1.41	1.41	1.41	1.41	1.40
1.50	1.49	1.49	1.49	1.49	1.48	1.47	1.46	1.46	1.46	1.46	1.45
1.55	1.54	1.54	1.54	1.53	1.52	1.52	1.51	1.51	1.51	1.50	1.50
1.60	1.59	1.59	1.59	1.58	1.57	1.57	1.56	1.56	1.56	1.55	1.55
1.65	1.64	1.64	1.64	1.63	1.62	1.62	1.61	1.61	1.60	1.60	1.60
1.70	1.69	1.69	1.69	1.68	1.67	1.67	1.66	1.66	1.65	1.65	1.65
1.75	1.74	1.74	1.74	1.73	1.72	1.72	1.71	1.70	1.70	1.70	1.69
1.80	1.79	1.79	1.79	1.78	1.77	1.76	1.76	1.75	1.75	1.75	1.74
1.85	1.84	1.84	1.84	1.83	1.82	1.81	1.80	1.80	1.80	1.79	1.79
1.90	1.89	1.89	1.89	1.88	1.87	1.86	1.85	1.85	1.85	1.84	1.84
1.95	1.94	1.94	1.94	1.93	1.92	1.91	1.90	1.90	1.90	1.89	1.89
2.00	1.99	1.99	1.99	1.98	1.97	1.96	1.95	1.95	1.94	1.94	1.94
2.05	2.04	2.04	2.04	2.03	2.02	2.01	2.00	2.00	1.99	1.99	1.98
2.10	2.09	2.09	2.09	2.08	2.07	2.06	2.05	2.05	2.04	2.04	2.03
2.15	2.14	2.14	2.14	2.13	2.11	2.11	2.10	2.09	2.09	2.09	2.08
2.20	2.19	2.19	2.19	2.18	2.16	2.16	2.15	2.14	2.14	2.13	2.13
2.25	2.24	2.24	2.24	2.23	2.21	2.21	2.20	2.19	2.19	2.18	2.18
2.30	2.29	2.29	2.28	2.28	2.26	2.25	2.24	2.24	2.24	2.23	2.23
2.35	2.34	2.34	2.33	2.33	2.31	2.30	2.29	2.29	2.28	2.28	2.27
2.40	2.39	2.39	2.38	2.38	2.36	2.35	2.34	2.34	2.33	2.33	2.32
2.45	2.44	2.44	2.43	2.43	2.41	2.40	2.39	2.39	2.38	2.38	2.37
2.50	2.49	2.49	2.48	2.48	2.46	2.45	2.44	2.44	2.43	2.43	2.42
2.55	2.54	2.54	2.53	2.52	2.51	2.50	2.49	2.48	2.48	2.47	2.47
2.60	2.59	2.59	2.58	2.57	2.56	2.55	2.54	2.53	2.53	2.52	2.52
2.65	2.64	2.64	2.63	2.62	2.61	2.60	2.59	2.58	2.58	2.57	2.56
2.70	2.69	2.69	2.68	2.67	2.66	2.65	2.63	2.63	2.62	2.62	2.61
2.75	2.74	2.74	2.73	2.72	2.70	2.70	2.68	2.68	2.67	2.67	2.66
2.80	2.79	2.79	2.78	2.77	2.75	2.75	2.73	2.73	2.72	2.72	2.71
2.85	2.84	2.84	2.83	2.82	2.80	2.79	2.78	2.78	2.77	2.76	2.76
2.90	2.89	2.89	2.88	2.87	2.85	2.84	2.83	2.82	2.82	2.81	2.81
2.95	2.94	2.94	2.93	2.92	2.90	2.89	2.88	2.87	2.87	2.86	2.85
3.00	2.99	2.99	2.98	2.97	2.95	2.94	2.93	2.92	2.92	2.91	2.90

TO = Turnover Rate

M = Average Number of Months Unit is Held in Stock

P/C = Current Ratio of (Unit Price)/(Unit Cost)

Table 6.2 Effective Ratio of (Unit Price)/(Unit Cost) by Turnover Rate (Continued)

h = 20% (Annual Holding Rate)
i = 0% (Annual Price Change Rate)

TO	5.50	5.00	4.50	4.00	3.50	3.00	2.50	2.00	1.50	1.00	.50
M	2.18	2.40	2.67	3.00	3.43	4.00	4.80	6.00	8.00	12.00	24.00
P/C											
.80	.77	.77	.77	.76	.76	.75	.74	.73	.71	.67	.57
.85	.82	.82	.81	.81	.80	.80	.79	.77	.75	.71	.61
.90	.87	.87	.86	.86	.85	.84	.83	.82	.79	.75	.64
.95	.92	.91	.91	.90	.90	.89	.88	.86	.84	.79	.68
1.00	.96	.96	.96	.95	.95	.94	.93	.91	.88	.83	.71
1.05	1.01	1.01	1.01	1.00	.99	.98	.97	.95	.93	.87	.75
1.10	1.06	1.06	1.05	1.05	1.04	1.03	1.02	1.00	.97	.92	.79
1.15	1.11	1.11	1.10	1.10	1.09	1.08	1.06	1.05	1.01	.96	.82
1.20	1.16	1.15	1.15	1.14	1.14	1.12	1.11	1.09	1.06	1.00	.86
1.25	1.21	1.20	1.20	1.19	1.18	1.17	1.16	1.14	1.10	1.04	.89
1.30	1.25	1.25	1.24	1.24	1.23	1.22	1.20	1.18	1.15	1.08	.93
1.35	1.30	1.30	1.29	1.29	1.28	1.27	1.25	1.23	1.19	1.12	.96
1.40	1.35	1.35	1.34	1.33	1.32	1.31	1.30	1.27	1.24	1.17	1.00
1.45	1.40	1.39	1.39	1.38	1.37	1.36	1.34	1.32	1.28	1.21	1.04
1.50	1.45	1.44	1.44	1.43	1.42	1.41	1.39	1.36	1.32	1.25	1.07
1.55	1.50	1.49	1.48	1.48	1.47	1.45	1.44	1.41	1.37	1.29	1.11
1.60	1.54	1.54	1.53	1.52	1.51	1.50	1.48	1.45	1.41	1.33	1.14
1.65	1.59	1.59	1.58	1.57	1.56	1.55	1.53	1.50	1.46	1.37	1.18
1.70	1.64	1.63	1.63	1.62	1.61	1.59	1.57	1.55	1.50	1.42	1.21
1.75	1.69	1.68	1.68	1.67	1.66	1.64	1.62	1.59	1.54	1.46	1.25
1.80	1.74	1.73	1.72	1.71	1.70	1.69	1.67	1.64	1.59	1.50	1.29
1.85	1.79	1.78	1.77	1.76	1.75	1.73	1.71	1.68	1.63	1.54	1.32
1.90	1.83	1.83	1.82	1.81	1.80	1.78	1.76	1.73	1.68	1.58	1.36
1.95	1.88	1.87	1.87	1.86	1.84	1.83	1.81	1.77	1.72	1.62	1.39
2.00	1.93	1.92	1.91	1.90	1.89	1.87	1.85	1.82	1.76	1.67	1.43
2.05	1.98	1.97	1.96	1.95	1.94	1.92	1.90	1.86	1.81	1.71	1.46
2.10	2.03	2.02	2.01	2.00	1.99	1.97	1.94	1.91	1.85	1.75	1.50
2.15	2.07	2.07	2.06	2.05	2.03	2.02	1.99	1.95	1.90	1.79	1.54
2.20	2.12	2.12	2.11	2.10	2.08	2.06	2.04	2.00	1.94	1.83	1.57
2.25	2.17	2.16	2.15	2.14	2.13	2.11	2.08	2.05	1.99	1.87	1.61
2.30	2.22	2.21	2.20	2.19	2.18	2.16	2.13	2.09	2.03	1.92	1.64
2.35	2.27	2.26	2.25	2.24	2.22	2.20	2.18	2.14	2.07	1.96	1.68
2.40	2.32	2.31	2.30	2.29	2.27	2.25	2.22	2.18	2.12	2.00	1.71
2.45	2.36	2.36	2.35	2.33	2.32	2.30	2.27	2.23	2.16	2.04	1.75
2.50	2.41	2.40	2.39	2.38	2.36	2.34	2.31	2.27	2.21	2.08	1.79
2.55	2.46	2.45	2.44	2.43	2.41	2.39	2.36	2.32	2.25	2.12	1.82
2.60	2.51	2.50	2.49	2.48	2.46	2.44	2.41	2.36	2.29	2.17	1.86
2.65	2.56	2.55	2.54	2.52	2.51	2.48	2.45	2.41	2.34	2.21	1.89
2.70	2.61	2.60	2.59	2.57	2.55	2.53	2.50	2.45	2.38	2.25	1.93
2.75	2.65	2.64	2.63	2.62	2.60	2.58	2.55	2.50	2.43	2.29	1.96
2.80	2.70	2.69	2.68	2.67	2.65	2.62	2.59	2.55	2.47	2.33	2.00
2.85	2.75	2.74	2.73	2.71	2.70	2.67	2.64	2.59	2.51	2.37	2.04
2.90	2.80	2.79	2.78	2.76	2.74	2.72	2.69	2.64	2.56	2.42	2.07
2.95	2.85	2.84	2.82	2.81	2.79	2.77	2.73	2.68	2.60	2.46	2.11
3.00	2.89	2.88	2.87	2.86	2.84	2.81	2.78	2.73	2.65	2.50	2.14

TO = Turnover Rate
M = Average Number of Months Unit is Held in Stock
P/C = Current Ratio of (Unit Price)/(Unit Cost)

Table 6.3 Effective Ratio of (Unit Price)/(Unit Cost) by Turnover Rate

h = 20% (Annual Holding Rate)

i = 10% (Annual Price Change Rate)

TO	50.00	40.00	30.00	20.00	12.00	10.00	8.00	7.50	7.00	6.50	6.00
M	.24	.30	.40	.60	1.00	1.20	1.50	1.60	1.71	1.85	2.00
P/C											
.80	.80	.80	.80	.80	.79	.79	.79	.79	.79	.79	.79
.85	.85	.85	.85	.85	.84	.84	.84	.84	.84	.84	.84
.90	.90	.90	.90	.90	.89	.89	.89	.89	.89	.89	.89
.95	.95	.95	.95	.95	.94	.94	.94	.94	.94	.94	.93
1.00	1.00	1.00	1.00	1.00	.99	.99	.99	.99	.99	.99	.98
1.05	1.05	1.05	1.05	1.04	1.04	1.04	1.04	1.04	1.04	1.03	1.03
1.10	1.10	1.10	1.10	1.09	1.09	1.09	1.09	1.09	1.08	1.08	1.08
1.15	1.15	1.15	1.15	1.14	1.14	1.14	1.14	1.14	1.13	1.13	1.13
1.20	1.20	1.20	1.20	1.19	1.19	1.19	1.19	1.18	1.18	1.18	1.18
1.25	1.25	1.25	1.25	1.24	1.24	1.24	1.23	1.23	1.23	1.23	1.23
1.30	1.30	1.30	1.30	1.29	1.29	1.29	1.28	1.28	1.28	1.28	1.28
1.35	1.35	1.35	1.35	1.34	1.34	1.34	1.33	1.33	1.33	1.33	1.33
1.40	1.40	1.40	1.40	1.39	1.39	1.39	1.38	1.38	1.38	1.38	1.38
1.45	1.45	1.45	1.45	1.44	1.44	1.44	1.43	1.43	1.43	1.43	1.43
1.50	1.50	1.50	1.50	1.49	1.49	1.49	1.48	1.48	1.48	1.48	1.48
1.55	1.55	1.55	1.54	1.54	1.54	1.53	1.53	1.53	1.53	1.53	1.52
1.60	1.60	1.60	1.59	1.59	1.59	1.58	1.58	1.58	1.58	1.58	1.57
1.65	1.65	1.65	1.64	1.64	1.64	1.63	1.63	1.63	1.63	1.63	1.62
1.70	1.70	1.70	1.69	1.69	1.69	1.68	1.68	1.68	1.68	1.67	1.67
1.75	1.75	1.75	1.74	1.74	1.74	1.73	1.73	1.73	1.73	1.72	1.72
1.80	1.80	1.80	1.79	1.79	1.79	1.78	1.78	1.78	1.77	1.77	1.77
1.85	1.85	1.85	1.84	1.84	1.83	1.83	1.83	1.83	1.82	1.82	1.82
1.90	1.90	1.90	1.89	1.89	1.88	1.88	1.88	1.88	1.87	1.87	1.87
1.95	1.95	1.95	1.94	1.94	1.93	1.93	1.93	1.92	1.92	1.92	1.92
2.00	2.00	2.00	1.99	1.99	1.98	1.98	1.98	1.97	1.97	1.97	1.97
2.05	2.05	2.04	2.04	2.04	2.03	2.03	2.02	2.02	2.02	2.02	2.02
2.10	2.10	2.09	2.09	2.09	2.08	2.08	2.07	2.07	2.07	2.07	2.07
2.15	2.15	2.14	2.14	2.14	2.13	2.13	2.12	2.12	2.12	2.12	2.12
2.20	2.20	2.19	2.19	2.19	2.18	2.18	2.17	2.17	2.17	2.17	2.16
2.25	2.25	2.24	2.24	2.24	2.23	2.23	2.22	2.22	2.22	2.22	2.21
2.30	2.30	2.29	2.29	2.29	2.28	2.28	2.27	2.27	2.27	2.27	2.26
2.35	2.35	2.34	2.34	2.34	2.33	2.33	2.32	2.32	2.32	2.31	2.31
2.40	2.40	2.39	2.39	2.39	2.38	2.38	2.37	2.37	2.37	2.36	2.36
2.45	2.45	2.44	2.44	2.44	2.43	2.43	2.42	2.42	2.42	2.41	2.41
2.50	2.50	2.49	2.49	2.49	2.48	2.48	2.47	2.47	2.47	2.46	2.46
2.55	2.54	2.54	2.54	2.54	2.53	2.52	2.52	2.52	2.51	2.51	2.51
2.60	2.59	2.59	2.59	2.59	2.58	2.57	2.57	2.57	2.56	2.56	2.56
2.65	2.64	2.64	2.64	2.64	2.63	2.62	2.62	2.62	2.61	2.61	2.61
2.70	2.69	2.69	2.69	2.69	2.68	2.67	2.67	2.66	2.66	2.66	2.66
2.75	2.74	2.74	2.74	2.74	2.73	2.72	2.72	2.71	2.71	2.71	2.71
2.80	2.79	2.79	2.79	2.79	2.78	2.77	2.77	2.76	2.76	2.76	2.75
2.85	2.84	2.84	2.84	2.84	2.83	2.82	2.82	2.81	2.81	2.81	2.80
2.90	2.89	2.89	2.89	2.89	2.88	2.87	2.86	2.86	2.86	2.86	2.85
2.95	2.94	2.94	2.94	2.94	2.93	2.92	2.91	2.91	2.91	2.91	2.90
3.00	2.99	2.99	2.99	2.99	2.98	2.97	2.96	2.96	2.96	2.96	2.95

TO = Turnover Rate

M = Average Number of Months Unit is Held in Stock

P/C = Current Ratio of (Unit Price)/(Unit Cost)

Table 6.3 Effective Ratio of (Unit Price)/(Unit Cost) by Turnover Rate

h = 20% (Annual Holding Rate) (Continued)

i = 10% (Annual Price Change Rate)

TO M P/C	5.50 2.18	5.00 2.40	4.50 2.67	4.00 3.00	3.50 3.43	3.00 4.00	2.50 4.80	2.00 6.00	1.50 8.00	1.00 12.00	.50 24.00
.80	.79	.78	.78	.78	.78	.78	.77	.76	.75	.73	.69
.85	.84	.83	.83	.83	.83	.82	.82	.81	.80	.78	.73
.90	.88	.88	.88	.88	.88	.87	.87	.86	.85	.83	.77
.95	.93	.93	.93	.93	.92	.92	.91	.91	.89	.87	.81
1.00	.98	.98	.98	.98	.97	.97	.96	.95	.94	.92	.86
1.05	1.03	1.03	1.03	1.03	1.02	1.02	1.01	1.00	.99	.96	.90
1.10	1.08	1.08	1.08	1.07	1.07	1.07	1.06	1.05	1.04	1.01	.94
1.15	1.13	1.13	1.13	1.12	1.12	1.11	1.11	1.10	1.08	1.05	.99
1.20	1.18	1.18	1.17	1.17	1.17	1.16	1.16	1.15	1.13	1.10	1.03
1.25	1.23	1.23	1.22	1.22	1.22	1.21	1.20	1.19	1.18	1.15	1.07
1.30	1.28	1.27	1.27	1.27	1.26	1.26	1.25	1.24	1.22	1.19	1.11
1.35	1.33	1.32	1.32	1.32	1.31	1.31	1.30	1.29	1.27	1.24	1.16
1.40	1.38	1.37	1.37	1.37	1.36	1.36	1.35	1.34	1.32	1.28	1.20
1.45	1.42	1.42	1.42	1.42	1.41	1.40	1.40	1.38	1.36	1.33	1.24
1.50	1.47	1.47	1.47	1.46	1.46	1.45	1.44	1.43	1.41	1.37	1.29
1.55	1.52	1.52	1.52	1.51	1.51	1.50	1.49	1.48	1.46	1.42	1.33
1.60	1.57	1.57	1.57	1.56	1.56	1.55	1.54	1.53	1.51	1.47	1.37
1.65	1.62	1.62	1.61	1.61	1.61	1.60	1.59	1.57	1.55	1.51	1.41
1.70	1.67	1.67	1.66	1.66	1.65	1.65	1.64	1.62	1.60	1.56	1.46
1.75	1.72	1.72	1.71	1.71	1.70	1.70	1.69	1.67	1.65	1.60	1.50
1.80	1.77	1.77	1.76	1.76	1.75	1.74	1.73	1.72	1.69	1.65	1.54
1.85	1.82	1.81	1.81	1.81	1.80	1.79	1.78	1.77	1.74	1.70	1.59
1.90	1.87	1.86	1.86	1.85	1.85	1.84	1.83	1.81	1.79	1.74	1.63
1.95	1.92	1.91	1.91	1.90	1.90	1.89	1.88	1.86	1.84	1.79	1.67
2.00	1.96	1.96	1.96	1.95	1.95	1.94	1.93	1.91	1.88	1.83	1.71
2.05	2.01	2.01	2.01	2.00	1.99	1.99	1.97	1.96	1.93	1.88	1.76
2.10	2.06	2.06	2.06	2.05	2.04	2.03	2.02	2.00	1.98	1.92	1.80
2.15	2.11	2.11	2.10	2.10	2.09	2.08	2.07	2.05	2.02	1.97	1.84
2.20	2.16	2.16	2.15	2.15	2.14	2.13	2.12	2.10	2.07	2.02	1.89
2.25	2.21	2.21	2.20	2.20	2.19	2.18	2.17	2.15	2.12	2.06	1.93
2.30	2.26	2.26	2.25	2.25	2.24	2.23	2.21	2.20	2.16	2.11	1.97
2.35	2.31	2.30	2.30	2.29	2.29	2.28	2.26	2.24	2.21	2.15	2.01
2.40	2.36	2.35	2.35	2.34	2.34	2.32	2.31	2.29	2.26	2.20	2.06
2.45	2.41	2.40	2.40	2.39	2.38	2.37	2.36	2.34	2.31	2.25	2.10
2.50	2.46	2.45	2.45	2.44	2.43	2.42	2.41	2.39	2.35	2.29	2.14
2.55	2.51	2.50	2.50	2.49	2.48	2.47	2.46	2.43	2.40	2.34	2.19
2.60	2.55	2.55	2.54	2.54	2.53	2.52	2.50	2.48	2.45	2.38	2.23
2.65	2.60	2.60	2.59	2.59	2.58	2.57	2.55	2.53	2.49	2.43	2.27
2.70	2.65	2.65	2.64	2.64	2.63	2.62	2.60	2.58	2.54	2.47	2.31
2.75	2.70	2.70	2.69	2.68	2.68	2.66	2.65	2.62	2.59	2.52	2.36
2.80	2.75	2.75	2.74	2.73	2.72	2.71	2.70	2.67	2.64	2.57	2.40
2.85	2.80	2.80	2.79	2.78	2.77	2.76	2.74	2.72	2.68	2.61	2.44
2.90	2.85	2.84	2.84	2.83	2.82	2.81	2.79	2.77	2.73	2.66	2.49
2.95	2.90	2.89	2.89	2.88	2.87	2.86	2.84	2.82	2.78	2.70	2.53
3.00	2.95	2.94	2.94	2.93	2.92	2.91	2.89	2.86	2.82	2.75	2.57

TO = Turnover Rate

M = Average Number of Months Unit is Held in Stock

P/C = Current Ratio of (Unit Price)/(Unit Cost)

Table 6.4 Effective Ratio of (Unit Price)/(Unit Cost) by Turnover Rate

h = 30% (Annual Holding Rate)

i = -10% (Annual Price Change Rate)

TO	50.00	40.00	30.00	20.00	12.00	10.00	8.00	7.50	7.00	6.50	6.00
M	.24	.30	.40	.60	1.00	1.20	1.50	1.60	1.71	1.85	2.00
P/C											
.80	.79	.79	.79	.78	.77	.77	.76	.76	.76	.75	.75
.85	.84	.84	.84	.83	.82	.82	.81	.81	.80	.80	.80
.90	.89	.89	.89	.88	.87	.87	.86	.85	.85	.85	.84
.95	.94	.94	.94	.93	.92	.91	.90	.90	.90	.89	.89
1.00	.99	.99	.99	.98	.97	.96	.95	.95	.95	.94	.94
1.05	1.04	1.04	1.04	1.03	1.02	1.01	1.00	1.00	.99	.99	.98
1.10	1.09	1.09	1.09	1.08	1.06	1.06	1.05	1.04	1.04	1.04	1.03
1.15	1.14	1.14	1.13	1.13	1.11	1.11	1.09	1.09	1.09	1.08	1.08
1.20	1.19	1.19	1.18	1.18	1.16	1.15	1.14	1.14	1.13	1.13	1.12
1.25	1.24	1.24	1.23	1.23	1.21	1.20	1.19	1.19	1.18	1.18	1.17
1.30	1.29	1.29	1.28	1.27	1.26	1.25	1.24	1.23	1.23	1.22	1.22
1.35	1.34	1.34	1.33	1.32	1.31	1.30	1.28	1.28	1.28	1.27	1.26
1.40	1.39	1.39	1.38	1.37	1.35	1.35	1.33	1.33	1.32	1.32	1.31
1.45	1.44	1.44	1.43	1.42	1.40	1.39	1.38	1.38	1.37	1.36	1.36
1.50	1.49	1.49	1.48	1.47	1.45	1.44	1.43	1.42	1.42	1.41	1.40
1.55	1.54	1.53	1.53	1.52	1.50	1.49	1.48	1.47	1.47	1.46	1.45
1.60	1.59	1.58	1.58	1.57	1.55	1.54	1.52	1.52	1.51	1.51	1.50
1.65	1.64	1.63	1.63	1.62	1.60	1.59	1.57	1.57	1.56	1.55	1.55
1.70	1.69	1.68	1.68	1.67	1.64	1.63	1.62	1.61	1.61	1.60	1.59
1.75	1.74	1.73	1.73	1.72	1.69	1.68	1.67	1.66	1.65	1.65	1.64
1.80	1.79	1.78	1.78	1.76	1.74	1.73	1.71	1.71	1.70	1.69	1.69
1.85	1.84	1.83	1.83	1.81	1.79	1.78	1.76	1.76	1.75	1.74	1.73
1.90	1.88	1.88	1.87	1.86	1.84	1.83	1.81	1.80	1.80	1.79	1.78
1.95	1.93	1.93	1.92	1.91	1.89	1.87	1.86	1.85	1.84	1.84	1.83
2.00	1.98	1.98	1.97	1.96	1.93	1.92	1.90	1.90	1.89	1.88	1.87
2.05	2.03	2.03	2.02	2.01	1.98	1.97	1.95	1.94	1.94	1.93	1.92
2.10	2.08	2.08	2.07	2.06	2.03	2.02	2.00	1.99	1.98	1.98	1.97
2.15	2.13	2.13	2.12	2.11	2.08	2.07	2.05	2.04	2.03	2.02	2.01
2.20	2.18	2.18	2.17	2.16	2.13	2.11	2.09	2.09	2.08	2.07	2.06
2.25	2.23	2.23	2.22	2.21	2.18	2.16	2.14	2.13	2.13	2.12	2.11
2.30	2.28	2.28	2.27	2.25	2.23	2.21	2.19	2.18	2.17	2.16	2.15
2.35	2.33	2.33	2.32	2.30	2.27	2.26	2.24	2.23	2.22	2.21	2.20
2.40	2.38	2.38	2.37	2.35	2.32	2.31	2.28	2.28	2.27	2.26	2.25
2.45	2.43	2.43	2.42	2.40	2.37	2.35	2.33	2.32	2.32	2.31	2.29
2.50	2.48	2.48	2.47	2.45	2.42	2.40	2.38	2.37	2.36	2.35	2.34
2.55	2.53	2.52	2.52	2.50	2.47	2.45	2.43	2.42	2.41	2.40	2.39
2.60	2.58	2.57	2.57	2.55	2.52	2.50	2.47	2.47	2.46	2.45	2.43
2.65	2.63	2.62	2.62	2.60	2.56	2.55	2.52	2.51	2.50	2.49	2.48
2.70	2.68	2.67	2.66	2.65	2.61	2.60	2.57	2.56	2.55	2.54	2.53
2.75	2.73	2.72	2.71	2.70	2.66	2.64	2.62	2.61	2.60	2.59	2.58
2.80	2.78	2.77	2.76	2.74	2.71	2.69	2.67	2.66	2.65	2.64	2.62
2.85	2.83	2.82	2.81	2.79	2.76	2.74	2.71	2.70	2.69	2.68	2.67
2.90	2.88	2.87	2.86	2.84	2.81	2.79	2.76	2.75	2.74	2.73	2.72
2.95	2.93	2.92	2.91	2.89	2.85	2.84	2.81	2.80	2.79	2.78	2.76
3.00	2.98	2.97	2.96	2.94	2.90	2.88	2.86	2.85	2.84	2.82	2.81

TO = Turnover Rate

M = Average Number of Months Unit is Held in Stock

P/C = Current Ratio of (Unit Price)/(Unit Cost)

Table 6.4   Effective Ratio of (Unit Price)/(Unit Cost) by Turnover Rate

h = 30% (Annual Holding Rate)

i = -10% (Annual Price Change Rate)

(Continued)

TO	5.50	5.00	4.50	4.00	3.50	3.00	2.50	2.00	1.50	1.00	.50
M	2.18	2.40	2.67	3.00	3.43	4.00	4.80	6.00	8.00	12.00	24.00
P/C											
.80	.74	.74	.73	.73	.72	.70	.69	.66	.62	.55	.40
.85	.79	.79	.78	.77	.76	.75	.73	.70	.66	.59	.43
.90	.84	.83	.82	.82	.81	.79	.77	.74	.70	.62	.45
.95	.88	.88	.87	.86	.85	.83	.81	.78	.74	.66	.48
1.00	.93	.92	.92	.91	.89	.88	.86	.83	.78	.69	.50
1.05	.98	.97	.96	.95	.94	.92	.90	.87	.82	.73	.53
1.10	1.02	1.02	1.01	1.00	.98	.97	.94	.91	.86	.76	.55
1.15	1.07	1.06	1.05	1.04	1.03	1.01	.99	.95	.89	.80	.57
1.20	1.12	1.11	1.10	1.09	1.07	1.05	1.03	.99	.93	.83	.60
1.25	1.16	1.16	1.15	1.13	1.12	1.10	1.07	1.03	.97	.87	.62
1.30	1.21	1.20	1.19	1.18	1.16	1.14	1.11	1.07	1.01	.90	.65
1.35	1.26	1.25	1.24	1.22	1.21	1.19	1.16	1.12	1.05	.93	.67
1.40	1.30	1.29	1.28	1.27	1.25	1.23	1.20	1.16	1.09	.97	.70
1.45	1.35	1.34	1.33	1.32	1.30	1.27	1.24	1.20	1.13	1.00	.72
1.50	1.40	1.39	1.37	1.36	1.34	1.32	1.29	1.24	1.17	1.04	.75
1.55	1.44	1.43	1.42	1.41	1.39	1.36	1.33	1.28	1.21	1.07	.77
1.60	1.49	1.48	1.47	1.45	1.43	1.41	1.37	1.32	1.24	1.11	.80
1.65	1.54	1.53	1.51	1.50	1.48	1.45	1.41	1.36	1.28	1.14	.82
1.70	1.58	1.57	1.56	1.54	1.52	1.49	1.46	1.40	1.32	1.18	.85
1.75	1.63	1.62	1.60	1.59	1.57	1.54	1.50	1.45	1.36	1.21	.87
1.80	1.68	1.66	1.65	1.63	1.61	1.58	1.54	1.49	1.40	1.25	.90
1.85	1.72	1.71	1.70	1.68	1.66	1.63	1.59	1.53	1.44	1.28	.92
1.90	1.77	1.76	1.74	1.72	1.70	1.67	1.63	1.57	1.48	1.32	.95
1.95	1.82	1.80	1.79	1.77	1.74	1.71	1.67	1.61	1.52	1.35	.97
2.00	1.86	1.85	1.83	1.81	1.79	1.76	1.71	1.65	1.56	1.38	1.00
2.05	1.91	1.90	1.88	1.86	1.83	1.80	1.76	1.69	1.59	1.42	1.02
2.10	1.96	1.94	1.92	1.90	1.88	1.85	1.80	1.73	1.63	1.45	1.05
2.15	2.00	1.99	1.97	1.95	1.92	1.89	1.84	1.78	1.67	1.49	1.07
2.20	2.05	2.03	2.02	2.00	1.97	1.93	1.89	1.82	1.71	1.52	1.10
2.25	2.09	2.08	2.06	2.04	2.01	1.98	1.93	1.86	1.75	1.56	1.12
2.30	2.14	2.13	2.11	2.09	2.06	2.02	1.97	1.90	1.79	1.59	1.15
2.35	2.19	2.17	2.15	2.13	2.10	2.07	2.01	1.94	1.83	1.63	1.17
2.40	2.23	2.22	2.20	2.18	2.15	2.11	2.06	1.98	1.87	1.66	1.20
2.45	2.28	2.27	2.25	2.22	2.19	2.15	2.10	2.02	1.91	1.70	1.22
2.50	2.33	2.31	2.29	2.27	2.24	2.20	2.14	2.07	1.94	1.73	1.25
2.55	2.37	2.36	2.34	2.31	2.28	2.24	2.19	2.11	1.98	1.77	1.27
2.60	2.42	2.40	2.38	2.36	2.33	2.28	2.23	2.15	2.02	1.80	1.30
2.65	2.47	2.45	2.43	2.40	2.37	2.33	2.27	2.19	2.06	1.83	1.32
2.70	2.51	2.50	2.47	2.45	2.42	2.37	2.31	2.23	2.10	1.87	1.35
2.75	2.56	2.54	2.52	2.49	2.46	2.42	2.36	2.27	2.14	1.90	1.37
2.80	2.61	2.59	2.57	2.54	2.51	2.46	2.40	2.31	2.18	1.94	1.40
2.85	2.65	2.63	2.61	2.58	2.55	2.50	2.44	2.35	2.22	1.97	1.42
2.90	2.70	2.68	2.66	2.63	2.59	2.55	2.49	2.40	2.26	2.01	1.45
2.95	2.75	2.73	2.70	2.68	2.64	2.59	2.53	2.44	2.29	2.04	1.47
3.00	2.79	2.77	2.75	2.72	2.68	2.64	2.57	2.48	2.33	2.08	1.50

TO = Turnover Rate

M   = Average Number of Months Unit is Held in Stock

P/C = Current Ratio of (Unit Price)/(Unit Cost)

Table 6.5   Effective Ratio of (Unit Price)/(Unit Cost) by Turnover Rate

h = 30% (Annual Holding Rate)

i = 0% (Annual Price Change Rate)

TO M P/C	50.00 .24	40.00 .30	30.00 .40	20.00 .60	12.00 1.00	10.00 1.20	8.00 1.50	7.50 1.60	7.00 1.71	6.50 1.85	6.00 2.00
.80	.80	.79	.79	.79	.78	.78	.77	.77	.77	.76	.76
.85	.84	.84	.84	.84	.83	.83	.82	.82	.82	.81	.81
.90	.89	.89	.89	.89	.88	.87	.87	.87	.86	.86	.86
.95	.94	.94	.94	.94	.93	.92	.92	.91	.91	.91	.90
1.00	.99	.99	.99	.99	.98	.97	.96	.96	.96	.96	.95
1.05	1.04	1.04	1.04	1.03	1.02	1.02	1.01	1.01	1.01	1.00	1.00
1.10	1.09	1.09	1.09	1.08	1.07	1.07	1.06	1.06	1.05	1.05	1.05
1.15	1.14	1.14	1.14	1.13	1.12	1.12	1.11	1.11	1.10	1.10	1.10
1.20	1.19	1.19	1.19	1.18	1.17	1.17	1.16	1.15	1.15	1.15	1.14
1.25	1.24	1.24	1.24	1.23	1.22	1.21	1.20	1.20	1.20	1.19	1.19
1.30	1.29	1.29	1.29	1.28	1.27	1.26	1.25	1.25	1.25	1.24	1.24
1.35	1.34	1.34	1.34	1.33	1.32	1.31	1.30	1.30	1.29	1.29	1.29
1.40	1.39	1.39	1.39	1.38	1.37	1.36	1.35	1.35	1.34	1.34	1.33
1.45	1.44	1.44	1.44	1.43	1.41	1.41	1.40	1.39	1.39	1.39	1.38
1.50	1.49	1.49	1.49	1.48	1.46	1.46	1.45	1.44	1.44	1.43	1.43
1.55	1.54	1.54	1.53	1.53	1.51	1.50	1.49	1.49	1.49	1.48	1.48
1.60	1.59	1.59	1.58	1.58	1.56	1.55	1.54	1.54	1.53	1.53	1.52
1.65	1.64	1.64	1.63	1.63	1.61	1.60	1.59	1.59	1.58	1.58	1.57
1.70	1.69	1.69	1.68	1.67	1.66	1.65	1.64	1.63	1.63	1.62	1.62
1.75	1.74	1.74	1.73	1.72	1.71	1.70	1.69	1.68	1.68	1.67	1.67
1.80	1.79	1.79	1.78	1.77	1.76	1.75	1.73	1.73	1.73	1.72	1.71
1.85	1.84	1.84	1.83	1.82	1.80	1.80	1.78	1.78	1.77	1.77	1.76
1.90	1.89	1.89	1.88	1.87	1.85	1.84	1.83	1.83	1.82	1.82	1.81
1.95	1.94	1.94	1.93	1.92	1.90	1.89	1.88	1.87	1.87	1.86	1.86
2.00	1.99	1.99	1.98	1.97	1.95	1.94	1.93	1.92	1.92	1.91	1.90
2.05	2.04	2.03	2.03	2.02	2.00	1.99	1.98	1.97	1.97	1.96	1.95
2.10	2.09	2.08	2.08	2.07	2.05	2.04	2.02	2.02	2.01	2.01	2.00
2.15	2.14	2.13	2.13	2.12	2.10	2.09	2.07	2.07	2.06	2.06	2.05
2.20	2.19	2.18	2.18	2.17	2.15	2.14	2.12	2.12	2.11	2.10	2.10
2.25	2.24	2.23	2.23	2.22	2.20	2.18	2.17	2.16	2.16	2.15	2.14
2.30	2.29	2.28	2.28	2.27	2.24	2.23	2.22	2.21	2.21	2.20	2.19
2.35	2.34	2.33	2.33	2.32	2.29	2.28	2.27	2.26	2.25	2.25	2.24
2.40	2.39	2.38	2.38	2.36	2.34	2.33	2.31	2.31	2.30	2.29	2.29
2.45	2.44	2.43	2.43	2.41	2.39	2.38	2.36	2.36	2.35	2.34	2.33
2.50	2.49	2.48	2.48	2.46	2.44	2.43	2.41	2.40	2.40	2.39	2.38
2.55	2.53	2.53	2.52	2.51	2.49	2.48	2.46	2.45	2.45	2.44	2.43
2.60	2.58	2.58	2.57	2.56	2.54	2.52	2.51	2.50	2.49	2.49	2.48
2.65	2.63	2.63	2.62	2.61	2.59	2.57	2.55	2.55	2.54	2.53	2.52
2.70	2.68	2.68	2.67	2.66	2.63	2.62	2.60	2.60	2.59	2.58	2.57
2.75	2.73	2.73	2.72	2.71	2.68	2.67	2.65	2.64	2.64	2.63	2.62
2.80	2.78	2.78	2.77	2.76	2.73	2.72	2.70	2.69	2.68	2.68	2.67
2.85	2.83	2.83	2.82	2.81	2.78	2.77	2.75	2.74	2.73	2.72	2.71
2.90	2.88	2.88	2.87	2.86	2.83	2.82	2.80	2.79	2.78	2.77	2.76
2.95	2.93	2.93	2.92	2.91	2.88	2.86	2.84	2.84	2.83	2.82	2.81
3.00	2.98	2.98	2.97	2.96	2.93	2.91	2.89	2.88	2.88	2.87	2.86

TO = Turnover Rate

M   = Average Number of Months Unit is Held in Stock

P/C = Current Ratio of (Unit Price)/(Unit Cost)

Table 6.5   Effective Ratio of (Unit Price)/(Unit Cost) by Turnover Rate   (Continued)

h =   30% (Annual Holding Rate)

i =   0% (Annual Price Change Rate)

TO	5.50	5.00	4.50	4.00	3.50	3.00	2.50	2.00	1.50	1.00	.50
M	2.18	2.40	2.67	3.00	3.43	4.00	4.80	6.00	8.00	12.00	24.00
P/C											
.80	.76	.75	.75	.74	.74	.73	.71	.70	.67	.62	.50
.85	.81	.80	.80	.79	.78	.77	.76	.74	.71	.65	.53
.90	.85	.85	.84	.84	.83	.82	.80	.78	.75	.69	.56
.95	.90	.90	.89	.88	.88	.86	.85	.83	.79	.73	.59
1.00	.95	.94	.94	.93	.92	.91	.89	.87	.83	.77	.63
1.05	1.00	.99	.98	.98	.97	.95	.94	.91	.87	.81	.66
1.10	1.04	1.04	1.03	1.02	1.01	1.00	.98	.96	.92	.85	.69
1.15	1.09	1.08	1.08	1.07	1.06	1.05	1.03	1.00	.96	.88	.72
1.20	1.14	1.13	1.12	1.12	1.11	1.09	1.07	1.04	1.00	.92	.75
1.25	1.19	1.18	1.17	1.16	1.15	1.14	1.12	1.09	1.04	.96	.78
1.30	1.23	1.23	1.22	1.21	1.20	1.18	1.16	1.13	1.08	1.00	.81
1.35	1.28	1.27	1.27	1.26	1.24	1.23	1.21	1.17	1.12	1.04	.84
1.40	1.33	1.32	1.31	1.30	1.29	1.27	1.25	1.22	1.17	1.08	.87
1.45	1.37	1.37	1.36	1.35	1.34	1.32	1.29	1.26	1.21	1.12	.91
1.50	1.42	1.42	1.41	1.40	1.38	1.36	1.34	1.30	1.25	1.15	.94
1.55	1.47	1.46	1.45	1.44	1.43	1.41	1.38	1.35	1.29	1.19	.97
1.60	1.52	1.51	1.50	1.49	1.47	1.45	1.43	1.39	1.33	1.23	1.00
1.65	1.56	1.56	1.55	1.53	1.52	1.50	1.47	1.43	1.37	1.27	1.03
1.70	1.61	1.60	1.59	1.58	1.57	1.55	1.52	1.48	1.42	1.31	1.06
1.75	1.66	1.65	1.64	1.63	1.61	1.59	1.56	1.52	1.46	1.35	1.09
1.80	1.71	1.70	1.69	1.67	1.66	1.64	1.61	1.57	1.50	1.38	1.12
1.85	1.75	1.75	1.73	1.72	1.70	1.68	1.65	1.61	1.54	1.42	1.16
1.90	1.80	1.79	1.78	1.77	1.75	1.73	1.70	1.65	1.58	1.46	1.19
1.95	1.85	1.84	1.83	1.81	1.80	1.77	1.74	1.70	1.62	1.50	1.22
2.00	1.90	1.89	1.87	1.86	1.84	1.82	1.79	1.74	1.67	1.54	1.25
2.05	1.94	1.93	1.92	1.91	1.89	1.86	1.83	1.78	1.71	1.58	1.28
2.10	1.99	1.98	1.97	1.95	1.93	1.91	1.87	1.83	1.75	1.62	1.31
2.15	2.04	2.03	2.02	2.00	1.98	1.95	1.92	1.87	1.79	1.65	1.34
2.20	2.09	2.08	2.06	2.05	2.03	2.00	1.96	1.91	1.83	1.69	1.37
2.25	2.13	2.12	2.11	2.09	2.07	2.05	2.01	1.96	1.87	1.73	1.41
2.30	2.18	2.17	2.16	2.14	2.12	2.09	2.05	2.00	1.92	1.77	1.44
2.35	2.23	2.22	2.20	2.19	2.16	2.14	2.10	2.04	1.96	1.81	1.47
2.40	2.28	2.26	2.25	2.23	2.21	2.18	2.14	2.09	2.00	1.85	1.50
2.45	2.32	2.31	2.30	2.28	2.26	2.23	2.19	2.13	2.04	1.88	1.53
2.50	2.37	2.36	2.34	2.33	2.30	2.27	2.23	2.17	2.08	1.92	1.56
2.55	2.42	2.41	2.39	2.37	2.35	2.32	2.28	2.22	2.12	1.96	1.59
2.60	2.47	2.45	2.44	2.42	2.39	2.36	2.32	2.26	2.17	2.00	1.62
2.65	2.51	2.50	2.48	2.47	2.44	2.41	2.37	2.30	2.21	2.04	1.66
2.70	2.56	2.55	2.53	2.51	2.49	2.45	2.41	2.35	2.25	2.08	1.69
2.75	2.61	2.59	2.58	2.56	2.53	2.50	2.46	2.39	2.29	2.12	1.72
2.80	2.66	2.64	2.62	2.60	2.58	2.55	2.50	2.43	2.33	2.15	1.75
2.85	2.70	2.69	2.67	2.65	2.62	2.59	2.54	2.48	2.37	2.19	1.78
2.90	2.75	2.74	2.72	2.70	2.67	2.64	2.59	2.52	2.42	2.23	1.81
2.95	2.80	2.78	2.77	2.74	2.72	2.68	2.63	2.57	2.46	2.27	1.84
3.00	2.84	2.83	2.81	2.79	2.76	2.73	2.68	2.61	2.50	2.31	1.87

TO = Turnover Rate

M   = Average Number of Months Unit is Held in Stock

P/C = Current Ratio of (Unit Price)/(Unit Cost)

Table 6.6 Effective Ratio of (Unit Price)/(Unit Cost) by Turnover Rate

h = 30% (Annual Holding Rate)
i = 10% (Annual Price Change Rate)

TO	50.00	40.00	30.00	20.00	12.00	10.00	8.00	7.50	7.00	6.50	6.00
M	.24	.30	.40	.60	1.00	1.20	1.50	1.60	1.71	1.85	2.00
P/C											
.80	.80	.80	.79	.79	.79	.78	.78	.78	.78	.78	.77
.85	.85	.85	.84	.84	.84	.83	.83	.83	.83	.83	.82
.90	.90	.90	.89	.89	.89	.88	.88	.88	.88	.87	.87
.95	.95	.95	.94	.94	.93	.93	.93	.93	.92	.92	.92
1.00	1.00	1.00	.99	.99	.98	.98	.98	.97	.97	.97	.97
1.05	1.05	1.04	1.04	1.04	1.03	1.03	1.02	1.02	1.02	1.02	1.02
1.10	1.10	1.09	1.09	1.09	1.08	1.08	1.07	1.07	1.07	1.07	1.07
1.15	1.15	1.14	1.14	1.14	1.13	1.13	1.12	1.12	1.12	1.12	1.11
1.20	1.20	1.19	1.19	1.19	1.18	1.18	1.17	1.17	1.17	1.16	1.16
1.25	1.25	1.24	1.24	1.24	1.23	1.23	1.22	1.22	1.22	1.21	1.21
1.30	1.29	1.29	1.29	1.29	1.28	1.27	1.27	1.27	1.26	1.26	1.26
1.35	1.34	1.34	1.34	1.34	1.33	1.32	1.32	1.32	1.31	1.31	1.31
1.40	1.39	1.39	1.39	1.39	1.38	1.37	1.37	1.36	1.36	1.36	1.36
1.45	1.44	1.44	1.44	1.44	1.43	1.42	1.42	1.41	1.41	1.41	1.40
1.50	1.49	1.49	1.49	1.49	1.48	1.47	1.46	1.46	1.46	1.46	1.45
1.55	1.54	1.54	1.54	1.53	1.52	1.52	1.51	1.51	1.51	1.50	1.50
1.60	1.59	1.59	1.59	1.58	1.57	1.57	1.56	1.56	1.56	1.55	1.55
1.65	1.64	1.64	1.64	1.63	1.62	1.62	1.61	1.61	1.60	1.60	1.60
1.70	1.69	1.69	1.69	1.68	1.67	1.67	1.66	1.66	1.65	1.65	1.65
1.75	1.74	1.74	1.74	1.73	1.72	1.72	1.71	1.71	1.70	1.70	1.69
1.80	1.79	1.79	1.79	1.78	1.77	1.77	1.76	1.75	1.75	1.75	1.74
1.85	1.84	1.84	1.84	1.83	1.82	1.81	1.81	1.80	1.80	1.80	1.79
1.90	1.89	1.89	1.89	1.88	1.87	1.86	1.85	1.85	1.85	1.84	1.84
1.95	1.94	1.94	1.94	1.93	1.92	1.91	1.90	1.90	1.90	1.89	1.89
2.00	1.99	1.99	1.99	1.98	1.97	1.96	1.95	1.95	1.95	1.94	1.94
2.05	2.04	2.04	2.04	2.03	2.02	2.01	2.00	2.00	1.99	1.99	1.98
2.10	2.09	2.09	2.09	2.08	2.07	2.06	2.05	2.05	2.04	2.04	2.03
2.15	2.14	2.14	2.14	2.13	2.12	2.11	2.10	2.09	2.09	2.09	2.08
2.20	2.19	2.19	2.19	2.18	2.16	2.16	2.15	2.14	2.14	2.14	2.13
2.25	2.24	2.24	2.24	2.23	2.21	2.21	2.20	2.19	2.19	2.18	2.18
2.30	2.29	2.29	2.28	2.28	2.26	2.26	2.24	2.24	2.24	2.23	2.23
2.35	2.34	2.34	2.33	2.33	2.31	2.30	2.29	2.29	2.29	2.28	2.28
2.40	2.39	2.39	2.38	2.38	2.36	2.35	2.34	2.34	2.33	2.33	2.32
2.45	2.44	2.44	2.43	2.43	2.41	2.40	2.39	2.39	2.38	2.38	2.37
2.50	2.49	2.49	2.48	2.48	2.46	2.45	2.44	2.44	2.43	2.43	2.42
2.55	2.54	2.54	2.53	2.52	2.51	2.50	2.49	2.48	2.48	2.47	2.47
2.60	2.59	2.59	2.58	2.57	2.56	2.55	2.54	2.53	2.53	2.52	2.52
2.65	2.64	2.64	2.63	2.62	2.61	2.60	2.59	2.58	2.58	2.57	2.57
2.70	2.69	2.69	2.68	2.67	2.66	2.65	2.63	2.63	2.63	2.62	2.61
2.75	2.74	2.74	2.73	2.72	2.71	2.70	2.68	2.68	2.67	2.67	2.66
2.80	2.79	2.79	2.78	2.77	2.75	2.75	2.73	2.73	2.72	2.72	2.71
2.85	2.84	2.84	2.83	2.82	2.80	2.79	2.78	2.78	2.77	2.77	2.76
2.90	2.89	2.89	2.88	2.87	2.85	2.84	2.83	2.83	2.82	2.81	2.81
2.95	2.94	2.94	2.93	2.92	2.90	2.89	2.88	2.87	2.87	2.86	2.86
3.00	2.99	2.99	2.98	2.97	2.95	2.94	2.93	2.92	2.92	2.91	2.90

TO = Turnover Rate
M = Average Number of Months Unit is Held in Stock
P/C = Current Ratio of (Unit Price)/(Unit Cost)

Table 6.6 Effective Ratio of (Unit Price)/(Unit Cost) by Turnover Rate (Continued)

h = 30% (Annual Holding Rate)
i = 10% (Annual Price Change Rate)

TO	5.50	5.00	4.50	4.00	3.50	3.00	2.50	2.00	1.50	1.00	.50
M	2.18	2.40	2.67	3.00	3.43	4.00	4.80	6.00	8.00	12.00	24.00
P/C											
.80	.77	.77	.77	.76	.76	.75	.74	.73	.71	.68	.60
.85	.82	.82	.81	.81	.81	.80	.79	.78	.76	.72	.64
.90	.87	.87	.86	.86	.85	.85	.84	.82	.80	.76	.68
.95	.92	.91	.91	.91	.90	.89	.88	.87	.84	.80	.71
1.00	.97	.96	.96	.95	.95	.94	.93	.91	.89	.85	.75
1.05	1.01	1.01	1.01	1.00	.99	.99	.97	.96	.93	.89	.79
1.10	1.06	1.06	1.05	1.05	1.04	1.03	1.02	1.00	.98	.93	.82
1.15	1.11	1.11	1.10	1.10	1.09	1.08	1.07	1.05	1.02	.97	.86
1.20	1.16	1.15	1.15	1.14	1.14	1.13	1.11	1.10	1.07	1.02	.90
1.25	1.21	1.20	1.20	1.19	1.18	1.17	1.16	1.14	1.11	1.06	.94
1.30	1.26	1.25	1.25	1.24	1.23	1.22	1.21	1.19	1.16	1.10	.97
1.35	1.30	1.30	1.29	1.29	1.28	1.27	1.25	1.23	1.20	1.14	1.01
1.40	1.35	1.35	1.34	1.33	1.33	1.32	1.30	1.28	1.24	1.18	1.05
1.45	1.40	1.40	1.39	1.38	1.37	1.36	1.35	1.32	1.29	1.23	1.09
1.50	1.45	1.44	1.44	1.43	1.42	1.41	1.39	1.37	1.33	1.27	1.12
1.55	1.50	1.49	1.49	1.48	1.47	1.46	1.44	1.42	1.38	1.31	1.16
1.60	1.54	1.54	1.53	1.53	1.52	1.50	1.49	1.46	1.42	1.35	1.20
1.65	1.59	1.59	1.58	1.57	1.56	1.55	1.53	1.51	1.47	1.40	1.24
1.70	1.64	1.64	1.63	1.62	1.61	1.60	1.58	1.55	1.51	1.44	1.27
1.75	1.69	1.68	1.68	1.67	1.66	1.64	1.62	1.60	1.56	1.48	1.31
1.80	1.74	1.73	1.72	1.72	1.71	1.69	1.67	1.64	1.60	1.52	1.35
1.85	1.79	1.78	1.77	1.76	1.75	1.74	1.72	1.69	1.64	1.57	1.39
1.90	1.83	1.83	1.82	1.81	1.80	1.78	1.76	1.73	1.69	1.61	1.42
1.95	1.88	1.88	1.87	1.86	1.85	1.83	1.81	1.78	1.73	1.65	1.46
2.00	1.93	1.92	1.92	1.91	1.89	1.88	1.86	1.83	1.78	1.69	1.50
2.05	1.98	1.97	1.96	1.95	1.94	1.93	1.90	1.87	1.82	1.73	1.54
2.10	2.03	2.02	2.01	2.00	1.99	1.97	1.95	1.92	1.87	1.78	1.57
2.15	2.08	2.07	2.06	2.05	2.04	2.02	2.00	1.96	1.91	1.82	1.61
2.20	2.12	2.12	2.11	2.10	2.08	2.07	2.04	2.01	1.96	1.86	1.65
2.25	2.17	2.17	2.16	2.15	2.13	2.11	2.09	2.05	2.00	1.90	1.69
2.30	2.22	2.21	2.20	2.19	2.18	2.16	2.14	2.10	2.04	1.95	1.72
2.35	2.27	2.26	2.25	2.24	2.23	2.21	2.18	2.15	2.09	1.99	1.76
2.40	2.32	2.31	2.30	2.29	2.27	2.25	2.23	2.19	2.13	2.03	1.80
2.45	2.37	2.36	2.35	2.34	2.32	2.30	2.27	2.24	2.18	2.07	1.84
2.50	2.41	2.41	2.40	2.38	2.37	2.35	2.32	2.28	2.22	2.12	1.87
2.55	2.46	2.45	2.44	2.43	2.42	2.40	2.37	2.33	2.27	2.16	1.91
2.60	2.51	2.50	2.49	2.48	2.46	2.44	2.41	2.37	2.31	2.20	1.95
2.65	2.56	2.55	2.54	2.53	2.51	2.49	2.46	2.42	2.36	2.24	1.99
2.70	2.61	2.60	2.59	2.57	2.56	2.54	2.51	2.47	2.40	2.28	2.02
2.75	2.66	2.65	2.64	2.62	2.61	2.58	2.55	2.51	2.44	2.33	2.06
2.80	2.70	2.69	2.68	2.67	2.65	2.63	2.60	2.56	2.49	2.37	2.10
2.85	2.75	2.74	2.73	2.72	2.70	2.68	2.65	2.60	2.53	2.41	2.14
2.90	2.80	2.79	2.78	2.77	2.75	2.72	2.69	2.65	2.58	2.45	2.17
2.95	2.85	2.84	2.83	2.81	2.79	2.77	2.74	2.69	2.62	2.50	2.21
3.00	2.90	2.89	2.87	2.86	2.84	2.82	2.79	2.74	2.67	2.54	2.25

TO = Turnover Rate
M = Average Number of Months Unit is Held in Stock
P/C = Current Ratio of (Unit Price)/(Unit Cost)

Table 6.7 Effective Ratio of (Unit Price)/(Unit Cost) by Turnover Rate

h = 40% (Annual Holding Rate)

i = -10% (Annual Price Change Rate)

TO	50.00	40.00	30.00	20.00	12.00	10.00	8.00	7.50	7.00	6.50	6.00
M	.24	.30	.40	.60	1.00	1.20	1.50	1.60	1.71	1.85	2.00
P/C											
.80	.79	.79	.79	.78	.77	.76	.75	.75	.75	.74	.74
.85	.84	.84	.84	.83	.82	.81	.80	.80	.79	.79	.78
.90	.89	.89	.89	.88	.86	.86	.85	.84	.84	.83	.83
.95	.94	.94	.93	.93	.91	.90	.89	.89	.89	.88	.88
1.00	.99	.99	.98	.98	.96	.95	.94	.94	.93	.93	.92
1.05	1.04	1.04	1.03	1.02	1.01	1.00	.99	.98	.98	.97	.97
1.10	1.09	1.09	1.08	1.07	1.06	1.05	1.03	1.03	1.03	1.02	1.01
1.15	1.14	1.14	1.13	1.12	1.10	1.09	1.08	1.08	1.07	1.07	1.06
1.20	1.19	1.19	1.18	1.17	1.15	1.14	1.13	1.12	1.12	1.11	1.11
1.25	1.24	1.23	1.23	1.22	1.20	1.19	1.18	1.17	1.17	1.16	1.15
1.30	1.29	1.28	1.28	1.27	1.25	1.24	1.22	1.22	1.21	1.21	1.20
1.35	1.34	1.33	1.33	1.32	1.30	1.29	1.27	1.26	1.26	1.25	1.24
1.40	1.39	1.38	1.38	1.37	1.34	1.33	1.32	1.31	1.31	1.30	1.29
1.45	1.44	1.43	1.43	1.41	1.39	1.38	1.36	1.36	1.35	1.34	1.34
1.50	1.49	1.48	1.48	1.46	1.44	1.43	1.41	1.41	1.40	1.39	1.38
1.55	1.53	1.53	1.52	1.51	1.49	1.48	1.46	1.45	1.45	1.44	1.43
1.60	1.58	1.58	1.57	1.56	1.54	1.52	1.50	1.50	1.49	1.48	1.47
1.65	1.63	1.63	1.62	1.61	1.58	1.57	1.55	1.55	1.54	1.53	1.52
1.70	1.68	1.68	1.67	1.66	1.63	1.62	1.60	1.59	1.59	1.58	1.57
1.75	1.73	1.73	1.72	1.71	1.68	1.67	1.65	1.64	1.63	1.62	1.61
1.80	1.78	1.78	1.77	1.76	1.73	1.71	1.69	1.69	1.68	1.67	1.66
1.85	1.83	1.83	1.82	1.80	1.78	1.76	1.74	1.73	1.72	1.72	1.71
1.90	1.88	1.88	1.87	1.85	1.82	1.81	1.79	1.78	1.77	1.76	1.75
1.95	1.93	1.93	1.92	1.90	1.87	1.86	1.83	1.83	1.82	1.81	1.80
2.00	1.98	1.98	1.97	1.95	1.92	1.90	1.88	1.87	1.86	1.86	1.84
2.05	2.03	2.02	2.02	2.00	1.97	1.95	1.93	1.92	1.91	1.90	1.89
2.10	2.08	2.07	2.07	2.05	2.02	2.00	1.97	1.97	1.96	1.95	1.94
2.15	2.13	2.12	2.11	2.10	2.06	2.05	2.02	2.01	2.00	1.99	1.98
2.20	2.18	2.17	2.16	2.15	2.11	2.09	2.07	2.06	2.05	2.04	2.03
2.25	2.23	2.22	2.21	2.19	2.16	2.14	2.12	2.11	2.10	2.09	2.07
2.30	2.28	2.27	2.26	2.24	2.21	2.19	2.16	2.15	2.14	2.13	2.12
2.35	2.33	2.32	2.31	2.29	2.26	2.24	2.21	2.20	2.19	2.18	2.17
2.40	2.38	2.37	2.36	2.34	2.30	2.28	2.26	2.25	2.24	2.23	2.21
2.45	2.43	2.42	2.41	2.39	2.35	2.33	2.30	2.29	2.28	2.27	2.26
2.50	2.48	2.47	2.46	2.44	2.40	2.38	2.35	2.34	2.33	2.32	2.30
2.55	2.52	2.52	2.51	2.49	2.45	2.43	2.40	2.39	2.38	2.37	2.35
2.60	2.57	2.57	2.56	2.54	2.50	2.47	2.45	2.44	2.42	2.41	2.40
2.65	2.62	2.62	2.61	2.59	2.54	2.52	2.49	2.48	2.47	2.46	2.44
2.70	2.67	2.67	2.66	2.63	2.59	2.57	2.54	2.53	2.52	2.50	2.49
2.75	2.72	2.72	2.70	2.68	2.64	2.62	2.59	2.58	2.56	2.55	2.54
2.80	2.77	2.77	2.75	2.73	2.69	2.67	2.63	2.62	2.61	2.60	2.58
2.85	2.82	2.81	2.80	2.78	2.74	2.71	2.68	2.67	2.66	2.64	2.63
2.90	2.87	2.86	2.85	2.83	2.78	2.76	2.73	2.72	2.70	2.69	2.67
2.95	2.92	2.91	2.90	2.88	2.83	2.81	2.77	2.76	2.75	2.74	2.72
3.00	2.97	2.96	2.95	2.93	2.88	2.86	2.82	2.81	2.80	2.78	2.77

TO = Turnover Rate

M = Average Number of Months Unit is Held in Stock

P/C = Current Ratio of (Unit Price)/(Unit Cost)

Table 6.7 Effective Ratio of (Unit Price)/(Unit Cost) by Turnover Rate (Continued)

h = 40% (Annual Holding Rate)

i = -10% (Annual Price Change Rate)

TO	5.50	5.00	4.50	4.00	3.50	3.00	2.50	2.00	1.50	1.00	.50
M	2.18	2.40	2.67	3.00	3.43	4.00	4.80	6.00	8.00	12.00	24.00
P/C											
.80	.73	.73	.72	.71	.70	.68	.66	.63	.59	.51	.36
.85	.78	.77	.76	.75	.74	.73	.70	.67	.63	.55	.38
.90	.82	.82	.81	.80	.78	.77	.74	.71	.66	.58	.40
.95	.87	.86	.85	.84	.83	.81	.79	.75	.70	.61	.42
1.00	.92	.91	.90	.89	.87	.85	.83	.79	.74	.64	.44
1.05	.96	.95	.94	.93	.92	.90	.87	.83	.77	.67	.47
1.10	1.01	1.00	.99	.97	.96	.94	.91	.87	.81	.71	.49
1.15	1.05	1.04	1.03	1.02	1.00	.98	.95	.91	.85	.74	.51
1.20	1.10	1.09	1.08	1.06	1.05	1.02	.99	.95	.88	.77	.53
1.25	1.14	1.13	1.12	1.11	1.09	1.07	1.03	.99	.92	.80	.56
1.30	1.19	1.18	1.17	1.15	1.13	1.11	1.08	1.03	.96	.84	.58
1.35	1.24	1.22	1.21	1.20	1.18	1.15	1.12	1.07	.99	.87	.60
1.40	1.28	1.27	1.26	1.24	1.22	1.19	1.16	1.11	1.03	.90	.62
1.45	1.33	1.32	1.30	1.29	1.26	1.24	1.20	1.15	1.07	.93	.64
1.50	1.37	1.36	1.35	1.33	1.31	1.28	1.24	1.19	1.11	.96	.67
1.55	1.42	1.41	1.39	1.37	1.35	1.32	1.28	1.23	1.14	1.00	.69
1.60	1.46	1.45	1.44	1.42	1.39	1.36	1.32	1.27	1.18	1.03	.71
1.65	1.51	1.50	1.48	1.46	1.44	1.41	1.37	1.31	1.22	1.06	.73
1.70	1.56	1.54	1.53	1.51	1.48	1.45	1.41	1.35	1.25	1.09	.76
1.75	1.60	1.59	1.57	1.55	1.53	1.49	1.45	1.39	1.29	1.12	.78
1.80	1.65	1.63	1.62	1.60	1.57	1.54	1.49	1.42	1.33	1.16	.80
1.85	1.69	1.68	1.66	1.64	1.61	1.58	1.53	1.46	1.36	1.19	.82
1.90	1.74	1.72	1.71	1.68	1.66	1.62	1.57	1.50	1.40	1.22	.84
1.95	1.78	1.77	1.75	1.73	1.70	1.66	1.61	1.54	1.44	1.25	.87
2.00	1.83	1.81	1.80	1.77	1.74	1.71	1.66	1.58	1.47	1.29	.89
2.05	1.88	1.86	1.84	1.82	1.79	1.75	1.70	1.62	1.51	1.32	.91
2.10	1.92	1.91	1.89	1.86	1.83	1.79	1.74	1.66	1.55	1.35	.93
2.15	1.97	1.95	1.93	1.91	1.87	1.83	1.78	1.70	1.58	1.38	.96
2.20	2.01	2.00	1.98	1.95	1.92	1.88	1.82	1.74	1.62	1.41	.98
2.25	2.06	2.04	2.02	1.99	1.96	1.92	1.86	1.78	1.66	1.45	1.00
2.30	2.11	2.09	2.07	2.04	2.01	1.96	1.90	1.82	1.69	1.48	1.02
2.35	2.15	2.13	2.11	2.08	2.05	2.00	1.94	1.86	1.73	1.51	1.04
2.40	2.20	2.18	2.16	2.13	2.09	2.05	1.99	1.90	1.77	1.54	1.07
2.45	2.24	2.22	2.20	2.17	2.14	2.09	2.03	1.94	1.81	1.57	1.09
2.50	2.29	2.27	2.24	2.22	2.18	2.13	2.07	1.98	1.84	1.61	1.11
2.55	2.33	2.31	2.29	2.26	2.22	2.17	2.11	2.02	1.88	1.64	1.13
2.60	2.38	2.36	2.33	2.30	2.27	2.22	2.15	2.06	1.92	1.67	1.16
2.65	2.43	2.40	2.38	2.35	2.31	2.26	2.19	2.10	1.95	1.70	1.18
2.70	2.47	2.45	2.42	2.39	2.35	2.30	2.23	2.14	1.99	1.74	1.20
2.75	2.52	2.50	2.47	2.44	2.40	2.35	2.28	2.18	2.03	1.77	1.22
2.80	2.56	2.54	2.51	2.48	2.44	2.39	2.32	2.22	2.06	1.80	1.24
2.85	2.61	2.59	2.56	2.53	2.48	2.43	2.36	2.26	2.10	1.83	1.27
2.90	2.65	2.63	2.60	2.57	2.53	2.47	2.40	2.30	2.14	1.86	1.29
2.95	2.70	2.68	2.65	2.61	2.57	2.52	2.44	2.34	2.17	1.90	1.31
3.00	2.75	2.72	2.69	2.66	2.62	2.56	2.48	2.37	2.21	1.93	1.33

TO = Turnover Rate

M = Average Number of Months Unit is Held in Stock

P/C = Current Ratio of (Unit Price)/(Unit Cost)

Table 6.8 Effective Ratio of (Unit Price)/(Unit Cost) by Turnover Rate

h = 40% (Annual Holding Rate)

i = 0% (Annual Price Change Rate)

TO	50.00	40.00	30.00	20.00	12.00	10.00	8.00	7.50	7.00	6.50	6.00
M	.24	.30	.40	.60	1.00	1.20	1.50	1.60	1.71	1.85	2.00
P/C											
.80	.79	.79	.79	.78	.77	.77	.76	.76	.76	.75	.75
.85	.84	.84	.84	.83	.82	.82	.81	.81	.80	.80	.80
.90	.89	.89	.89	.88	.87	.87	.86	.85	.85	.85	.84
.95	.94	.94	.94	.93	.92	.91	.90	.90	.90	.89	.89
1.00	.99	.99	.99	.98	.97	.96	.95	.95	.95	.94	.94
1.05	1.04	1.04	1.04	1.03	1.02	1.01	1.00	1.00	.99	.99	.98
1.10	1.09	1.09	1.09	1.08	1.06	1.06	1.05	1.04	1.04	1.04	1.03
1.15	1.14	1.14	1.13	1.13	1.11	1.11	1.10	1.09	1.09	1.08	1.08
1.20	1.19	1.19	1.18	1.18	1.16	1.15	1.14	1.14	1.14	1.13	1.12
1.25	1.24	1.24	1.23	1.23	1.21	1.20	1.19	1.19	1.18	1.18	1.17
1.30	1.29	1.29	1.28	1.27	1.26	1.25	1.24	1.23	1.23	1.22	1.22
1.35	1.34	1.34	1.33	1.32	1.31	1.30	1.29	1.28	1.28	1.27	1.27
1.40	1.39	1.39	1.38	1.37	1.35	1.35	1.33	1.33	1.32	1.32	1.31
1.45	1.44	1.44	1.43	1.42	1.40	1.39	1.38	1.38	1.37	1.37	1.36
1.50	1.49	1.49	1.48	1.47	1.45	1.44	1.43	1.42	1.42	1.41	1.41
1.55	1.54	1.53	1.53	1.52	1.50	1.49	1.48	1.47	1.47	1.46	1.45
1.60	1.59	1.58	1.58	1.57	1.55	1.54	1.52	1.52	1.51	1.51	1.50
1.65	1.64	1.63	1.63	1.62	1.60	1.59	1.57	1.57	1.56	1.55	1.55
1.70	1.69	1.68	1.68	1.67	1.65	1.63	1.62	1.61	1.61	1.60	1.59
1.75	1.74	1.73	1.73	1.72	1.69	1.68	1.67	1.66	1.66	1.65	1.64
1.80	1.79	1.78	1.78	1.76	1.74	1.73	1.71	1.71	1.70	1.70	1.69
1.85	1.84	1.83	1.83	1.81	1.79	1.78	1.76	1.76	1.75	1.74	1.73
1.90	1.88	1.88	1.87	1.86	1.84	1.83	1.81	1.80	1.80	1.79	1.78
1.95	1.93	1.93	1.92	1.91	1.89	1.87	1.86	1.85	1.84	1.84	1.83
2.00	1.98	1.98	1.97	1.96	1.94	1.92	1.90	1.90	1.89	1.88	1.87
2.05	2.03	2.03	2.02	2.01	1.98	1.97	1.95	1.95	1.94	1.93	1.92
2.10	2.08	2.08	2.07	2.06	2.03	2.02	2.00	1.99	1.99	1.98	1.97
2.15	2.13	2.13	2.12	2.11	2.08	2.07	2.05	2.04	2.03	2.03	2.02
2.20	2.18	2.18	2.17	2.16	2.13	2.12	2.10	2.09	2.08	2.07	2.06
2.25	2.23	2.23	2.22	2.21	2.18	2.16	2.14	2.14	2.13	2.12	2.11
2.30	2.28	2.28	2.27	2.25	2.23	2.21	2.19	2.18	2.18	2.17	2.16
2.35	2.33	2.33	2.32	2.30	2.27	2.26	2.24	2.23	2.22	2.21	2.20
2.40	2.38	2.38	2.37	2.35	2.32	2.31	2.29	2.28	2.27	2.26	2.25
2.45	2.43	2.43	2.42	2.40	2.37	2.36	2.33	2.33	2.32	2.31	2.30
2.50	2.48	2.48	2.47	2.45	2.42	2.40	2.38	2.37	2.36	2.36	2.34
2.55	2.53	2.52	2.52	2.50	2.47	2.45	2.43	2.42	2.41	2.40	2.39
2.60	2.58	2.57	2.57	2.55	2.52	2.50	2.48	2.47	2.46	2.45	2.44
2.65	2.63	2.62	2.62	2.60	2.56	2.55	2.52	2.52	2.51	2.50	2.48
2.70	2.68	2.67	2.66	2.65	2.61	2.60	2.57	2.56	2.55	2.54	2.53
2.75	2.73	2.72	2.71	2.70	2.66	2.64	2.62	2.61	2.60	2.59	2.58
2.80	2.78	2.77	2.76	2.75	2.71	2.69	2.67	2.66	2.65	2.64	2.62
2.85	2.83	2.82	2.81	2.79	2.76	2.74	2.71	2.71	2.70	2.68	2.67
2.90	2.88	2.87	2.86	2.84	2.81	2.79	2.76	2.75	2.74	2.73	2.72
2.95	2.93	2.92	2.91	2.89	2.85	2.84	2.81	2.80	2.79	2.78	2.77
3.00	2.98	2.97	2.96	2.94	2.90	2.88	2.86	2.85	2.84	2.83	2.81

TO = Turnover Rate

M = Average Number of Months Unit is Held in Stock

P/C = Current Ratio of (Unit Price)/(Unit Cost)

Table 6.8   Effective Ratio of (Unit Price)/(Unit Cost) by Turnover Rate

Table 6.8   Effective Ratio of (Unit Price)/(Unit Cost) by Turnover Rate
                                                                    (Continued)

h =   40%   (Annual Holding Rate)

i =   0%   (Annual Price Change Rate)

TO	5.50	5.00	4.50	4.00	3.50	3.00	2.50	2.00	1.50	1.00	.50
M	2.18	2.40	2.67	3.00	3.43	4.00	4.80	6.00	8.00	12.00	24.00
P/C											
.80	.75	.74	.73	.73	.72	.71	.69	.67	.63	.57	.44
.85	.79	.79	.78	.77	.76	.75	.73	.71	.67	.61	.47
.90	.84	.83	.83	.82	.81	.79	.78	.75	.71	.64	.50
.95	.89	.88	.87	.86	.85	.84	.82	.79	.75	.68	.53
1.00	.93	.93	.92	.91	.90	.88	.86	.83	.79	.71	.56
1.05	.98	.97	.96	.95	.94	.93	.91	.87	.83	.75	.58
1.10	1.03	1.02	1.01	1.00	.99	.97	.95	.92	.87	.79	.61
1.15	1.07	1.06	1.06	1.05	1.03	1.01	.99	.96	.91	.82	.64
1.20	1.12	1.11	1.10	1.09	1.08	1.06	1.03	1.00	.95	.86	.67
1.25	1.17	1.16	1.15	1.14	1.12	1.10	1.08	1.04	.99	.89	.69
1.30	1.21	1.20	1.19	1.18	1.17	1.15	1.12	1.08	1.03	.93	.72
1.35	1.26	1.25	1.24	1.23	1.21	1.19	1.16	1.12	1.07	.96	.75
1.40	1.31	1.30	1.29	1.27	1.26	1.24	1.21	1.17	1.11	1.00	.78
1.45	1.35	1.34	1.33	1.32	1.30	1.28	1.25	1.21	1.14	1.04	.81
1.50	1.40	1.39	1.38	1.36	1.35	1.32	1.29	1.25	1.18	1.07	.83
1.55	1.44	1.44	1.42	1.41	1.39	1.37	1.34	1.29	1.22	1.11	.86
1.60	1.49	1.48	1.47	1.45	1.44	1.41	1.38	1.33	1.26	1.14	.89
1.65	1.54	1.53	1.52	1.50	1.48	1.46	1.42	1.37	1.30	1.18	.92
1.70	1.58	1.57	1.56	1.55	1.53	1.50	1.47	1.42	1.34	1.21	.94
1.75	1.63	1.62	1.61	1.59	1.57	1.54	1.51	1.46	1.38	1.25	.97
1.80	1.68	1.67	1.65	1.64	1.62	1.59	1.55	1.50	1.42	1.29	1.00
1.85	1.72	1.71	1.70	1.68	1.66	1.63	1.59	1.54	1.46	1.32	1.03
1.90	1.77	1.76	1.74	1.73	1.71	1.68	1.64	1.58	1.50	1.36	1.06
1.95	1.82	1.81	1.79	1.77	1.75	1.72	1.68	1.62	1.54	1.39	1.08
2.00	1.86	1.85	1.84	1.82	1.79	1.76	1.72	1.67	1.58	1.43	1.11
2.05	1.91	1.90	1.88	1.86	1.84	1.81	1.77	1.71	1.62	1.46	1.14
2.10	1.96	1.94	1.93	1.91	1.88	1.85	1.81	1.75	1.66	1.50	1.17
2.15	2.00	1.99	1.97	1.95	1.93	1.90	1.85	1.79	1.70	1.54	1.19
2.20	2.05	2.04	2.02	2.00	1.97	1.94	1.90	1.83	1.74	1.57	1.22
2.25	2.10	2.08	2.07	2.05	2.02	1.99	1.94	1.87	1.78	1.61	1.25
2.30	2.14	2.13	2.11	2.09	2.06	2.03	1.98	1.92	1.82	1.64	1.28
2.35	2.19	2.18	2.16	2.14	2.11	2.07	2.03	1.96	1.86	1.68	1.31
2.40	2.24	2.22	2.20	2.18	2.15	2.12	2.07	2.00	1.89	1.71	1.33
2.45	2.28	2.27	2.25	2.23	2.20	2.16	2.11	2.04	1.93	1.75	1.36
2.50	2.33	2.31	2.30	2.27	2.24	2.21	2.16	2.08	1.97	1.79	1.39
2.55	2.38	2.36	2.34	2.32	2.29	2.25	2.20	2.12	2.01	1.82	1.42
2.60	2.42	2.41	2.39	2.36	2.33	2.29	2.24	2.17	2.05	1.86	1.44
2.65	2.47	2.45	2.43	2.41	2.38	2.34	2.28	2.21	2.09	1.89	1.47
2.70	2.52	2.50	2.48	2.45	2.42	2.38	2.33	2.25	2.13	1.93	1.50
2.75	2.56	2.55	2.53	2.50	2.47	2.43	2.37	2.29	2.17	1.96	1.53
2.80	2.61	2.59	2.57	2.55	2.51	2.47	2.41	2.33	2.21	2.00	1.56
2.85	2.66	2.64	2.62	2.59	2.56	2.51	2.46	2.37	2.25	2.04	1.58
2.90	2.70	2.69	2.66	2.64	2.60	2.56	2.50	2.42	2.29	2.07	1.61
2.95	2.75	2.73	2.71	2.68	2.65	2.60	2.54	2.46	2.33	2.11	1.64
3.00	2.80	2.78	2.76	2.73	2.69	2.65	2.59	2.50	2.37	2.14	1.67

TO = Turnover Rate

M   = Average Number of Months Unit is Held in Stock

P/C = Current Ratio of (Unit Price)/(Unit Cost)

Table 6.9 Effective Ratio of (Unit Price)/(Unit Cost) by Turnover Rate

h = 40% (Annual Holding Rate)

i = 10% (Annual Price Change Rate)

TO	50.00	40.00	30.00	20.00	12.00	10.00	8.00	7.50	7.00	6.50	6.00
M	.24	.30	.40	.60	1.00	1.20	1.50	1.60	1.71	1.85	2.00
P/C											
.80	.80	.79	.79	.79	.78	.78	.77	.77	.77	.77	.76
.85	.84	.84	.84	.84	.83	.83	.82	.82	.82	.81	.81
.90	.89	.89	.89	.89	.88	.87	.87	.87	.86	.86	.86
.95	.94	.94	.94	.94	.93	.92	.92	.91	.91	.91	.91
1.00	.99	.99	.99	.99	.98	.97	.96	.96	.96	.96	.95
1.05	1.04	1.04	1.04	1.03	1.02	1.02	1.01	1.01	1.01	1.00	1.00
1.10	1.09	1.09	1.09	1.08	1.07	1.07	1.06	1.06	1.06	1.05	1.05
1.15	1.14	1.14	1.14	1.13	1.12	1.12	1.11	1.11	1.10	1.10	1.10
1.20	1.19	1.19	1.19	1.18	1.17	1.17	1.16	1.15	1.15	1.15	1.14
1.25	1.24	1.24	1.24	1.23	1.22	1.21	1.21	1.20	1.20	1.20	1.19
1.30	1.29	1.29	1.29	1.28	1.27	1.26	1.25	1.25	1.25	1.24	1.24
1.35	1.34	1.34	1.34	1.33	1.32	1.31	1.30	1.30	1.30	1.29	1.29
1.40	1.39	1.39	1.39	1.38	1.37	1.36	1.35	1.35	1.34	1.34	1.33
1.45	1.44	1.44	1.44	1.43	1.41	1.41	1.40	1.39	1.39	1.39	1.38
1.50	1.49	1.49	1.49	1.48	1.46	1.46	1.45	1.44	1.44	1.43	1.43
1.55	1.54	1.54	1.53	1.53	1.51	1.51	1.49	1.49	1.49	1.48	1.48
1.60	1.59	1.59	1.58	1.58	1.56	1.55	1.54	1.54	1.54	1.53	1.52
1.65	1.64	1.64	1.63	1.63	1.61	1.60	1.59	1.59	1.58	1.58	1.57
1.70	1.69	1.69	1.68	1.67	1.66	1.65	1.64	1.64	1.63	1.63	1.62
1.75	1.74	1.74	1.73	1.72	1.71	1.70	1.69	1.68	1.68	1.67	1.67
1.80	1.79	1.79	1.78	1.77	1.76	1.75	1.74	1.73	1.73	1.72	1.72
1.85	1.84	1.84	1.83	1.82	1.81	1.80	1.78	1.78	1.77	1.77	1.76
1.90	1.89	1.89	1.88	1.87	1.85	1.85	1.83	1.83	1.82	1.82	1.81
1.95	1.94	1.94	1.93	1.92	1.90	1.89	1.88	1.88	1.87	1.87	1.86
2.00	1.99	1.99	1.98	1.97	1.95	1.94	1.93	1.92	1.92	1.91	1.91
2.05	2.04	2.03	2.03	2.02	2.00	1.99	1.98	1.97	1.97	1.96	1.95
2.10	2.09	2.08	2.08	2.07	2.05	2.04	2.02	2.02	2.01	2.01	2.00
2.15	2.14	2.13	2.13	2.12	2.10	2.09	2.07	2.07	2.06	2.06	2.05
2.20	2.19	2.18	2.18	2.17	2.15	2.14	2.12	2.12	2.11	2.10	2.10
2.25	2.24	2.23	2.23	2.22	2.20	2.19	2.17	2.16	2.16	2.15	2.14
2.30	2.29	2.28	2.28	2.27	2.24	2.23	2.22	2.21	2.21	2.20	2.19
2.35	2.34	2.33	2.33	2.32	2.29	2.28	2.27	2.26	2.25	2.25	2.24
2.40	2.39	2.38	2.38	2.36	2.34	2.33	2.31	2.31	2.30	2.30	2.29
2.45	2.44	2.43	2.43	2.41	2.39	2.38	2.36	2.36	2.35	2.34	2.34
2.50	2.49	2.48	2.48	2.46	2.44	2.43	2.41	2.41	2.40	2.39	2.38
2.55	2.53	2.53	2.52	2.51	2.49	2.48	2.46	2.45	2.45	2.44	2.43
2.60	2.58	2.58	2.57	2.56	2.54	2.52	2.51	2.50	2.49	2.49	2.48
2.65	2.63	2.63	2.62	2.61	2.59	2.57	2.56	2.55	2.54	2.53	2.53
2.70	2.68	2.68	2.67	2.66	2.63	2.62	2.60	2.60	2.59	2.58	2.57
2.75	2.73	2.73	2.72	2.71	2.68	2.67	2.65	2.65	2.64	2.63	2.62
2.80	2.78	2.78	2.77	2.76	2.73	2.72	2.70	2.69	2.69	2.68	2.67
2.85	2.83	2.83	2.82	2.81	2.78	2.77	2.75	2.74	2.73	2.73	2.72
2.90	2.88	2.88	2.87	2.86	2.83	2.82	2.80	2.79	2.78	2.77	2.76
2.95	2.93	2.93	2.92	2.91	2.88	2.86	2.84	2.84	2.83	2.82	2.81
3.00	2.98	2.98	2.97	2.96	2.93	2.91	2.89	2.89	2.88	2.87	2.86

TO = Turnover Rate

M = Average Number of Months Unit is Held in Stock

P/C = Current Ratio of (Unit Price)/(Unit Cost)

Table 6.9   Effective Ratio of (Unit Price)/(Unit Cost) by Turnover Rate
(Continued)

h = 40%   (Annual Holding Rate)
i = 10%   (Annual Price Change Rate)

TO	5.50	5.00	4.50	4.00	3.50	3.00	2.50	2.00	1.50	1.00	.50
M	2.18	2.40	2.67	3.00	3.43	4.00	4.80	6.00	8.00	12.00	24.00
P/C											
.80	.76	.76	.75	.75	.74	.73	.72	.70	.67	.63	.53
.85	.81	.80	.80	.79	.78	.78	.76	.74	.72	.67	.57
.90	.85	.85	.84	.84	.83	.82	.81	.79	.76	.71	.60
.95	.90	.90	.89	.89	.88	.87	.85	.83	.80	.75	.63
1.00	.95	.94	.94	.93	.92	.91	.90	.87	.84	.79	.67
1.05	1.00	.99	.99	.98	.97	.96	.94	.92	.88	.83	.70
1.10	1.04	1.04	1.03	1.02	1.02	1.00	.99	.96	.93	.86	.73
1.15	1.09	1.09	1.08	1.07	1.06	1.05	1.03	1.01	.97	.90	.77
1.20	1.14	1.13	1.13	1.12	1.11	1.09	1.08	1.05	1.01	.94	.80
1.25	1.19	1.18	1.17	1.16	1.15	1.14	1.12	1.09	1.05	.98	.83
1.30	1.23	1.23	1.22	1.21	1.20	1.19	1.17	1.14	1.09	1.02	.87
1.35	1.28	1.27	1.27	1.26	1.25	1.23	1.21	1.18	1.14	1.06	.90
1.40	1.33	1.32	1.31	1.30	1.29	1.28	1.26	1.22	1.18	1.10	.93
1.45	1.38	1.37	1.36	1.35	1.34	1.32	1.30	1.27	1.22	1.14	.97
1.50	1.42	1.42	1.41	1.40	1.38	1.37	1.34	1.31	1.26	1.18	1.00
1.55	1.47	1.46	1.46	1.44	1.43	1.41	1.39	1.36	1.31	1.22	1.03
1.60	1.52	1.51	1.50	1.49	1.48	1.46	1.43	1.40	1.35	1.26	1.07
1.65	1.57	1.56	1.55	1.54	1.52	1.50	1.48	1.44	1.39	1.30	1.10
1.70	1.61	1.61	1.60	1.58	1.57	1.55	1.52	1.49	1.43	1.34	1.13
1.75	1.66	1.65	1.64	1.63	1.62	1.60	1.57	1.53	1.47	1.37	1.17
1.80	1.71	1.70	1.69	1.68	1.66	1.64	1.61	1.57	1.52	1.41	1.20
1.85	1.76	1.75	1.74	1.72	1.71	1.69	1.66	1.62	1.56	1.45	1.23
1.90	1.80	1.79	1.78	1.77	1.75	1.73	1.70	1.66	1.60	1.49	1.27
1.95	1.85	1.84	1.83	1.82	1.80	1.78	1.75	1.71	1.64	1.53	1.30
2.00	1.90	1.89	1.88	1.86	1.85	1.82	1.79	1.75	1.68	1.57	1.33
2.05	1.95	1.94	1.92	1.91	1.89	1.87	1.84	1.79	1.73	1.61	1.37
2.10	1.99	1.98	1.97	1.96	1.94	1.91	1.88	1.84	1.77	1.65	1.40
2.15	2.04	2.03	2.02	2.00	1.98	1.96	1.93	1.88	1.81	1.69	1.43
2.20	2.09	2.08	2.07	2.05	2.03	2.01	1.97	1.92	1.85	1.73	1.47
2.25	2.14	2.12	2.11	2.10	2.08	2.05	2.02	1.97	1.89	1.77	1.50
2.30	2.18	2.17	2.16	2.14	2.12	2.10	2.06	2.01	1.94	1.81	1.53
2.35	2.23	2.22	2.21	2.19	2.17	2.14	2.11	2.06	1.98	1.85	1.57
2.40	2.28	2.27	2.25	2.24	2.22	2.19	2.15	2.10	2.02	1.89	1.60
2.45	2.33	2.31	2.30	2.28	2.26	2.23	2.20	2.14	2.06	1.92	1.63
2.50	2.37	2.36	2.35	2.33	2.31	2.28	2.24	2.19	2.11	1.96	1.67
2.55	2.42	2.41	2.39	2.38	2.35	2.32	2.29	2.23	2.15	2.00	1.70
2.60	2.47	2.46	2.44	2.42	2.40	2.37	2.33	2.27	2.19	2.04	1.73
2.65	2.52	2.50	2.49	2.47	2.45	2.42	2.38	2.32	2.23	2.08	1.77
2.70	2.56	2.55	2.53	2.52	2.49	2.46	2.42	2.36	2.27	2.12	1.80
2.75	2.61	2.60	2.58	2.56	2.54	2.51	2.47	2.41	2.32	2.16	1.83
2.80	2.66	2.64	2.63	2.61	2.58	2.55	2.51	2.45	2.36	2.20	1.87
2.85	2.71	2.69	2.68	2.66	2.63	2.60	2.56	2.49	2.40	2.24	1.90
2.90	2.75	2.74	2.72	2.70	2.68	2.64	2.60	2.54	2.44	2.28	1.93
2.95	2.80	2.79	2.77	2.75	2.72	2.69	2.64	2.58	2.48	2.32	1.97
3.00	2.85	2.83	2.82	2.80	2.77	2.74	2.69	2.62	2.53	2.36	2.00

TO = Turnover Rate

M   = Average Number of Months Unit is Held in Stock

P/C = Current Ratio of (Unit Price)/(Unit Cost)

CHAPTER 7

The Standard Normal Distribution

The standard normal distribution (reference 1) is perhaps the most commonly used probability distribution in materials management as well as in many other scientific developments. The primary use in inventory applications occurs when future demands of an item are not known for certain and a forecast of these demands is generated for inventory decision making. Actual demands are generally assumed to follow a normal distribution with a mean and standard deviation estimated by the forecast of the demands. In this way subsequent inventory decisions may be made using the shape of the normal probability distribution as a basis. In Chapters 9 to 13 the normal distribution is used in determining the size of safety stock for individual items.

A variable **x** with a normal distribution has a particular mean μ and standard deviation σ. The shape of the distribution appears as in Figure 7.1; note that always **x** almost always ranges from $\mu - 3\sigma$ to $\mu + 3\sigma$ and the most likely value of **x** is the mean μ.

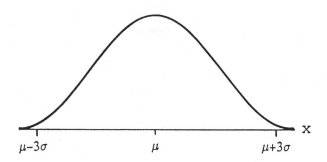

Figure 7.1. The normal distribution

A companion distribution—called the standard normal distribution—has a mean of zero and a standard deviation of one and appears as in Figure 7.2. The variable **z** is the standard normal variate and is related to **x** by the relation:

$$z = \frac{x - \mu}{\sigma}$$

In the same way, **x** is obtained from **z** by:

$$x = \mu + z\sigma$$

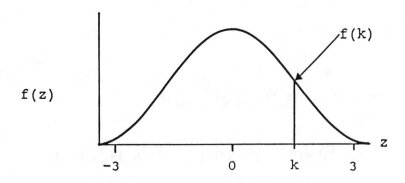

Figure 7.2. The standard normal distribution

Probability Density

If **k** represents a particular value of **z**, then the probability density of **k**, denoted as **f(k)**, is:

$$f(k) = \sqrt{1/2\,\pi}\,\exp\left(-k^2/2\right)$$

as shown in Figure 7.2. Note that **f(k)** gives the height of the probability density at the particular value of z = k.

Cumulative Probability Distribution

When **k** is a particular value of **z**, the probability that **z** is less than or equal to **k**, called the cumulative probability distribution, **F(k)**, becomes:

$$F(k) = \int_{-\infty}^{k} f(z)\,dz$$

as shown in Figure 7.3. Note, as **k** approaches −3, F(k) = 0; and as **k** approaches +3, F(k) = 1. Also, if k = 0, then F(k) = .5, indicating that the probability is one-half (50/50) that **z** is less than zero.

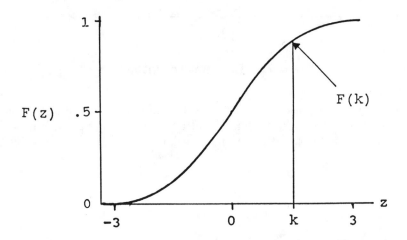

Figure 7.3. The cumulative standard normal distribution

For convenience later, the complement of **F(k)** is noted at this time. This calculation gives the probability that **k** is larger than **z** and is here denoted as **H(k)**, where:

$$H(k) = 1 - F(k)$$

Partial Expectation

Consider **k** (a particular value of z) and imagine all values of **z** larger than **k**. Now let $(z - k)$ identify the measure of how much larger these values of **z** are above **k** and where $(z - k)$ is always larger than zero. The average of $(z - k)$ can be determined—this average is called the *partial expectation*—and is here denoted as **E(k)**. **E(k)** is evaluated by the relation:

$$E(k) = \int_{k}^{\infty} (z - k) f(z) \, dz$$

that is,

$$E(k) = f(k) - k H(k)$$

The partial expectation is used in subsequent chapters to determine the size of the safety stock to use (references 2 and 3).

Tables

Three adjoining tables are presented in this chapter. Table 7.1, arranged by values of **k** from k = −3 to +3, lists the corresponding values of **f(k)**, **F(k)** and **E(k)**.

Table 7.2 is arranged from the low to high values of **E(k)**. Observe in Table 7.1 that the positive values of **k** correspond with the **E(k)** values ranging from 0 to .3989. Also, the negative values of **k** yield **E(k)** values above .3989. Table 7.2 has 400 entries, with the first 200 listing the **E(k)** values ranging from .002 to .400 in intervals of .002 to span the associated positive values of **k**. The next 200 entries range from .413 to 3.000 in intervals of .013 to span the negative values of **k**. For each value of **E(k)**, the associated values of **k**, **F(k)** and **f(k)** are listed.

Table 7.3 is arranged from low to high values of **F(k)** ranging from .005 to .995. The associated entries are **k**, **f(k)** and **E(k)**.

Example 7.1

Suppose the monthly demands for a particular brand of soap are normally shaped with a mean of 10,000 bars and a standard deviation of 1000. Find the probability that the demand for the soap will not exceed 11,000 bars. This probability is often called the *availability* and represents the percent of order cycles where item stock is sufficient to cover the demands that occur over the order cycle. (An order cycle is the elapsed time between two replenishments of stock for an item).

With $\mu = 10,000$ and $\sigma = 1,000$, the standard normal variate corresponding to x = 11,000 is derived by:

$$k = \frac{x - \mu}{\sigma} = \frac{11,000 - 10,000}{1,000} = 1$$

Now the probability that the demand of the soap will not exceed 11,000 bars is the same as the probability that **z** will not exceed a value of k = 1. Table 7.1 is used (with k = 1) to find F(1) = .8413, the probability that demand will not exceed 11,000 bars; therefore, the availability is 84.13 percent.

Example 7.2

The demand for a popular shoe style is normally shaped and the average demand is 4,000 pairs per month with a standard deviation of 500 pairs. How many pairs of the shoe should be stocked in the warehouse at the start of the month to be 95 percent certain of not running out of stock? This criterion corresponds to an availability of 95 percent.

In this situation, it is necessary to find the value of k, where the probability is .95 that z will be less than or equal to k. Table 7.3 is used with $F(k) = .95$ to seek the corresponding value of $k = 1.645$. The number of pairs to have available should then be:

$$x = \mu + k\sigma = 4000 + 1.645 \, (500) = 4822$$

Example 7.3

The demand for a service parts kit is estimated as 100 units a month with a standard deviation of 20 units, and the demand distribution is normally shaped. If the number of units available for the month to meet these demands is 110, what then is the probability that the demand will exceed the stock available? Also, what is the corresponding measure of availability for the kit?

Note that since $\mu = 100$, $\sigma = 20$ and $x = 110$, then:

$$k = (x - \mu)/\sigma = (110 - 100)/20 = .50$$

Thus, the probability that the demand will exceed 110 units is the same as z exceeding $k = .5$. Table 7.1 shows that $F(.5) = .6915$, which is the probability that z will be less than or equal to $k = .5$; therefore, the probability that demand will exceed the available stock of 110 is $H(.5) = 1 - F(.5) = .3085$. Also, the availability becomes 69.15 percent.

Example 7.4

A cosmetic firm stocks shampoo in a regional warehouse to fill local demands. The shampoo demands are normally shaped with a monthly mean of 20,000 cases and a standard deviation of 3,000 cases. At the start of a month, 22,000 cases are available and no replenishment will be forthcoming over the month. Find the expected number of demands that may exceed the supply of 22,000 cases.

A relation that is more fully described in Chapter 9, where safety stocks are considered, is needed to solve this problem. However, the method proceeds in the following manner. First the value of k is found, where $x = 22,000$, $\mu = 20,000$ and $\sigma = 3,000$:

$$k = (x - \mu)/\sigma = (22,000 - 20,000)/3,000 = 0.67$$

Second, Chapter 9 shows that the average number of demands x exceeding a particular value, say x_0, is found by the relation:

$$E(x > x_0) = \sigma \, E(k)$$

Therefore, when $\mu = 20,000$, $\sigma = 3,000$ and $x_0 = 22,000$, $k = 0.67$. Now—using $k = 0.67$ in Table 7.1—the partial expectation $E(0.67) = 0.150$ is found and the expected number of cases unfilled is:

$$\sigma \, E(k) = 3000 \, (.150) = 450$$

Example 7.5

Suppose the cosmetic firm from Example 7.4 desires that the expected number of shortages should not exceed 100 cases. How much stock should be available at the start of the month, in order to accomplish this goal?

To find this solution, first the relation:

$$E(x > x_o) = \sigma \, E(k)$$

is reversed to find:

$$E(k) = E(x > x_o)/\sigma = 100/3,000 = .0333$$

Second, Table 7.2 is now used to find the corresponding value of **k** where $E(k) = 0.0333$. This point occurs when $k = 1.45$, and thereby the stock to have available becomes:

$$x_o = \mu + k \, \sigma$$

therefore,

$$x_o = 20,000 + 1.45 \, (3000) = 24,350$$

Example 7.6

A grocery firm stocks lettuce in its produce section each third day. The average demand over these days is 300 head of lettuce with a standard deviation is 50 head. If 310 head of lettuce are stocked at the outset, what is the probability the store will run out of lettuce over the three days? Also find the availability for the lettuce.

Using $\mu = 300$ and $\sigma = 50$, with $x = 310$, then:

$$k = (x - \mu)/\sigma = (310 - 300)/50 = 0.20$$

Table 7.1 is next used to find $F(0.20) = .5793$, which is the probability that **z** will be less than or equal to $k = 0.20$. Thus, $H(0.20) = 1 - .5793 = .4207$ is the probability that **z** will exceed $k = 0.20$. This calculation is the same as the probability that the demand of lettuce will exceed 310 head over the three days. The availability consequently becomes $100F(0.20) = 57.93$ percent.

Example 7.7

Consider the stocking of lettuce in Example 7.6; suppose that the store management desires to stock enough lettuce that the probability of not running out of stock is .90. How many head of lettuce should be stocked?

In this situation Table 7.3 is used, with $F(k) = .90$, finding that the corresponding value of $k = 1.2817$. Recalling $\mu = 300$ and $\sigma = 50$, the number of head of lettuce to stock is then:

$$x = \mu + k \, \sigma = 300 + 1.2817 \, (50) = 364.085$$

or approximately 364.

Table 7.1   k of the Standard Normal Distribution and Related Measures

k	f(k)	F(k)	E(k)	k	f(k)	F(k)	E(k)
-3.00	.0044	.0013	3.0004	-2.20	.0355	.0139	2.2049
-2.98	.0047	.0014	2.9804	-2.18	.0371	.0146	2.1852
-2.96	.0050	.0015	2.9604	-2.16	.0387	.0154	2.1655
-2.94	.0053	.0016	2.9405	-2.14	.0404	.0162	2.1458
-2.92	.0056	.0018	2.9205	-2.12	.0422	.0170	2.1261
-2.90	.0060	.0019	2.9005	-2.10	.0440	.0179	2.1065
-2.88	.0063	.0020	2.8806	-2.08	.0459	.0188	2.0868
-2.86	.0067	.0021	2.8606	-2.06	.0478	.0197	2.0672
-2.84	.0071	.0023	2.8407	-2.04	.0498	.0207	2.0476
-2.82	.0075	.0024	2.8207	-2.02	.0519	.0217	2.0280
-2.80	.0079	.0026	2.8008	-2.00	.0540	.0228	2.0085
-2.78	.0084	.0027	2.7808	-1.98	.0562	.0239	1.9890
-2.76	.0088	.0029	2.7609	-1.96	.0584	.0250	1.9694
-2.74	.0093	.0031	2.7409	-1.94	.0608	.0262	1.9500
-2.72	.0099	.0033	2.7210	-1.92	.0632	.0274	1.9305
-2.70	.0104	.0035	2.7011	-1.90	.0656	.0287	1.9111
-2.68	.0110	.0037	2.6811	-1.88	.0681	.0301	1.8916
-2.66	.0116	.0039	2.6612	-1.86	.0707	.0314	1.8723
-2.64	.0122	.0041	2.6413	-1.84	.0734	.0329	1.8529
-2.62	.0129	.0044	2.6214	-1.82	.0761	.0344	1.8336
-2.60	.0136	.0047	2.6015	-1.80	.0790	.0359	1.8143
-2.58	.0143	.0049	2.5816	-1.78	.0818	.0375	1.7950
-2.56	.0151	.0052	2.5617	-1.76	.0848	.0392	1.7758
-2.54	.0158	.0055	2.5418	-1.74	.0878	.0409	1.7566
-2.52	.0167	.0059	2.5219	-1.72	.0909	.0427	1.7374
-2.50	.0175	.0062	2.5020	-1.70	.0940	.0446	1.7183
-2.48	.0184	.0066	2.4821	-1.68	.0973	.0465	1.6992
-2.46	.0194	.0069	2.4623	-1.66	.1006	.0485	1.6801
-2.44	.0203	.0073	2.4424	-1.64	.1040	.0505	1.6611
-2.42	.0213	.0078	2.4226	-1.62	.1074	.0526	1.6422
-2.40	.0224	.0082	2.4027	-1.60	.1109	.0548	1.6232
-2.38	.0235	.0087	2.3829	-1.58	.1145	.0571	1.6044
-2.36	.0246	.0091	2.3631	-1.56	.1182	.0594	1.5855
-2.34	.0258	.0096	2.3433	-1.54	.1219	.0618	1.5667
-2.32	.0270	.0102	2.3235	-1.52	.1257	.0643	1.5480
-2.30	.0283	.0107	2.3037	-1.50	.1295	.0668	1.5293
-2.28	.0297	.0113	2.2839	-1.48	.1334	.0694	1.5107
-2.26	.0310	.0119	2.2641	-1.46	.1374	.0721	1.4921
-2.24	.0325	.0125	2.2444	-1.44	.1415	.0749	1.4736
-2.22	.0339	.0132	2.2246	-1.42	.1456	.0778	1.4551

k	f(k)	F(k)	E(k)	k	f(k)	F(k)	E(k)
-1.40	.1497	.0808	1.4367	-.60	.3332	.2743	.7687
-1.38	.1539	.0838	1.4183	-.58	.3372	.2810	.7542
-1.36	.1582	.0869	1.4000	-.56	.3410	.2877	.7399
-1.34	.1626	.0901	1.3818	-.54	.3448	.2946	.7257
-1.32	.1669	.0934	1.3636	-.52	.3485	.3015	.7117
-1.30	.1714	.0968	1.3455	-.50	.3521	.3085	.6978
-1.28	.1758	.1003	1.3275	-.48	.3555	.3156	.6840
-1.26	.1804	.1038	1.3095	-.46	.3589	.3228	.6704
-1.24	.1849	.1075	1.2917	-.44	.3621	.3300	.6569
-1.22	.1895	.1112	1.2738	-.42	.3653	.3372	.6436
-1.20	.1942	.1151	1.2561	-.40	.3683	.3446	.6304
-1.18	.1989	.1190	1.2384	-.38	.3712	.3520	.6174
-1.16	.2036	.1230	1.2209	-.36	.3739	.3594	.6045
-1.14	.2083	.1271	1.2034	-.34	.3765	.3669	.5918
-1.12	.2131	.1314	1.1859	-.32	.3790	.3745	.5792
-1.10	.2179	.1357	1.1686	-.30	.3814	.3821	.5668
-1.08	.2227	.1401	1.1514	-.28	.3836	.3897	.5545
-1.06	.2275	.1446	1.1342	-.26	.3857	.3974	.5424
-1.04	.2323	.1492	1.1172	-.24	.3876	.4052	.5304
-1.02	.2371	.1539	1.1002	-.22	.3894	.4129	.5186
-1.00	.2420	.1587	1.0833	-.20	.3910	.4207	.5069
-.98	.2468	.1635	1.0665	-.18	.3925	.4286	.4954
-.96	.2516	.1685	1.0499	-.16	.3939	.4364	.4840
-.94	.2565	.1736	1.0333	-.14	.3951	.4443	.4728
-.92	.2613	.1788	1.0168	-.12	.3961	.4522	.4618
-.90	.2661	.1841	1.0004	-.10	.3970	.4602	.4509
-.88	.2709	.1894	.9842	-.08	.3977	.4681	.4402
-.86	.2756	.1949	.9680	-.06	.3982	.4761	.4297
-.84	.2803	.2005	.9520	-.04	.3986	.4840	.4193
-.82	.2850	.2061	.9360	-.02	.3989	.4920	.4090
-.80	.2897	.2119	.9202	.00	.3989	.5000	.3989
-.78	.2943	.2177	.9045	.02	.3989	.5080	.3890
-.76	.2989	.2236	.8889	.04	.3986	.5160	.3793
-.74	.3034	.2296	.8734	.06	.3982	.5239	.3697
-.72	.3079	.2358	.8581	.08	.3977	.5319	.3602
-.70	.3123	.2420	.8429	.10	.3970	.5398	.3509
-.68	.3166	.2483	.8278	.12	.3961	.5478	.3418
-.66	.3209	.2546	.8128	.14	.3951	.5557	.3328
-.64	.3251	.2611	.7980	.16	.3939	.5636	.3240
-.62	.3292	.2676	.7833	.18	.3925	.5714	.3154

k	f(k)	F(k)	E(k)	k	f(k)	F(k)	E(k)
.20	.3910	.5793	.3069	1.00	.2420	.8413	.0833
.22	.3894	.5871	.2986	1.02	.2371	.8461	.0802
.24	.3876	.5948	.2904	1.04	.2323	.8508	.0772
.26	.3857	.6026	.2824	1.06	.2275	.8554	.0742
.28	.3836	.6103	.2745	1.08	.2227	.8599	.0714
.30	.3814	.6179	.2668	1.10	.2179	.8643	.0686
.32	.3790	.6255	.2592	1.12	.2131	.8686	.0659
.34	.3765	.6331	.2518	1.14	.2083	.8729	.0634
.36	.3739	.6406	.2445	1.16	.2036	.8770	.0609
.38	.3712	.6480	.2374	1.18	.1989	.8810	.0584
.40	.3683	.6554	.2304	1.20	.1942	.8849	.0561
.42	.3653	.6628	.2236	1.22	.1895	.8888	.0538
.44	.3621	.6700	.2169	1.24	.1849	.8925	.0517
.46	.3589	.6772	.2104	1.26	.1804	.8962	.0495
.48	.3555	.6844	.2040	1.28	.1758	.8997	.0475
.50	.3521	.6915	.1978	1.30	.1714	.9032	.0455
.52	.3485	.6985	.1917	1.32	.1669	.9066	.0436
.54	.3448	.7054	.1857	1.34	.1626	.9099	.0418
.56	.3410	.7123	.1799	1.36	.1582	.9131	.0400
.58	.3372	.7190	.1742	1.38	.1539	.9162	.0383
.60	.3332	.7257	.1687	1.40	.1497	.9192	.0367
.62	.3292	.7324	.1633	1.42	.1456	.9222	.0351
.64	.3251	.7389	.1580	1.44	.1415	.9251	.0336
.66	.3209	.7454	.1528	1.46	.1374	.9279	.0321
.68	.3166	.7517	.1478	1.48	.1334	.9306	.0307
.70	.3123	.7580	.1429	1.50	.1295	.9332	.0293
.72	.3079	.7642	.1381	1.52	.1257	.9357	.0280
.74	.3034	.7704	.1334	1.54	.1219	.9382	.0267
.76	.2989	.7764	.1289	1.56	.1182	.9406	.0255
.78	.2943	.7823	.1245	1.58	.1145	.9429	.0244
.80	.2897	.7881	.1202	1.60	.1109	.9452	.0232
.82	.2850	.7939	.1160	1.62	.1074	.9474	.0222
.84	.2803	.7995	.1120	1.64	.1040	.9495	.0211
.86	.2756	.8051	.1080	1.66	.1006	.9515	.0201
.88	.2709	.8106	.1042	1.68	.0973	.9535	.0192
.90	.2661	.8159	.1004	1.70	.0940	.9554	.0183
.92	.2613	.8212	.0968	1.72	.0909	.9573	.0174
.94	.2565	.8264	.0933	1.74	.0878	.9591	.0166
.96	.2516	.8315	.0899	1.76	.0848	.9608	.0158
.98	.2468	.8365	.0865	1.78	.0818	.9625	.0150

k	f(k)	F(k)	E(k)	k	f(k)	F(k)	E(k)
1.80	.0790	.9641	.0143	2.40	.0224	.9918	.0027
1.82	.0761	.9656	.0136	2.42	.0213	.9922	.0026
1.84	.0734	.9671	.0129	2.44	.0203	.9927	.0024
1.86	.0707	.9686	.0123	2.46	.0194	.9931	.0023
1.88	.0681	.9699	.0116	2.48	.0184	.9934	.0021
1.90	.0656	.9713	.0111	2.50	.0175	.9938	.0020
1.92	.0632	.9726	.0105	2.52	.0167	.9941	.0019
1.94	.0608	.9738	.0100	2.54	.0158	.9945	.0018
1.96	.0584	.9750	.0094	2.56	.0151	.9948	.0017
1.98	.0562	.9761	.0090	2.58	.0143	.9951	.0016
2.00	.0540	.9772	.0085	2.60	.0136	.9953	.0015
2.02	.0519	.9783	.0080	2.62	.0129	.9956	.0014
2.04	.0498	.9793	.0076	2.64	.0122	.9959	.0013
2.06	.0478	.9803	.0072	2.66	.0116	.9961	.0012
2.08	.0459	.9812	.0068	2.68	.0110	.9963	.0011
2.10	.0440	.9821	.0065	2.70	.0104	.9965	.0011
2.12	.0422	.9830	.0061	2.72	.0099	.9967	.0010
2.14	.0404	.9838	.0058	2.74	.0093	.9969	.0009
2.16	.0387	.9846	.0055	2.76	.0088	.9971	.0009
2.18	.0371	.9854	.0052	2.78	.0084	.9973	.0008
2.20	.0355	.9861	.0049	2.80	.0079	.9974	.0008
2.22	.0339	.9868	.0046	2.82	.0075	.9976	.0007
2.24	.0325	.9875	.0044	2.84	.0071	.9977	.0007
2.26	.0310	.9881	.0041	2.86	.0067	.9979	.0006
2.28	.0297	.9887	.0039	2.88	.0063	.9980	.0006
2.30	.0283	.9893	.0037	2.90	.0060	.9981	.0005
2.32	.0270	.9898	.0035	2.92	.0056	.9982	.0005
2.34	.0258	.9904	.0033	2.94	.0053	.9984	.0005
2.36	.0246	.9909	.0031	2.96	.0050	.9985	.0004
2.38	.0235	.9913	.0029	2.98	.0047	.9986	.0004
				3.00	.0044	.9987	.0004

Table 7.2   E(k) of the Standard Normal Distribution and Related Measures

E(k)	k	F(k)	f(k)	E(k)	k	F(k)	f(k)
.002	2.5049	.9939	.0173	.102	.8917	.8137	.2681
.004	2.2691	.9884	.0304	.104	.8811	.8109	.2706
.006	2.1257	.9832	.0417	.106	.8706	.8080	.2731
.008	2.0206	.9783	.0518	.108	.8602	.8052	.2756
.010	1.9369	.9736	.0611	.110	.8500	.8024	.2780
.012	1.8668	.9690	.0698	.112	.8400	.7995	.2803
.014	1.8063	.9646	.0781	.114	.8301	.7968	.2827
.016	1.7529	.9602	.0858	.116	.8204	.7940	.2850
.018	1.7053	.9559	.0932	.118	.8107	.7912	.2872
.020	1.6619	.9517	.1003	.120	.8012	.7885	.2894
.022	1.6221	.9476	.1070	.122	.7918	.7858	.2916
.024	1.5854	.9436	.1135	.124	.7825	.7831	.2937
.026	1.5511	.9396	.1198	.126	.7734	.7804	.2958
.028	1.5191	.9356	.1258	.128	.7643	.7777	.2979
.030	1.4890	.9318	.1317	.130	.7554	.7750	.2999
.032	1.4604	.9279	.1373	.132	.7466	.7723	.3019
.034	1.4334	.9241	.1428	.134	.7378	.7697	.3039
.036	1.4077	.9204	.1481	.136	.7292	.7671	.3058
.038	1.3832	.9167	.1533	.138	.7207	.7644	.3077
.040	1.3597	.9130	.1583	.140	.7123	.7618	.3096
.042	1.3372	.9094	.1632	.142	.7039	.7593	.3114
.044	1.3156	.9058	.1679	.144	.6956	.7567	.3132
.046	1.2947	.9023	.1725	.146	.6875	.7541	.3150
.048	1.2747	.8988	.1770	.148	.6794	.7516	.3167
.050	1.2553	.8953	.1815	.150	.6714	.7490	.3184
.052	1.2365	.8919	.1857	.152	.6635	.7465	.3201
.054	1.2183	.8884	.1899	.154	.6556	.7440	.3218
.056	1.2006	.8851	.1940	.156	.6478	.7415	.3234
.058	1.1835	.8817	.1980	.158	.6401	.7390	.3250
.060	1.1669	.8784	.2019	.160	.6325	.7365	.3266
.062	1.1507	.8751	.2058	.162	.6250	.7340	.3282
.064	1.1349	.8718	.2095	.164	.6175	.7315	.3297
.066	1.1195	.8685	.2132	.166	.6101	.7291	.3312
.068	1.1045	.8653	.2168	.168	.6027	.7267	.3327
.070	1.0899	.8621	.2203	.170	.5954	.7242	.3341
.072	1.0755	.8589	.2237	.172	.5882	.7218	.3356
.074	1.0615	.8558	.2271	.174	.5811	.7194	.3370
.076	1.0478	.8526	.2304	.176	.5740	.7170	.3384
.078	1.0344	.8495	.2336	.178	.5669	.7146	.3397
.080	1.0213	.8464	.2368	.180	.5599	.7122	.3411
.082	1.0084	.8434	.2399	.182	.5530	.7099	.3424
.084	.9958	.8403	.2430	.184	.5462	.7075	.3437
.086	.9834	.8373	.2460	.186	.5394	.7052	.3449
.088	.9712	.8343	.2489	.188	.5326	.7028	.3462
.090	.9593	.8313	.2518	.190	.5259	.7005	.3474
.092	.9475	.8283	.2547	.192	.5192	.6982	.3486
.094	.9360	.8254	.2574	.194	.5126	.6959	.3498
.096	.9246	.8224	.2602	.196	.5061	.6936	.3510
.098	.9135	.8195	.2629	.198	.4996	.6913	.3521
.100	.9025	.8166	.2655	.200	.4931	.6890	.3533

Table 7.2   E(k) of the Standard Normal Distribution and Related Measures
(Continued)

E(k)	k	F(k)	f(k)	E(k)	k	F(k)	f(k)
.202	.4867	.6868	.3544	.302	.2118	.5839	.3901
.204	.4804	.6845	.3555	.304	.2070	.5820	.3905
.206	.4740	.6823	.3565	.306	.2022	.5801	.3909
.208	.4678	.6800	.3576	.308	.1974	.5783	.3912
.210	.4615	.6778	.3586	.310	.1927	.5764	.3916
.212	.4553	.6756	.3597	.312	.1880	.5746	.3920
.214	.4492	.6734	.3607	.314	.1833	.5727	.3923
.216	.4431	.6712	.3616	.316	.1786	.5709	.3926
.218	.4370	.6690	.3626	.318	.1740	.5691	.3929
.220	.4310	.6668	.3636	.320	.1693	.5672	.3933
.222	.4250	.6646	.3645	.322	.1647	.5654	.3936
.224	.4191	.6624	.3654	.324	.1601	.5636	.3939
.226	.4132	.6603	.3663	.326	.1556	.5618	.3941
.228	.4073	.6581	.3672	.328	.1510	.5600	.3944
.230	.4015	.6560	.3681	.330	.1465	.5582	.3947
.232	.3957	.6538	.3689	.332	.1419	.5564	.3949
.234	.3899	.6517	.3697	.334	.1374	.5547	.3952
.236	.3842	.6496	.3706	.336	.1330	.5529	.3954
.238	.3785	.6475	.3714	.338	.1285	.5511	.3957
.240	.3728	.6454	.3722	.340	.1240	.5494	.3959
.242	.3672	.6433	.3729	.342	.1196	.5476	.3961
.244	.3616	.6412	.3737	.344	.1152	.5459	.3963
.246	.3561	.6391	.3744	.346	.1108	.5441	.3965
.248	.3505	.6370	.3752	.348	.1064	.5424	.3967
.250	.3450	.6350	.3759	.350	.1021	.5406	.3969
.252	.3396	.6329	.3766	.352	.0977	.5389	.3970
.254	.3341	.6309	.3773	.354	.0934	.5372	.3972
.256	.3287	.6288	.3780	.356	.0891	.5355	.3974
.258	.3233	.6268	.3786	.358	.0848	.5338	.3975
.260	.3180	.6248	.3793	.360	.0805	.5321	.3977
.262	.3127	.6227	.3799	.362	.0762	.5304	.3978
.264	.3074	.6207	.3805	.364	.0720	.5287	.3979
.266	.3021	.6187	.3811	.366	.0677	.5270	.3980
.268	.2969	.6167	.3817	.368	.0635	.5253	.3981
.270	.2917	.6147	.3823	.370	.0593	.5236	.3982
.272	.2865	.6128	.3829	.372	.0551	.5220	.3983
.274	.2814	.6108	.3835	.374	.0509	.5203	.3984
.276	.2762	.6088	.3840	.376	.0468	.5187	.3985
.278	.2711	.6069	.3845	.378	.0426	.5170	.3986
.280	.2660	.6049	.3851	.380	.0385	.5153	.3986
.282	.2610	.6030	.3856	.382	.0344	.5137	.3987
.284	.2560	.6010	.3861	.384	.0303	.5121	.3988
.286	.2510	.5991	.3866	.386	.0262	.5104	.3988
.288	.2460	.5972	.3871	.388	.0221	.5088	.3988
.290	.2410	.5952	.3875	.390	.0180	.5072	.3989
.292	.2361	.5933	.3880	.392	.0140	.5056	.3989
.294	.2312	.5914	.3884	.394	.0099	.5040	.3989
.296	.2263	.5895	.3889	.396	.0059	.5024	.3989
.298	.2214	.5876	.3893	.398	.0019	.5008	.3989
.300	.2166	.5857	.3897	.400	-.0021	.4992	.3989

Table 7.2 E(k) of the Standard Normal Distribution and Related Measures (Continued)

E(k)	k	F(k)	f(k)	E(k)	k	F(k)	f(k)
.413	-0.0278	.4889	.3988	1.063	-0.9758	.1646	.2478
.426	-0.0530	.4789	.3984	1.076	-0.9913	.1608	.2441
.439	-0.0777	.4690	.3977	1.089	-1.0067	.1570	.2403
.452	-0.1019	.4594	.3969	1.102	-1.0221	.1534	.2366
.465	-0.1258	.4500	.3958	1.115	-1.0375	.1498	.2329
.478	-0.1492	.4407	.3945	1.128	-1.0527	.1462	.2292
.491	-0.1723	.4316	.3931	1.141	-1.0679	.1428	.2256
.504	-0.1949	.4227	.3914	1.154	-1.0831	.1394	.2219
.517	-0.2173	.4140	.3896	1.167	-1.0981	.1361	.2183
.530	-0.2393	.4054	.3877	1.180	-1.1132	.1328	.2147
.543	-0.2610	.3970	.3856	1.193	-1.1281	.1296	.2111
.556	-0.2824	.3888	.3833	1.206	-1.1430	.1265	.2076
.569	-0.3035	.3807	.3810	1.219	-1.1579	.1235	.2041
.582	-0.3244	.3728	.3785	1.232	-1.1727	.1205	.2006
.595	-0.3450	.3651	.3759	1.245	-1.1875	.1175	.1971
.608	-0.3653	.3574	.3732	1.258	-1.2022	.1146	.1937
.621	-0.3854	.3500	.3704	1.271	-1.2168	.1118	.1903
.634	-0.4053	.3426	.3675	1.284	-1.2315	.1091	.1869
.647	-0.4250	.3354	.3645	1.297	-1.2460	.1064	.1836
.660	-0.4444	.3284	.3614	1.310	-1.2606	.1037	.1802
.673	-0.4637	.3214	.3583	1.323	-1.2750	.1011	.1770
.686	-0.4828	.3146	.3551	1.336	-1.2895	.0986	.1737
.699	-0.5016	.3080	.3518	1.349	-1.3039	.0961	.1705
.712	-0.5203	.3014	.3484	1.362	-1.3182	.0937	.1673
.725	-0.5389	.2950	.3450	1.375	-1.3326	.0913	.1642
.738	-0.5572	.2887	.3416	1.388	-1.3469	.0890	.1611
.751	-0.5754	.2825	.3381	1.401	-1.3611	.0867	.1580
.764	-0.5935	.2764	.3345	1.414	-1.3753	.0845	.1549
.777	-0.6113	.2705	.3309	1.427	-1.3895	.0823	.1519
.790	-0.6291	.2646	.3273	1.440	-1.4037	.0802	.1490
.803	-0.6467	.2589	.3237	1.453	-1.4178	.0781	.1460
.816	-0.6642	.2533	.3200	1.466	-1.4319	.0761	.1431
.829	-0.6815	.2478	.3163	1.479	-1.4459	.0741	.1403
.842	-0.6988	.2424	.3125	1.492	-1.4600	.0721	.1374
.855	-0.7159	.2370	.3088	1.505	-1.4740	.0702	.1346
.868	-0.7328	.2318	.3050	1.518	-1.4879	.0684	.1319
.881	-0.7497	.2267	.3012	1.531	-1.5019	.0666	.1292
.894	-0.7665	.2217	.2974	1.544	-1.5158	.0648	.1265
.907	-0.7831	.2168	.2936	1.557	-1.5297	.0630	.1238
.920	-0.7997	.2119	.2898	1.570	-1.5435	.0614	.1212
.933	-0.8161	.2072	.2859	1.583	-1.5574	.0597	.1186
.946	-0.8325	.2026	.2821	1.596	-1.5712	.0581	.1161
.959	-0.8487	.1980	.2783	1.609	-1.5850	.0565	.1136
.972	-0.8649	.1935	.2745	1.622	-1.5987	.0549	.1111
.985	-0.8810	.1892	.2706	1.635	-1.6125	.0534	.1087
.998	-0.8970	.1849	.2668	1.648	-1.6262	.0520	.1063
1.011	-0.9129	.1806	.2630	1.661	-1.6399	.0505	.1040
1.024	-0.9287	.1765	.2592	1.674	-1.6536	.0491	.1017
1.037	-0.9445	.1725	.2554	1.687	-1.6673	.0477	.0994
1.050	-0.9601	.1685	.2516	1.700	-1.6809	.0464	.0971

Table 7.2   E(k) of the Standard Normal Distribution and Related Measures
(Continued)

E(k)	k	F(k)	f(k)	E(k)	k	F(k)	f(k)
1.713	-1.6945	.0451	.0949	2.363	-2.3599	.0091	.0246
1.726	-1.7081	.0438	.0928	2.376	-2.3730	.0088	.0239
1.739	-1.7217	.0426	.0906	2.389	-2.3862	.0085	.0231
1.752	-1.7353	.0413	.0885	2.402	-2.3993	.0082	.0224
1.765	-1.7488	.0402	.0865	2.415	-2.4124	.0079	.0217
1.778	-1.7624	.0390	.0844	2.428	-2.4255	.0076	.0211
1.791	-1.7759	.0379	.0824	2.441	-2.4386	.0074	.0204
1.804	-1.7894	.0368	.0805	2.454	-2.4517	.0071	.0198
1.817	-1.8029	.0357	.0785	2.467	-2.4648	.0069	.0191
1.830	-1.8164	.0347	.0766	2.480	-2.4778	.0066	.0185
1.843	-1.8298	.0336	.0748	2.493	-2.4909	.0064	.0179
1.856	-1.8433	.0326	.0730	2.506	-2.5040	.0061	.0174
1.869	-1.8567	.0317	.0712	2.519	-2.5171	.0059	.0168
1.882	-1.8701	.0307	.0694	2.532	-2.5302	.0057	.0162
1.895	-1.8835	.0298	.0677	2.545	-2.5432	.0055	.0157
1.908	-1.8969	.0289	.0660	2.558	-2.5563	.0053	.0152
1.921	-1.9103	.0280	.0643	2.571	-2.5694	.0051	.0147
1.934	-1.9237	.0272	.0627	2.584	-2.5825	.0049	.0142
1.947	-1.9370	.0264	.0611	2.597	-2.5955	.0047	.0137
1.960	-1.9504	.0256	.0596	2.610	-2.6086	.0045	.0133
1.973	-1.9637	.0248	.0580	2.623	-2.6216	.0044	.0128
1.986	-1.9770	.0240	.0565	2.636	-2.6346	.0042	.0124
1.999	-1.9903	.0233	.0550	2.649	-2.6477	.0041	.0120
2.012	-2.0036	.0226	.0536	2.662	-2.6607	.0039	.0116
2.025	-2.0169	.0219	.0522	2.675	-2.6738	.0038	.0112
2.038	-2.0302	.0212	.0508	2.688	-2.6868	.0036	.0108
2.051	-2.0435	.0205	.0494	2.701	-2.6999	.0035	.0104
2.064	-2.0568	.0199	.0481	2.714	-2.7129	.0033	.0101
2.077	-2.0700	.0192	.0468	2.727	-2.7260	.0032	.0097
2.090	-2.0833	.0186	.0456	2.740	-2.7390	.0031	.0094
2.103	-2.0965	.0180	.0443	2.753	-2.7521	.0030	.0090
2.116	-2.1097	.0174	.0431	2.766	-2.7651	.0028	.0087
2.129	-2.1230	.0169	.0419	2.779	-2.7782	.0027	.0084
2.142	-2.1362	.0163	.0407	2.792	-2.7912	.0026	.0081
2.155	-2.1494	.0158	.0396	2.805	-2.8043	.0025	.0078
2.168	-2.1626	.0153	.0385	2.818	-2.8173	.0024	.0075
2.181	-2.1758	.0148	.0374	2.831	-2.8303	.0023	.0073
2.194	-2.1890	.0143	.0363	2.844	-2.8433	.0022	.0070
2.207	-2.2022	.0138	.0353	2.857	-2.8564	.0021	.0067
2.220	-2.2153	.0134	.0343	2.870	-2.8694	.0021	.0065
2.233	-2.2285	.0129	.0333	2.883	-2.8824	.0020	.0063
2.246	-2.2417	.0125	.0323	2.896	-2.8954	.0019	.0060
2.259	-2.2548	.0121	.0314	2.909	-2.9085	.0018	.0058
2.272	-2.2680	.0117	.0305	2.922	-2.9215	.0017	.0056
2.285	-2.2811	.0113	.0296	2.935	-2.9345	.0017	.0054
2.298	-2.2943	.0109	.0287	2.948	-2.9475	.0016	.0052
2.311	-2.3074	.0105	.0278	2.961	-2.9605	.0015	.0050
2.324	-2.3206	.0102	.0270	2.974	-2.9736	.0015	.0048
2.337	-2.3337	.0098	.0262	2.987	-2.9866	.0014	.0046
2.350	-2.3468	.0095	.0254	3.000	-2.9996	.0014	.0044

Table 7.3 F(k) of the Standard Normal Distribution and Related Measures

F(k)	k	f(k)	E(k)	F(k)	k	f(k)	E(k)
.005	-2.5762	.0144	2.5778	.255	-.6585	.3212	.8118
.010	-2.3268	.0266	2.3301	.260	-.6430	.3244	.8003
.015	-2.1705	.0378	2.1758	.265	-.6277	.3276	.7890
.020	-2.0542	.0484	2.0615	.270	-.6125	.3307	.7778
.025	-1.9604	.0584	1.9698	.275	-.5974	.3337	.7669
.030	-1.8812	.0680	1.8928	.280	-.5825	.3367	.7561
.035	-1.8123	.0772	1.8261	.285	-.5677	.3396	.7455
.040	-1.7511	.0861	1.7671	.290	-.5530	.3424	.7350
.045	-1.6958	.0947	1.7142	.295	-.5384	.3451	.7247
.050	-1.6452	.1031	1.6660	.300	-.5240	.3478	.7146
.055	-1.5985	.1112	1.6218	.305	-.5097	.3504	.7046
.060	-1.5551	.1191	1.5809	.310	-.4954	.3529	.6947
.065	-1.5144	.1267	1.5427	.315	-.4813	.3553	.6850
.070	-1.4761	.1342	1.5070	.320	-.4673	.3577	.6754
.075	-1.4398	.1415	1.4733	.325	-.4533	.3600	.6660
.080	-1.4053	.1486	1.4415	.330	-.4395	.3622	.6567
.085	-1.3724	.1556	1.4113	.335	-.4257	.3644	.6475
.090	-1.3410	.1623	1.3826	.340	-.4120	.3665	.6384
.095	-1.3108	.1690	1.3552	.345	-.3984	.3685	.6295
.100	-1.2817	.1755	1.3290	.350	-.3849	.3705	.6206
.105	-1.2537	.1818	1.3039	.355	-.3714	.3724	.6119
.110	-1.2267	.1880	1.2797	.360	-.3580	.3742	.6033
.115	-1.2005	.1941	1.2565	.365	-.3447	.3759	.5948
.120	-1.1751	.2000	1.2341	.370	-.3314	.3776	.5864
.125	-1.1504	.2058	1.2125	.375	-.3182	.3792	.5781
.130	-1.1265	.2115	1.1915	.380	-.3050	.3808	.5699
.135	-1.1031	.2171	1.1713	.385	-.2919	.3823	.5618
.140	-1.0804	.2226	1.1517	.390	-.2789	.3837	.5538
.145	-1.0581	.2279	1.1326	.395	-.2659	.3851	.5459
.150	-1.0364	.2332	1.1141	.400	-.2529	.3864	.5381
.155	-1.0152	.2383	1.0961	.405	-.2400	.3876	.5304
.160	-.9944	.2433	1.0786	.410	-.2271	.3888	.5228
.165	-.9741	.2482	1.0616	.415	-.2143	.3899	.5153
.170	-.9541	.2531	1.0450	.420	-.2015	.3909	.5078
.175	-.9345	.2578	1.0288	.425	-.1888	.3919	.5004
.180	-.9153	.2624	1.0129	.430	-.1760	.3928	.4931
.185	-.8964	.2670	.9975	.435	-.1633	.3937	.4859
.190	-.8778	.2714	.9824	.440	-.1507	.3944	.4788
.195	-.8595	.2757	.9676	.445	-.1380	.3952	.4718
.200	-.8415	.2800	.9532	.450	-.1254	.3958	.4648
.205	-.8237	.2842	.9390	.455	-.1128	.3964	.4579
.210	-.8062	.2882	.9252	.460	-.1002	.3969	.4511
.215	-.7890	.2922	.9116	.465	-.0876	.3974	.4443
.220	-.7720	.2961	.8983	.470	-.0751	.3978	.4376
.225	-.7552	.3000	.8852	.475	-.0625	.3982	.4310
.230	-.7386	.3037	.8724	.480	-.0500	.3984	.4245
.235	-.7222	.3074	.8599	.485	-.0375	.3987	.4180
.240	-.7060	.3109	.8475	.490	-.0250	.3988	.4116
.245	-.6900	.3144	.8354	.495	-.0125	.3989	.4052
.250	-.6742	.3178	.8235	.500	-.0000	.3989	.3989

Table 7.3   F(k) of the Standard Normal Distribution and Related Measures
(Continued)

F(k)	k	f(k)	E(k)	F(k)	k	f(k)	E(k)
.505	.0125	.3989	.3927	.755	.6900	.3144	.1454
.510	.0250	.3988	.3866	.760	.7060	.3109	.1415
.515	.0375	.3987	.3805	.765	.7222	.3074	.1376
.520	.0500	.3984	.3744	.770	.7386	.3037	.1338
.525	.0625	.3982	.3685	.775	.7552	.3000	.1301
.530	.0751	.3978	.3625	.780	.7720	.2961	.1263
.535	.0876	.3974	.3567	.785	.7890	.2922	.1226
.540	.1002	.3969	.3509	.790	.8062	.2882	.1189
.545	.1128	.3964	.3451	.795	.8237	.2842	.1153
.550	.1254	.3958	.3394	.800	.8415	.2800	.1117
.555	.1380	.3952	.3337	.805	.8595	.2757	.1081
.560	.1507	.3944	.3282	.810	.8778	.2714	.1046
.565	.1633	.3937	.3226	.815	.8964	.2670	.1011
.570	.1760	.3928	.3171	.820	.9153	.2624	.0977
.575	.1888	.3919	.3117	.825	.9345	.2578	.0943
.580	.2015	.3909	.3063	.830	.9541	.2531	.0909
.585	.2143	.3899	.3009	.835	.9741	.2482	.0875
.590	.2271	.3888	.2957	.840	.9944	.2433	.0842
.595	.2400	.3876	.2904	.845	1.0152	.2383	.0809
.600	.2529	.3864	.2852	.850	1.0364	.2332	.0777
.605	.2659	.3851	.2801	.855	1.0581	.2279	.0745
.610	.2789	.3837	.2750	.860	1.0804	.2226	.0713
.615	.2919	.3823	.2699	.865	1.1031	.2171	.0682
.620	.3050	.3808	.2649	.870	1.1265	.2115	.0651
.625	.3182	.3792	.2599	.875	1.1504	.2058	.0620
.630	.3314	.3776	.2550	.880	1.1751	.2000	.0590
.635	.3447	.3759	.2501	.885	1.2005	.1941	.0560
.640	.3580	.3742	.2453	.890	1.2267	.1880	.0531
.645	.3714	.3724	.2405	.895	1.2537	.1818	.0502
.650	.3849	.3705	.2358	.900	1.2817	.1755	.0473
.655	.3984	.3685	.2311	.905	1.3108	.1690	.0445
.660	.4120	.3665	.2264	.910	1.3410	.1623	.0417
.665	.4257	.3644	.2218	.915	1.3724	.1556	.0389
.670	.4395	.3622	.2172	.920	1.4053	.1486	.0362
.675	.4533	.3600	.2127	.925	1.4398	.1415	.0335
.680	.4673	.3577	.2082	.930	1.4761	.1342	.0309
.685	.4813	.3553	.2037	.935	1.5144	.1267	.0283
.690	.4954	.3529	.1993	.940	1.5551	.1191	.0258
.695	.5097	.3504	.1949	.945	1.5985	.1112	.0233
.700	.5240	.3478	.1906	.950	1.6452	.1031	.0208
.705	.5384	.3451	.1863	.955	1.6958	.0947	.0184
.710	.5530	.3424	.1820	.960	1.7511	.0861	.0161
.715	.5677	.3396	.1778	.965	1.8123	.0772	.0138
.720	.5825	.3367	.1736	.970	1.8812	.0680	.0116
.725	.5974	.3337	.1695	.975	1.9604	.0584	.0094
.730	.6125	.3307	.1653	.980	2.0542	.0484	.0073
.735	.6277	.3276	.1613	.985	2.1705	.0378	.0053
.740	.6430	.3244	.1572	.990	2.3268	.0266	.0034
.745	.6585	.3212	.1533	.995	2.5762	.0144	.0016
.750	.6742	.3178	.1493				

CHAPTER 8

The Poisson Distribution

The Poisson probability distribution is applicable in many situations where observations occur over a unit of time or a unit of space (reference 1). Examples would include the number of customer demands for an item in a week, the number of customers arriving to a sales counter in ten minute intervals, the number of telephone calls to a store per minute, the number of flaws observed in a square yard of material and so on. The number of such observations may conveniently be labeled as **x**, which can occur in values of x = 0, 1, 2, . . . The average value of **x**, called the mean, here is labeled as *m*. With a particular mean *m*, probabilities can be determined for each possible **x**. The shape of the probability distribution varies depending on the mean value of **x**. When the mean increases to values of ten or larger, the shape begins to resemble a normal distribution.

The Probability Distribution

If **x** represents a random variable that has a Poisson distribution, **x** may then take on any integer value of zero or larger. The average (or mean) of **x** is denoted here as *m*, and the probability for a particular value of **x** to occur, i.e., **P(x)**, is determined by:

$$P(x) = e^{-m} m^x / x!$$

where e = 2.71828. The standard deviation of **x** (denoted as σ) turns out to be:

$$\sigma = \sqrt{m}$$

When values of **P(x)** are calculated, it is useful to apply the recursive relation shown below. First note that at x = 0, then:

$$P(0) = e^{-m}$$

and when x > 1, then **P(x)** is related to the probability of the preceding value of **x**, P(x − 1), by the relation:

$$P(x) = \frac{P(x-1)\, m}{x}$$

Table

Table 8.1 gives the values of **P(x)** for the mean values ranging from 0.10 to 10.0. For values larger than *m* = 10, approximations to the probabilities can be obtained using the normal distribution with a mean of *m* and a standard deviation of $\sigma = \sqrt{m}$.

Example 8.1

Suppose the demand on a particular brand refrigerator in a department store averages 1.4 per week. What is the probability of no demand in a week and for demands of 4 or more in a week.

By using Table 8.1 with $m = 1.4$, the probability of $x = 0$ is $P(0) = .247$. The probability for x greater or equal to 4 is:

$$P(x \geq 4) = .039 + .011 + .003 + .001 = .054$$

Example 8.2

For the refrigerator situation in Example 8.1, suppose the department store is open seven days a week and demands for the refrigerators are likely to be equal on any given day. Find the probability that a demand of one or more will occur on a given day.

As the average demand is 1.4 for one week (seven days), the average daily demand is $m = 1.4 / 7 = 0.2$, whereby Table 8.1 gives the probability:

$$P(x \geq 1) = .164 + .016 + .001 = .181$$

Example 8.3

The average demand for a popular sweater in a sporting goods store is 20 per week. The sweater comes in three sizes; on the average, 20 percent of the demands are for size small, 50 percent for size medium and 30 percent for size large. Find the number of sweaters to have—by size—at the start of the week in order to be at least 95 percent certain of filling all demands.

For size small, the average weekly demand is 20 percent of 20, which gives $m = 4$. Table 8.1 shows that 8 sweaters are needed, as $P(x > 8) = .013 + .005 + .002 + .001 = .021$, or, $P(x \leq 8) = 1 - .021 = .979$. Note that if seven sweaters are stocked, then $P(x > 7) = .051$ and $P(x \leq 7) = .949$, which falls short of the criterion.

For size medium, the average weekly demand is 50 percent of 20 or $m = 10$. Therefore, 15 sweaters should be stocked because $P(x > 15) = .049$ and $P(x \leq 15) = .951$.

For size large, the average weekly demand is 30 percent of 20 or $m = 6$. Table 8.1 shows that 10 sweaters should be stocked, since $P(x > 10) = .042$ and $P(x \leq 10) = .958$.

Example 8.4

Suppose the demand for a luxury car is 0.50 per week. If the car dealer keeps one such model in stock at the start of each week, find the probability that the demand for the week will exceed the supply of one. Also, find the average demand larger than 1.

First, Table 8.1 is used with $m = 0.50$ to give $P(x > 1) = .076 + .013 + .002 = .091$, which is the probability that the demand will exceed 1.

Second, the average demand larger than 1 is labeled as $E(x > 1)$, where:

$$E(x > 1) = (2 - 1)P(2) + (3 - 1)P(3) + (4 - 1)P(4)$$

that is,

$$E(x > 1) = 1(.076) + 2(.013) + 3(.002)$$

therefore,

$$E(x > 1) = .108$$

This average is also called the *partial expectation* and in this case represents the expected value of **x** larger than one. The above calculation shows that the average number of demands in a week larger than 1 is 0.108.

Table 8.1 Poisson Probability Distribution

x \ m	0.1	0.2	0.3	0.4	0.5	0.6	0.7	0.8	0.9	1.0
0	.905	.819	.741	.670	.607	.549	.497	.449	.407	.368
1	.090	.164	.222	.268	.303	.329	.348	.359	.366	.368
2	.005	.016	.033	.054	.076	.099	.122	.144	.165	.184
3		.001	.003	.007	.013	.020	.028	.038	.049	.061
4				.001	.002	.003	.005	.008	.011	.015
5							.001	.001	.002	.003
6										.001

x \ m	1.1	1.2	1.3	1.4	1.5	1.6	1.7	1.8	1.9	2.0
0	.333	.301	.273	.247	.223	.202	.183	.165	.150	.135
1	.366	.361	.354	.345	.335	.323	.311	.298	.284	.271
2	.201	.217	.230	.242	.251	.258	.264	.268	.270	.271
3	.074	.087	.100	.113	.126	.138	.150	.161	.171	.180
4	.020	.026	.032	.039	.047	.055	.064	.072	.081	.090
5	.004	.006	.008	.011	.014	.018	.022	.026	.031	.036
6	.001	.001	.002	.003	.004	.005	.006	.008	.010	.012
7				.001	.001	.001	.001	.002	.003	.003
8									.001	.001

x \ m	2.1	2.2	2.3	2.4	2.5	2.6	2.7	2.8	2.9	3.0
0	.122	.111	.100	.091	.082	.074	.067	.061	.055	.050
1	.257	.244	.231	.218	.205	.193	.181	.170	.160	.149
2	.270	.268	.265	.261	.257	.251	.245	.238	.231	.224
3	.189	.197	.203	.209	.214	.218	.220	.222	.224	.224
4	.099	.108	.117	.125	.134	.141	.149	.156	.162	.168
5	.042	.048	.054	.060	.067	.074	.080	.087	.094	.101
6	.015	.017	.021	.024	.028	.032	.036	.041	.045	.050
7	.004	.005	.007	.008	.010	.012	.014	.016	.019	.022
8	.001	.002	.002	.002	.003	.004	.005	.006	.007	.008
9				.001	.001	.001	.001	.002	.002	.003
10									.001	.001

x \ m	3.1	3.2	3.3	3.4	3.5	3.6	3.7	3.8	3.9	4.0
0	.045	.041	.037	.033	.030	.027	.025	.022	.020	.018
1	.140	.130	.122	.113	.106	.098	.091	.085	.079	.073
2	.216	.209	.201	.193	.185	.177	.169	.162	.154	.147
3	.224	.223	.221	.219	.216	.212	.209	.205	.200	.195
4	.173	.178	.182	.186	.189	.191	.193	.194	.195	.195
5	.107	.114	.120	.126	.132	.138	.143	.148	.152	.156
6	.056	.061	.066	.072	.077	.083	.088	.094	.099	.104
7	.025	.028	.031	.035	.039	.042	.047	.051	.055	.060
8	.010	.011	.013	.015	.017	.019	.022	.024	.027	.030
9	.003	.004	.005	.006	.007	.008	.009	.010	.012	.013
10	.001	.001	.002	.002	.002	.003	.003	.004	.005	.005
11				.001	.001	.001	.001	.001	.002	.002
12									.001	.001

Table 8.1   Poisson Probability Distribution   (Continued)

m / x	4.1	4.2	4.3	4.4	4.5	4.6	4.7	4.8	4.9	5.0
0	.017	.015	.014	.012	.011	.010	.009	.008	.007	.007
1	.068	.063	.058	.054	.050	.046	.043	.040	.036	.034
2	.139	.132	.125	.119	.112	.106	.100	.095	.089	.084
3	.190	.185	.180	.174	.169	.163	.157	.152	.146	.140
4	.195	.194	.193	.192	.190	.188	.185	.182	.179	.175
5	.160	.163	.166	.169	.171	.173	.174	.175	.175	.175
6	.109	.114	.119	.124	.128	.132	.136	.140	.143	.146
7	.064	.069	.073	.078	.082	.087	.091	.096	.100	.104
8	.033	.036	.039	.043	.046	.050	.054	.058	.061	.065
9	.015	.017	.019	.021	.023	.026	.028	.031	.033	.036
10	.006	.007	.008	.009	.010	.012	.013	.015	.016	.018
11	.002	.003	.003	.004	.004	.005	.006	.006	.007	.008
12	.001	.001	.001	.001	.002	.002	.002	.003	.003	.003
13					.001	.001	.001	.001	.001	.001

m / x	5.1	5.2	5.3	5.4	5.5	5.6	5.7	5.8	5.9	6.0
0	.006	.006	.005	.005	.004	.004	.003	.003	.003	.002
1	.031	.029	.026	.024	.022	.021	.019	.018	.016	.015
2	.079	.075	.070	.066	.062	.058	.054	.051	.048	.045
3	.135	.129	.124	.119	.113	.108	.103	.098	.094	.089
4	.172	.168	.164	.160	.156	.152	.147	.143	.138	.134
5	.175	.175	.174	.173	.171	.170	.168	.166	.163	.161
6	.149	.151	.154	.156	.157	.158	.159	.160	.160	.161
7	.109	.113	.116	.120	.123	.127	.130	.133	.135	.138
8	.069	.073	.077	.081	.085	.089	.092	.096	.100	.103
9	.039	.042	.045	.049	.052	.055	.059	.062	.065	.069
10	.020	.022	.024	.026	.029	.031	.033	.036	.039	.041
11	.009	.010	.012	.013	.014	.016	.017	.019	.021	.023
12	.004	.005	.005	.006	.007	.007	.008	.009	.010	.011
13	.002	.002	.002	.002	.003	.003	.004	.004	.005	.005
14	.001	.001	.001	.001	.001	.001	.001	.002	.002	.002
15							.001	.001	.001	.001

Table 8.1 Poisson Probability Distribution (Continued)

m	6.1	6.2	6.3	6.4	6.5	6.6	6.7	6.8	6.9	7.0
x										
0	.002	.002	.002	.002	.002	.001	.001	.001	.001	.001
1	.014	.013	.012	.011	.010	.009	.008	.008	.007	.006
2	.042	.039	.036	.034	.032	.030	.028	.026	.024	.022
3	.085	.081	.077	.073	.069	.065	.062	.058	.055	.052
4	.129	.125	.121	.116	.112	.108	.103	.099	.095	.091
5	.158	.155	.152	.149	.145	.142	.138	.135	.131	.128
6	.160	.160	.159	.159	.157	.156	.155	.153	.151	.149
7	.140	.142	.144	.145	.146	.147	.148	.149	.149	.149
8	.107	.110	.113	.116	.119	.121	.124	.126	.128	.130
9	.072	.076	.079	.082	.086	.089	.092	.095	.098	.101
10	.044	.047	.050	.053	.056	.059	.062	.065	.068	.071
11	.024	.026	.029	.031	.033	.035	.038	.040	.043	.045
12	.012	.014	.015	.016	.018	.019	.021	.023	.025	.026
13	.006	.007	.007	.008	.009	.010	.011	.012	.013	.014
14	.003	.003	.003	.004	.004	.005	.005	.006	.006	.007
15	.001	.001	.001	.002	.002	.002	.002	.003	.003	.003
16			.001	.001	.001	.001	.001	.001	.001	.001
17									.001	.001

m	7.1	7.2	7.3	7.4	7.5	7.6	7.7	7.8	7.9	8.0
x										
0	.001	.001	.001	.001	.001	.001				
1	.006	.005	.005	.005	.004	.004	.003	.003	.003	.003
2	.021	.019	.018	.017	.016	.014	.013	.012	.012	.011
3	.049	.046	.044	.041	.039	.037	.034	.032	.030	.029
4	.087	.084	.080	.076	.073	.070	.066	.063	.060	.057
5	.124	.120	.117	.113	.109	.106	.102	.099	.095	.092
6	.147	.144	.142	.139	.137	.134	.131	.128	.125	.122
7	.149	.149	.148	.147	.146	.145	.144	.143	.141	.140
8	.132	.134	.135	.136	.137	.138	.139	.139	.139	.140
9	.104	.107	.110	.112	.114	.117	.119	.121	.122	.124
10	.074	.077	.080	.083	.086	.089	.091	.094	.097	.099
11	.048	.050	.053	.056	.059	.061	.064	.067	.069	.072
12	.028	.030	.032	.034	.037	.039	.041	.043	.046	.048
13	.015	.017	.018	.020	.021	.023	.024	.026	.028	.030
14	.008	.009	.009	.010	.011	.012	.013	.015	.016	.017
15	.004	.004	.005	.005	.006	.006	.007	.008	.008	.009
16	.002	.002	.002	.002	.003	.003	.003	.004	.004	.005
17	.001	.001	.001	.001	.001	.001	.001	.002	.002	.002
18						.001	.001	.001	.001	.001

Table 8.1 Poisson Probability Distribution (Continued)

m	8.1	8.2	8.3	8.4	8.5	8.6	8.7	8.8	8.9	9.0
x										
0										
1	.002	.002	.002	.002	.002	.002	.001	.001	.001	.001
2	.010	.009	.009	.008	.007	.007	.006	.006	.005	.005
3	.027	.025	.024	.022	.021	.020	.018	.017	.016	.015
4	.054	.052	.049	.047	.044	.042	.040	.038	.036	.034
5	.088	.085	.082	.078	.075	.072	.069	.066	.063	.061
6	.119	.116	.113	.110	.107	.103	.100	.097	.094	.091
7	.138	.136	.134	.132	.129	.127	.125	.122	.120	.117
8	.140	.139	.139	.138	.138	.137	.136	.134	.133	.132
9	.126	.127	.128	.129	.130	.131	.131	.131	.132	.132
10	.102	.104	.106	.108	.110	.112	.114	.116	.117	.119
11	.075	.078	.080	.083	.085	.088	.090	.093	.095	.097
12	.051	.053	.055	.058	.060	.063	.065	.068	.070	.073
13	.031	.033	.035	.037	.040	.042	.044	.046	.048	.050
14	.018	.020	.021	.022	.024	.026	.027	.029	.031	.032
15	.010	.011	.012	.013	.014	.015	.016	.017	.018	.019
16	.005	.005	.006	.007	.007	.008	.009	.009	.010	.011
17	.002	.003	.003	.003	.004	.004	.004	.005	.005	.006
18	.001	.001	.001	.002	.002	.002	.002	.002	.003	.003
19		.001	.001	.001	.001	.001	.001	.001	.001	.001
20									.001	.001

m	9.1	9.2	9.3	9.4	9.5	9.6	9.7	9.8	9.9	10.0
x										
0										
1	.001	.001	.001	.001	.001	.001	.001	.001		
2	.005	.004	.004	.004	.003	.003	.003	.003	.002	.002
3	.014	.013	.012	.011	.011	.010	.009	.009	.008	.008
4	.032	.030	.028	.027	.025	.024	.023	.021	.020	.019
5	.058	.055	.053	.051	.048	.046	.044	.042	.040	.038
6	.088	.085	.082	.079	.076	.074	.071	.068	.066	.063
7	.114	.112	.109	.106	.104	.101	.098	.096	.093	.090
8	.130	.129	.127	.125	.123	.121	.119	.117	.115	.113
9	.132	.131	.131	.131	.130	.129	.128	.127	.126	.125
10	.120	.121	.122	.123	.124	.124	.125	.125	.125	.125
11	.099	.101	.103	.105	.107	.108	.110	.111	.113	.114
12	.075	.078	.080	.082	.084	.087	.089	.091	.093	.095
13	.053	.055	.057	.059	.062	.064	.066	.068	.071	.073
14	.034	.036	.038	.040	.042	.044	.046	.048	.050	.052
15	.021	.022	.024	.025	.027	.028	.030	.031	.033	.035
16	.012	.013	.014	.015	.016	.017	.018	.019	.020	.022
17	.006	.007	.007	.008	.009	.010	.010	.011	.012	.013
18	.003	.004	.004	.004	.005	.005	.006	.006	.007	.007
19	.002	.002	.002	.002	.002	.003	.003	.003	.003	.004
20	.001	.001	.001	.001	.001	.001	.001	.002	.002	.002
21						.001	.001	.001	.001	.001

CHAPTER 9

Safety Stock For A Desired Service Level

Safety stock for an item is the amount of stock housed in the inventory in the event it is needed to fill any demands that may occur above the forecast quantity. When all future demands are known in advance, such as in many production facilities, no safety stock is needed. In most retail and service parts facilities, however, future demands for items are not known in advance and the inventory planning is driven by a forecast of the future demands. The stock level for the item therefore depends on the economic order quantity and the safety stock. The amount of safety stock is derived from various information associated with the item, such as the forecast error, the lead time, the size of the order quantity and the desired service level.

The most common measure of forecast error is the standard deviation of the one period ahead error in the forecasts. This standard deviation can be obtained from tracking the history of the forecasts and the corresponding actual demands. The standard deviation is then projected over the lead time and is used to measure the total variation that is possible over the lead time duration. With the above information, statistical methods may be used to determine the minimum amount of safety stock that is necessary for the item in order to fulfill customer service goals set by management. The customer service goal is usually stated in terms of a desired service level.

The service level may be defined in various ways, depending on the way the inventory is used in the determination. For purposes of this chapter, the service level SL is the percent of the total demand that is filled from the available stock, i.e.:

$$SL = \frac{\text{demand filled from stock}}{\text{total demand}}$$

Generally a service level of 90 to 95 percent is acceptable to most managements, although the level may be set higher or lower for particular items depending on their value or use. In order to achieve the service level goals, the stock level must be continually in review and replenished whenever stock becomes dangerously low.

It is common to refer to the inventory for an item as the total stock TS, which is divided into two components called the cycle stock CS and the safety stock SS, i.e.:

$$TS = CS + SS$$

The cycle stock is set at a level that is consistent with an economical order quantity Q and where over time the average stock is $CS = Q/2$. The safety stock is planned in a precautionary manner to fill demands that rise above the average forecasts.

Safety stock plays a key role in yielding the service level sought. This chapter shows how the safety stock is determined for an item when a desired service level is specified (references 1, 2 and 3).

Data
The data required to determine the safety stock are the following:

$$SL = \text{desired service level}$$
$$F = \text{monthly forecast of demand}$$
$$\sigma = \text{standard deviation of the error in F}$$
$$L = \text{lead time}$$
$$Q = \text{order quantity}$$

Model
In order to determine the safety stock from the above data, it is helpful to study the relation (in Figure 9.1) that depicts the flow of inventory over time. At time t_1 the on-hand (OH) plus on-order (OO) inventory reaches the order point (OP) level, whereupon the quantity **Q** is ordered from the supplier. This quantity is not received until time t_2, which is a lead time beyond t_1, i.e., $t_2 = t_1 + L$. This process repeats as shown in the diagram, where the next order is placed at t_3 and is received at t_4. An order cycle represents the elapsed time between the receipts of two successive orders, such as between t_2 and t_4.

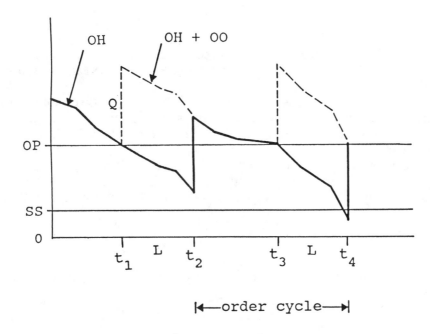

Figure 9.1. On-hand and on-order relations for a continuous review order-point system

Safety stock and order point quantities can be found using statistical methods to satisfy the particular service level desired for the item. Safety stock is found by the relation:

$$SS = k\,\sigma_L$$

where $\sigma_L = \sqrt{L}\,\sigma$ is the standard deviation of the lead time forecast error and **k** is called the safety factor. The order point is obtained as below:

$$OP = F_L + SS$$

where $F_L = L \times F$ is the lead time forecast. The objective is to find the appropriate value of **k** that yields the desired service level.

Over an order cycle, the expected demand is **Q**. If the lead time demand x_L exceeds the order point, a shortage occurs. The expected number of pieces short is denoted as $E(x_L > OP)$ and is obtained from the relation:

$$E(x_L > OP) = E(k)\,\sigma_L$$

where **E(k)** is the partial expectation (with table entries in Chapter 7). The service level becomes:

$$SL = 1 - \frac{\text{pieces short over the order cycle}}{\text{average demand over the order cycle}}$$

that is,

$$SL = 1 - E(x_L > OP) / Q$$

Thus, with σ_L, **Q** and **SL** known for an item, the partial expectation **E(k)** can be calculated as:

$$E(k) = \frac{(1 - SL)\,Q}{\sigma_L}$$

E(k) is now used in Table 7.2 to find the corresponding value of **k**. Hence, the safety stock ($SS = k\,\sigma_L$) and the order point ($OP = F_L + SS$) are determined for the item.

Note that **k** could be less than zero—resulting in a negative safety stock. When this situation occurs, the order point is set at a level that is less than the lead time forecast. In order to achieve the desired service level, only this quantity of the order point is needed. A usual practice is to set any negative safety stock to zero, and the result will be to achieve a service level larger than the desired service level. In the tables to follow, if the safety stock becomes negative, it is then set to zero; therefore, only positive safety stocks are listed.

Tables

In the adjoining tables of this chapter, the input data are normalized in the following manner. First, the coefficient of variation for one month of forecast demand is defined by:

$$cov = \sigma / F$$

Note that the smaller the coefficient of variation, the more accurate the forecasts. The tables show results when **cov** ranges from 0.10 (very accurate forecasts) to 1.0 (poor forecasts). Second, the order quantity in months of demand is determined by the relation:

$$M = Q / F$$

The safety stock listed in the tables is also standardized by finding the safety stock in months of demand **ss**. This is determined by:

$$ss = SS / F$$

For the following tables of this chapter, the lead time spans from one week to 12 months. Also, the months in the order quantity spans one week to 12 months, and the coefficient of variation ranges from 0.10 to 1.0. Each table pertains to a particular service level as listed below:

Table	SL (%)
9.1	85
9.2	90
9.3	92.5
9.4	95
9.5	97.5
9.6	99

In addition, Table 9.7 is developed and lists the months of safety stock when the coefficient of variation ranges from 0.30 to 0.50 and the service level spans from 0.90 to 0.99.

Just-in-Time Applications

Just-in-Time (JIT) methods concern the flow of materials that meets demands (as they occur) with the minimal amount of inventory. The goal is to eliminate waste where inventory is a key target. In most production facilities, demands on the facility are scheduled in advance and JIT has ample opportunity to be applied and can realize great potential in savings. In a distribution center type environment, the inventory is housed to meet uncertain levels of oncoming demands. The level of inventory to hold depends on forecasts of the demands; these forecasts subsequently yield the order quantity and the safety stock to meet a desired level of customer service. JIT methods are more difficult to apply in this latter environment, as advance demands are not known for certain. Nevertheless, the spirit of JIT is strong in such environments, and management continuously seeks methods of reducing inventories to a minimum and yet fulfilling customer service needs

Two levels of inventory may be singled out for reduction—cycle stock and safety stock. The cycle stock inventory is directly related to the order quantity, and the factors that allow reducing this stock are described in Chapters 2 to 4. In this chapter, the adjoining tables reveal how the safety stock may be lowered as the procurement lead time is reduced accordingly. The inventory management may easily review the tables to determine the potential benefits to be gained in reduced sizes of safety stock and yet to maintain the level of customer service sought by the firm.

Example 9.1

A tire dealer receives an average of 100 requests for a particular brand tire per month. There is an associated standard deviation of 50 tires. Assume the replenishment lead time is one week and the dealer orders two weeks of replenishments when the need arises. If the desired service level is .95, how much safety stock is needed for this tire and what is the corresponding order point?

Table 9.4 is used with SL = .95, cov = 50/100 = .50, L = .25 (one week) and M = .50 (two weeks). The table shows that the months of safety stock should be 0.22 months. Hence, SS = .22 (100) = 22. Also, since the lead time forecast is F_L = .25 (100) = 25, the order point becomes:

$$OP = 25 + 22 = 47$$

Example 9.2

A hose is stocked as a service part for an auto manufacturer. The forecast calls for 1000 units per month with a standard deviation of the error in the forecast of 300. Assume the lead time is 4 months, the replenishment quantity is 1000, and the desired service level is .95. Find the safety stock and order point for the hose.

Since SL = .95, then Table 9.4 is used with cov = 300/1000 = .30, L = 4 (months) and M = 1000/1000 = 1 month. The table shows the need for ss = 0.60 months of safety stock, so SS = .60 (1000) = 600. Since the lead time forecast is 4 (1000) = 4000, the order point is then:

$$OP = 4000 + 600 = 4600$$

Example 9.3

Consider the hose in Example 9.2 and assume the lead time could be reduced to three months. What change in the safety stock takes place?

Using Table 9.4 with L = 3, M = 1 and cov = 0.30, SS = .48 (1000) = 480. Thus the reduction in safety stock is 20 percent (from 600 to 480).

Example 9.4

Consider the hose in Example 9.2; assume the order quantity is increased to two months and all else remains the same. How does this change affect the safety stock?

Using Table 9.4 with L = 4, M = 2 and cov = 0.30, then SS = .36 (1000) = 360, which is a reduction of 40 percent of safety stock (from 600 to 360).

Example 9.5

Consider the hose in Example 9.2 and suppose the forecast is improved to where the forecast standard error per month reduces to 100 (from 300). Assuming also that all else remains the same, what affect on the safety stock takes place?

Using Table 9.4 with L = 4, M = 1 and cov = .1, SS = .07 (1000) = 70. This improvement reduces the safety stock by 88 percent (600 to 70).

Example 9.6

Consider the hose in Example 9.2 and suppose the desired service level is decreased to 92.5 percent, and all else remains the same. What is the change in the safety stock?

Table 9.3 is used with L = 4, M = 1, and cov = 0.30 to give SS = .47 (1000) = 470. This change yields a 22 percent reduction in safety stock (600 to 470).

Example 9.7

The monthly demand for a lawnmower is 120 units with a standard deviation of 50. Suppose the lead time is one month and the order quantity is a one-half month's supply (Q = 60). If the safety stock held is 40 units, determine approximately the service level for the item.

Since the lead time is one month, the standard error for the lead time is $\sigma_L = \sqrt{1} \times 50 = 50$. Note the safety stock is SS = 40 = k σ_L. Now the safety factor **k** can be determined by the relation k = 40/50 = .8. With k = 0.80, Table 7.1 shows that E(.8) = .1202. Hence,

$$(1 - SL) = E (k) \sigma_L/Q = .1202 (50)/60 = .100$$

gives the percent of demands that will not be filled from the available stock. This formula yields SL = 1 − .100 = .90 or 90 percent.

Example 9.8

Assume a truck dealer has average demands for a battery of 50 per month with a standard deviation of 15. Suppose the lead time on these batteries is two weeks, and the policy is to order one week of new batteries per replenishment. If the desired service level is 95 percent, find the safety stock needed for the batteries.

Using Table 9.4 with SL = .95, L = .50, M = .25 and cov = 15/50 = .30, ss = .25 of a month. This figure is now used to derive the safety stock, SS = ss × F = .25 × 50 = 12.5.

Table 9.1 Safety Stock in months

SL = Service Level   COV = Coefficient of Variation
M = Order Quantity (in months of forecast)   L = Lead Time (in months)

SL = .85   COV = .1

M \ L	.25	.50	.75	1	2	3	4	5	6	8	10	12
.25												
.50												
.75												
1												
2	.04											
3	.08											
4	.11	.01										
5	.13	.03										
6	.16	.05										
8	.21	.09										
10	.25	.12	.03									
12	.30	.15	.05									

SL = .85   COV = .3

M \ L	.25	.50	.75	1	2	3	4	5	6	8	10	12
.25	.05											
.50	.12	.02										
.75	.18	.06										
1	.23	.10	.01									
2	.41	.24	.13	.04								
3	.56	.36	.23	.13								
4	.69	.47	.32	.20								
5	.80	.56	.40	.28								
6	.91	.65	.48	.35								
8	1.11	.82	.63	.48	.08							
10	1.29	.97	.76	.60	.17							
12	1.46	1.11	.89	.72	.25							

SL = .85   COV = .5

M \ L	.25	.50	.75	1	2	3	4	5	6	8	10	12
.25	.17	.05										
.50	.31	.16	.06									
.75	.42	.25	.14	.05								
1	.53	.33	.21	.11								
2	.87	.61	.45	.32								
3	1.14	.85	.65	.50	.09							
4	1.39	1.05	.83	.67	.21							
5	1.61	1.24	1.00	.82	.33							
6	1.81	1.41	1.16	.96	.44	.07						
8	2.18	1.73	1.44	1.23	.64	.24						
10	2.51	2.02	1.71	1.47	.83	.40	.06					
12	2.82	2.29	1.95	1.69	1.01	.55	.18					

Table 9.1 Safety Stock in months (Continued)

SL = Service Level COV = Coefficient of Variation
M = Order Quantity (in months of forecast) L = Lead Time (in months)

SL = .85   COV = .6

M \ L	.25	.50	.75	1	2	3	4	5	6	8	10	12
.25	.23	.10	.01									
.50	.41	.24	.13	.04								
.75	.56	.36	.23	.13								
1	.69	.47	.32	.20								
2	1.11	.82	.63	.48	.08							
3	1.46	1.11	.89	.72	.25							
4	1.76	1.37	1.12	.93	.41	.05						
5	2.04	1.61	1.33	1.12	.56	.18						
6	2.29	1.83	1.53	1.31	.70	.29						
8	2.75	2.23	1.89	1.64	.96	.51	.15					
10	3.16	2.59	2.22	1.94	1.21	.72	.33	.01				
12	3.54	2.92	2.53	2.23	1.44	.91	.50	.16				

SL = .85   COV = .8

M \ L	.25	.50	.75	1	2	3	4	5	6	8	10	12
.25	.37	.21	.10	.02								
.50	.63	.42	.28	.17								
.75	.84	.59	.43	.30								
1	1.03	.75	.57	.42	.04							
2	1.63	1.26	1.02	.84	.34							
3	2.12	1.68	1.40	1.19	.61	.21						
4	2.55	2.05	1.74	1.50	.85	.41	.07					
5	2.94	2.39	2.04	1.78	1.07	.60	.23					
6	3.29	2.70	2.32	2.04	1.29	.78	.39	.06				
8	3.93	3.26	2.84	2.52	1.68	1.12	.68	.32				
10	4.51	3.77	3.31	2.96	2.04	1.43	.95	.56	.22			
12	5.04	4.25	3.74	3.37	2.37	1.72	1.21	.79	.43			

SL = .85   COV = 1.0

M \ L	.25	.50	.75	1	2	3	4	5	6	8	10	12
.25	.53	.33	.21	.11								
.50	.87	.61	.45	.32								
.75	1.14	.85	.65	.50	.09							
1	1.39	1.05	.83	.67	.21							
2	2.18	1.73	1.44	1.23	.64	.24						
3	2.82	2.29	1.95	1.69	1.01	.55	.18					
4	3.37	2.77	2.39	2.10	1.34	.83	.43	.09				
5	3.87	3.21	2.80	2.48	1.64	1.09	.65	.29				
6	4.33	3.62	3.17	2.83	1.93	1.33	.87	.49	.15			
8	5.17	4.36	3.85	3.46	2.45	1.79	1.28	.85	.48			
10	5.91	5.02	4.46	4.04	2.94	2.21	1.66	1.19	.79	.11		
12	6.60	5.64	5.03	4.58	3.38	2.61	2.01	1.52	1.09	.37		

Table 9.2 Safety Stock in months

SL = Service Level   COV = Coefficient of Variation
M = Order Quantity (in months of forecast)   L = Lead Time (in months)

SL = .90   COV = .1

M	.25	.50	.75	1	2	3	4	5	6	8	10	12
L												
.25												
.50	.01											
.75	.02											
1	.03											
2	.08	.01										
3	.12	.04										
4	.16	.07	.01									
5	.19	.09	.03									
6	.22	.12	.05									
8	.27	.16	.09	.03								
10	.32	.20	.12	.06								
12	.37	.24	.15	.08								

SL = .90   COV = .3

M	.25	.50	.75	1	2	3	4	5	6	8	10	12
L												
.25	.09	.02										
.50	.17	.08	.02									
.75	.24	.13	.06	.01								
1	.30	.18	.10	.04								
2	.50	.34	.24	.16								
3	.66	.48	.36	.27	.01							
4	.80	.60	.47	.36	.08							
5	.93	.71	.56	.45	.15							
6	1.05	.81	.65	.53	.21							
8	1.27	1.00	.82	.69	.32	.08						
10	1.46	1.16	.97	.83	.43	.17						
12	1.64	1.32	1.11	.96	.53	.25	.03					

SL = .90   COV = .5

M	.25	.50	.75	1	2	3	4	5	6	8	10	12
L												
.25	.22	.12	.05									
.50	.38	.25	.16	.09								
.75	.51	.36	.25	.17								
1	.63	.45	.33	.24								
2	1.00	.77	.61	.50	.18							
3	1.30	1.02	.85	.71	.34	.09						
4	1.57	1.25	1.05	.90	.49	.21						
5	1.80	1.46	1.24	1.07	.63	.33	.09					
6	2.02	1.65	1.41	1.23	.76	.44	.18					
8	2.42	2.00	1.73	1.53	.99	.64	.36	.13				
10	2.78	2.31	2.02	1.80	1.21	.83	.53	.28	.06			
12	3.11	2.60	2.29	2.05	1.42	1.01	.68	.42	.18			

Table 9.2 Safety Stock in months (Continued)

SL = Service Level   COV = Coefficient of Variation
M = Order Quantity (in months of forecast)   L = Lead Time (in months)

SL = .90   COV = .6

L \ M	.25	.50	.75	1	2	3	4	5	6	8	10	12
.25	.30	.18	.10	.04								
.50	.50	.34	.24	.16								
.75	.66	.48	.36	.27	.01							
1	.80	.60	.47	.36	.08							
2	1.27	1.00	.82	.69	.32	.08						
3	1.64	1.32	1.11	.96	.53	.25	.03					
4	1.97	1.61	1.37	1.20	.73	.41	.16					
5	2.27	1.86	1.61	1.42	.90	.56	.29	.07				
6	2.54	2.10	1.83	1.62	1.07	.70	.42	.18				
8	3.03	2.54	2.23	1.99	1.37	.96	.65	.38	.15			
10	3.47	2.93	2.59	2.33	1.65	1.21	.86	.58	.33			
12	3.88	3.29	2.92	2.64	1.91	1.44	1.07	.76	.50	.05		

SL = .90   COV = .8

L \ M	.25	.50	.75	1	2	3	4	5	6	8	10	12
.25	.46	.31	.21	.14								
.50	.74	.55	.42	.32	.05							
.75	.97	.74	.59	.48	.17							
1	1.18	.92	.75	.62	.27	.04						
2	1.83	1.48	1.26	1.09	.64	.34	.10					
3	2.36	1.95	1.68	1.49	.96	.61	.33	.10				
4	2.82	2.35	2.05	1.83	1.24	.85	.55	.29	.07			
5	3.23	2.72	2.39	2.15	1.50	1.07	.75	.47	.23			
6	3.61	3.05	2.70	2.44	1.74	1.29	.93	.64	.39			
8	4.30	3.66	3.26	2.97	2.19	1.68	1.29	.96	.68	.20		
10	4.91	4.21	3.77	3.45	2.59	2.04	1.61	1.26	.95	.44	.01	
12	5.48	4.72	4.25	3.89	2.97	2.37	1.92	1.54	1.21	.67	.21	

SL = .90   COV = 1.0

L \ M	.25	.50	.75	1	2	3	4	5	6	8	10	12
.25	.63	.45	.33	.24								
.50	1.00	.77	.61	.50	.18							
.75	1.30	1.02	.85	.71	.34	.09						
1	1.57	1.25	1.05	.90	.49	.21						
2	2.42	2.00	1.73	1.53	.99	.64	.36	.13				
3	3.11	2.60	2.29	2.05	1.42	1.01	.68	.42	.18			
4	3.70	3.13	2.77	2.51	1.80	1.34	.98	.68	.43			
5	4.23	3.61	3.21	2.92	2.15	1.64	1.25	.93	.65	.18		
6	4.72	4.05	3.62	3.30	2.47	1.93	1.51	1.17	.87	.37		
8	5.61	4.84	4.36	4.00	3.06	2.45	1.99	1.61	1.28	.72	.26	
10	6.40	5.55	5.02	4.63	3.60	2.94	2.43	2.01	1.66	1.05	.55	.11
12	7.14	6.21	5.64	5.21	4.10	3.38	2.84	2.39	2.01	1.37	.83	.37

Table 9.3 Safety Stock in months

SL = Service Level   COV = Coefficient of Variation
M = Order Quantity (in months of forecast)   L = Lead Time (in months)

SL = .925   COV = .1

M	.25	.50	.75	1	2	3	4	5	6	8	10	12
L												
.25												
.50	.02											
.75	.04											
1	.05												
2	.10	.04										
3	.15	.08	.03									
4	.19	.11	.05	.01								
5	.22	.13	.08	.03								
6	.26	.16	.10	.05								
8	.32	.21	.14	.09								
10	.37	.25	.18	.12								
12	.42	.30	.21	.15								

SL = .925   COV = .3

M	.25	.50	.75	1	2	3	4	5	6	8	10	12
L												
.25	.12	.05	.01									
.50	.20	.12	.06	.02								
.75	.28	.18	.11	.06								
1	.34	.23	.16	.10								
2	.56	.41	.31	.24	.04							
3	.73	.56	.44	.36	.13							
4	.88	.69	.56	.47	.20	.03						
5	1.02	.80	.67	.56	.28	.09						
6	1.14	.91	.77	.65	.35	.15						
8	1.37	1.11	.95	.82	.48	.26	.08					
10	1.58	1.29	1.11	.97	.60	.36	.17					
12	1.77	1.46	1.26	1.11	.72	.46	.25	.08				

SL = .925   COV = .5

M	.25	.50	.75	1	2	3	4	5	6	8	10	12
L												
.25	.26	.17	.10	.05								
.50	.43	.31	.22	.16								
.75	.57	.42	.33	.25	.05							
1	.69	.53	.42	.33	.11							
2	1.09	.87	.72	.61	.32	.12						
3	1.41	1.14	.97	.85	.50	.27	.09					
4	1.69	1.39	1.20	1.05	.67	.41	.21	.04				
5	1.94	1.61	1.40	1.24	.82	.54	.33	.15				
6	2.17	1.81	1.58	1.41	.96	.67	.44	.24	.07			
8	2.58	2.18	1.92	1.73	1.23	.90	.64	.43	.24			
10	2.96	2.51	2.23	2.02	1.47	1.11	.83	.60	.40	.06		
12	3.30	2.82	2.51	2.29	1.69	1.30	1.01	.76	.55	.18		

Table 9.3 Safety Stock in months (Continued)

SL = Service Level   COV = Coefficient of Variation

M = Order Quantity (in months of forecast)   L = Lead Time (in months)

SL = .925   COV = .6

M	.25	.50	.75	1	2	3	4	5	6	8	10	12
L												
.25	.34	.23	.16	.10								
.50	.56	.41	.31	.24	.04							
.75	.73	.56	.44	.36	.13							
1	.88	.69	.56	.47	.20	.03						
2	1.37	1.11	.95	.82	.48	.26	.08					
3	1.77	1.46	1.26	1.11	.72	.46	.25	.08				
4	2.11	1.76	1.54	1.37	.93	.64	.41	.22	.05			
5	2.42	2.04	1.79	1.61	1.12	.81	.56	.35	.18			
6	2.71	2.29	2.03	1.83	1.31	.96	.70	.48	.29			
8	3.22	2.75	2.45	2.23	1.64	1.26	.96	.72	.51	.15		
10	3.68	3.16	2.83	2.59	1.94	1.53	1.21	.94	.72	.33	.01	
12	4.11	3.54	3.18	2.92	2.23	1.78	1.44	1.15	.91	.50	.16	

SL = .925   COV = .8

M	.25	.50	.75	1	2	3	4	5	6	8	10	12
L												
.25	.51	.37	.28	.21	.02							
.50	.82	.63	.51	.42	.17							
.75	1.06	.84	.70	.59	.30	.11						
1	1.27	1.03	.87	.75	.42	.21	.04					
2	1.97	1.63	1.42	1.26	.84	.56	.34	.16				
3	2.52	2.12	1.87	1.68	1.19	.86	.61	.40	.21			
4	3.00	2.55	2.27	2.05	1.50	1.13	.85	.62	.41	.07		
5	3.43	2.94	2.62	2.39	1.78	1.38	1.07	.82	.60	.23		
6	3.83	3.29	2.95	2.70	2.04	1.61	1.29	1.02	.78	.39	.06	
8	4.54	3.93	3.55	3.26	2.52	2.04	1.68	1.38	1.12	.68	.32	
10	5.19	4.51	4.09	3.77	2.96	2.44	2.04	1.71	1.43	.95	.56	.22
12	5.78	5.04	4.58	4.25	3.37	2.80	2.37	2.02	1.72	1.21	.79	.43

SL = .925   COV = 1.0

M	.25	.50	.75	1	2	3	4	5	6	8	10	12
L												
.25	.69	.53	.42	.33	.11							
.50	1.09	.87	.72	.61	.32	.12						
.75	1.41	1.14	.97	.85	.50	.27	.09					
1	1.69	1.39	1.20	1.05	.67	.41	.21	.04				
2	2.58	2.18	1.92	1.73	1.23	.90	.64	.43	.24			
3	3.30	2.82	2.51	2.29	1.69	1.30	1.01	.76	.55	.18		
4	3.92	3.37	3.03	2.77	2.10	1.67	1.34	1.06	.83	.43	.09	
5	4.48	3.87	3.50	3.21	2.48	2.00	1.64	1.34	1.09	.65	.29	
6	4.99	4.33	3.93	3.62	2.83	2.32	1.93	1.61	1.33	.87	.49	.15
8	5.92	5.17	4.70	4.36	3.46	2.89	2.45	2.10	1.79	1.28	.85	.48
10	6.73	5.91	5.40	5.02	4.04	3.41	2.94	2.55	2.21	1.66	1.19	.79
12	7.51	6.60	6.05	5.64	4.58	3.90	3.38	2.97	2.61	2.01	1.52	1.09

Table 9.4 Safety Stock in months

SL = Service Level COV = Coefficient of Variation
M = Order Quantity (in months of forecast) L = Lead Time (in months)

SL = .95 COV = .1

M	.25	.50	.75	1	2	3	4	5	6	8	10	12
L												
.25	.02											
.50	.04	.01										
.75	.06	.02										
1	.08	.03										
2	.14	.08	.04	.01								
3	.19	.12	.08	.04								
4	.23	.16	.11	.07								
5	.27	.19	.13	.09								
6	.30	.22	.16	.12								
8	.37	.27	.21	.16	.03							
10	.43	.32	.25	.20	.06							
12	.49	.37	.30	.24	.08							

SL = .95 COV = .3

M	.25	.50	.75	1	2	3	4	5	6	8	10	12
L												
.25	.15	.09	.05	.02								
.50	.25	.17	.12	.08								
.75	.33	.24	.18	.13	.01							
1	.40	.30	.23	.18	.04							
2	.63	.50	.41	.34	.16	.04						
3	.82	.66	.56	.48	.27	.13	.01					
4	.99	.80	.69	.60	.36	.20	.08					
5	1.13	.93	.80	.71	.45	.28	.15	.03				
6	1.27	1.05	.91	.81	.53	.35	.21	.09				
8	1.51	1.27	1.11	1.00	.69	.48	.32	.19	.08			
10	1.74	1.46	1.29	1.16	.83	.60	.43	.29	.17			
12	1.94	1.64	1.46	1.32	.96	.72	.53	.38	.25	.03		

SL = .95 COV = .5

M	.25	.50	.75	1	2	3	4	5	6	8	10	12
L												
.25	.31	.22	.17	.12								
.50	.50	.38	.31	.25	.09							
.75	.65	.51	.42	.36	.17	.05						
1	.78	.63	.53	.45	.24	.11						
2	1.21	1.00	.87	.77	.50	.32	.18	.06				
3	1.55	1.30	1.14	1.02	.71	.50	.34	.21	.09			
4	1.85	1.57	1.39	1.25	.90	.67	.49	.34	.21			
5	2.12	1.80	1.61	1.46	1.07	.82	.63	.47	.33	.09		
6	2.36	2.02	1.81	1.65	1.23	.96	.76	.58	.44	.18		
8	2.81	2.42	2.18	2.00	1.53	1.23	.99	.80	.64	.36	.13	
10	3.20	2.78	2.51	2.31	1.80	1.47	1.21	1.01	.83	.53	.28	.06
12	3.57	3.11	2.82	2.60	2.05	1.69	1.42	1.20	1.01	.68	.42	.18

Table 9.4   Safety Stock in months   (Continued)

SL = Service Level   COV = Coefficient of Variation
M = Order Quantity (in months of forecast)   L = Lead Time (in months)

SL = .95   COV = .6

M	.25	.50	.75	1	2	3	4	5	6	8	10	12
L												
.25	.40	.30	.23	.18	.04							
.50	.63	.50	.41	.34	.16	.04						
.75	.82	.66	.56	.48	.27	.13	.01					
1	.99	.80	.69	.60	.36	.20	.08					
2	1.51	1.27	1.11	1.00	.69	.48	.32	.19	.08			
3	1.94	1.64	1.46	1.32	.96	.72	.53	.38	.25	.03		
4	2.30	1.97	1.76	1.61	1.20	.93	.73	.56	.41	.16		
5	2.63	2.27	2.04	1.86	1.42	1.12	.90	.72	.56	.29	.07	
6	2.94	2.54	2.29	2.10	1.62	1.31	1.07	.87	.70	.42	.18	
8	3.48	3.03	2.75	2.54	1.99	1.64	1.37	1.15	.96	.65	.38	.15
10	3.97	3.47	3.16	2.93	2.33	1.94	1.65	1.41	1.21	.86	.58	.33
12	4.41	3.88	3.54	3.29	2.64	2.23	1.91	1.66	1.44	1.07	.76	.50

SL = .95   COV = .8

M	.25	.50	.75	1	2	3	4	5	6	8	10	12
L												
.25	.59	.46	.37	.31	.14	.02						
.50	.92	.74	.63	.55	.32	.17	.05					
.75	1.18	.97	.84	.74	.48	.30	.17	.05				
1	1.41	1.18	1.03	.92	.62	.42	.27	.15	.04			
2	2.15	1.83	1.63	1.48	1.09	.84	.64	.48	.34	.10		
3	2.74	2.36	2.12	1.95	1.49	1.19	.96	.77	.61	.33	.10	
4	3.25	2.82	2.55	2.35	1.83	1.50	1.24	1.03	.85	.55	.29	.07
5	3.71	3.23	2.94	2.72	2.15	1.78	1.50	1.27	1.07	.75	.47	.23
6	4.12	3.61	3.29	3.05	2.44	2.04	1.74	1.50	1.29	.93	.64	.39
8	4.88	4.30	3.93	3.66	2.97	2.52	2.19	1.91	1.68	1.29	.96	.68
10	5.57	4.91	4.51	4.21	3.45	2.96	2.59	2.29	2.04	1.61	1.26	.95
12	6.18	5.48	5.04	4.72	3.89	3.37	2.97	2.65	2.37	1.92	1.54	1.21

SL = .95   COV = 1.0

M	.25	.50	.75	1	2	3	4	5	6	8	10	12
L												
.25	.78	.63	.53	.45	.24	.11						
.50	1.21	1.00	.87	.77	.50	.32	.18	.06				
.75	1.55	1.30	1.14	1.02	.71	.50	.34	.21	.09			
1	1.85	1.57	1.39	1.25	.90	.67	.49	.34	.21			
2	2.81	2.42	2.18	2.00	1.53	1.23	.99	.80	.64	.36	.13	
3	3.57	3.11	2.82	2.60	2.05	1.69	1.42	1.20	1.01	.68	.42	.18
4	4.22	3.70	3.37	3.13	2.51	2.10	1.80	1.55	1.34	.98	.68	.43
5	4.82	4.23	3.87	3.61	2.92	2.48	2.15	1.87	1.64	1.25	.93	.65
6	5.36	4.72	4.33	4.05	3.30	2.83	2.47	2.18	1.93	1.51	1.17	.87
8	6.33	5.61	5.17	4.84	4.00	3.46	3.06	2.73	2.45	1.99	1.61	1.28
10	7.19	6.40	5.91	5.55	4.63	4.04	3.60	3.24	2.94	2.43	2.01	1.66
12	8.02	7.14	6.60	6.21	5.21	4.58	4.10	3.71	3.38	2.84	2.39	2.01

Table 9.5   Safety Stock in months

SL = Service Level   COV = Coefficient of Variation
M = Order Quantity (in months of forecast)   L = Lead Time (in months)

SL = .975   COV = .1

L \ M	.25	.50	.75	1	2	3	4	5	6	8	10	12
.25	.04	.02										
.50	.07	.04	.02	.01								
.75	.09	.06	.04	.02								
1	.11	.08	.05	.03								
2	.19	.14	.10	.08	.01							
3	.24	.19	.15	.12	.04							
4	.29	.23	.19	.16	.07	.01						
5	.34	.27	.22	.19	.09	.03						
6	.38	.30	.26	.22	.12	.05						
8	.46	.37	.32	.27	.16	.09	.03					
10	.53	.43	.37	.32	.20	.12	.06					
12	.59	.49	.42	.37	.24	.15	.08	.03				

SL = .975   COV = .3

L \ M	.25	.50	.75	1	2	3	4	5	6	8	10	12
.25	.20	.15	.12	.09	.02							
.50	.32	.25	.20	.17	.08	.02						
.75	.41	.33	.28	.24	.13	.06	.01					
1	.49	.40	.34	.30	.18	.10	.04					
2	.76	.63	.56	.50	.34	.24	.16	.10	.04			
3	.97	.82	.73	.66	.48	.36	.27	.19	.13	.01		
4	1.15	.99	.88	.80	.60	.47	.36	.28	.20	.08		
5	1.32	1.13	1.02	.93	.71	.56	.45	.36	.28	.15	.03	
6	1.47	1.27	1.14	1.05	.81	.65	.53	.44	.35	.21	.09	
8	1.74	1.51	1.37	1.27	1.00	.82	.69	.58	.48	.32	.19	.08
10	1.99	1.74	1.58	1.46	1.16	.97	.83	.71	.60	.43	.29	.17
12	2.21	1.94	1.77	1.64	1.32	1.11	.96	.83	.72	.53	.38	.25

SL = .975   COV = .5

L \ M	.25	.50	.75	1	2	3	4	5	6	8	10	12
.25	.39	.31	.26	.22	.12	.05						
.50	.60	.50	.43	.38	.25	.16	.09	.03				
.75	.78	.65	.57	.51	.36	.25	.17	.10	.05			
1	.93	.78	.69	.63	.45	.33	.24	.17	.11			
2	1.40	1.21	1.09	1.00	.77	.61	.50	.40	.32	.18	.06	
3	1.78	1.55	1.41	1.30	1.02	.85	.71	.60	.50	.34	.21	.09
4	2.11	1.85	1.69	1.57	1.25	1.05	.90	.78	.67	.49	.34	.21
5	2.41	2.12	1.94	1.80	1.46	1.24	1.07	.94	.82	.63	.47	.33
6	2.68	2.36	2.17	2.02	1.65	1.41	1.23	1.09	.96	.76	.58	.44
8	3.17	2.81	2.58	2.42	2.00	1.73	1.53	1.37	1.23	.99	.80	.64
10	3.59	3.20	2.96	2.78	2.31	2.02	1.80	1.62	1.47	1.21	1.01	.83
12	4.01	3.57	3.30	3.11	2.60	2.29	2.05	1.86	1.69	1.42	1.20	1.01

Table 9.5   Safety Stock in months   (Continued)

SL = Service Level   COV = Coefficient of Variation
M = Order Quantity (in months of forecast)   L = Lead Time (in months)

SL = .975   COV = .6

M	.25	.50	.75	1	2	3	4	5	6	8	10	12
L
.25	.49	.40	.34	.30	.18	.10	.04					
.50	.76	.63	.56	.50	.34	.24	.16	.10	.04			
.75	.97	.82	.73	.66	.48	.36	.27	.19	.13	.01		
1	1.15	.99	.88	.80	.60	.47	.36	.28	.20	.08		
2	1.74	1.51	1.37	1.27	1.00	.82	.69	.58	.48	.32	.19	.08
3	2.21	1.94	1.77	1.64	1.32	1.11	.96	.83	.72	.53	.38	.25
4	2.62	2.30	2.11	1.97	1.61	1.37	1.20	1.05	.93	.73	.56	.41
5	2.98	2.63	2.42	2.27	1.86	1.61	1.42	1.26	1.12	.90	.72	.56
6	3.31	2.94	2.71	2.54	2.10	1.83	1.62	1.45	1.31	1.07	.87	.70
8	3.91	3.48	3.22	3.03	2.54	2.23	1.99	1.80	1.64	1.37	1.15	.96
10	4.46	3.97	3.68	3.47	2.93	2.59	2.33	2.12	1.94	1.65	1.41	1.21
12	4.96	4.41	4.11	3.88	3.29	2.92	2.64	2.42	2.23	1.91	1.66	1.44

SL = .975   COV = .8

M	.25	.50	.75	1	2	3	4	5	6	8	10	12
L
.25	.70	.59	.51	.46	.31	.21	.14	.07	.02			
.50	1.07	.92	.82	.74	.55	.42	.32	.24	.17	.05		
.75	1.37	1.18	1.06	.97	.74	.59	.48	.38	.30	.17	.05	
1	1.62	1.41	1.27	1.18	.92	.75	.62	.52	.42	.27	.15	.04
2	2.44	2.15	1.97	1.83	1.48	1.26	1.09	.96	.84	.64	.48	.34
3	3.09	2.74	2.52	2.36	1.95	1.68	1.49	1.32	1.19	.96	.77	.61
4	3.65	3.25	3.00	2.82	2.35	2.05	1.83	1.65	1.50	1.24	1.03	.85
5	4.16	3.71	3.43	3.23	2.72	2.39	2.15	1.95	1.78	1.50	1.27	1.07
6	4.63	4.12	3.83	3.61	3.05	2.70	2.44	2.22	2.04	1.74	1.50	1.29
8	5.46	4.88	4.54	4.30	3.66	3.26	2.97	2.73	2.52	2.19	1.91	1.68
10	6.20	5.57	5.19	4.91	4.21	3.77	3.45	3.18	2.96	2.59	2.29	2.04
12	6.86	6.18	5.78	5.48	4.72	4.25	3.89	3.61	3.37	2.97	2.65	2.37

SL = .975   COV = 1.0

M	.25	.50	.75	1	2	3	4	5	6	8	10	12
L
.25	.93	.78	.69	.63	.45	.33	.24	.17	.11			
.50	1.40	1.21	1.09	1.00	.77	.61	.50	.40	.32	.18	.06	
.75	1.78	1.55	1.41	1.30	1.02	.85	.71	.60	.50	.34	.21	.09
1	2.11	1.85	1.69	1.57	1.25	1.05	.90	.78	.67	.49	.34	.21
2	3.17	2.81	2.58	2.42	2.00	1.73	1.53	1.37	1.23	.99	.80	.64
3	4.01	3.57	3.30	3.11	2.60	2.29	2.05	1.86	1.69	1.42	1.20	1.01
4	4.74	4.22	3.92	3.70	3.13	2.77	2.51	2.29	2.10	1.80	1.55	1.34
5	5.39	4.82	4.48	4.23	3.61	3.21	2.92	2.68	2.48	2.15	1.87	1.64
6	5.98	5.36	4.99	4.72	4.05	3.62	3.30	3.05	2.83	2.47	2.18	1.93
8	7.01	6.33	5.92	5.61	4.84	4.36	4.00	3.71	3.46	3.06	2.73	2.45
10	7.93	7.19	6.73	6.40	5.55	5.02	4.63	4.31	4.04	3.60	3.24	2.94
12	8.79	8.02	7.51	7.14	6.21	5.64	5.21	4.87	4.58	4.10	3.71	3.38

Table 9.6 Safety Stock in months

SL = Service Level   COV = Coefficient of Variation
   M = Order Quantity (in months of forecast)   L = Lead Time (in months)

SL = .99   COV = .1

L \ M	.25	.50	.75	1	2	3	4	5	6	8	10	12
.25	.06	.04	.03	.02								
.50	.10	.08	.06	.05	.02							
.75	.13	.10	.08	.07	.03	.01						
1	.16	.13	.11	.09	.05	.02						
2	.24	.20	.17	.15	.10	.06	.04	.01				
3	.31	.26	.23	.20	.14	.10	.07	.04	.02			
4	.37	.31	.28	.25	.18	.13	.10	.07	.04			
5	.42	.36	.32	.29	.21	.16	.13	.09	.07	.02		
6	.47	.40	.36	.33	.25	.19	.15	.12	.09	.04		
8	.56	.48	.44	.40	.31	.25	.20	.16	.13	.07	.03	
10	.64	.56	.50	.46	.36	.29	.24	.20	.17	.11	.06	.01
12	.71	.62	.56	.52	.41	.34	.28	.24	.20	.14	.08	.04

SL = .99   COV = .3

L \ M	.25	.50	.75	1	2	3	4	5	6	8	10	12
.25	.26	.22	.19	.17	.11	.07	.04	.02				
.50	.40	.34	.30	.27	.20	.15	.11	.08	.05	.01		
.75	.51	.44	.39	.36	.27	.21	.17	.13	.10	.05	.01	
1	.60	.52	.47	.43	.33	.27	.22	.18	.15	.09	.04	
2	.90	.79	.73	.68	.54	.46	.40	.34	.30	.22	.16	.11
3	1.15	1.01	.93	.87	.71	.61	.54	.48	.43	.34	.27	.21
4	1.35	1.20	1.11	1.04	.86	.75	.67	.60	.54	.44	.36	.29
5	1.54	1.37	1.27	1.19	1.00	.88	.78	.71	.64	.54	.45	.38
6	1.72	1.53	1.42	1.33	1.12	.99	.89	.81	.74	.63	.53	.45
8	2.03	1.81	1.68	1.59	1.35	1.20	1.09	1.00	.92	.79	.69	.60
10	2.30	2.07	1.92	1.82	1.55	1.39	1.26	1.16	1.08	.94	.83	.73
12	2.55	2.30	2.14	2.03	1.74	1.56	1.43	1.32	1.23	1.08	.96	.85

SL = .99   COV = .5

L \ M	.25	.50	.75	1	2	3	4	5	6	8	10	12
.25	.48	.42	.37	.34	.25	.20	.16	.12	.09	.04		
.50	.73	.64	.58	.53	.42	.35	.29	.25	.21	.14	.09	.04
.75	.93	.81	.74	.69	.56	.47	.41	.36	.31	.23	.17	.12
1	1.10	.97	.89	.83	.68	.58	.51	.45	.40	.31	.24	.18
2	1.64	1.46	1.35	1.27	1.07	.94	.84	.77	.70	.59	.50	.42
3	2.08	1.85	1.72	1.63	1.39	1.23	1.12	1.02	.95	.82	.71	.62
4	2.45	2.20	2.05	1.94	1.66	1.49	1.36	1.25	1.16	1.02	.90	.80
5	2.77	2.50	2.33	2.21	1.91	1.72	1.57	1.46	1.36	1.20	1.07	.96
6	3.06	2.77	2.59	2.46	2.14	1.93	1.78	1.65	1.55	1.37	1.23	1.12
8	3.60	3.29	3.08	2.92	2.55	2.31	2.14	2.00	1.88	1.69	1.53	1.40
10	4.08	3.74	3.50	3.33	2.92	2.66	2.47	2.31	2.18	1.97	1.80	1.65
12	4.52	4.16	3.89	3.71	3.26	2.98	2.77	2.60	2.46	2.24	2.05	1.89

Table 9.6 Safety Stock in months (Continued)

SL = Service Level   COV = Coefficient of Variation
M = Order Quantity (in months of forecast)   L = Lead Time (in months)

SL = .99   COV = .6

M	.25	.50	.75	1	2	3	4	5	6	8	10	12
L
.25	.60	.52	.47	.43	.33	.27	.22	.18	.15	.09	.04	
.50	.90	.79	.73	.68	.54	.46	.40	.34	.30	.22	.16	.11
.75	1.15	1.01	.93	.87	.71	.61	.54	.48	.43	.34	.27	.21
1	1.35	1.20	1.11	1.04	.86	.75	.67	.60	.54	.44	.36	.29
2	2.03	1.81	1.68	1.59	1.35	1.20	1.09	1.00	.92	.79	.69	.60
3	2.55	2.30	2.14	2.03	1.74	1.56	1.43	1.32	1.23	1.08	.96	.85
4	2.99	2.71	2.53	2.41	2.08	1.88	1.73	1.61	1.50	1.33	1.20	1.08
5	3.39	3.09	2.89	2.75	2.39	2.16	2.00	1.86	1.75	1.57	1.42	1.29
6	3.76	3.44	3.22	3.06	2.67	2.43	2.25	2.10	1.98	1.78	1.62	1.48
8	4.42	4.06	3.80	3.62	3.18	2.90	2.70	2.54	2.40	2.17	1.99	1.84
10	5.00	4.61	4.31	4.13	3.64	3.33	3.11	2.93	2.78	2.53	2.33	2.16
12	5.54	5.11	4.81	4.59	4.06	3.73	3.48	3.29	3.13	2.86	2.64	2.46

SL = .99   COV = .8

M	.25	.50	.75	1	2	3	4	5	6	8	10	12
L
.25	.84	.74	.67	.63	.50	.42	.36	.31	.27	.20	.14	.09
.50	1.27	1.12	1.03	.97	.80	.69	.61	.55	.49	.40	.32	.26
.75	1.60	1.43	1.32	1.24	1.04	.92	.82	.74	.68	.57	.48	.40
1	1.90	1.69	1.57	1.48	1.25	1.11	1.00	.92	.84	.72	.62	.53
2	2.81	2.53	2.37	2.24	1.94	1.74	1.60	1.48	1.39	1.22	1.09	.98
3	3.52	3.21	3.00	2.85	2.48	2.25	2.08	1.95	1.83	1.64	1.49	1.35
4	4.13	3.79	3.55	3.38	2.96	2.70	2.51	2.35	2.22	2.00	1.83	1.68
5	4.68	4.31	4.03	3.85	3.39	3.10	2.89	2.72	2.57	2.34	2.15	1.98
6	5.19	4.78	4.48	4.29	3.78	3.47	3.24	3.05	2.90	2.64	2.44	2.26
8	6.09	5.61	5.32	5.06	4.49	4.13	3.87	3.66	3.49	3.20	2.97	2.77
10	6.90	6.35	6.05	5.75	5.12	4.73	4.44	4.21	4.02	3.70	3.45	3.23
12	7.64	7.03	6.71	6.41	5.71	5.28	4.97	4.72	4.51	4.17	3.89	3.66

SL = .99   COV = 1.0

M	.25	.50	.75	1	2	3	4	5	6	8	10	12
L
.25	1.10	.97	.89	.83	.68	.58	.51	.45	.40	.31	.24	.18
.50	1.64	1.46	1.35	1.27	1.07	.94	.84	.77	.70	.59	.50	.42
.75	2.08	1.85	1.72	1.63	1.39	1.23	1.12	1.02	.95	.82	.71	.62
1	2.45	2.20	2.05	1.94	1.66	1.49	1.36	1.25	1.16	1.02	.90	.80
2	3.60	3.29	3.08	2.92	2.55	2.31	2.14	2.00	1.88	1.69	1.53	1.40
3	4.52	4.16	3.89	3.71	3.26	2.98	2.77	2.60	2.46	2.24	2.05	1.89
4	5.31	4.89	4.60	4.39	3.87	3.56	3.32	3.13	2.97	2.72	2.51	2.33
5	6.01	5.54	5.24	5.00	4.43	4.07	3.81	3.61	3.43	3.15	2.92	2.73
6	6.66	6.12	5.83	5.54	4.93	4.55	4.27	4.05	3.86	3.55	3.30	3.09
8	7.82	7.20	6.87	6.57	5.85	5.41	5.09	4.84	4.63	4.28	4.00	3.76
10	8.85	8.16	7.78	7.49	6.66	6.19	5.84	5.55	5.32	4.94	4.63	4.37
12	9.80	9.04	8.61	8.31	7.42	6.90	6.52	6.21	5.96	5.54	5.21	4.93

Table 9.7 Safety Stock in months

SL = Service Level COV = Coefficient of Variation
M = Order Quantity (in months of forecast) L = Lead Time (in months)

SL = .90   COV = .3

M	.25	.50	.75	1	2	3	4	5	6	8	10	12
L												
.25	.09	.02										
.50	.17	.08	.02									
.75	.24	.13	.06	.01								
1	.30	.18	.10	.04								
2	.50	.34	.24	.16								
3	.66	.48	.36	.27	.01							
4	.80	.60	.47	.36	.08							
5	.93	.71	.56	.45	.15							
6	1.05	.81	.65	.53	.21							
8	1.27	1.00	.82	.69	.32	.08						
10	1.46	1.16	.97	.83	.43	.17						
12	1.64	1.32	1.11	.96	.53	.25	.03					

SL = .95   COV = .3

M	.25	.50	.75	1	2	3	4	5	6	8	10	12
L												
.25	.15	.09	.05	.02								
.50	.25	.17	.12	.08								
.75	.33	.24	.18	.13	.01							
1	.40	.30	.23	.18	.04							
2	.63	.50	.41	.34	.16	.04						
3	.82	.66	.56	.48	.27	.13	.01					
4	.99	.80	.69	.60	.36	.20	.08					
5	1.13	.93	.80	.71	.45	.28	.15	.03				
6	1.27	1.05	.91	.81	.53	.35	.21	.09				
8	1.51	1.27	1.11	1.00	.69	.48	.32	.19	.08			
10	1.74	1.46	1.29	1.1c	.83	.60	.43	.29	.17			
12	1.94	1.64	1.46	1.32	.96	.72	.53	.38	.25	.03		

SL = .99   COV = .3

M	.25	.50	.75	1	2	3	4	5	6	8	10	12
L												
.25	.26	.22	.19	.17	.11	.07	.04	.02				
.50	.40	.34	.30	.27	.20	.15	.11	.08	.05	.01		
.75	.51	.44	.39	.36	.27	.21	.17	.13	.10	.05	.01	
1	.60	.52	.47	.43	.33	.27	.22	.18	.15	.09	.04	
2	.90	.79	.73	.68	.54	.46	.40	.34	.30	.22	.16	.11
3	1.15	1.01	.93	.87	.71	.61	.54	.48	.43	.34	.27	.21
4	1.35	1.20	1.11	1.04	.86	.75	.67	.60	.54	.44	.36	.29
5	1.54	1.37	1.27	1.19	1.00	.88	.78	.71	.64	.54	.45	.38
6	1.72	1.53	1.42	1.33	1.12	.99	.89	.81	.74	.63	.53	.45
8	2.03	1.81	1.68	1.59	1.35	1.20	1.09	1.00	.92	.79	.69	.60
10	2.30	2.07	1.92	1.82	1.55	1.39	1.26	1.16	1.08	.94	.83	.73
12	2.55	2.30	2.14	2.03	1.74	1.56	1.43	1.32	1.23	1.08	.96	.85

Table 9.7 Safety Stock in months (Continued)

SL = Service Level   COV = Coefficient of Variation
M = Order Quantity (in months of forecast)   L = Lead Time (in months)

SL = .90   COV = .5

L \ M	.25	.50	.75	1	2	3	4	5	6	8	10	12
.25	.22	.12	.05									
.50	.38	.25	.16	.09								
.75	.51	.36	.25	.17								
1	.63	.45	.33	.24								
2	1.00	.77	.61	.50	.18							
3	1.30	1.02	.85	.71	.34	.09						
4	1.57	1.25	1.05	.90	.49	.21						
5	1.80	1.46	1.24	1.07	.63	.33	.09					
6	2.02	1.65	1.41	1.23	.76	.44	.18					
8	2.42	2.00	1.73	1.53	.99	.64	.36	.13				
10	2.78	2.31	2.02	1.80	1.21	.83	.53	.28	.06			
12	3.11	2.60	2.29	2.05	1.42	1.01	.68	.42	.18			

SL = .95   COV = .5

L \ M	.25	.50	.75	1	2	3	4	5	6	8	10	12
.25	.31	.22	.17	.12								
.50	.50	.38	.31	.25	.09							
.75	.65	.51	.42	.36	.17	.05						
1	.78	.63	.53	.45	.24	.11						
2	1.21	1.00	.87	.77	.50	.32	.18	.06				
3	1.55	1.30	1.14	1.02	.71	.50	.34	.21	.09			
4	1.85	1.57	1.39	1.25	.90	.67	.49	.34	.21			
5	2.12	1.80	1.61	1.46	1.07	.82	.63	.47	.33	.09		
6	2.36	2.02	1.81	1.65	1.23	.96	.76	.58	.44	.18		
8	2.81	2.42	2.18	2.00	1.53	1.23	.99	.80	.64	.36	.13	
10	3.20	2.78	2.51	2.31	1.80	1.47	1.21	1.01	.83	.53	.28	.06
12	3.57	3.11	2.82	2.60	2.05	1.69	1.42	1.20	1.01	.68	.42	.18

SL = .99   COV = .5

L \ M	.25	.50	.75	1	2	3	4	5	6	8	10	12
.25	.48	.42	.37	.34	.25	.20	.16	.12	.09	.04		
.50	.73	.64	.58	.53	.42	.35	.29	.25	.21	.14	.09	.04
.75	.93	.81	.74	.69	.56	.47	.41	.36	.31	.23	.17	.12
1	1.10	.97	.89	.83	.68	.58	.51	.45	.40	.31	.24	.18
2	1.64	1.46	1.35	1.27	1.07	.94	.84	.77	.70	.59	.50	.42
3	2.08	1.85	1.72	1.63	1.39	1.23	1.12	1.02	.95	.82	.71	.62
4	2.45	2.20	2.05	1.94	1.66	1.49	1.36	1.25	1.16	1.02	.90	.80
5	2.77	2.50	2.33	2.21	1.91	1.72	1.57	1.46	1.36	1.20	1.07	.96
6	3.06	2.77	2.59	2.46	2.14	1.93	1.78	1.65	1.55	1.37	1.23	1.12
8	3.60	3.29	3.08	2.92	2.55	2.31	2.14	2.00	1.88	1.69	1.53	1.40
10	4.09	3.74	3.50	3.33	2.92	2.66	2.47	2.31	2.18	1.97	1.80	1.65
12	4.53	4.16	3.89	3.71	3.26	2.98	2.77	2.60	2.46	2.24	2.05	1.89

CHAPTER 10

Safety Stock For Items With Various Stockkeeping Units

In many inventory situations, an item is stocked in a multiple of variations called stockkeeping units (**SKU**'s), such as by model, size or location. For example, a car comes in various colors, a shirt in several sizes and a truck service part is stocked in various regional distribution centers. The forecast for such items are often generated on the total item basis first, and then the total forecast is proportionately allocated to the individual **SKU**'s in relation to the percent of the **SKU**'s past demands.

The purpose of this chapter is to demonstrate how the safety stock for individual **SKU**'s may be determined and how the total safety stock of the item (over all **SKU**'s) may vary by the number of **SKU**'s. The results assume that the service level, lead time and replenishment policies are the same for all **SKU**'s of the item. Further it is assumed that the **SKU** demands are mutually exclusive and cannot be interchanged one for another **SKU**. For example, if a customer has a desire to purchase a particular color sofa, which at the moment is out of stock, he/she will not buy another color sofa in its place.

Data

The data needed to apply the model are the following:

$$SL = \text{desired service level}$$
$$F = \text{forecast per month for the item}$$
$$\sigma = \text{standard error of F}$$
$$L = \text{lead time (in months)}$$
$$Q = \text{order quantity for the item}$$
$$N = \text{number of SKU's}$$
$$P_i = \text{probability a demand is for SKU i } (i = 1, \dots, N)$$

Note in the above that the sum of the probabilities over all **N** of the **SKU**'s is one.

Model

Certain calculations—first carried out for the item itself—concern the forecast of demand over the procurement lead time F_L and the corresponding standard error of the lead time for the item σ_L. These calculations are obtained from:

$$F_L = L\,F$$
$$\sigma_L = \sqrt{L}\,\sigma$$

In addition, when a replenishment for the item occurs, it is assumed that the order size Q is determined from economic factors or other considerations with the supplier.

Consider **SKU i** of the item where P_i = the probability that a demand for the item occurs for **SKU i**. Using F_L and P_i, it is possible to determine the lead time forecast f_i for **SKU i**:

$$f_i = P_i F_L$$

If F_L were exactly known, the standard error of the lead time forecast for **SKU i** (denoted as σ_i) could be determined from use of the binomial distribution as below:

$$\sigma_i = \sqrt{F_L P_i (1 - P_i)}$$

However, since F_L is *not* known for certain and may vary with a standard error σ_L, the associated standard error for **SKU i** becomes:

$$\sigma_i = \sqrt{F_L P_i (1 - P_i) + P_i^2 \sigma_L^2}$$

Now—using Q as the order quantity for the item—the order quantity for **SKU i** is determined by:

$$q_i = P_i Q$$

In this way, the individual **SKU**'s will be replenished in quantities proportional to their probability distribution over the item.

Determining the safety stock for **SKU i** is now possible in a manner where the **SKU** achieves the service level goal set for the item. Using q_i, σ_i, and **SL**, the partial expectation is found in the same manner as in Chapter 9, where:

$$E(k_i) = (1 - SL) q_i / \sigma_i$$

k_i, the safety factory for **SKU i**, is obtained from use of Table 7.2. The safety stock for **SKU i** becomes:

$$SS_i = k_i \sigma_i$$

The safety stock **SS** for the item is obtained by summing all **SKU** safety stocks, i.e.:

$$SS = SS_1 + \ldots + SS_N$$

Tables

For the purpose of developing the adjoining tables, certain standardizing of input data and output results is useful. The first step is to determine the coefficient of variation **COV** for the item's one month forecast:

$$COV = \sigma / F$$

Second, the order quantity in months of forecast, denoted as **M**, is obtained by:

$$M = Q / F$$

Third, in order to develop the tables for presentation, the probability distribution over the **SKU**'s must be stipulated. For purposes here, the average of the probabilities is used throughout, i.e., $P_i = 1/N$ for $i = 1, \ldots,$ N. This usage assumes all **SKU**'s are equally likely to occur. Note here that other distributions on the P_i were tested and the results are very close to those presented in the adjoining tables; therefore, it seems the probability distribution on P_i has little significance when measuring the total safety stock for the items.

Finally, the output results are listed in months of safety stock for the item. Because **SS** is the total safety stock for the item, the associated months of safety stock for the item, **ss**, becomes:

$$ss = SS/F$$

The adjoining tables are arranged in the following manner:

Table	SL	cov
10.1	.90	.30
10.2	.90	.50
10.3	.90	.70
10.4	.95	.30
10.5	.95	.50
10.6	.95	.70

For each table, selected values of the lead time and months of order quantity are given. The monthly forecasts for which results are listed are 10, 50, 100, 500 and 1000. Note that when the forecasts rise above 1000 per month, the results are much like those reported when F = 1000. Finally, also note that the safety stock may sometimes become a negative quantity. This situation occurs when a safety stock of zero will yield a service level that is larger than the desired service level. In the adjoining tables, should any of the safety stocks become negative, they are then listed as calculated.

Example 10.1

Suppose a clothing warehouse outlet stocks a particular coat in 5 sizes. The monthly forecast for the coat is 100 and with a corresponding standard error of 30. Suppose also the procurement lead time is one half of a month and replenishments to stock are in one month quantities. If the management desires a 95 percent service level on orders received, how much total safety stock is needed?

Because SL = .95 and COV = 30/100 = .30, Table 10.4 is used along with F = 100, N = 5, L = 0.5 and M = 1. The table entry shows that the safety stock should cover 0.13 of a month, whereby SS = .13 × F = .13 × 100 = 13.

Example 10.2

In Example 10.1, suppose the coats are to be stocked in ten different sizes and all else is the same. How much safety stock is needed now?

By using Table 10.4 with N = 10, the safety stock becomes SS = .18 × 100 = 18. Note this is almost a 38 percent increase in the safety stock.

Example 10.3

Assume a sporting goods distribution center stocks a particular model ski with demands of 500 per month with a standard deviation of 150. The skis have a procurement lead time of one month and are replenished in quantities of one half of a month. Suppose the skis come in 10 sizes and a service level of 95 percent is desired. How much safety stock is needed over all sizes?

Table 10.4 indicates that SL = .95 and COV = 150/500 = .3. Using F = 500, L = 1, M = .5 and N = 10, then ss = .35, whereby SS = .35 × 500 = 175.

Example 10.4

Assume a firm is considering using 1, 5, or 10 distribution centers to stock items. Typically, the lead time is 3 months and the replenish quantity is for one month. Also the forecast generally yields a coefficient of variation near COV = .30 and the desired service level is .95. Compare the total safety stock requirements for the three distribution options.

Table 10.4 is used with SL = .95, COV = .30, L = 3 and M = 1 for N = 5 and 10, and Table 9.4 is used when N = 1. The table below summarizes the findings:

Months of Safety Stock

Monthly Forecast	Number of Distribution Centers		
	1	5	10
10	.48	1.66	2.64
50	.48	.79	1.10
100	.48	.64	.82
500	.48	.52	.56
1000	.48	.50	.52

The results show that for the lower volume items a more significant increase in the safety stock is needed as the number of distribution centers increases from 1 to 10.

Example 10.5

Consider an automotive equipment distributor with 5 branches. The forecasts are generated on a total basis (over all branches) and for a certain filter the forecast yields 500 units per month with a standard deviation of 150 units. When the filters are purchased, they are procured in lots of one month supply, and the lead time is one half of a month. The distribution management seeks a 95 percent service level with each branch. How much safety stock should be held in each branch to achieve the service goal when the percent of demands by branch are 30, 25, 20, 15 and 10 percent for branches 1, 2, 3, 4 and 5, respectively?

The results for the 5 branches are listed below, where the calculations are attained separately for each branch using the relations described in the chapter.

	Branch					
	1	2	3	4	5	sum
P	.30	.25	.20	.15	.10	1
f	75	62.5	50	37.5	25	250
σ	32.6	27.4	22.1	16.9	11.6	—
q	150	125	100	75	50	500
SS	13.1	11.2	9.1	7.2	5.2	45.8
ss	.087	.089	.091	.096	.104	.091

Note in the above that **f** is the lead time forecast, σ is the lead time standard deviation, **q** is the size of the order quantity, **SS** is the safety stock and **ss** is the safety stock in month's supply.

Table 10.1   Safety Stock in months of forecast for items with N SKU's

SL = .90 (service level)   COV = .30 (coefficient of variation)

F =	10		N = 5				10		N = 10			
L	M .25	.50	1	3	6	9	.25	.50	1	3	6	9
.25	.38	.25	.09	-.25	-.59	-.90	.63	.45	.25	-.18	-.57	-.89
.50	.63	.45	.24	-.18	-.57	-.89	1.01	.77	.50	-.04	-.50	-.86
1	1.00	.76	.49	-.04	-.50	-.86	1.59	1.26	.90	.21	-.36	-.78
3	2.05	1.66	1.23	.43	-.22	-.68	3.19	2.64	2.06	1.01	.18	-.39
6	3.17	2.62	2.05	1.00	.18	-.40	4.89	4.12	3.34	1.93	.87	.15
9	4.07	3.41	2.72	1.48	.53	-.13	6.28	5.33	4.37	2.71	1.47	.64

F =	50		N = 5				10		N = 10			
L	M .25	.50	1	3	6	9	.25	.50	1	3	6	9
.25	.17	.08	-.03	-.29	-.60	-.90	.24	.14	.01	-.28	-.60	-.90
.50	.29	.17	.03	-.27	-.60	-.90	.41	.27	.11	-.24	-.59	-.90
1	.48	.33	.15	-.22	-.59	-.90	.67	.48	.27	-.17	-.56	-.89
3	1.03	.79	.51	-.03	-.50	-.86	1.40	1.10	.77	.13	-.41	-.81
6	1.62	1.29	.93	.23	-.35	-.77	2.18	1.77	1.33	.49	-.18	-.66
9	2.10	1.70	1.27	.46	-.20	-.67	2.81	2.32	1.79	.81	.04	-.50

F =	100		N = 5				10		N = 10			
L	M .25	.50	1	3	6	9	.25	.50	1	3	6	9
.25	.13	.05	-.05	-.30	-.60	-.90	.17	.08	-.03	-.29	-.60	-.90
.50	.23	.13	.00	-.28	-.60	-.90	.30	.18	.04	-.27	-.60	-.90
1	.40	.26	.10	-.25	-.59	-.90	.50	.35	.16	-.22	-.58	-.90
3	.86	.64	.40	-.10	-.53	-.88	1.07	.82	.54	-.02	-.49	-.86
6	1.36	1.07	.74	.11	-.42	-.82	1.68	1.34	.97	.26	-.33	-.76
9	1.77	1.42	1.03	.30	-.31	-.74	2.18	1.77	1.33	.49	-.18	-.66

F =	500		N = 5				10		N = 10			
L	M .25	.50	1	3	6	9	.25	.50	1	3	6	9
.25	.10	.03	-.06	-.30	-.60	-.90	.11	.03	-.06	-.30	-.60	-.90
.50	.19	.09	-.02	-.29	-.60	-.90	.20	.10	-.01	-.29	-.60	-.90
1	.32	.20	.05	-.27	-.60	-.90	.35	.22	.07	-.26	-.60	-.90
3	.71	.52	.30	-.15	-.56	-.89	.76	.56	.33	-.13	-.55	-.89
6	1.13	.87	.58	.01	-.48	-.85	1.21	.94	.63	.04	-.46	-.84
9	1.48	1.17	.82	.16	-.39	-.80	1.57	1.25	.89	.20	-.36	-.78

F =	1,000		N = 5				10		N = 10			
L	M .25	.50	1	3	6	9	.25	.50	1	3	6	9
.25	.10	.02	-.07	-.30	-.60	-.90	.10	.03	-.06	-.30	-.60	-.90
.50	.18	.09	-.03	-.29	-.60	-.90	.19	.09	-.02	-.29	-.60	-.90
1	.31	.19	.05	-.27	-.60	-.90	.33	.20	.06	-.27	-.60	-.90
3	.69	.50	.28	-.16	-.56	-.89	.72	.52	.30	-.15	-.56	-.89
6	1.10	.85	.56	-.02	-.48	-.85	1.14	.88	.59	.02	-.47	-.85
9	1.44	1.13	.79	.14	-.40	-.80	1.49	1.17	.83	.17	-.39	-.80

F = forecast per month   N = number of stockkeeping units (SKU'S)

L = lead time in months   M = order quantity in months of forecast

SL = .90 (service level)   COV = .30 (coefficient of variation)

F =	10		N = 25						N = 50			
L	M	.25	.50	1	3	6	9	.25	.50	1	3	6	9
.25		1.18	.91	.61	.03	-.47	-.84	1.85	1.48	1.08	.33	-.28	-.73
.50		1.84	1.48	1.08	.33	-.28	-.73	2.86	2.36	1.82	.84	.06	-.48
1		2.85	2.35	1.82	.83	.06	-.49	4.40	3.69	2.96	1.66	.66	-.06
3		5.64	4.77	3.89	2.35	1.19	.41	8.65	7.36	6.14	4.06	2.54	1.53
6		8.63	7.35	6.13	4.05	2.53	1.53	13.33	11.29	9.55	6.71	4.70	3.39
9		11.13	9.45	7.95	5.46	3.67	2.50	16.79	14.49	12.31	8.89	6.51	4.98

F =	50		N = 25						N = 50			
L	M	.25	.50	1	3	6	9	.25	.50	1	3	6	9
.25		.43	.28	.12	-.24	-.59	-.90	.67	.48	.27	-.17	-.56	-.89
.50		.70	.51	.29	-.16	-.56	-.89	1.06	.82	.54	-.02	-.49	-.86
1		1.11	.85	.57	.00	-.48	-.85	1.67	1.33	.96	.25	-.33	-.76
3		2.25	1.83	1.38	.53	-.15	-.64	3.34	2.78	2.18	1.09	.24	-.35
6		3.48	2.90	2.28	1.16	.30	-.31	5.13	4.33	3.52	2.07	.97	.23
9		4.47	3.76	3.02	1.70	.69	.01	6.58	5.59	4.60	2.88	1.61	.75

F =	100		N = 25						N = 50			
L	M	.25	.50	1	3	6	9	.25	.50	1	3	6	9
.25		.28	.17	.03	-.27	-.60	-.90	.43	.29	.12	-.24	-.59	-.90
.50		.47	.32	.15	-.23	-.59	-.90	.70	.51	.29	-.15	-.56	-.89
1		.77	.57	.34	-.13	-.55	-.89	1.12	.86	.58	.01	-.48	-.85
3		1.59	1.26	.90	.21	-.36	-.78	2.28	1.86	1.40	.54	-.14	-.63
6		2.47	2.02	1.54	.64	-.08	-.58	3.52	2.93	2.31	1.18	.31	-.30
9		3.19	2.64	2.06	1.01	.18	-.39	4.52	3.80	3.06	1.73	.71	.02

F =	500		N = 25						N = 50			
L	M	.25	.50	1	3	6	9	.25	.50	1	3	6	9
.25		.14	.05	-.05	-.30	-.60	-.90	.18	.09	-.03	-.29	-.60	-.90
.50		.25	.14	.01	-.28	-.60	-.90	.31	.19	.05	-.27	-.60	-.90
1		.42	.28	.11	-.24	-.59	-.90	.52	.36	.17	-.21	-.58	-.90
3		.90	.67	.42	-.08	-.53	-.87	1.10	.85	.56	-.02	-.48	-.85
6		1.42	1.12	.78	.13	-.40	-.81	1.73	1.38	1.00	.28	-.32	-.75
9		1.84	1.48	1.08	.33	-.28	-.73	2.24	1.82	1.37	.52	-.16	-.64

F =	1,000		N = 25						N = 50			
L	M	.25	.50	1	3	6	9	.25	.50	1	3	6	9
.25		.12	.04	-.06	-.30	-.60	-.90	.14	.06	-.05	-.30	-.60	-.90
.50		.21	.11	-.01	-.29	-.60	-.90	.25	.14	.01	-.28	-.60	-.90
1		.36	.23	.08	-.26	-.59	-.90	.42	.28	.11	-.24	-.59	-.90
3		.79	.58	.35	-.12	-.55	-.88	.90	.68	.42	-.08	-.52	-.87
6		1.25	.97	.66	.06	-.45	-.83	1.42	1.12	.79	.14	-.40	-.81
9		1.63	1.30	.93	.23	-.35	-.77	1.85	1.48	1.09	.33	-.28	-.73

F = forecast per month   N = number of stockkeeping units (SKU'S)
L = lead time in months   M = order quantity in months of forecast

Table 10.2 Safety Stock in months of forecast for items with N SKU's

SL = .90 (service level)   COV = .50 (coefficient of variation)

F = 10	N = 5						N = 10					
L \ M	.25	.50	1	3	6	9	.25	.50	1	3	6	9
.25	.47	.32	.14	-.23	-.59	-.90	.70	.51	.29	-.16	-.56	-.89
.50	.76	.56	.33	-.13	-.55	-.89	1.12	.86	.57	.01	-.48	-.85
1	1.21	.94	.64	.04	-.46	-.84	1.75	1.40	1.02	.29	-.31	-.75
3	2.45	2.00	1.52	.63	-.09	-.59	3.50	2.91	2.30	1.17	.30	-.30
6	3.78	3.15	2.50	1.32	.41	-.22	5.37	4.53	3.69	2.20	1.07	.31
9	4.85	4.08	3.30	1.91	.85	.13	6.88	5.85	4.83	3.05	1.74	.86

F = 50	N = 5						N = 10					
L \ M	.25	.50	1	3	6	9	.25	.50	1	3	6	9
.25	.28	.17	.03	-.27	-.60	-.90	.35	.22	.07	-.26	-.60	-.90
.50	.47	.32	.15	-.23	-.59	-.90	.57	.40	.21	-.20	-.58	-.90
1	.77	.57	.34	-.13	-.55	-.89	.92	.69	.44	-.07	-.52	-.87
3	1.59	1.26	.90	.21	-.36	-.78	1.89	1.52	1.11	.35	-.27	-.72
6	2.47	2.02	1.54	.64	-.08	-.58	2.92	2.41	1.87	.87	.08	-.47
9	3.19	2.64	2.06	1.01	.18	-.39	3.76	3.14	2.49	1.31	.40	-.22

F = 100	N = 5						N = 10					
L \ M	.25	.50	1	3	6	9	.25	.50	1	3	6	9
.25	.26	.15	.02	-.28	-.60	-.90	.29	.17	.03	-.27	-.60	-.90
.50	.43	.29	.12	-.24	-.59	-.90	.48	.33	.15	-.22	-.59	-.90
1	.70	.51	.29	-.15	-.56	-.89	.79	.58	.35	-.13	-.55	-.88
3	1.46	1.15	.81	.16	-.39	-.80	1.62	1.29	.93	.23	-.35	-.77
6	2.28	1.86	1.40	.54	-.14	-.63	2.52	2.06	1.57	.66	-.06	-.57
9	2.94	2.43	1.88	.88	.09	-.46	3.25	2.69	2.11	1.04	.21	-.38

F = 500	N = 5						N = 10					
L \ M	.25	.50	1	3	6	9	.25	.50	1	3	6	9
.25	.23	.13	.00	-.28	-.60	-.90	.24	.13	.01	-.28	-.60	-.90
.50	.40	.26	.10	-.25	-.59	-.90	.41	.27	.10	-.25	-.59	-.90
1	.65	.47	.26	-.17	-.57	-.89	.67	.48	.27	-.17	-.56	-.89
3	1.36	1.06	.74	.11	-.42	-.82	1.39	1.09	.76	.12	-.41	-.81
6	2.12	1.72	1.28	.46	-.20	-.67	2.17	1.76	1.32	.49	-.18	-.66
9	2.73	2.25	1.73	.77	.02	-.52	2.80	2.30	1.78	.81	.04	-.50

F = 1,000	N = 5						N = 10					
L \ M	.25	.50	1	3	6	9	.25	.50	1	3	6	9
.25	.23	.13	.00	-.28	-.60	-.90	.23	.13	.00	-.28	-.60	-.90
.50	.39	.26	.09	-.25	-.59	-.90	.40	.26	.10	-.25	-.59	-.90
1	.64	.46	.25	-.17	-.57	-.89	.65	.47	.26	-.17	-.57	-.89
3	1.34	1.05	.73	.10	-.42	-.82	1.36	1.07	.74	.11	-.42	-.82
6	2.10	1.70	1.27	.45	-.20	-.67	2.12	1.72	1.28	.47	-.20	-.67
9	2.71	2.22	1.71	.76	.01	-.52	2.74	2.25	1.73	.78	.02	-.52

F = forecast per month   N = number of stockkeeping units (SKU'S)

L = lead time in months   M = order quantity in months of forecast

148 Inventory Management and Planning

Table 10.2 Safety Stock in months of forecast for items with N SKU's (Continued)

SL = .90 (service level)   COV = .50 (coefficient of variation)

F = 10							N = 25	N = 50					
L	M	.25	.50	1	3	6	9	.25	.50	1	3	6	9
.25		1.23	.95	.65	.05	-.45	-.84	1.88	1.51	1.11	.35	-.27	-.72
.50		1.92	1.54	1.14	.37	-.26	-.71	2.92	2.41	1.86	.87	.08	-.47
1		2.97	2.45	1.90	.89	.10	-.45	4.48	3.77	3.03	1.71	.70	.01
3		5.86	4.96	4.06	2.47	1.29	.49	8.81	7.51	6.26	4.15	2.62	1.60
6		8.96	7.64	6.38	4.24	2.69	1.66	13.59	11.52	9.73	6.86	4.83	3.50
9		11.58	9.81	8.27	5.71	3.88	2.68	17.05	14.78	12.55	9.08	6.67	5.12

F = 50							N = 25	N = 50					
L	M	.25	.50	1	3	6	9	.25	.50	1	3	6	9
.25		.51	.35	.17	-.22	-.58	-.90	.73	.54	.31	-.14	-.55	-.89
.50		.82	.61	.37	-.11	-.54	-.88	1.17	.90	.61	.03	-.47	-.84
1		1.31	1.02	.70	.09	-.43	-.82	1.83	1.47	1.07	.32	-.29	-.73
3		2.63	2.16	1.66	.72	-.04	-.54	3.65	3.04	2.41	1.25	.36	-.26
6		4.05	3.39	2.71	1.47	.52	-.13	5.60	4.73	3.86	2.32	1.17	.39
9		5.21	4.40	3.57	2.11	1.00	.26	7.18	6.10	5.04	3.22	1.87	.97

F = 100							N = 25	N = 50					
L	M	.25	.50	1	3	6	9	.25	.50	1	3	6	9
.25		.38	.25	.09	-.25	-.59	-.90	.51	.36	.17	-.22	-.58	-.90
.50		.63	.45	.24	-.18	-.57	-.89	.83	.62	.38	-.11	-.54	-.88
1		1.00	.76	.49	-.04	-.50	-.86	1.32	1.03	.71	.09	-.43	-.82
3		2.05	1.66	1.23	.43	-.22	-.68	2.66	2.18	1.67	.73	-.04	-.54
6		3.17	2.62	2.05	1.00	.18	-.40	4.09	3.42	2.74	1.49	.54	-.12
9		4.07	3.41	2.72	1.48	.53	-.13	5.25	4.43	3.60	2.13	1.02	.27

F = 500							N = 25	N = 50					
L	M	.25	.50	1	3	6	9	.25	.50	1	3	6	9
.25		.26	.15	.02	-.28	-.60	-.90	.30	.18	.04	-.27	-.60	-.90
.50		.44	.29	.12	-.24	-.59	-.90	.49	.34	.16	-.22	-.59	-.90
1		.72	.52	.30	-.15	-.56	-.89	.80	.59	.35	-.12	-.54	-.88
3		1.49	1.18	.83	.17	-.39	-.80	1.65	1.31	.94	.24	-.34	-.77
6		2.32	1.89	1.43	.56	-.13	-.62	2.56	2.10	1.60	.68	-.05	-.56
9		2.99	2.47	1.92	.91	.11	-.45	3.29	2.73	2.14	1.06	.22	-.36

F = 1,000							N = 25	N = 50					
L	M	.25	.50	1	3	6	9	.25	.50	1	3	6	9
.25		.24	.14	.01	-.28	-.60	-.90	.26	.15	.02	-.28	-.60	-.90
.50		.41	.27	.11	-.24	-.59	-.90	.44	.30	.13	-.24	-.59	-.90
1		.68	.49	.28	-.16	-.56	-.89	.72	.52	.30	-.15	-.56	-.89
3		1.41	1.11	.78	.13	-.41	-.81	1.49	1.18	.83	.17	-.38	-.79
6		2.20	1.79	1.34	.50	-.17	-.65	2.32	1.89	1.43	.56	-.13	-.62
9		2.84	2.34	1.81	.83	.05	-.49	3.00	2.48	1.92	.91	.11	-.45

F = forecast per month   N = number of stockkeeping units (SKU'S)

L = lead time in months   M = order quantity in months of forecast

Table 10.3 Safety Stock in months of forecast for items with N SKU's

SL = .90 (service level)   COV = .70 (coefficient of variation)

F =	10		N =	5				10		N =	10		
L	M	.25	.50	1	3	6	9	.25	.50	1	3	6	9
.25		.59	.41	.22	-.19	-.57	-.89	.80	.59	.35	-.12	-.54	-.88
.50		.94	.71	.45	-.07	-.52	-.87	1.26	.98	.67	.07	-.44	-.83
1		1.49	1.17	.83	.17	-.39	-.80	1.98	1.59	1.18	.39	-.24	-.70
3		2.98	2.46	1.91	.90	.11	-.45	3.93	3.29	2.62	1.41	.48	-.17
6		4.59	3.85	3.10	1.76	.74	.04	6.03	5.11	4.19	2.57	1.36	.55
9		5.89	4.98	4.08	2.49	1.30	.50	7.75	6.58	5.46	3.54	2.13	1.18

F =	50		N =	5						N =	10		
L	M	.25	.50	1	3	6	9	.25	.50	1	3	6	9
.25		.43	.28	.12	-.24	-.59	-.90	.48	.33	.15	-.23	-.59	-.90
.50		.70	.51	.29	-.16	-.56	-.89	.78	.57	.34	-.13	-.55	-.88
1		1.11	.85	.57	.00	-.48	-.85	1.23	.96	.65	.05	-.45	-.84
3		2.25	1.83	1.38	.53	-.15	-.64	2.50	2.04	1.56	.65	-.07	-.58
6		3.48	2.90	2.28	1.16	.30	-.31	3.85	3.21	2.55	1.36	.44	-.20
9		4.47	3.76	3.02	1.70	.69	.01	4.94	4.16	3.37	1.96	.89	.16

F =	100		N =	5						N =	10		
L	M	.25	.50	1	3	6	9	.25	.50	1	3	6	9
.25		.40	.27	.10	-.25	-.59	-.90	.43	.29	.12	-.24	-.59	-.90
.50		.66	.48	.27	-.17	-.56	-.89	.70	.51	.29	-.15	-.56	-.89
1		1.06	.81	.53	-.02	-.49	-.86	1.12	.86	.58	.01	-.48	-.85
3		2.15	1.75	1.31	.48	-.19	-.66	2.28	1.86	1.40	.54	-.14	-.63
6		3.32	2.76	2.17	1.08	.24	-.35	3.52	2.93	2.31	1.18	.31	-.30
9		4.28	3.59	2.87	1.59	.61	-.06	4.52	3.80	3.06	1.73	.71	.02

F =	500		N =	5						N =	10		
L	M	.25	.50	1	3	6	9	.25	.50	1	3	6	9
.25		.39	.25	.09	-.25	-.59	-.90	.39	.26	.09	-.25	-.59	-.90
.50		.63	.45	.25	-.18	-.57	-.89	.64	.46	.25	-.17	-.57	-.89
1		1.02	.77	.50	-.04	-.50	-.86	1.03	.78	.51	-.03	-.50	-.86
3		2.07	1.67	1.25	.44	-.21	-.68	2.10	1.70	1.27	.45	-.20	-.67
6		3.20	2.65	2.07	1.01	.19	-.39	3.24	2.69	2.10	1.04	.20	-.38
9		4.11	3.45	2.75	1.50	.55	-.11	4.16	3.49	2.79	1.53	.57	-.10

F =	1,000		N =	5						N =	10		
L	M	.25	.50	1	3	6	9	.25	.50	1	3	6	9
.25		.38	.25	.09	-.25	-.59	-.90	.39	.25	.09	-.25	-.59	-.90
.50		.63	.45	.24	-.18	-.57	-.89	.64	.45	.25	-.18	-.57	-.89
1		1.01	.77	.50	-.04	-.50	-.86	1.02	.77	.50	-.04	-.50	-.86
3		2.06	1.67	1.24	.43	-.22	-.68	2.07	1.68	1.25	.44	-.21	-.68
6		3.18	2.64	2.06	1.01	.18	-.39	3.20	2.66	2.08	1.02	.19	-.39
9		4.09	3.43	2.74	1.49	.54	-.12	4.12	3.45	2.76	1.51	.55	-.12

F = forecast per month
L = lead time in months
N = number of stockkeeping units (SKU'S)
M = order quantity in months of forecast

SL = .90 (service level)   COV = .70   (coefficient of variation)

F = 10		N = 25					N = 50				
L \ M	.25	.50	1	3	6	9	.25	.50	1	3	6	9
.25	1.30	1.01	.70	.08	-.44	-.83	1.94	1.56	1.15	.38	-.25	-.71
.50	2.03	1.64	1.22	.42	-.23	-.69	3.00	2.48	1.93	.91	.11	-.45
1	3.13	2.59	2.02	.98	.16	-.41	4.61	3.88	3.12	1.78	.75	.05
3	6.18	5.24	4.30	2.65	1.43	.60	9.06	7.72	6.45	4.30	2.73	1.70
6	9.44	8.06	6.74	4.53	2.92	1.86	13.97	11.84	10.02	7.08	5.01	3.66
9	12.22	10.35	8.73	6.07	4.18	2.94	17.45	15.20	12.91	9.37	6.91	5.33

F = 50		N = 25					N = 50				
L \ M	.25	.50	1	3	6	9	.25	.50	1	3	6	9
.25	.62	.44	.24	-.18	-.57	-.89	.83	.62	.37	-.11	-.54	-.88
.50	1.00	.76	.49	-.04	-.51	-.86	1.31	1.02	.71	.09	-.43	-.82
1	1.57	1.25	.89	.20	-.36	-.78	2.05	1.66	1.23	.43	-.22	-.68
3	3.15	2.61	2.03	.99	.17	-.40	4.07	3.41	2.72	1.48	.53	-.13
6	4.83	4.07	3.29	1.90	.85	.13	6.24	5.29	4.34	2.69	1.45	.62
9	6.20	5.26	4.31	2.67	1.44	.61	8.02	6.82	5.67	3.69	2.25	1.29

F = 100		N = 25					N = 50				
L \ M	.25	.50	1	3	6	9	.25	.50	1	3	6	9
.25	.51	.35	.17	-.22	-.58	-.90	.63	.45	.24	-.18	-.57	-.89
.50	.82	.61	.37	-.11	-.54	-.88	1.00	.76	.49	-.04	-.50	-.86
1	1.31	1.02	.70	.09	-.43	-.82	1.58	1.25	.90	.21	-.36	-.78
3	2.63	2.16	1.66	.72	-.04	-.54	3.17	2.62	2.05	1.00	.18	-.40
6	4.05	3.39	2.71	1.47	.52	-.13	4.86	4.10	3.31	1.92	.86	.14
9	5.21	4.40	3.57	2.11	1.00	.26	6.24	5.29	4.34	2.69	1.45	.62

F = 500		N = 25					N = 50				
L \ M	.25	.50	1	3	6	9	.25	.50	1	3	6	9
.25	.41	.27	.11	-.25	-.59	-.90	.44	.29	.12	-.24	-.59	-.90
.50	.67	.48	.27	-.17	-.56	-.89	.71	.52	.30	-.15	-.56	-.89
1	1.07	.82	.54	-.02	-.49	-.86	1.13	.87	.58	.01	-.48	-.85
3	2.17	1.76	1.32	.49	-.18	-.66	2.30	1.87	1.41	.55	-.14	-.63
6	3.36	2.79	2.19	1.10	.25	-.34	3.55	2.95	2.33	1.20	.32	-.29
9	4.32	3.62	2.90	1.61	.63	-.06	4.56	3.83	3.08	1.75	.73	.04

F = 1,000		N = 25					N = 50				
L \ M	.25	.50	1	3	6	9	.25	.50	1	3	6	9
.25	.40	.26	.10	-.25	-.59	-.90	.41	.27	.11	-.24	-.59	-.90
.50	.65	.47	.26	-.17	-.57	-.89	.67	.48	.27	-.17	-.56	-.89
1	1.04	.79	.52	-.03	-.50	-.86	1.07	.82	.54	-.02	-.49	-.86
3	2.11	1.71	1.28	.46	-.20	-.67	2.18	1.77	1.32	.49	-.18	-.66
6	3.26	2.71	2.12	1.05	.21	-.37	3.36	2.79	2.19	1.10	.25	-.34
9	4.20	3.52	2.81	1.55	.58	-.09	4.32	3.63	2.91	1.62	.63	-.06

F = forecast per month   N = number of stockkeeping units (SKU'S)
L = lead time in months   M = order quantity in months of forecast

Table 10.4 Safety Stock in months of forecast for items with N SKU's

SL = .95 (service level)   COV = .30 (coefficient of variation)

F = 10

L	M	N = 5 .25	.50	1	3	6	9	N = 10 .25	.50	1	3	6	9
.25		.50	.38	.25	-.02	-.25	-.43	.80	.63	.45	.11	-.18	-.39
.50		.79	.63	.45	.10	-.18	-.39	1.24	1.01	.77	.32	-.04	-.29
1		1.23	1.00	.76	.32	-.04	-.29	1.91	1.59	1.26	.67	.21	-.10
3		2.43	2.05	1.66	.96	.43	.07	3.75	3.19	2.64	1.70	1.01	.55
6		3.73	3.17	2.62	1.69	1.00	.54	5.78	4.89	4.12	2.85	1.93	1.33
9		4.77	4.07	3.41	2.29	1.48	.95	7.41	6.28	5.33	3.79	2.71	2.01

F = 50

L	M	N = 5 .25	.50	1	3	6	9	N = 10 .25	.50	1	3	6	9
.25		.24	.17	.08	-.11	-.29	-.45	.34	.24	.14	-.08	-.28	-.45
.50		.39	.29	.17	-.06	-.27	-.44	.54	.41	.27	-.01	-.24	-.43
1		.62	.48	.33	.03	-.22	-.42	.84	.67	.48	.13	-.17	-.38
3		1.26	1.03	.79	.33	-.03	-.29	1.68	1.40	1.10	.55	.13	-.17
6		1.94	1.62	1.29	.69	.23	-.09	2.58	2.18	1.77	1.04	.49	.12
9		2.49	2.10	1.70	.99	.46	.09	3.31	2.81	2.32	1.45	.81	.38

F = 100

L	M	N = 5 .25	.50	1	3	6	9	N = 10 .25	.50	1	3	6	9
.25		.20	.13	.05	-.12	-.30	-.45	.25	.17	.08	-.11	-.29	-.45
.50		.33	.23	.13	-.09	-.28	-.45	.41	.30	.18	-.06	-.27	-.44
1		.52	.40	.26	-.01	-.25	-.43	.65	.50	.35	.04	-.22	-.41
3		1.06	.86	.64	.23	-.10	-.33	1.31	1.07	.82	.35	-.02	-.27
6		1.64	1.36	1.07	.53	.11	-.18	2.01	1.68	1.34	.73	.26	-.07
9		2.11	1.77	1.42	.78	.30	-.04	2.58	2.18	1.77	1.04	.49	.12

F = 500

L	M	N = 5 .25	.50	1	3	6	9	N = 10 .25	.50	1	3	6	9
.25		.16	.10	.03	-.13	-.30	-.45	.17	.11	.03	-.13	-.30	-.45
.50		.27	.19	.09	-.10	-.29	-.45	.29	.20	.10	-.10	-.29	-.45
1		.43	.32	.20	-.05	-.27	-.44	.46	.35	.22	-.04	-.26	-.44
3		.89	.71	.52	.15	-.15	-.37	.95	.76	.56	.18	-.13	-.36
6		1.38	1.13	.87	.39	.01	-.26	1.46	1.21	.94	.44	.04	-.23
9		1.77	1.48	1.17	.60	.16	-.14	1.88	1.57	1.25	.66	.20	-.11

F = 1,000

L	M	N = 5 .25	.50	1	3	6	9	N = 10 .25	.50	1	3	6	9
.25		.16	.10	.02	-.13	-.30	-.45	.16	.10	.03	-.13	-.30	-.45
.50		.26	.18	.09	-.11	-.29	-.45	.27	.19	.09	-.10	-.29	-.45
1		.42	.31	.19	-.05	-.27	-.44	.44	.33	.20	-.05	-.27	-.44
3		.87	.69	.50	.14	-.16	-.38	.89	.72	.52	.15	-.15	-.37
6		1.34	1.10	.85	.37	-.02	-.27	1.39	1.14	.88	.40	.02	-.25
9		1.73	1.44	1.13	.58	.14	-.16	1.79	1.49	1.17	.61	.17	-.14

F = forecast per month
L = lead time in months
N = number of stockkeeping units (SKU'S)
M = order quantity in months of forecast

SL = .95 (service level) COV = .30 (coefficient of variation)

F = 10

L	M = .25	.50	1	3	6	9	N=50 .25	.50	1	3	6	9
.25	1.43	1.18	.91	.42	.03	-.24	2.20	1.85	1.48	.83	.33	-.03
.50	2.20	1.84	1.48	.83	.33	-.03	3.36	2.86	2.36	1.48	.84	.40
1	3.36	2.85	2.35	1.48	.83	.40	5.17	4.40	3.69	2.51	1.66	1.10
3	6.66	5.64	4.77	3.35	2.35	1.69	9.69	8.65	7.36	5.40	4.06	3.20
6	9.68	8.63	7.35	5.39	4.05	3.19	13.71	13.33	11.29	8.53	6.71	5.57
9	11.86	11.13	9.45	7.06	5.46	4.44	16.80	16.79	14.49	11.07	8.89	7.53

F = 50

L	M = .25	.50	1	3	6	9	N=50 .25	.50	1	3	6	9
.25	.56	.43	.28	.00	-.24	-.43	.84	.67	.48	.13	-.17	-.38
.50	.87	.70	.51	.14	-.16	-.37	1.30	1.06	.82	.35	-.02	-.28
1	1.35	1.11	.85	.38	.00	-.26	2.00	1.67	1.33	.72	.25	-.08
3	2.67	2.25	1.83	1.09	.53	.15	3.94	3.34	2.78	1.81	1.09	.62
6	4.09	3.48	2.90	1.89	1.16	.68	6.06	5.13	4.33	3.01	2.07	1.45
9	5.26	4.47	3.76	2.56	1.70	1.13	7.76	6.58	5.59	4.00	2.88	2.16

F = 100

L	M = .25	.50	1	3	6	9	N=50 .25	.50	1	3	6	9
.25	.38	.28	.17	-.07	-.27	-.44	.56	.43	.29	.00	-.24	-.42
.50	.61	.47	.32	.02	-.23	-.42	.88	.70	.51	.15	-.15	-.37
1	.96	.77	.57	.18	-.13	-.36	1.37	1.12	.86	.39	.01	-.26
3	1.91	1.59	1.26	.67	.21	-.10	2.70	2.28	1.86	1.11	.54	.16
6	2.92	2.47	2.02	1.23	.64	.24	4.14	3.52	2.93	1.92	1.18	.69
9	3.75	3.19	2.64	1.70	1.01	.55	5.32	4.52	3.80	2.59	1.73	1.16

F = 500

L	M = .25	.50	1	3	6	9	N=50 .25	.50	1	3	6	9
.25	.21	.14	.05	-.12	-.30	-.45	.26	.18	.09	-.11	-.29	-.45
.50	.34	.25	.14	-.08	-.28	-.45	.42	.31	.19	-.05	-.27	-.44
1	.54	.42	.28	-.01	-.24	-.43	.67	.52	.36	.05	-.21	-.41
3	1.10	.90	.67	.25	-.08	-.32	1.34	1.10	.85	.37	-.02	-.27
6	1.71	1.42	1.12	.56	.13	-.16	2.07	1.73	1.38	.76	.28	-.06
9	2.19	1.84	1.48	.83	.33	-.03	2.65	2.24	1.82	1.08	.52	.15

F = 1,000

L	M = .25	.50	1	3	6	9	N=50 .25	.50	1	3	6	9
.25	.18	.12	.04	-.13	-.30	-.45	.21	.14	.06	-.12	-.30	-.45
.50	.30	.21	.11	-.10	-.29	-.45	.34	.25	.14	-.08	-.28	-.45
1	.48	.36	.23	-.03	-.26	-.43	.55	.42	.28	-.01	-.24	-.43
3	.98	.79	.58	.19	-.12	-.35	1.11	.90	.68	.26	-.08	-.32
6	1.51	1.25	.97	.46	.06	-.22	1.71	1.42	1.12	.57	.14	-.16
9	1.95	1.63	1.30	.69	.23	-.09	2.20	1.85	1.48	.83	.33	-.03

F = forecast per month   N = number of stockkeeping units (SKU'S)
L = lead time in months   M = order quantity in months of forecast

Table 10.5 Safety Stock in months of forecast for items with N SKU's

SL = .95 (service level)   COV = .50 (coefficient of variation)

F = 10		N = 5						N = 10					
L	M	.25	.50	1	3	6	9	.25	.50	1	3	6	9
.25		.61	.47	.32	.02	-.23	-.42	.88	.70	.51	.14	-.16	-.37
.50		.95	.76	.56	.18	-.13	-.36	1.36	1.12	.86	.38	.01	-.26
1		1.47	1.21	.94	.44	.04	-.23	2.09	1.75	1.40	.77	.29	-.05
3		2.90	2.45	2.00	1.22	.63	.23	4.11	3.50	2.91	1.91	1.17	.68
6		4.43	3.78	3.15	2.09	1.32	.81	6.34	5.37	4.53	3.17	2.20	1.56
9		5.72	4.85	4.08	2.82	1.91	1.31	8.06	6.88	5.85	4.20	3.05	2.31

F = 50		N = 5						N = 10					
L	M	.25	.50	1	3	6	9	.25	.50	1	3	6	9
.25		.38	.28	.17	-.07	-.27	-.44	.46	.35	.22	-.04	-.26	-.44
.50		.61	.47	.32	.02	-.23	-.42	.73	.57	.40	.08	-.20	-.40
1		.96	.77	.57	.18	-.13	-.36	1.13	.92	.69	.27	-.07	-.32
3		1.91	1.59	1.26	.67	.21	-.10	2.25	1.89	1.52	.85	.35	.01
6		2.92	2.47	2.02	1.23	.64	.24	3.44	2.92	2.41	1.52	.87	.43
9		3.75	3.19	2.64	1.70	1.01	.55	4.41	3.76	3.14	2.08	1.31	.80

F = 100		N = 5						N = 10					
L	M	.25	.50	1	3	6	9	.25	.50	1	3	6	9
.25		.35	.26	.15	-.08	-.28	-.44	.39	.29	.17	-.06	-.27	-.44
.50		.56	.43	.29	.00	-.24	-.42	.62	.48	.33	.03	-.22	-.42
1		.88	.70	.51	.15	-.15	-.37	.97	.79	.58	.19	-.13	-.35
3		1.76	1.46	1.15	.59	.16	-.15	1.94	1.62	1.29	.69	.23	-.09
6		2.70	2.28	1.86	1.11	.54	.16	2.98	2.52	2.06	1.26	.66	.26
9		3.46	2.94	2.43	1.54	.88	.44	3.82	3.25	2.69	1.74	1.04	.57

F = 500		N = 5						N = 10					
L	M	.25	.50	1	3	6	9	.25	.50	1	3	6	9
.25		.33	.23	.13	-.09	-.28	-.45	.33	.24	.13	-.08	-.28	-.45
.50		.52	.40	.26	-.01	-.25	-.43	.53	.41	.27	-.01	-.25	-.43
1		.82	.65	.47	.12	-.17	-.38	.84	.67	.48	.13	-.17	-.38
3		1.64	1.36	1.06	.53	.11	-.18	1.67	1.39	1.09	.55	.12	-.17
6		2.51	2.12	1.72	1.00	.46	.10	2.57	2.17	1.76	1.03	.49	.12
9		3.22	2.73	2.25	1.40	.77	.35	3.29	2.80	2.30	1.44	.81	.38

F = 1,000		N = 5						N = 10					
L	M	.25	.50	1	3	6	9	.25	.50	1	3	6	9
.25		.32	.23	.13	-.09	-.28	-.45	.33	.23	.13	-.09	-.28	-.45
.50		.51	.39	.26	-.02	-.25	-.43	.52	.40	.26	-.01	-.25	-.43
1		.81	.64	.46	.11	-.17	-.39	.82	.65	.47	.12	-.17	-.38
3		1.62	1.34	1.05	.52	.10	-.19	1.64	1.36	1.07	.53	.11	-.18
6		2.49	2.10	1.70	.99	.45	.09	2.52	2.12	1.72	1.01	.47	.10
9		3.19	2.71	2.22	1.38	.76	.34	3.23	2.74	2.25	1.41	.78	.35

F = forecast per month   N = number of stockkeeping units (SKU'S)
L = lead time in months   M = order quantity in months of forecast

Table 10.5 Safety Stock in months of forecast for items with N SKU's (Continued)

SL = .95 (service level)   COV = .50 (coefficient of variation)

F =	10		N =	25			50		N =	50		
L	M	.25	.50	1	3	6	9	.25	.50	1	3	6	9
.25		1.48	1.23	.95	.45	.05	-.23	2.24	1.88	1.51	.85	.35	.01
.50		2.28	1.92	1.54	.87	.37	.02	3.43	2.92	2.41	1.52	.87	.43
1		3.49	2.97	2.45	1.56	.89	.45	5.28	4.48	3.77	2.57	1.71	1.14
3		6.91	5.86	4.96	3.50	2.47	1.80	9.85	8.81	7.51	5.52	4.15	3.28
6		9.99	8.96	7.64	5.62	4.24	3.36	13.92	13.59	11.52	8.71	6.86	5.70
9		12.23	11.58	9.81	7.36	5.71	4.67	17.07	17.05	14.78	11.30	9.08	7.70

F =	50		N =	25					N =	50		
L	M	.25	.50	1	3	6	9	.25	.50	1	3	6	9
.25		.65	.51	.35	.04	-.22	-.41	.91	.73	.54	.16	-.14	-.37
.50		1.02	.82	.61	.21	-.11	-.34	1.42	1.17	.90	.41	.03	-.25
1		1.58	1.31	1.02	.50	.09	-.20	2.18	1.83	1.47	.82	.32	-.03
3		3.11	2.63	2.16	1.34	.72	.31	4.29	3.65	3.04	2.01	1.25	.75
6		4.75	4.05	3.39	2.28	1.47	.94	6.61	5.60	4.73	3.32	2.32	1.67
9		6.15	5.21	4.40	3.06	2.11	1.49	8.33	7.18	6.10	4.40	3.22	2.46

F =	100		N =	25					N =	50		
L	M	.25	.50	1	3	6	9	.25	.50	1	3	6	9
.25		.50	.38	.25	-.02	-.25	-.43	.66	.51	.36	.05	-.22	-.41
.50		.79	.63	.45	.10	-.18	-.39	1.03	.83	.62	.22	-.11	-.34
1		1.23	1.00	.76	.32	-.04	-.29	1.59	1.32	1.03	.50	.09	-.20
3		2.43	2.05	1.66	.96	.43	.07	3.13	2.66	2.18	1.35	.73	.32
6		3.73	3.17	2.62	1.69	1.00	.54	4.79	4.09	3.42	2.30	1.49	.96
9		4.77	4.07	3.41	2.29	1.48	.95	6.20	5.25	4.43	3.09	2.13	1.51

F =	500		N =	25					N =	50		
L	M	.25	.50	1	3	6	9	.25	.50	1	3	6	9
.25		.36	.26	.15	-.07	-.28	-.44	.40	.30	.18	-.06	-.27	-.44
.50		.57	.44	.29	.01	-.24	-.42	.63	.49	.34	.03	-.22	-.42
1		.90	.72	.52	.15	-.15	-.37	.99	.80	.59	.20	-.12	-.35
3		1.79	1.49	1.18	.61	.17	-.14	1.97	1.65	1.31	.70	.24	-.08
6		2.75	2.32	1.89	1.13	.56	.18	3.02	2.56	2.10	1.29	.68	.28
9		3.52	2.99	2.47	1.57	.91	.46	3.88	3.29	2.73	1.77	1.06	.59

F =	1,000		N =	25					N =	50		
L	M	.25	.50	1	3	6	9	.25	.50	1	3	6	9
.25		.34	.24	.14	-.08	-.28	-.45	.36	.26	.15	-.07	-.28	-.44
.50		.54	.41	.27	-.01	-.24	-.43	.57	.44	.30	.01	-.24	-.42
1		.85	.68	.49	.13	-.16	-.38	.90	.72	.52	.15	-.15	-.37
3		1.70	1.41	1.11	.56	.13	-.17	1.79	1.49	1.18	.61	.17	-.14
6		2.61	2.20	1.79	1.05	.50	.13	2.75	2.32	1.89	1.13	.56	.18
9		3.34	2.84	2.34	1.47	.83	.39	3.53	3.00	2.48	1.57	.91	.46

F = forecast per month   N = number of stockkeeping units (SKU'S)
L = lead time in months   M = order quantity in months of forecast

Table 10.6   Safety Stock in months of forecast for items with N SKU's

SL = .95 (service level)   COV = .70   (coefficient of variation)

F = 10	N = 5						N = 10					
L \ M	.25	.50	1	3	6	9	.25	.50	1	3	6	9
.25	.74	.59	.41	.08	-.19	-.40	.99	.80	.59	.20	-.12	-.35
.50	1.16	.94	.71	.28	-.07	-.31	1.53	1.26	.98	.47	.07	-.21
1	1.78	1.49	1.17	.60	.17	-.14	2.35	1.98	1.59	.91	.39	.04
3	3.51	2.98	2.46	1.57	.90	.46	4.61	3.93	3.29	2.20	1.41	.88
6	5.40	4.59	3.85	2.64	1.76	1.19	7.12	6.03	5.11	3.62	2.57	1.89
9	6.95	5.89	4.98	3.52	2.49	1.81	8.86	7.75	6.58	4.78	3.54	2.74

F = 50	N = 5						N = 10					
L \ M	.25	.50	1	3	6	9	.25	.50	1	3	6	9
.25	.56	.43	.28	.00	-.24	-.43	.62	.48	.33	.03	-.23	-.42
.50	.87	.70	.51	.14	-.16	-.37	.97	.78	.57	.19	-.13	-.35
1	1.35	1.11	.85	.38	.00	-.26	1.49	1.23	.96	.45	.05	-.22
3	2.67	2.25	1.83	1.09	.53	.15	2.95	2.50	2.04	1.25	.65	.25
6	4.09	3.48	2.90	1.89	1.16	.68	4.51	3.85	3.21	2.14	1.36	.84
9	5.26	4.47	3.76	2.56	1.70	1.13	5.83	4.94	4.16	2.88	1.96	1.36

F = 100	N = 5						N = 10					
L \ M	.25	.50	1	3	6	9	.25	.50	1	3	6	9
.25	.53	.40	.27	-.01	-.25	-.43	.56	.43	.29	.00	-.24	-.42
.50	.83	.66	.48	.12	-.17	-.38	.88	.70	.51	.15	-.15	-.37
1	1.29	1.06	.81	.35	-.02	-.28	1.37	1.12	.86	.39	.01	-.26
3	2.55	2.15	1.75	1.03	.48	.11	2.70	2.28	1.86	1.11	.54	.16
6	3.91	3.32	2.76	1.79	1.08	.61	4.14	3.52	2.93	1.92	1.18	.69
9	5.02	4.28	3.59	2.43	1.59	1.04	5.32	4.52	3.80	2.59	1.73	1.16

F = 500	N = 5						N = 10					
L \ M	.25	.50	1	3	6	9	.25	.50	1	3	6	9
.25	.51	.39	.25	-.02	-.25	-.43	.51	.39	.26	-.02	-.25	-.43
.50	.80	.63	.45	.11	-.18	-.39	.81	.64	.46	.11	-.17	-.39
1	1.24	1.02	.77	.32	-.04	-.29	1.26	1.03	.78	.33	-.03	-.29
3	2.46	2.07	1.67	.97	.44	.08	2.49	2.10	1.70	.99	.45	.09
6	3.77	3.20	2.65	1.71	1.01	.55	3.81	3.24	2.69	1.73	1.04	.57
9	4.82	4.11	3.45	2.32	1.50	.97	4.89	4.16	3.49	2.35	1.53	.99

F = 1,000	N = 5						N = 10					
L \ M	.25	.50	1	3	6	9	.25	.50	1	3	6	9
.25	.50	.38	.25	-.02	-.25	-.43	.51	.39	.25	-.02	-.25	-.43
.50	.79	.63	.45	.11	-.18	-.39	.80	.64	.45	.11	-.18	-.39
1	1.23	1.01	.77	.32	-.04	-.29	1.24	1.02	.77	.32	-.04	-.29
3	2.44	2.06	1.67	.96	.43	.07	2.46	2.07	1.68	.97	.44	.08
6	3.75	3.18	2.64	1.70	1.01	.54	3.77	3.20	2.66	1.71	1.02	.55
9	4.80	4.09	3.43	2.31	1.49	.96	4.83	4.12	3.45	2.32	1.51	.97

F = forecast per month   N = number of stockkeeping units (SKU'S)

L = lead time in months   M = order quantity in months of forecast

SL = .95 (service level)   COV = .70 (coefficient of variation)

F =	10		N =	25					N =	50		
L	M	.25	.50	1	3	6	9	.25	.50	1	3	6	9
.25		1.57	1.30	1.01	.49	.08	-.20	2.31	1.94	1.56	.89	.38	.03
.50		2.41	2.03	1.64	.94	.42	.06	3.53	3.00	2.48	1.58	.91	.46
1		3.69	3.13	2.59	1.66	.98	.52	5.43	4.61	3.88	2.65	1.78	1.20
3		7.29	6.18	5.24	3.72	2.65	1.96	10.07	9.06	7.72	5.69	4.30	3.41
6		10.43	9.44	8.06	5.96	4.53	3.61	14.25	13.97	11.84	8.97	7.08	5.90
9		12.78	12.22	10.35	7.78	6.07	4.99	17.47	17.45	15.20	11.63	9.37	7.96

F =	50		N =	25					N =	50		
L	M	.25	.50	1	3	6	9	.25	.50	1	3	6	9
.25		.79	.62	.44	.10	-.18	-.39	1.02	.83	.62	.21	-.11	-.34
.50		1.22	1.00	.76	.31	-.04	-.30	1.58	1.31	1.02	.50	.09	-.20
1		1.88	1.57	1.25	.66	.20	-.11	2.43	2.05	1.66	.96	.43	.07
3		3.71	3.15	2.61	1.67	.99	.53	4.77	4.07	3.41	2.29	1.48	.95
6		5.70	4.83	4.07	2.81	1.90	1.31	7.36	6.24	5.29	3.76	2.69	1.99
9		7.32	6.20	5.26	3.74	2.67	1.97	9.11	8.02	6.82	4.97	3.69	2.87

F =	100		N =	25					N =	50		
L	M	.25	.50	1	3	6	9	.25	.50	1	3	6	9
.25		.65	.51	.35	.04	-.22	-.41	.79	.63	.45	.10	-.18	-.39
.50		1.02	.82	.61	.21	-.11	-.34	1.23	1.00	.76	.32	-.04	-.29
1		1.58	1.31	1.02	.50	.09	-.20	1.89	1.58	1.25	.66	.21	-.11
3		3.11	2.63	2.16	1.34	.72	.31	3.73	3.17	2.62	1.69	1.00	.54
6		4.75	4.05	3.39	2.28	1.47	.94	5.74	4.86	4.10	2.83	1.92	1.32
9		6.15	5.21	4.40	3.06	2.11	1.49	7.36	6.24	5.29	3.76	2.69	1.99

F =	500		N =	25					N =	50		
L	M	.25	.50	1	3	6	9	.25	.50	1	3	6	9
.25		.53	.41	.27	-.01	-.25	-.43	.57	.44	.29	.01	-.24	-.42
.50		.84	.67	.48	.13	-.17	-.38	.89	.71	.52	.15	-.15	-.37
1		1.30	1.07	.82	.35	-.02	-.28	1.38	1.13	.87	.39	.01	-.26
3		2.58	2.17	1.76	1.04	.49	.12	2.72	2.30	1.87	1.12	.55	.17
6		3.95	3.36	2.79	1.81	1.10	.62	4.17	3.55	2.95	1.94	1.20	.71
9		5.07	4.32	3.62	2.46	1.61	1.06	5.37	4.56	3.83	2.62	1.75	1.17

F =	1,000		N =	25					N =	50		
L	M	.25	.50	1	3	6	9	.25	.50	1	3	6	9
.25		.52	.40	.26	-.01	-.25	-.43	.54	.41	.27	-.01	-.24	-.43
.50		.82	.65	.47	.12	-.17	-.39	.84	.67	.48	.13	-.17	-.38
1		1.27	1.04	.79	.33	-.03	-.28	1.30	1.07	.82	.35	-.02	-.28
3		2.50	2.11	1.71	1.00	.46	.09	2.58	2.18	1.77	1.04	.49	.12
6		3.84	3.26	2.71	1.75	1.05	.58	3.95	3.36	2.79	1.82	1.10	.62
9		4.92	4.20	3.52	2.37	1.55	1.00	5.08	4.32	3.63	2.46	1.62	1.06

F = forecast per month   N = number of stockkeeping units (SKU'S)
L = lead time in months   M = order quantity in months of forecast

CHAPTER 11

Cycle Stock, Safety Stock, Turnover And Stocking Costs

As described in Chapter 9, inventory may be separated into two categories, called the cycle stock **CS** and the safety stock **SS**, which in total becomes the total stock (TS = CS + SS). The cycle stock represents stock that is available to meet the average demands and is generally based on economic considerations. The safety stock is stock that is carried as a protection for those occasions when demands exceed the average but yet it is necessary to attain the service level goals set forth by management.

Perhaps the most common measure of inventory investment is the turnover ratio (annual sales over average on-hand inventory). In this chapter, the total stock **TS** is the same as the average on-hand inventory as used in Chapter 6. Therefore, the **TO** ratio becomes annual sales over total stock. Although management may designate an ideal turnover ratio for the inventory, this ideal value is necessarily an average for all the items in the inventory and is not meant to be a fixed value for each and every item. The economic turnover for an item depends on both the economic level of cycle stock and the level of safety stock that satisfies the service level goals.

Another measure of the inventory, described in Chapters 2, 3 and 4, is called the stocking cost. This measure is the cost pertaining to ordering and holding of stock in inventory. In this chapter (unlike the earlier chapters) the stocking cost now includes the *combined* costs for safety stock and cycle stock.

In this chapter, also, the methods of determining the economic order quantity (from Chapter 2) and the safety stock (from Chapter 9) are combined in the endeavor to determine the total stock for an item and all related measures described above. The chapter further shows all data needed for this purpose and the role they play. At the same time, the sensitivity relations between the measures and the data are observed.

The goal of this chapter is to generate tables that will show how the above measures are related to each other and to the input data that play important roles in their determination. The model assumes the demands are evenly distributed throughout the year. The forecast of these demands and the associated standard error of the forecast are used in the decision making process of this chapter.

Data

The data needed to carry out the calculations are the following:

$$A = \text{forecast of the annual demand}$$
$$\sigma = \text{standard error of the one month forecast}$$
$$h = \text{annual holding rate}$$
$$Co = \text{cost per order}$$
$$C = \text{cost per unit}$$
$$SL = \text{desired service level}$$
$$L = \text{procurement lead time}$$

Model

The model proceeds in the following manner. The above input data for an item are used to derive the economic order quantity from which the cycle stock is determined. Next the safety stock needed to yield the desired service level is obtained. Cycle stock **CS** and safety stock **SS** are combined—to give the total stock **TS** for the item. These results lead to measuring the turnover and the stocking rate for the item.

The first step is to determine the economic order quantity **Q** for the item. Assuming the simple lot size model of Chapter 9 pertains, then:

$$Q = \sqrt{\frac{2 \, A \, Co}{C \, h}}$$

When the order quantity arrives to replenish the stock, it arrives in one lump sum. This stock is gradually used up until the next replenishment arrives. This process takes place in a sawtooth manner and, on the average, the amount of stock to meet the daily demands is **Q/2**, which is the average cycle stock (reference 1), i.e.:

$$CS = Q/2$$

The next step is to derive the safety stock **SS** necessary to satisfy the desired service level **SL** for the item. Recall from Chapter 9 that the following service level function is used for this purpose (references 2 and 3):

$$SL = 1 - E(k) \, \sigma_L / Q$$

In the above, **SL** is specified by management as an input parameter and **Q** is calculated from the earlier results. Now σ_L, the standard deviation of demand over the lead time, is derived from:

$$\sigma_L = \sqrt{L} \, \sigma$$

Thus, using **SL**, **Q** and σ_L, the partial expectation **E(k)** is found:

$$E(k) = (1 - SL) \, Q / \sigma_L$$

and then (by way of Table 7.2) the associated safety factor **k** is determined. Hence, the safety stock needed for the item becomes:

$$SS = k \, \sigma_L$$

The total stock **TS** is merely the sum of the cycle stock and the safety stock:

$$TS = CS + SS$$

This sum represents the average on-hand inventory needed to meet all demands placed on the item.

Now it is possible to measure the turnover ratio **TO** for the item, as in the following manner:

$$TO = \frac{\text{annual demand}}{\text{total stock}} = \frac{A}{TS}$$

Thus the turnover ratio for a particular item and its corresponding set of data is measured.

The annual stocking cost **S** for an item is here defined as the annual add-on cost of ordering and holding the item in inventory for both its cycle stock and safety stock needs. This calculation becomes:

$$S = A\,C_o/Q + hC\,(CS + SS)$$

that is,

$$S = (\text{order cost}) + (\text{holding cost})$$

The stocking rate **s** for one unit of the item is the ratio of stocking cost over the corresponding procurement cost. This rate is found by the relation:

$$s = S/AC$$

Tables

The following standardization of data is used to develop the tables of this chapter. Using **A/12** as the average forecast per month and recalling that σ is the standard deviation of this forecast, the coefficient of variation for one month is then:

$$cov = 12\sigma/A$$

Further, the cost per order and the procurement cost per unit are combined to give:

$$R = C_o/C$$

The tables also report the cycle stock and the safety stock in standardized form, where:

cs = cycle stock in months
ss = safety stock in months

In addition, the tables list the corresponding values of the turnover and stocking rate. Also, if the months of safety stock ever become a negative value, then for purposes of the tables the safety stock is set to zero.

The adjoining tables are developed using selected values of input data, **h, L, A, SL, cov** and **R**. The tables are arranged as follows:

Tables	h	L (months)
11.1	.25	.5
11.2	.25	1
11.3	.25	3
11.4	.25	5
11.5	.35	.5
11.6	.35	1
11.7	.35	3
11.8	.35	5

Example 11.1

Suppose the forecast for a service part calls for a monthly demand of 83 units and the associated standard error of the forecast is 41. Assume the part has a procurement cost of $4 per unit, the cost per order is $40, lead time is five months and a 95 percent service level is sought. Assume also that the annual holding rate is set at 35 percent. For this part, find the months of cycle stock, safety stock and total stock. Also determine the turnover and the stocking cost per unit.

With $h = .35$ and $L = 5$, Table 11.8 is used along with $SL = .95$, $cov = 41/83 = .50$, $A = 12 \times 83 = 1000$ and $R = 40/4 = 10$. The table entries show the cycle stock and safety stock are:

$$cs = 1.43 \text{ months}$$
$$ss = 0.85 \text{ months}$$

Thereby the total stock is:

$$ts = 2.28 \text{ months}$$

The tables also give the turnover:

$$TO = 5.25 \text{ months (which is derived from } 12/2.28)$$

and the stocking rate:

$$s = .108$$

Hence, the stocking cost per unit is $4 \times .108 = 0.432.

Example 11.2

For the service part in Example 11.1, show the effects on inventory when the lead time is reduced to 3 months and all else remains as before.

Table 11.7 is here used, as $h = .35$ and $L = 3$. The comparison of results are:

	L = 5	L = 3	% change
cs	1.43	1.43	0
ss	0.85	0.53	38 decrease
ts	2.28	1.96	14 decrease
TO	5.25	6.12	17 increase
s	0.108	0.099	8 decrease

Example 11.3

Using the service part in Example 11.1, show the inventory changes that occur when the service level is reduced to 90 percent and all else remains the same.

Table 11.8 is used where $h = .35$ and $L = 5$ to give the following results:

	SL = 95%	SL = 90%	% change
cs	1.43	1.43	0
ss	0.85	0.36	58 decrease
ts	2.28	1.79	21 decrease
TO	5.25	6.68	27 increase
s	0.108	0.094	13 decrease

Example 11.4

For the service part in Example 11.1, suppose the forecast could be improved to bring the standard deviation from 41 down to 25, whereby the coefficient of variation is $cov = 25/83 = .30$. Assuming all else remains as before, what are the effects on the inventory?

Table 11.8, with h = .35 and L = 5, yields the following:

	cov = .5	cov = .3	% change
cs	1.43	1.43	0
ss	0.85	0.30	65 decrease
ts	2.28	1.73	24 decrease
TO	5.25	6.92	32 increase
s	0.108	0.092	15 decrease

Example 11.5

For the service part in Example 11.1, show the inventory effects that take place when the holding rate is changed to 25 percent per year and all else remains as before.

Table 11.4 is used (h = .25 and L = 5) to give the results:

	h = .35	h = .25	% change
cs	1.43	1.70	19 increase
ss	0.85	0.74	13 decrease
ts	2.28	2.44	7 increase
TO	5.25	4.93	6 decrease

The stocking rates are not compared here because they are based on two different holding rates.

Table 11.1   Cycle Stock, Safety Stock, Turnover and Stocking Rate

h = .25 (Annual Holding Rate)   L = .5 (Lead Time in Months)

	SL = .90 COV = .30					SL = .95 COV = .30				
R	500	100	10	1	.1	500	100	10	1	.1
A	---------------------CS------------------					---------------------CS------------------				
100	37.95	16.97	5.37	1.70	.54	37.95	16.97	5.37	1.70	.54
1000	12.00	5.37	1.70	.54	.17	12.00	5.37	1.70	.54	.17
10000	3.79	1.70	.54	.17	.05	3.79	1.70	.54	.17	.05
100000	1.20	.54	.17	.05	.02	1.20	.54	.17	.05	.02
A	---------------------SS------------------					---------------------SS------------------				
100	.00	.00	.00	.00	.00	.00	.00	.00	.00	.07
1000	.00	.00	.00	.00	.13	.00	.00	.00	.07	.22
10000	.00	.00	.00	.13	.26	.00	.00	.07	.22	.33
100000	.00	.00	.13	.26	.37	.00	.07	.22	.33	.43
A	---------------------TO------------------					---------------------TO------------------				
100	.32	.71	2.24	7.07	22.36	.32	.71	2.24	7.07	19.76
1000	1.00	2.24	7.07	22.36	39.57	1.00	2.24	7.07	19.76	31.10
10000	3.16	7.07	22.36	39.57	37.70	3.16	7.07	19.76	31.10	31.18
100000	10.00	22.36	39.57	37.70	30.89	10.00	19.76	31.10	31.18	26.95
A	---------------------s------------------					---------------------s------------------				
100	1.581	.707	.224	.071	.022	1.581	.707	.224	.071	.024
1000	.500	.224	.071	.022	.010	.500	.224	.071	.024	.012
10000	.158	.071	.022	.010	.008	.158	.071	.024	.012	.009
100000	.050	.022	.010	.008	.008	.050	.024	.012	.009	.010

	SL = .90 COV = .50					SL = .95 COV = .50				
R	500	100	10	1	.1	500	100	10	1	.1
A	---------------------CS------------------					---------------------CS------------------				
100	37.95	16.97	5.37	1.70	.54	37.95	16.97	5.37	1.70	.54
1000	12.00	5.37	1.70	.54	.17	12.00	5.37	1.70	.54	.17
10000	3.79	1.70	.54	.17	.05	3.79	1.70	.54	.17	.05
100000	1.20	.54	.17	.05	.02	1.20	.54	.17	.05	.02
A	---------------------SS------------------					---------------------SS------------------				
100	.00	.00	.00	.00	.07	.00	.00	.00	.00	.23
1000	.00	.00	.00	.07	.33	.00	.00	.00	.23	.45
10000	.00	.00	.07	.33	.52	.00	.00	.23	.45	.63
100000	.00	.07	.33	.52	.69	.04	.23	.45	.63	.78
A	---------------------TO------------------					---------------------TO------------------				
100	.32	.71	2.24	7.07	19.71	.32	.71	2.24	7.07	15.57
1000	1.00	2.24	7.07	19.71	24.21	1.00	2.24	7.07	15.57	19.37
10000	3.16	7.07	19.71	24.21	20.78	3.16	7.07	15.57	19.37	17.63
100000	10.00	19.71	24.21	20.78	16.97	9.65	15.57	19.37	17.63	15.03
A	---------------------s------------------					---------------------s------------------				
100	1.581	.707	.224	.071	.024	1.581	.707	.224	.071	.027
1000	.500	.224	.071	.024	.014	.500	.224	.071	.027	.016
10000	.158	.071	.024	.014	.013	.158	.071	.027	.016	.015
100000	.050	.024	.014	.013	.015	.051	.027	.016	.015	.017

A = Annual Demand   R = Cost to Order/Cost per Unit
SL = Service Level   COV = Coefficient of Variation
CS = Cycle Stock (in months of forecast)   SS = Safety Stock (in months of forecast)
TO = Turnover   s = Stocking Rate (Economic Order plus Holding Cost / Cost per Unit)

Table 11.2 Cycle Stock, Safety Stock, Turnover and Stocking Rate

h = .25 (Annual Holding Rate)   L = 1 (Lead Time in Months)

	SL = .90 COV = .30					SL = .95 COV = .30				
R	500	100	10	1	.1	500	100	10	1	.1
A	----------------CS----------------					----------------CS----------------				
100	37.95	16.97	5.37	1.70	.54	37.95	16.97	5.37	1.70	.54
1000	12.00	5.37	1.70	.54	.17	12.00	5.37	1.70	.54	.17
10000	3.79	1.70	.54	.17	.05	3.79	1.70	.54	.17	.05
100000	1.20	.54	.17	.05	.02	1.20	.54	.17	.05	.02
A	----------------SS----------------					----------------SS----------------				
100	.00	.00	.00	.00	.02	.00	.00	.00	.00	.17
1000	.00	.00	.00	.02	.25	.00	.00	.00	.17	.36
10000	.00	.00	.02	.25	.42	.00	.00	.17	.36	.51
100000	.00	.02	.25	.42	.57	.00	.17	.36	.51	.64
A	----------------TO----------------					----------------TO----------------				
100	.32	.71	2.24	7.07	21.39	.32	.71	2.24	7.07	17.02
1000	1.00	2.24	7.07	21.39	28.63	1.00	2.24	7.07	17.02	22.74
10000	3.16	7.07	21.39	28.63	25.20	3.16	7.07	17.02	22.74	21.22
100000	10.00	21.39	28.63	25.20	20.56	10.00	17.02	22.74	21.22	18.14
A	----------------s----------------					----------------s----------------				
100	1.581	.707	.224	.071	.023	1.581	.707	.224	.071	.026
1000	.500	.224	.071	.023	.012	.500	.224	.071	.026	.015
10000	.158	.071	.023	.012	.011	.158	.071	.026	.015	.013
100000	.050	.023	.012	.011	.013	.050	.026	.015	.013	.014

	SL = .90 COV = .50					SL = .95 COV = .50				
R	500	100	10	1	.1	500	100	10	1	.1
A	----------------CS----------------					----------------CS----------------				
100	37.95	16.97	5.37	1.70	.54	37.95	16.97	5.37	1.70	.54
1000	12.00	5.37	1.70	.54	.17	12.00	5.37	1.70	.54	.17
10000	3.79	1.70	.54	.17	.05	3.79	1.70	.54	.17	.05
100000	1.20	.54	.17	.05	.02	1.20	.54	.17	.05	.02
A	----------------SS----------------					----------------SS----------------				
100	.00	.00	.00	.00	.22	.00	.00	.00	.06	.43
1000	.00	.00	.00	.22	.55	.00	.00	.06	.43	.72
10000	.00	.00	.22	.55	.82	.00	.06	.43	.72	.95
100000	.00	.22	.55	.82	1.04	.18	.43	.72	.95	1.17
A	----------------TO----------------					----------------TO----------------				
100	.32	.71	2.24	7.07	15.82	.32	.71	2.24	6.83	12.41
1000	1.00	2.24	7.07	15.82	16.64	1.00	2.24	6.83	12.41	13.55
10000	3.16	7.07	15.82	16.64	13.81	3.16	6.83	12.41	13.55	11.90
100000	10.00	15.82	16.64	13.81	11.34	8.67	12.41	13.55	11.90	10.11
A	----------------s----------------					----------------s----------------				
100	1.581	.707	.224	.071	.027	1.581	.707	.224	.072	.031
1000	.500	.224	.071	.027	.019	.500	.224	.072	.031	.022
10000	.158	.071	.027	.019	.019	.158	.072	.031	.022	.022
100000	.050	.027	.019	.019	.022	.054	.031	.022	.022	.025

A = Annual Demand   R = Cost to Order/Cost per Unit
SL = Service Level   COV = Coefficient of Variation
CS = Cycle Stock (in months of forecast)   SS = Safety Stock (in months of forecast)
TO = Turnover   s = Stocking Rate (Economic Order plus Holding Cost / Cost per Unit)

Table 11.3 Cycle Stock, Safety Stock, Turnover and Stocking Rate

h = .25 (Annual Holding Rate)   L = 3 (Lead Time in Months)

	SL = .90 COV = .30					SL = .95 COV = .30				
R	500	100	10	1	.1	500	100	10	1	.1
A	----CS----					----CS----				
100	37.95	16.97	5.37	1.70	.54	37.95	16.97	5.37	1.70	.54
1000	12.00	5.37	1.70	.54	.17	12.00	5.37	1.70	.54	.17
10000	3.79	1.70	.54	.17	.05	3.79	1.70	.54	.17	.05
100000	1.20	.54	.17	.05	.02	1.20	.54	.17	.05	.02
A	----SS----					----SS----				
100	.00	.00	.00	.00	.24	.00	.00	.00	.08	.46
1000	.00	.00	.00	.24	.58	.00	.00	.08	.46	.75
10000	.00	.00	.24	.58	.86	.00	.08	.46	.75	1.00
100000	.00	.24	.58	.86	1.09	.21	.46	.75	1.00	1.22
A	----TO----					----TO----				
100	.32	.71	2.24	7.07	15.38	.32	.71	2.24	6.76	12.06
1000	1.00	2.24	7.07	15.38	15.94	1.00	2.24	6.76	12.06	13.00
10000	3.16	7.07	15.38	15.94	13.19	3.16	6.76	12.06	13.00	11.39
100000	10.00	15.38	15.94	13.19	10.85	8.54	12.06	13.00	11.39	9.67
A	----s----					----s----				
100	1.581	.707	.224	.071	.027	1.581	.707	.224	.072	.032
1000	.500	.224	.071	.027	.019	.500	.224	.072	.032	.023
10000	.158	.071	.027	.019	.020	.158	.072	.032	.023	.023
100000	.050	.027	.019	.020	.023	.054	.032	.023	.023	.026

	SL = .90 COV = .50					SL = .95 COV = .50				
R	500	100	10	1	.1	500	100	10	1	.1
A	----CS----					----CS----				
100	37.95	16.97	5.37	1.70	.54	37.95	16.97	5.37	1.70	.54
1000	12.00	5.37	1.70	.54	.17	12.00	5.37	1.70	.54	.17
10000	3.79	1.70	.54	.17	.05	3.79	1.70	.54	.17	.05
100000	1.20	.54	.17	.05	.02	1.20	.54	.17	.05	.02
A	----SS----					----SS----				
100	.00	.00	.00	.01	.68	.00	.00	.00	.44	.99
1000	.00	.00	.01	.68	1.18	.00	.00	.44	.99	1.45
10000	.00	.01	.68	1.18	1.61	.00	.44	.99	1.45	1.83
100000	.23	.68	1.18	1.61	1.97	.62	.99	1.45	1.83	2.17
A	----TO----					----TO----				
100	.32	.71	2.24	7.03	9.90	.32	.71	2.24	5.63	7.84
1000	1.00	2.24	7.03	9.90	8.87	1.00	2.24	5.63	7.84	7.43
10000	3.16	7.03	9.90	8.87	7.23	3.16	5.63	7.84	7.43	6.37
100000	8.37	9.90	8.87	7.23	6.03	6.59	7.84	7.43	6.37	5.49
A	----s----					----s----				
100	1.581	.707	.224	.071	.036	1.581	.707	.224	.080	.043
1000	.500	.224	.071	.036	.032	.500	.224	.080	.043	.037
10000	.158	.071	.036	.032	.036	.158	.080	.043	.037	.040
100000	.055	.036	.032	.036	.042	.063	.043	.037	.040	.046

A = Annual Demand   R = Cost to Order/Cost per Unit
SL = Service Level   COV = Coefficient of Variation
CS = Cycle Stock (in months of forecast)   SS = Safety Stock (in months of forecast)
TO = Turnover   s = Stocking Rate (Economic Order plus Holding Cost / Cost per Unit)

Table 11.4 Cycle Stock, Safety Stock, Turnover and Stocking Rate

h = .25 (Annual Holding Rate)   L = 5 (Lead Time in Months)

| | SL = .90 COV = .30 | | | | | SL = .95 COV = .30 | | | | |
R	500	100	10	1	.1	500	100	10	1	.1
A			--CS--					--CS--		
100	37.95	16.97	5.37	1.70	.54	37.95	16.97	5.37	1.70	.54
1000	12.00	5.37	1.70	.54	.17	12.00	5.37	1.70	.54	.17
10000	3.79	1.70	.54	.17	.05	3.79	1.70	.54	.17	.05
100000	1.20	.54	.17	.05	.02	1.20	.54	.17	.05	.02
A			--SS--					--SS--		
100	.00	.00	.00	.00	.42	.00	.00	.00	.22	.68
1000	.00	.00	.00	.42	.84	.00	.00	.22	.68	1.05
10000	.00	.00	.42	.84	1.17	.00	.22	.68	1.05	1.35
100000	.05	.42	.84	1.17	1.47	.38	.68	1.05	1.35	1.64
A			--TO--					--TO--		
100	.32	.71	2.24	7.07	12.51	.32	.71	2.24	6.25	9.84
1000	1.00	2.24	7.07	12.51	11.92	1.00	2.24	6.25	9.84	9.86
10000	3.16	7.07	12.51	11.92	9.77	3.16	6.25	9.84	9.86	8.52
100000	9.56	12.51	11.92	9.77	8.07	7.61	9.84	9.86	8.52	7.25
A			--s--					--s--		
100	1.581	.707	.224	.071	.031	1.581	.707	.224	.075	.037
1000	.500	.224	.071	.031	.025	.500	.224	.075	.037	.029
10000	.158	.071	.031	.025	.027	.158	.075	.037	.029	.030
100000	.051	.031	.025	.027	.031	.058	.037	.029	.030	.035

| | SL = .90 COV = .50 | | | | | SL = .95 COV = .50 | | | | |
R	500	100	10	1	.1	500	100	10	1	.1
A			--CS--					--CS--		
100	37.95	16.97	5.37	1.70	.54	37.95	16.97	5.37	1.70	.54
1000	12.00	5.37	1.70	.54	.17	12.00	5.37	1.70	.54	.17
10000	3.79	1.70	.54	.17	.05	3.79	1.70	.54	.17	.05
100000	1.20	.54	.17	.05	.02	1.20	.54	.17	.05	.02
A			--SS--					--SS--		
100	.00	.00	.00	.23	1.03	.00	.00	.00	.74	1.42
1000	.00	.00	.23	1.03	1.66	.00	.00	.74	1.42	1.98
10000	.00	.23	1.03	1.66	2.18	.14	.74	1.42	1.98	2.47
100000	.50	1.03	1.66	2.18	2.66	.96	1.42	1.98	2.47	2.81
A			--TO--					--TO--		
100	.32	.71	2.24	6.23	7.66	.32	.71	2.24	4.93	6.12
1000	1.00	2.24	6.23	7.66	6.57	1.00	2.24	4.93	6.12	5.58
10000	3.16	6.23	7.66	6.57	5.37	3.05	4.93	6.12	5.58	4.75
100000	7.07	7.66	6.57	5.37	4.48	5.55	6.12	5.58	4.75	4.24
A			--s--					--s--		
100	1.581	.707	.224	.075	.044	1.581	.707	.224	.086	.052
1000	.500	.224	.075	.044	.042	.500	.224	.086	.052	.048
10000	.158	.075	.044	.042	.048	.161	.086	.052	.048	.054
100000	.060	.044	.042	.048	.056	.070	.052	.048	.054	.059

A = Annual Demand   R = Cost to Order/Cost per Unit
SL = Service Level   COV = Coefficient of Variation
CS = Cycle Stock (in months of forecast)   SS = Safety Stock (in months of forecast)
TO = Turnover   s = Stocking Rate (Economic Order plus Holding Cost / Cost per Unit)

Table 11.5 Cycle Stock, Safety Stock, Turnover and Stocking Rate

h = .35 (Annual Holding Rate)   L = .5 (Lead Time in Months)

| | SL = .90 COV = .30 | | | | | SL = .95 COV = .30 | | | | |
R	500	100	10	1	.1	500	100	10	1	.1
A	----------CS----------					----------CS----------				
100	32.07	14.34	4.54	1.43	.45	32.07	14.34	4.54	1.43	.45
1000	10.14	4.54	1.43	.45	.14	10.14	4.54	1.43	.45	.14
10000	3.21	1.43	.45	.14	.05	3.21	1.43	.45	.14	.05
100000	1.01	.45	.14	.05	.01	1.01	.45	.14	.05	.01
A	----------SS----------					----------SS----------				
100	.00	.00	.00	.00	.00	.00	.00	.00	.00	.09
1000	.00	.00	.00	.00	.15	.00	.00	.00	.09	.23
10000	.00	.00	.00	.15	.28	.00	.00	.09	.23	.35
100000	.00	.00	.15	.28	.39	.00	.09	.23	.35	.44
A	----------TO----------					----------TO----------				
100	.37	.84	2.65	8.37	26.46	.37	.84	2.65	8.37	21.89
1000	1.18	2.65	8.37	26.46	40.24	1.18	2.65	8.37	21.89	31.76
10000	3.74	8.37	26.46	40.24	36.72	3.74	8.37	21.89	31.76	30.64
100000	11.83	26.46	40.24	36.72	29.98	11.83	21.89	31.76	30.64	26.29
A	----------s----------					----------s----------				
100	1.871	.837	.265	.084	.026	1.871	.837	.265	.084	.029
1000	.592	.265	.084	.026	.013	.592	.265	.084	.029	.015
10000	.187	.084	.026	.013	.011	.187	.084	.029	.015	.013
100000	.059	.026	.013	.011	.012	.059	.029	.015	.013	.014

| | SL = .90 COV = .50 | | | | | SL = .95 COV = .50 | | | | |
R	500	100	10	1	.1	500	100	10	1	.1
A	----------CS----------					----------CS----------				
100	32.07	14.34	4.54	1.43	.45	32.07	14.34	4.54	1.43	.45
1000	10.14	4.54	1.43	.45	.14	10.14	4.54	1.43	.45	.14
10000	3.21	1.43	.45	.14	.05	3.21	1.43	.45	.14	.05
100000	1.01	.45	.14	.05	.01	1.01	.45	.14	.05	.01
A	----------SS----------					----------SS----------				
100	.00	.00	.00	.00	.11	.00	.00	.00	.00	.27
1000	.00	.00	.00	.11	.36	.00	.00	.00	.27	.48
10000	.00	.00	.11	.36	.55	.00	.00	.27	.48	.65
100000	.00	.11	.36	.55	.71	.09	.27	.48	.65	.80
A	----------TO----------					----------TO----------				
100	.37	.84	2.65	8.37	21.13	.37	.84	2.65	8.37	16.61
1000	1.18	2.65	8.37	21.13	23.95	1.18	2.65	8.37	16.61	19.32
10000	3.74	8.37	21.13	23.95	20.16	3.74	8.37	16.61	19.32	17.24
100000	11.83	21.13	23.95	20.16	16.51	10.90	16.61	19.32	17.24	14.73
A	----------s----------					----------s----------				
100	1.871	.837	.265	.084	.030	1.871	.837	.265	.084	.034
1000	.592	.265	.084	.030	.019	.592	.265	.084	.034	.022
10000	.187	.084	.030	.019	.019	.187	.084	.034	.022	.022
100000	.059	.030	.019	.019	.022	.062	.034	.022	.022	.024

A = Annual Demand   R = Cost to Order/Cost per Unit

SL = Service Level   COV = Coefficient of Variation

CS = Cycle Stock (in months of forecast)   SS = Safety Stock (in months of forecast)

TO = Turnover   s = Stocking Rate (Economic Order plus Holding Cost / Cost per Unit)

Table 11.6 Cycle Stock, Safety Stock, Turnover and Stocking Rate

h = .35 (Annual Holding Rate) L = 1 (Lead Time in Months)

	SL = .90 COV = .30					SL = .95 COV = .30				
R	500	100	10	1	.1	500	100	10	1	.1
A	----------CS----------					----------CS----------				
100	32.07	14.34	4.54	1.43	.45	32.07	14.34	4.54	1.43	.45
1000	10.14	4.54	1.43	.45	.14	10.14	4.54	1.43	.45	.14
10000	3.21	1.43	.45	.14	.05	3.21	1.43	.45	.14	.05
100000	1.01	.45	.14	.05	.01	1.01	.45	.14	.05	.01
A	----------SS----------					----------SS----------				
100	.00	.00	.00	.00	.06	.00	.00	.00	.00	.20
1000	.00	.00	.00	.06	.28	.00	.00	.00	.20	.38
10000	.00	.00	.06	.28	.45	.00	.00	.20	.38	.53
100000	.00	.06	.28	.45	.59	.04	.20	.38	.53	.66
A	----------TO----------					----------TO----------				
100	.37	.84	2.65	8.37	23.27	.37	.84	2.65	8.37	18.39
1000	1.18	2.65	8.37	23.27	28.53	1.18	2.65	8.37	18.39	22.83
10000	3.74	8.37	23.27	28.53	24.47	3.74	8.37	18.39	22.83	20.77
100000	11.83	23.27	28.53	24.47	19.99	11.41	18.39	22.83	20.77	17.70
A	----------s----------					----------s----------				
100	1.871	.837	.265	.084	.028	1.871	.837	.265	.084	.032
1000	.592	.265	.084	.028	.016	.592	.265	.084	.032	.020
10000	.187	.084	.028	.016	.016	.187	.084	.032	.020	.018
100000	.059	.028	.016	.016	.018	.060	.032	.020	.018	.020

	SL = .90 COV = .50					SL = .95 COV = .50				
R	500	100	10	1	.1	500	100	10	1	.1
A	----------CS----------					----------CS----------				
100	32.07	14.34	4.54	1.43	.45	32.07	14.34	4.54	1.43	.45
1000	10.14	4.54	1.43	.45	.14	10.14	4.54	1.43	.45	.14
10000	3.21	1.43	.45	.14	.05	3.21	1.43	.45	.14	.05
100000	1.01	.45	.14	.05	.01	1.01	.45	.14	.05	.01
A	----------SS----------					----------SS----------				
100	.00	.00	.00	.00	.28	.00	.00	.00	.12	.48
1000	.00	.00	.00	.28	.59	.00	.00	.12	.48	.75
10000	.00	.00	.28	.59	.85	.00	.12	.48	.75	.99
100000	.00	.28	.59	.85	1.07	.24	.48	.75	.99	1.20
A	----------TO----------					----------TO----------				
100	.37	.84	2.65	8.37	16.45	.37	.84	2.65	7.71	12.91
1000	1.18	2.65	8.37	16.45	16.29	1.18	2.65	7.71	12.91	13.38
10000	3.74	8.37	16.45	16.29	13.40	3.74	7.71	12.91	13.38	11.62
100000	11.83	16.45	16.29	13.40	11.05	9.56	12.91	13.38	11.62	9.87
A	----------s----------					----------s----------				
100	1.871	.837	.265	.084	.035	1.871	.837	.265	.087	.040
1000	.592	.265	.084	.035	.026	.592	.265	.087	.040	.030
10000	.187	.084	.035	.026	.027	.187	.087	.040	.030	.031
100000	.059	.035	.026	.027	.032	.066	.040	.030	.031	.036

A = Annual Demand R = Cost to Order/Cost per Unit

SL = Service Level COV = Coefficient of Variation

CS = Cycle Stock (in months of forecast) SS = Safety Stock (in months of forecast)

TO = Turnover s = Stocking Rate (Economic Order plus Holding Cost / Cost per Unit)

Table 11.7 Cycle Stock, Safety Stock, Turnover and Stocking Rate

h = .35 (Annual Holding Rate)   L = 3 (Lead Time in Months)

	SL = .90 COV = .30						SL = .95 COV = .30				
R	500	100	10	1	.1		500	100	10	1	.1
A	------------------CS------------------						------------------CS------------------				
100	32.07	14.34	4.54	1.43	.45		32.07	14.34	4.54	1.43	.45
1000	10.14	4.54	1.43	.45	.14		10.14	4.54	1.43	.45	.14
10000	3.21	1.43	.45	.14	.05		3.21	1.43	.45	.14	.05
100000	1.01	.45	.14	.05	.01		1.01	.45	.14	.05	.01
A	------------------SS------------------						------------------SS------------------				
100	.00	.00	.00	.00	.30		.00	.00	.00	.14	.51
1000	.00	.00	.00	.30	.63		.00	.00	.14	.51	.79
10000	.00	.00	.30	.63	.89		.00	.14	.51	.79	1.03
100000	.01	.30	.63	.89	1.12		.26	.51	.79	1.03	1.25
A	------------------TO------------------						------------------TO------------------				
100	.37	.84	2.65	8.37	15.94		.37	.84	2.65	7.61	12.51
1000	1.18	2.65	8.37	15.94	15.59		1.18	2.65	7.61	12.51	12.83
10000	3.74	8.37	15.94	15.59	12.80		3.74	7.61	12.51	12.83	11.12
100000	11.75	15.94	15.59	12.80	10.56		9.40	12.51	12.83	11.12	9.46
A	------------------s------------------						------------------s------------------				
100	1.871	.837	.265	.084	.035		1.871	.837	.265	.088	.041
1000	.592	.265	.084	.035	.027		.592	.265	.088	.041	.031
10000	.187	.084	.035	.027	.029		.187	.088	.041	.031	.033
100000	.059	.035	.027	.029	.034		.067	.041	.031	.033	.037

	SL = .90 COV = .50						SL = .95 COV = .50				
R	500	100	10	1	.1		500	100	10	1	.1
A	------------------CS------------------						------------------CS------------------				
100	32.07	14.34	4.54	1.43	.45		32.07	14.34	4.54	1.43	.45
1000	10.14	4.54	1.43	.45	.14		10.14	4.54	1.43	.45	.14
10000	3.21	1.43	.45	.14	.05		3.21	1.43	.45	.14	.05
100000	1.01	.45	.14	.05	.01		1.01	.45	.14	.05	.01
A	------------------SS------------------						------------------SS------------------				
100	.00	.00	.00	.12	.76		.00	.00	.00	.53	1.07
1000	.00	.00	.12	.76	1.25		.00	.00	.53	1.07	1.50
10000	.00	.12	.76	1.25	1.66		.05	.53	1.07	1.50	1.89
100000	.33	.76	1.25	1.66	2.03		.70	1.07	1.50	1.89	2.17
A	------------------TO------------------						------------------TO------------------				
100	.37	.84	2.65	7.71	9.91		.37	.84	2.65	6.12	7.90
1000	1.18	2.65	7.71	9.91	8.61		1.18	2.65	6.12	7.90	7.28
10000	3.74	7.71	9.91	8.61	7.03		3.69	6.12	7.90	7.28	6.21
100000	8.90	9.91	8.61	7.03	5.86		6.99	7.90	7.28	6.21	5.48
A	------------------s------------------						------------------s------------------				
100	1.871	.837	.265	.087	.049		1.871	.837	.265	.099	.058
1000	.592	.265	.087	.049	.045		.592	.265	.099	.058	.052
10000	.187	.087	.049	.045	.051		.188	.099	.058	.052	.058
100000	.069	.049	.045	.051	.060		.080	.058	.052	.058	.064

A = Annual Demand   R = Cost to Order/Cost per Unit
SL = Service Level   COV = Coefficient of Variation
CS = Cycle Stock (in months of forecast)   SS = Safety Stock (in months of forecast)
TO = Turnover   s = Stocking Rate (Economic Order plus Holding Cost / Cost per Unit)

Table 11.8 Cycle Stock, Safety Stock, Turnover and Stocking Rate

h = .35 (Annual Holding Rate)　　　　　　　L = 5 (Lead Time in Months)

	SL = .90 COV = .30					SL = .95 COV = .30				
R	500	100	10	1	.1	500	100	10	1	.1
A	----CS----					----CS----				
100	32.07	14.34	4.54	1.43	.45	32.07	14.34	4.54	1.43	.45
1000	10.14	4.54	1.43	.45	.14	10.14	4.54	1.43	.45	.14
10000	3.21	1.43	.45	.14	.05	3.21	1.43	.45	.14	.05
100000	1.01	.45	.14	.05	.01	1.01	.45	.14	.05	.01
A	----SS----					----SS----				
100	.00	.00	.00	.00	.49	.00	.00	.00	.30	.74
1000	.00	.00	.00	.49	.89	.00	.00	.30	.74	1.10
10000	.00	.00	.49	.89	1.22	.00	.30	.74	1.10	1.40
100000	.14	.49	.89	1.22	1.51	.45	.74	1.10	1.40	1.67
A	----TO----					----TO----				
100	.37	.84	2.65	8.37	12.72	.37	.84	2.65	6.92	10.04
1000	1.18	2.65	8.37	12.72	11.61	1.18	2.65	6.92	10.04	9.69
10000	3.74	8.37	12.72	11.61	9.48	3.74	6.92	10.04	9.69	8.31
100000	10.41	12.72	11.61	9.48	7.88	8.22	10.04	9.69	8.31	7.13
A	----s----					----s----				
100	1.871	.837	.265	.084	.041	1.871	.837	.265	.092	.048
1000	.592	.265	.084	.041	.034	.592	.265	.092	.048	.040
10000	.187	.084	.041	.034	.038	.187	.092	.048	.040	.043
100000	.063	.041	.034	.038	.045	.072	.048	.040	.043	.050

	SL = .90 COV = .50					SL = .95 COV = .50				
R	500	100	10	1	.1	500	100	10	1	.1
A	----CS----					----CS----				
100	32.07	14.34	4.54	1.43	.45	32.07	14.34	4.54	1.43	.45
1000	10.14	4.54	1.43	.45	.14	10.14	4.54	1.43	.45	.14
10000	3.21	1.43	.45	.14	.05	3.21	1.43	.45	.14	.05
100000	1.01	.45	.14	.05	.01	1.01	.45	.14	.05	.01
A	----SS----					----SS----				
100	.00	.00	.00	.36	1.13	.00	.00	.00	.85	1.51
1000	.00	.00	.36	1.13	1.74	.00	.00	.85	1.51	2.06
10000	.00	.36	1.13	1.74	2.25	.27	.85	1.51	2.06	2.53
100000	.62	1.13	1.74	2.25	2.73	1.06	1.51	2.06	2.53	2.82
A	----TO----					----TO----				
100	.37	.84	2.65	6.68	7.57	.37	.84	2.65	5.25	6.11
1000	1.18	2.65	6.68	7.57	6.38	1.18	2.65	5.25	6.11	5.45
10000	3.74	6.68	7.57	6.38	5.22	3.45	5.25	6.11	5.45	4.66
100000	7.36	7.57	6.38	5.22	4.38	5.77	6.11	5.45	4.66	4.24
A	----s----					----s----				
100	1.871	.837	.265	.094	.059	1.871	.837	.265	.108	.071
1000	.592	.265	.094	.059	.059	.592	.265	.108	.071	.068
10000	.187	.094	.059	.059	.068	.195	.108	.071	.068	.076
100000	.077	.059	.059	.068	.080	.090	.071	.068	.076	.083

A = Annual Demand　　　　　　　　R = Cost to Order/Cost per Unit
SL = Service Level　　　　　　　COV = Coefficient of Variation
CS = Cycle Stock (in months of forecast)　　SS = Safety Stock (in months of forecast)
TO = Turnover　　s = Stocking Rate (Economic Order plus Holding Cost / Cost per Unit)

CHAPTER 12

Economic Safety Stock With Lost Sales

This chapter illustrates how to determine the economic size of the safety stock when shortages of stock might represent lost sales (reference 1). Lost sales with finished good items may occur, for example, when a customer seeks to purchase an item that is out of stock. The potential sale of the item is lost if the customer does not place a backorder with the store or purchases the item at another store.

An economic cost relation is formulated in a model that includes the combined costs of holding safety stock and the cost of incurring a lost sale. The model assumes the stock is reordered in quantities of size **Q** every time the on-hand plus on-order inventory reaches the order point quantity. A lead time period later, the quantity **Q** arrives and replenishes the on-hand stock. For purposes of developing the adjoining tables of this chapter, the lead time demand in the model is assumed to follow a normal distribution.

Data

The data used in applying the model are the following:

$$A = \text{annual demand}$$
$$Q = \text{order quantity}$$
$$h = \text{annual holding rate}$$
$$C_s = \text{cost per shortage}$$
$$C = \text{cost per unit}$$
$$F_L = \text{lead time forecast}$$
$$\sigma_L = \text{standard error of the lead time forecast}$$

Model

As in the safety stock models of Chapters 9, 10 and 11, safety stock **SS** is determined from the relation $SS = k\,\sigma_L$, where **k** is the safety factor and σ_L is the standard error of the lead time forecast. The goal of the model is to find the value of **k** that is economically optimal for the item. In pursuing this goal, consider the following relations between the lead time demand and the order point. Recall also that the order point **OP** consists of the lead time forecast F_L plus the safety stock **SS**, i.e.:

$$OP = F_L + SS$$

Let **x** = demand over the lead time. If $x < OP$, then at the end of the order cycle some stock is unused and left over for the next cycle. The average of this stock, called safety stock per order cycle, can be measured by the relation:

$$\text{Average Safety Stock} = SS = \sigma_L \int_{-\infty}^{k} (k - z)\, f(z)\, dz$$

where $f(z)$ is the standard normal density and z is the standard normal variate as described in Chapter 7.

On the other hand, if $x \geq OP$, then the order point is not adequate to meet all the demand for the order cycle and some shortages do occur. The average of the shortages per order cycle is obtained from:

$$\text{Average Shortage per Order Cycle} = SH = \sigma_L \int_{k}^{\infty} (z - k)\, f(z)\, dz$$

Now the annual cost relation, which includes the costs associated with shortages of stock and holding of safety stock, can be formulated. The cost relation K is given below:

$$K = C h (SS) + Cs\, A/Q\, (SH)$$

that is,

$$K = (\text{annual cost to hold the safety stock}) + (\text{annual cost for the shortages})$$

By using optimization methods, the particular value of the safety factor k can be determined, yielding the minimum annual cost. Carrying out the optimization yields the relation:

$$1 - F(k) = \frac{1}{1 + \dfrac{A\, Cs}{Q\, h\, C}}$$

Since $F(k)$ gives the probability that a shortage will not occur in an order cycle, the above expression $(1 - F(k))$ can be interpreted as the probability that a shortage will occur over an order cycle. Because the probability is obtained from optimizing methods, it is here called the *economic probability of a shortage*.

To find the safety factor k, $F(k)$ is used along with the entries in Table 7.3 to find the corresponding value of k. In this chapter, this value is called the *economic safety factor*. Therefore, the safety stock that minimizes the above cost relation may be determined using:

$$SS = k\, \sigma_L$$

Tables

In developing the adjoining tables of this chapter, the following standardizations of the input data are used. First, the cost per shortage Cs and the procurement cost per unit C are combined to give:

$$R = Cs/C = \text{cost per shortage / cost per unit}$$

Second, the order quantity is stated in months of demand M. Since $A/12$ gives the average demand per month,

$$M = 12\, Q/A = \text{order quantity in months of demand}$$

The only other input data required to use the tables is the annual holding rate h. The tables list the economic probability that a shortage will occur over the order cycle $[P(\text{shortage}) = 1 - F(k)]$ and the economic safety factor k.

The tables are arranged in the following manner:

Table	h
12.1	.10
12.2	.20
12.3	.30
12.4	.40

Example 12.1

Suppose a computer outlet store stocks a particular computer model with a monthly forecast of 8 units per month, and the standard error of the monthly forecast σ is 4 units (i.e., $\sigma = 4$). Also suppose the store replenishes its stock for the computer model in sizes of 6 per order. Assume also the computer procurement cost to the store is $1600 and the selling price is $2400. Further, the annual holding rate for the store is 20 percent (i.e., $h = .2$). Also suppose that when a demand occurs and the store is out of stock, the shortage then represents a lost sale. If the lead time is one-half month, how much safety stock should be carried on this computer model?

Table 12.2 is used since $h = .20$. Also, $M = 6/8 = 0.75$ is the size of the order quantity in months. As the profit per computer is ($2400 − $1600) = $800, the cost per shortage is approximately this value ($800); thereby $R = 800/1600 = .5$. The table entries yield P (shortage) = .024 and $k = 1.97$. The lead time standard error is:

$$\sigma_L = \sqrt{L}\sigma$$

therefore,

$$\sigma_L = \sqrt{0.5}\,(4) = 2.83$$

and the economic safety stock becomes:

$$\text{Safety Stock (SS)} = k\,(\sigma_L)$$

therefore,

$$SS = 1.97\,(2.83) = 5.58$$

which may be rounded to 6. Note also that P (shortage) = .024 interprets that (using the above safety stock) the computer model can be expected to be short on 2.4 percent of the order cycles.

Example 12.2

Suppose a gas station sells a gas supplement in cans at a price of $1.10 and the station's cost is $1.00. The monthly demands for this product average 100 cans with a standard deviation of 30 cans. Assume the holding rate for the station is 40 percent, the gas supplement is ordered in quantities of size 600 and the lead time is one week. How much safety stock should be carried for this item?

Table 12.4 is used, since $h = .40$. Also, $M = 600/100 = 6$ and $R = (\text{price} - \text{cost})/\text{cost} = (1.10 - 1.00)/1.00 = 0.10$. The table entries show that it is economical for the station to incur a shortage on .667 (66.7 percent) of its order cycles and also that the economic safety stock is $k = -0.43$. Since k is a negative value in this situation, the corresponding safety stock will be negative. With the lead time standard error of $\sigma_L = \sqrt{.25}\ 30 = 15$, the safety stock is obtained by $SS = -0.43 \times 15 = -6.45$. This implies that the order point $OP = (F_L + SS)$ should be smaller than the lead time forecast F_L. In this situation F_L is about 25 percent of one month's demand, i.e., $F_L = .25 \times 100 = 25$. Hence, the economic order point becomes:

$$OP = 25 - 6.45 = 18.55$$

Example 12.3

Assume a grocery store stocks lawn chairs in quantities of 25 with a lead time of two weeks. Suppose also that the forecast of demands is 50 chairs per month and the standard error of this forecast is 20. The lawn chairs cost $5 and sell for $10 each and the holding rate to the store is 30 percent per year. Find the safety stock and order point for these lawnchairs.

Table 12.3 is used, since $h = .30$. Because $M = 25/50 = .50$ and $R = (\text{Price} - \text{Cost})/\text{Cost} = (10 - 5)/5 = 1$, the probability of a shortage is $P(\text{shortage}) = 0.012$. Also the economic safety factor is $k = 2.25$. The lead time standard deviation becomes:

$$\sigma_L = \sqrt{.50}\ 20 = 14.1$$

Thus the safety stock is $SS = 2.25 \times 14.1 = 31.7$ (about 32).

With the lead time forecast of $F_L = .5 \times 50 = 25$, the order point is $F_L = 25 + 32 = 57$. Note in this situation the economic probability of a shortage is quite small (0.012) and consequently the on-hand inventory should seldom be out of stock.

Table 12.1 Economic Safety Stock for Stock Replenishments where Shortages Represent Lost Sales

h = .10 (annual holding rate)

Economic Probability of a Shortage

R M	.1	.2	.3	.4	.5	.6	.7	.8	.9	1.0
.25	.020	.010	.007	.005	.004	.003	.003	.003	.002	.002
.50	.040	.020	.014	.010	.008	.007	.006	.005	.005	.004
.75	.059	.030	.020	.015	.012	.010	.009	.008	.007	.006
1	.077	.040	.027	.020	.016	.014	.012	.010	.009	.008
2	.143	.077	.053	.040	.032	.027	.023	.020	.018	.016
3	.200	.111	.077	.059	.048	.040	.034	.030	.027	.024
4	.250	.143	.100	.077	.063	.053	.045	.040	.036	.032
5	.294	.172	.122	.094	.077	.065	.056	.050	.044	.040
6	.333	.200	.143	.111	.091	.077	.067	.059	.053	.048
7	.368	.226	.163	.127	.104	.089	.077	.068	.061	.055
8	.400	.250	.182	.143	.118	.100	.087	.077	.069	.063
9	.429	.273	.200	.158	.130	.111	.097	.086	.077	.070
10	.455	.294	.217	.172	.143	.122	.106	.094	.085	.077
11	.478	.314	.234	.186	.155	.133	.116	.103	.092	.084
12	.500	.333	.250	.200	.167	.143	.125	.111	.100	.091
18	.600	.429	.333	.273	.231	.200	.176	.158	.143	.130
24	.667	.500	.400	.333	.286	.250	.222	.200	.182	.167

Economic Safety Factor

R M	.1	.2	.3	.4	.5	.6	.7	.8	.9	1.0
.25	2.05	2.32	2.46	2.56	2.64	2.70	2.75	2.80	2.83	2.87
.50	1.75	2.05	2.21	2.32	2.40	2.46	2.52	2.56	2.60	2.64
.75	1.57	1.88	2.05	2.16	2.25	2.32	2.37	2.42	2.46	2.50
1	1.43	1.75	1.93	2.05	2.14	2.21	2.27	2.32	2.36	2.40
2	1.07	1.43	1.62	1.75	1.85	1.93	1.99	2.05	2.09	2.14
3	.84	1.22	1.43	1.57	1.67	1.75	1.82	1.88	1.93	1.97
4	.67	1.07	1.28	1.43	1.53	1.62	1.69	1.75	1.80	1.85
5	.54	.94	1.17	1.31	1.43	1.51	1.59	1.65	1.70	1.75
6	.43	.84	1.07	1.22	1.34	1.43	1.50	1.57	1.62	1.67
7	.34	.75	.98	1.14	1.26	1.35	1.43	1.49	1.55	1.60
8	.25	.67	.91	1.07	1.19	1.28	1.36	1.43	1.48	1.53
9	.18	.60	.84	1.00	1.12	1.22	1.30	1.37	1.43	1.48
10	.11	.54	.78	.94	1.07	1.17	1.25	1.31	1.37	1.43
11	.05	.48	.73	.89	1.02	1.11	1.20	1.27	1.33	1.38
12	-.00	.43	.67	.84	.97	1.07	1.15	1.22	1.28	1.34
18	-.25	.18	.43	.60	.74	.84	.93	1.00	1.07	1.12
24	-.43	-.00	.25	.43	.57	.67	.76	.84	.91	.97

R = (cost per shortage) / (cost per unit)

M = order quantity (in months of forecast)

Table 12.2 Economic Safety Stock for Stock Replenishments where Shortages Represent Lost Sales

h   = .20   (annual holding rate)

Economic Probability of a Shortage

R M	.1	.2	.3	.4	.5	.6	.7	.8	.9	1.0
.25	.040	.020	.014	.010	.008	.007	.006	.005	.005	.004
.50	.077	.040	.027	.020	.016	.014	.012	.010	.009	.008
.75	.111	.059	.040	.030	.024	.020	.018	.015	.014	.012
1	.143	.077	.053	.040	.032	.027	.023	.020	.018	.016
2	.250	.143	.100	.077	.063	.053	.045	.040	.036	.032
3	.333	.200	.143	.111	.091	.077	.067	.059	.053	.048
4	.400	.250	.182	.143	.118	.100	.087	.077	.069	.063
5	.455	.294	.217	.172	.143	.122	.106	.094	.085	.077
6	.500	.333	.250	.200	.167	.143	.125	.111	.100	.091
7	.538	.368	.280	.226	.189	.163	.143	.127	.115	.104
8	.571	.400	.308	.250	.211	.182	.160	.143	.129	.118
9	.600	.429	.333	.273	.231	.200	.176	.158	.143	.130
10	.625	.455	.357	.294	.250	.217	.192	.172	.156	.143
11	.647	.478	.379	.314	.268	.234	.208	.186	.169	.155
12	.667	.500	.400	.333	.286	.250	.222	.200	.182	.167
18	.750	.600	.500	.429	.375	.333	.300	.273	.250	.231
24	.800	.667	.571	.500	.444	.400	.364	.333	.308	.286

Economic Safety Factor

R M	.1	.2	.3	.4	.5	.6	.7	.8	.9	1.0
.25	1.75	2.05	2.21	2.32	2.40	2.46	2.52	2.56	2.60	2.64
.50	1.43	1.75	1.93	2.05	2.14	2.21	2.27	2.32	2.36	2.40
.75	1.22	1.57	1.75	1.88	1.97	2.05	2.11	2.16	2.21	2.25
1	1.07	1.43	1.62	1.75	1.85	1.93	1.99	2.05	2.09	2.14
2	.67	1.07	1.28	1.43	1.53	1.62	1.69	1.75	1.80	1.85
3	.43	.84	1.07	1.22	1.34	1.43	1.50	1.57	1.62	1.67
4	.25	.67	.91	1.07	1.19	1.28	1.36	1.43	1.48	1.53
5	.11	.54	.78	.94	1.07	1.17	1.25	1.31	1.37	1.43
6	-.00	.43	.67	.84	.97	1.07	1.15	1.22	1.28	1.34
7	-.10	.34	.58	.75	.88	.98	1.07	1.14	1.20	1.26
8	-.18	.25	.50	.67	.80	.91	.99	1.07	1.13	1.19
9	-.25	.18	.43	.60	.74	.84	.93	1.00	1.07	1.12
10	-.32	.11	.37	.54	.67	.78	.87	.94	1.01	1.07
11	-.38	.05	.31	.48	.62	.73	.81	.89	.96	1.02
12	-.43	-.00	.25	.43	.57	.67	.76	.84	.91	.97
18	-.67	-.25	-.00	.18	.32	.43	.52	.60	.67	.74
24	-.84	-.43	-.18	-.00	.14	.25	.35	.43	.50	.57

R   = (cost per shortage) / (cost per unit)

M   = order quantity (in months of forecast)

Table 12.3 Economic Safety Stock for Stock Replenishments
where Shortages Represent Lost Sales

h = .30   (annual holding rate)

Economic Probability of a Shortage

M \ R	.1	.2	.3	.4	.5	.6	.7	.8	.9	1.0
.25	.059	.030	.020	.015	.012	.010	.009	.008	.007	.006
.50	.111	.059	.040	.030	.024	.020	.018	.015	.014	.012
.75	.158	.086	.059	.045	.036	.030	.026	.023	.020	.018
1	.200	.111	.077	.059	.048	.040	.034	.030	.027	.024
2	.333	.200	.143	.111	.091	.077	.067	.059	.053	.048
3	.429	.273	.200	.158	.130	.111	.097	.086	.077	.070
4	.500	.333	.250	.200	.167	.143	.125	.111	.100	.091
5	.556	.385	.294	.238	.200	.172	.152	.135	.122	.111
6	.600	.429	.333	.273	.231	.200	.176	.158	.143	.130
7	.636	.467	.368	.304	.259	.226	.200	.179	.163	.149
8	.667	.500	.400	.333	.286	.250	.222	.200	.182	.167
9	.692	.529	.429	.360	.310	.273	.243	.220	.200	.184
10	.714	.556	.455	.385	.333	.294	.263	.238	.217	.200
11	.733	.579	.478	.407	.355	.314	.282	.256	.234	.216
12	.750	.600	.500	.429	.375	.333	.300	.273	.250	.231
18	.818	.692	.600	.529	.474	.429	.391	.360	.333	.310
24	.857	.750	.667	.600	.545	.500	.462	.429	.400	.375

Economic Safety Factor

M \ R	.1	.2	.3	.4	.5	.6	.7	.8	.9	1.0
.25	1.57	1.88	2.05	2.16	2.25	2.32	2.37	2.42	2.46	2.50
.50	1.22	1.57	1.75	1.88	1.97	2.05	2.11	2.16	2.21	2.25
.75	1.00	1.37	1.57	1.70	1.80	1.88	1.94	2.00	2.05	2.09
1	.84	1.22	1.43	1.57	1.67	1.75	1.82	1.88	1.93	1.97
2	.43	.84	1.07	1.22	1.34	1.43	1.50	1.57	1.62	1.67
3	.18	.60	.84	1.00	1.12	1.22	1.30	1.37	1.43	1.48
4	-.00	.43	.67	.84	.97	1.07	1.15	1.22	1.28	1.34
5	-.14	.29	.54	.71	.84	.94	1.03	1.10	1.17	1.22
6	-.25	.18	.43	.60	.74	.84	.93	1.00	1.07	1.12
7	-.35	.08	.34	.51	.65	.75	.84	.92	.98	1.04
8	-.43	-.00	.25	.43	.57	.67	.76	.84	.91	.97
9	-.50	-.07	.18	.36	.49	.60	.70	.77	.84	.90
10	-.57	-.14	.11	.29	.43	.54	.63	.71	.78	.84
11	-.62	-.20	.05	.23	.37	.48	.58	.66	.73	.79
12	-.67	-.25	-.00	.18	.32	.43	.52	.60	.67	.74
18	-.91	-.50	-.25	-.07	.07	.18	.28	.36	.43	.49
24	-1.07	-.67	-.43	-.25	-.11	-.00	.10	.18	.25	.32

R = (cost per shortage) / (cost per unit)

M = order quantity (in months of forecast)

Table 12.4 Economic Safety Stock for Stock Replenishments where Shortages Represent Lost Sales

h = .40   (annual holding rate)

Economic Probability of a Shortage

M \ R	.1	.2	.3	.4	.5	.6	.7	.8	.9	1.0
.25	.077	.040	.027	.020	.016	.014	.012	.010	.009	.008
.50	.143	.077	.053	.040	.032	.027	.023	.020	.018	.016
.75	.200	.111	.077	.059	.048	.040	.034	.030	.027	.024
1	.250	.143	.100	.077	.063	.053	.045	.040	.036	.032
2	.400	.250	.182	.143	.118	.100	.087	.077	.069	.063
3	.500	.333	.250	.200	.167	.143	.125	.111	.100	.091
4	.571	.400	.308	.250	.211	.182	.160	.143	.129	.118
5	.625	.455	.357	.294	.250	.217	.192	.172	.156	.143
6	.667	.500	.400	.333	.286	.250	.222	.200	.182	.167
7	.700	.538	.437	.368	.318	.280	.250	.226	.206	.189
8	.727	.571	.471	.400	.348	.308	.276	.250	.229	.211
9	.750	.600	.500	.429	.375	.333	.300	.273	.250	.231
10	.769	.625	.526	.455	.400	.357	.323	.294	.270	.250
11	.786	.647	.550	.478	.423	.379	.344	.314	.289	.268
12	.800	.667	.571	.500	.444	.400	.364	.333	.308	.286
18	.857	.750	.667	.600	.545	.500	.462	.429	.400	.375
24	.889	.800	.727	.667	.615	.571	.533	.500	.471	.444

Economic Safety Factor

M \ R	.1	.2	.3	.4	.5	.6	.7	.8	.9	1.0
.25	1.43	1.75	1.93	2.05	2.14	2.21	2.27	2.32	2.36	2.40
.50	1.07	1.43	1.62	1.75	1.85	1.93	1.99	2.05	2.09	2.14
.75	.84	1.22	1.43	1.57	1.67	1.75	1.82	1.88	1.93	1.97
1	.67	1.07	1.28	1.43	1.53	1.62	1.69	1.75	1.80	1.85
2	.25	.67	.91	1.07	1.19	1.28	1.36	1.43	1.48	1.53
3	-.00	.43	.67	.84	.97	1.07	1.15	1.22	1.28	1.34
4	-.18	.25	.50	.67	.80	.91	.99	1.07	1.13	1.19
5	-.32	.11	.37	.54	.67	.78	.87	.94	1.01	1.07
6	-.43	-.00	.25	.43	.57	.67	.76	.84	.91	.97
7	-.52	-.10	.16	.34	.47	.58	.67	.75	.82	.88
8	-.60	-.18	.07	.25	.39	.50	.59	.67	.74	.80
9	-.67	-.25	-.00	.18	.32	.43	.52	.60	.67	.74
10	-.74	-.32	-.07	.11	.25	.37	.46	.54	.61	.67
11	-.79	-.38	-.13	.05	.19	.31	.40	.48	.55	.62
12	-.84	-.43	-.18	-.00	.14	.25	.35	.43	.50	.57
18	-1.07	-.67	-.43	-.25	-.11	-.00	.10	.18	.25	.32
24	-1.22	-.84	-.60	-.43	-.29	-.18	-.08	-.00	.07	.14

R = (cost per shortage) / (cost per unit)

M = order quantity (in months of forecast)

CHAPTER 13

Economic Safety Stock With Backorders

This chapter seeks to determine the economical amount of safety stock to have available when a shortage becomes a backorder (reference 1). The size of the safety stock is set to minimize the combined cost of backorders and the holding cost of safety stock. Backorders are likely to occur when the item the customer needs is out of stock and not available from another source and when there is no substitute item available. When a backorder occurs in an order cycle, the backorder is filled as soon as the next sufficient replenishment is received. The model assumes that the stock is reordered in size **Q** whenever the on-hand plus on-order inventory falls to the order point level of the stock. A lead time later, the replenishment of size **Q** arrives. The probability distribution of demands over the lead time period is assumed to follow a normal distribution.

Data
The following data are used in applying the model:

$$A = \text{annual demand}$$
$$Q = \text{order quantity}$$
$$h = \text{annual holding rate}$$
$$C_b = \text{cost per backorder}$$
$$C = \text{cost per unit}$$
$$F_L = \text{lead time forecast}$$
$$\sigma_L = \text{standard error of the lead time forecast}$$

Model
The safety stock **SS** is determined by the relation $SS = k\,\sigma_L$ where **k** is the safety factor and σ_L is the standard deviation of demand over the lead time. The goal of the model is to find the value of the safety factor **k** that yields economically optimal results. The model is developed in the following manner.

Let **x** be the demand for an item over the lead time period and let **OP** be the corresponding order point. Recall that **OP** is the amount of stock to meet the lead time demands until the next replenishment arrives; **OP** is the lead time forecast plus the safety stock. If $x < OP$, at the end of the order cycle some stock is unused and left over for the next order cycle. The average amount of this stock, called safety stock per order cycle, is measured by:

$$\text{Average Safety Stock} = SS = \sigma_L \int_{-\infty}^{k} (k - z)\, f(z)\,dz$$

where **f(z)** is the standard normal density and **z** is the standard normal variate as described in Chapter 7.

If, however, $x > OP$, the lead time demand exceeds the order point and the excess demands become backorders. The average of these backorders per order cycle is obtained from:

$$\text{Backorder per Order Cycle} = BO = \sigma_L \int_k^\infty (z - k)f(z)dz$$

Note in this backorder situation that the next replenishment of stock is used to fill the outstanding backorders; consequently, the cycle stock over the subsequent order cycle is at a smaller level than planned. As a result the holding cost of the cycle stock is reduced accordingly.

Using the above reasoning, the annual cost **K** associated with the safety stock is then developed as:

$$K = C\, h\, [SS - BO] + [BO]\, C_b\, A/Q$$

that is,

$$K = (\text{annual hold cost of safety stock}) + (\text{annual backorder cost})$$

So now optimization methods are used with the above relation to seek the value of the safety factor **k** that minimizes the annual cost. The outcome of the optimization yields the following relation:

$$1 - F(k) = \frac{Q\, h\, C}{A\, C_b}$$

Since **F(k)** is the probability that a shortage will not occur over an order cycle, $[1 - F(k)]$ is thus the probability that a shortage will occur in an order cycle. In this model, since a shortage is a backorder, then:

$$1 - F(k) = \text{probability that a backorder will occur}$$

For convenience, the above is here called the *economic probability of a backorder*. This probability having been found, the corresponding value of **k** is obtained from use of Table 7.3 and is here called the *economic safety factor*. The economic safety stock becomes:

$$SS = k\, \sigma_L$$

Tables

In developing the tables of this chapter, the following standardizings of the input data are used. First, the cost per backorder C_b and the procurement cost per unit **C** are combined to give:

$$R = C_b/C = \text{cost per backorder / cost per unit}$$

Second, since **A/12** is the average demand per month, the order quantity in months of demand is:

$$M = 12\, Q/A = \text{order quantity in months of forecast}$$

In addition, the tables require use of the annual holding rate **h**.

The tables list the economic probability of a backorder and the associated economic safety factor. Note that in the tables the probability of a backorder may take on values that are larger than one, depending on the combination of input data **h**, **M** and **R**. When this situation occurs, the corresponding table entries are set to .999 in order to avoid confusion. Also, the associated safety factors are listed as -3.00.

The tables are arranged as follows:

Tables	h
13.1	.10
13.2	.20
13.3	.30
13.4	.40

Example 13.1

Consider an appliance center where a certain part for a refrigerator is ordered in quantities of 12 units and where the procurement lead time is one month. Suppose the monthly forecast for this service part is six units per month with a standard deviation of $\sigma = 3$ units. Suppose shortages of stock are treated as backorders; assume further that the cost of the service part is $20, the cost whenever a backorder occurs is set at $8, and the annual holding rate for the center is placed at 30 percent. Find the economic safety stock and the corresponding order point for this item.

Table 13.3 is used, as $h = .30$; also, $M = 12/6 = 2$ and $R = 8/20 = .4$. Hence the economic probability of a backorder per order cycle is .125. The table shows the economic safety factor is $k = 1.15$. Because $L = 1$ and $\sigma = 3$, the lead time standard deviation of demand is $\sigma_L = \sqrt{1}\ 3 = 3$. The economic safety stock now becomes $SS = 1.15 \times 3 = 3.45$.

In order to find the order point, the lead time forecast is also needed, or, $F_L = L \times 6 = 1 \times 6 = 6$. The order point is therefore $OP = 6 + 3.45 = 9.45$.

Example 13.2

Consider the service part in Example 13.1, but suppose the lead time is shortened to one week (about .25 of a month). What effect does this change have on servicing the part?

The economic safety factor, unaffected by the lead time, remains as $k = 1.15$; however, the lead time standard deviation now becomes $\sigma_L = \sqrt{.25}\ 3 = 1.5$ and the lead time forecast is $F_L = .25 \times 6 = 1.5$. These changes in the lead time yield a safety stock of $SS = 1.15 \times 1.5 = 1.73$ and an order point of $OP = F_L + SS = 1.5 + 1.73 = 3.23$. This change in the order point from 9.45 to 3.23 is due to the reduction in the lead time from one month to one week.

Example 13.3

Consider an auto service center where demands of a particular radiator service part occurs on the average of 8 per month with a standard deviation of 3 per month. Suppose the part is ordered in quantities of 4 with a procurement lead time of one-half month, and the procurement cost is $10 each. Assume the cost per backorder is also $10 and the annual holding rate for the center is 20 percent. Determine the economic safety stock and order point for this part.

Table 13.2 is used, since $h = .20$, along with $M = 4/8 = .50$ and $R = 10/10 = 1$. The results show that the economic probability of a backorder is .008, thus signifying that a backorder should seldom occur, 8 times in 1000 order cycles. The associated economic safety factor is $k = 2.39$.

As $L = 0.5$ of a month and $\sigma = 3$, the lead time standard deviation is $\sigma_L = \sqrt{.5}\ 3 = 2.12$. The safety stock becomes $SS = 2.39 \times 2.12 = 5.06$. To find the order point, the lead time forecast is needed. This figure is $F_L = .5 \times 8 = 4$; hence, the order point becomes $OP = 4 + 5.06 = 9.06$, which may be rounded to $OP = 9$.

Table 13.1 Economic Safety Stock for Stock Replenishments where Shortages Represent Backorders

h = .10   (annual holding rate)

Economic Probability of a Shortage

R M	.1	.2	.3	.4	.5	.6	.7	.8	.9	1.0
.25	.021	.010	.007	.005	.004	.003	.003	.003	.002	.002
.50	.042	.021	.014	.010	.008	.007	.006	.005	.005	.004
.75	.063	.031	.021	.016	.013	.010	.009	.008	.007	.006
1	.083	.042	.028	.021	.017	.014	.012	.010	.009	.008
2	.167	.083	.056	.042	.033	.028	.024	.021	.019	.017
3	.250	.125	.083	.063	.050	.042	.036	.031	.028	.025
4	.333	.167	.111	.083	.067	.056	.048	.042	.037	.033
5	.417	.208	.139	.104	.083	.069	.060	.052	.046	.042
6	.500	.250	.167	.125	.100	.083	.071	.063	.056	.050
7	.583	.292	.194	.146	.117	.097	.083	.073	.065	.058
8	.667	.333	.222	.167	.133	.111	.095	.083	.074	.067
9	.750	.375	.250	.188	.150	.125	.107	.094	.083	.075
10	.833	.417	.278	.208	.167	.139	.119	.104	.093	.083
11	.917	.458	.306	.229	.183	.153	.131	.115	.102	.092
12	.999	.500	.333	.250	.200	.167	.143	.125	.111	.100
18	.999	.750	.500	.375	.300	.250	.214	.188	.167	.150
24	.999	.999	.667	.500	.400	.333	.286	.250	.222	.200

Economic Safety Factor

R M	.1	.2	.3	.4	.5	.6	.7	.8	.9	1.0
.25	2.04	2.31	2.46	2.56	2.64	2.70	2.75	2.79	2.83	2.87
.50	1.73	2.04	2.20	2.31	2.39	2.46	2.52	2.56	2.60	2.64
.75	1.53	1.86	2.04	2.15	2.24	2.31	2.37	2.42	2.46	2.50
1	1.38	1.73	1.91	2.04	2.13	2.20	2.26	2.31	2.36	2.39
2	.97	1.38	1.59	1.73	1.83	1.91	1.98	2.04	2.09	2.13
3	.67	1.15	1.38	1.53	1.65	1.73	1.80	1.86	1.91	1.96
4	.43	.97	1.22	1.38	1.50	1.59	1.67	1.73	1.79	1.83
5	.21	.81	1.09	1.26	1.38	1.48	1.56	1.63	1.68	1.73
6	-.00	.67	.97	1.15	1.28	1.38	1.47	1.53	1.59	1.65
7	-.21	.55	.86	1.05	1.19	1.30	1.38	1.45	1.52	1.57
8	-.43	.43	.76	.97	1.11	1.22	1.31	1.38	1.45	1.50
9	-.67	.32	.67	.89	1.04	1.15	1.24	1.32	1.38	1.44
10	-.97	.21	.59	.81	.97	1.09	1.18	1.26	1.33	1.38
11	-1.38	.10	.51	.74	.90	1.02	1.12	1.20	1.27	1.33
12	-3.00	-.00	.43	.67	.84	.97	1.07	1.15	1.22	1.28
18	-3.00	-.67	-.00	.32	.52	.67	.79	.89	.97	1.04
24	-3.00	-3.00	-.43	-.00	.25	.43	.57	.67	.76	.84

R = (cost per shortage) / (cost per unit)

M = order quantity (in months of forecast)

Table 13.2 Economic Safety Stock for Stock Replenishments where Shortages Represent Backorders

h = .20 (annual holding rate)

Economic Probability of a Shortage

R M	.1	.2	.3	.4	.5	.6	.7	.8	.9	1.0
.25	.042	.021	.014	.010	.008	.007	.006	.005	.005	.004
.50	.083	.042	.028	.021	.017	.014	.012	.010	.009	.008
.75	.125	.063	.042	.031	.025	.021	.018	.016	.014	.013
1	.167	.083	.056	.042	.033	.028	.024	.021	.019	.017
2	.333	.167	.111	.083	.067	.056	.048	.042	.037	.033
3	.500	.250	.167	.125	.100	.083	.071	.063	.056	.050
4	.667	.333	.222	.167	.133	.111	.095	.083	.074	.067
5	.833	.417	.278	.208	.167	.139	.119	.104	.093	.083
6	.999	.500	.333	.250	.200	.167	.143	.125	.111	.100
7	.999	.583	.389	.292	.233	.194	.167	.146	.130	.117
8	.999	.667	.444	.333	.267	.222	.190	.167	.148	.133
9	.999	.750	.500	.375	.300	.250	.214	.188	.167	.150
10	.999	.833	.556	.417	.333	.278	.238	.208	.185	.167
11	.999	.917	.611	.458	.367	.306	.262	.229	.204	.183
12	.999	.999	.667	.500	.400	.333	.286	.250	.222	.200
18	.999	.999	.999	.750	.600	.500	.429	.375	.333	.300
24	.999	.999	.999	.999	.800	.667	.571	.500	.444	.400

Economic Safety Factor

R M	.1	.2	.3	.4	.5	.6	.7	.8	.9	1.0
.25	1.73	2.04	2.20	2.31	2.39	2.46	2.52	2.56	2.60	2.64
.50	1.38	1.73	1.91	2.04	2.13	2.20	2.26	2.31	2.36	2.39
.75	1.15	1.53	1.73	1.86	1.96	2.04	2.10	2.15	2.20	2.24
1	.97	1.38	1.59	1.73	1.83	1.91	1.98	2.04	2.09	2.13
2	.43	.97	1.22	1.38	1.50	1.59	1.67	1.73	1.79	1.83
3	-.00	.67	.97	1.15	1.28	1.38	1.47	1.53	1.59	1.65
4	-.43	.43	.76	.97	1.11	1.22	1.31	1.38	1.45	1.50
5	-.97	.21	.59	.81	.97	1.09	1.18	1.26	1.33	1.38
6	-3.00	-.00	.43	.67	.84	.97	1.07	1.15	1.22	1.28
7	-3.00	-.21	.28	.55	.73	.86	.97	1.05	1.13	1.19
8	-3.00	-.43	.14	.43	.62	.76	.88	.97	1.04	1.11
9	-3.00	-.67	-.00	.32	.52	.67	.79	.89	.97	1.04
10	-3.00	-.97	-.14	.21	.43	.59	.71	.81	.90	.97
11	-3.00	-1.38	-.28	.10	.34	.51	.64	.74	.83	.90
12	-3.00	-3.00	-.43	-.00	.25	.43	.57	.67	.76	.84
18	-3.00	-3.00	-3.00	-.67	-.25	-.00	.18	.32	.43	.52
24	-3.00	-3.00	-3.00	-3.00	-.84	-.43	-.18	-.00	.14	.25

R = (cost per shortage) / (cost per unit)

M = order quantity (in months of forecast)

Table 13.3 Economic Safety Stock for Stock Replenishments where Shortages Represent Backorders

h = .30   (annual holding rate)

Economic Probability of a Shortage

R \ M	.1	.2	.3	.4	.5	.6	.7	.8	.9	1.0
.25	.063	.031	.021	.016	.013	.010	.009	.008	.007	.006
.50	.125	.063	.042	.031	.025	.021	.018	.016	.014	.013
.75	.188	.094	.063	.047	.038	.031	.027	.023	.021	.019
1	.250	.125	.083	.063	.050	.042	.036	.031	.028	.025
2	.500	.250	.167	.125	.100	.083	.071	.063	.056	.050
3	.750	.375	.250	.188	.150	.125	.107	.094	.083	.075
4	.999	.500	.333	.250	.200	.167	.143	.125	.111	.100
5	.999	.625	.417	.313	.250	.208	.179	.156	.139	.125
6	.999	.750	.500	.375	.300	.250	.214	.188	.167	.150
7	.999	.875	.583	.438	.350	.292	.250	.219	.194	.175
8	.999	.999	.667	.500	.400	.333	.286	.250	.222	.200
9	.999	.999	.750	.563	.450	.375	.321	.281	.250	.225
10	.999	.999	.833	.625	.500	.417	.357	.313	.278	.250
11	.999	.999	.917	.688	.550	.458	.393	.344	.306	.275
12	.999	.999	.999	.750	.600	.500	.429	.375	.333	.300
18	.999	.999	.999	.999	.900	.750	.643	.563	.500	.450
24	.999	.999	.999	.999	.999	.999	.857	.750	.667	.600

Economic Safety Factor

R \ M	.1	.2	.3	.4	.5	.6	.7	.8	.9	1.0
.25	1.53	1.86	2.04	2.15	2.24	2.31	2.37	2.42	2.46	2.50
.50	1.15	1.53	1.73	1.86	1.96	2.04	2.10	2.15	2.20	2.24
.75	.89	1.32	1.53	1.68	1.78	1.86	1.93	1.99	2.04	2.08
1	.67	1.15	1.38	1.53	1.65	1.73	1.80	1.86	1.91	1.96
2	-.00	.67	.97	1.15	1.28	1.38	1.47	1.53	1.59	1.65
3	-.67	.32	.67	.89	1.04	1.15	1.24	1.32	1.38	1.44
4	-3.00	-.00	.43	.67	.84	.97	1.07	1.15	1.22	1.28
5	-3.00	-.32	.21	.49	.67	.81	.92	1.01	1.09	1.15
6	-3.00	-.67	-.00	.32	.52	.67	.79	.89	.97	1.04
7	-3.00	-1.15	-.21	.16	.38	.55	.67	.78	.86	.93
8	-3.00	-3.00	-.43	-.00	.25	.43	.57	.67	.76	.84
9	-3.00	-3.00	-.67	-.16	.13	.32	.46	.58	.67	.76
10	-3.00	-3.00	-.97	-.32	-.00	.21	.37	.49	.59	.67
11	-3.00	-3.00	-1.38	-.49	-.13	.10	.27	.40	.51	.60
12	-3.00	-3.00	-3.00	-.67	-.25	-.00	.18	.32	.43	.52
18	-3.00	-3.00	-3.00	-3.00	-1.28	-.67	-.37	-.16	-.00	.13
24	-3.00	-3.00	-3.00	-3.00	-3.00	-3.00	-1.07	-.67	-.43	-.25

R = (cost per shortage) / (cost per unit)

M = order quantity (in months of forecast)

Table 13.4 Economic Safety Stock for Stock Replenishments where Shortages Represent Backorders

h = .40   (annual holding rate)

Economic Probability of a Shortage

R \ M	.1	.2	.3	.4	.5	.6	.7	.8	.9	1.0
.25	.083	.042	.028	.021	.017	.014	.012	.010	.009	.008
.50	.167	.083	.056	.042	.033	.028	.024	.021	.019	.017
.75	.250	.125	.083	.063	.050	.042	.036	.031	.028	.025
1	.333	.167	.111	.083	.067	.056	.048	.042	.037	.033
2	.667	.333	.222	.167	.133	.111	.095	.083	.074	.067
3	.999	.500	.333	.250	.200	.167	.143	.125	.111	.100
4	.999	.667	.444	.333	.267	.222	.190	.167	.148	.133
5	.999	.833	.556	.417	.333	.278	.238	.208	.185	.167
6	.999	.999	.667	.500	.400	.333	.286	.250	.222	.200
7	.999	.999	.778	.583	.467	.389	.333	.292	.259	.233
8	.999	.999	.889	.667	.533	.444	.381	.333	.296	.267
9	.999	.999	.999	.750	.600	.500	.429	.375	.333	.300
10	.999	.999	.999	.833	.667	.556	.476	.417	.370	.333
11	.999	.999	.999	.917	.733	.611	.524	.458	.407	.367
12	.999	.999	.999	.999	.800	.667	.571	.500	.444	.400
18	.999	.999	.999	.999	.999	.999	.857	.750	.667	.600
24	.999	.999	.999	.999	.999	.999	.999	.999	.889	.800

Economic Safety Factor

R \ M	.1	.2	.3	.4	.5	.6	.7	.8	.9	1.0
.25	1.38	1.73	1.91	2.04	2.13	2.20	2.26	2.31	2.36	2.39
.50	.97	1.38	1.59	1.73	1.83	1.91	1.98	2.04	2.09	2.13
.75	.67	1.15	1.38	1.53	1.65	1.73	1.80	1.86	1.91	1.96
1	.43	.97	1.22	1.38	1.50	1.59	1.67	1.73	1.79	1.83
2	-.43	.43	.76	.97	1.11	1.22	1.31	1.38	1.45	1.50
3	-3.00	-.00	.43	.67	.84	.97	1.07	1.15	1.22	1.28
4	-3.00	-.43	.14	.43	.62	.76	.88	.97	1.04	1.11
5	-3.00	-.97	-.14	.21	.43	.59	.71	.81	.90	.97
6	-3.00	-3.00	-.43	-.00	.25	.43	.57	.67	.76	.84
7	-3.00	-3.00	-.76	-.21	.08	.28	.43	.55	.65	.73
8	-3.00	-3.00	-1.22	-.43	-.08	.14	.30	.43	.53	.62
9	-3.00	-3.00	-3.00	-.67	-.25	-.00	.18	.32	.43	.52
10	-3.00	-3.00	-3.00	-.97	-.43	-.14	.06	.21	.33	.43
11	-3.00	-3.00	-3.00	-1.38	-.62	-.28	-.06	.10	.23	.34
12	-3.00	-3.00	-3.00	-3.00	-.84	-.43	-.18	-.00	.14	.25
18	-3.00	-3.00	-3.00	-3.00	-3.00	-3.00	-1.07	-.67	-.43	-.25
24	-3.00	-3.00	-3.00	-3.00	-3.00	-3.00	-3.00	-3.00	-1.22	-.84

R = (cost per shortage) / (cost per unit)

M = order quantity (in months of forecast)

CHAPTER 14

Order Point And Order Level For Low Demand Items

In an order point and order level system, the on-hand plus on-order quantity of stock (OH + OO) is monitored to lie always within two limits. The low limit is called the order point and the high limit is the order level. When the (OH + OO) reaches the order point, an order quantity is placed to bring the (OH + OO) back up to the order level. In this chapter it is assumed that when a demand for the item occurs, the demand becomes a sale so long as the on-hand inventory is adequate; otherwise the demand becomes a lost sale. Also, the chapter considers items where demands are relatively low and follows the Poisson probability distribution. The goal is to show how the order point and order level are determined in relation to the average demand, the lead time and the service level.

The chapter may be more applicable for retail store establishments. If an item is not on-hand when a customer arrives to purchase, the customer may decide to substitute another item or may seek another such establishment to obtain the item. This situation may occur, for example, when a customer seeks a particular style shoe of a certain size or when a particular book is sought in a bookstore. Store management is faced with the task of deciding how to stock these items in a manner that is consistent with their service level goals. When too little stock is carried, lost sales may occur; and when too much stock is carried, the item faces the risk of not being sold within the normal flow of demands. In the latter case, the item's price may need to be reduced in order to entice a sale, or else the item may be scrapped.

Data

The data used in this model are the following:

$$m = \text{average demand per month}$$
$$L = \text{lead time (in months)}$$
$$SL = \text{service level}$$

Note that the average lead time demand (denoted as **d**) can be determined by the relation:

$$d = L\,m$$

In the model of this chapter, the order point is labeled as **OP** and the order level as **OL**.

Model

Consider Figure 14.1, where the level of inventory for an item is plotted against time. Suppose at time t = 0 that the on-hand inventory is at the order level quantity. At time t_1, the on-hand reaches the order point quantity, whereupon an order is placed to bring the on-hand plus on-order inventory back up to the order level. This quantity will arrive at time t_2, which is a lead time beyond t_1. This time elapsing from **0** to t_2 is here called the *order cycle*.

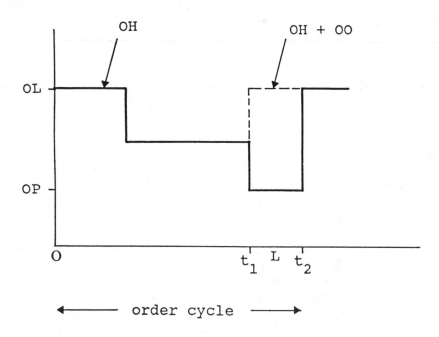

Figure 14.1. On-hand and on-order inventory for the order-level and order-point system

In this model, demands that occur against the item will be filled as long as the on-hand inventory is greater than zero; these filled demands are denoted as sales. When the on-hand inventory is zero, the demands are not filled and sales are lost. Measuring the expected demands and sales that occur over the order cycle is of interest in this model. These findings are needed to calculate the service level **SL**, which is defined in this model by the relation:

$$SL = \frac{\text{sales}}{\text{demand}}$$

Consider first the demands over the order cycle. From time **0** to t_1, the demands are $(OL - OP)$. From t_1 to t_2 (which spans a lead time) the expected demands are merely the average lead time demand **d**. For the order cycle, the expected demands are:

$$\text{demands} = (OL - OP) + d$$

Consider the sales that occur over the order cycle. Recall that a sale occurs with each demand as long as the on-hand inventory is greater than zero. From the time span of **0** to t_1, the sales are $(OL - OP)$. For the lead time period t_1 to t_2, the sales cannot rise above the order point **OP** value. Letting **x** designate the lead time demand and P_x the probability of the demand **x** occurring, the expected sales **s** over the lead time becomes:

$$s = \sum_{x=0}^{OP} xP_x + OP \sum_{x>OP} P_x$$

In this model, **x** is assumed to follow a Poisson probability distribution with a mean of **d**. By using P_x accordingly, the expected sales over the lead time **s** is tabulated. Hence, the expected sales over the order cycle becomes:

$$sales = (OL - OP) + s$$

The expected demands and sales for the item having been determined, the service level can be measured by the relation given earlier. This result is the service level used in developing the adjoining tables.

Tables

The tables of this chapter are arranged in two different formats. The only input required in using Table 14.1 is the average lead time demand **d**. For **d** ranging from 0.10 to 5.0, the service levels are listed for each combination of the order point and order level ranging from (OP,OL) = (0,1) to (5,6).

In Table 14.2 the input data includes the average monthly demand, the lead time and the desired service level. The table lists the corresponding quantities needed for the order point and order level to reach the service level goal. In this table, the monthly demands **m** range from 0.10 to 5.0. The lead time is given in months where L = .25, .50, .75 and 1.00. Note, for a given combination of **m** and **L**, the average monthly lead time demand is d = m × L. The desired service levels are SL = .85, .90, .95 and .99. The table entry of (**OP, OL**) is the first combination from (0,1), (0,2), (1,2), (0,3), so forth, that yields a calculated service level greater or equal to the desired service level.

Example 14.1

Suppose a sporting goods store stocks a rubber life boat with a lead time of two weeks. During the warm weather season, the demand for the boat is estimated as 2 per month. The store manager normally keeps an on-hand plus on-order quantity of 2, and when the on-hand plus on-order quantity falls to 1, then he/she orders another. Assume also that when the boat is out of stock, the sale is lost. Find the service level for this item.

Table 14.1 is used with the average lead time demand of d = .5 × 2 = 1. Also note that OP = 1 and OL = 2. A search of the table shows that the service level is SL = .82.

Example 14.2

For the life boat from the above example, find the order point and order level necessary to bring the service level up to at least SL = .95.

Table 14.1 may be used along with d = 1 to search for the required value of OP and OL. Note the smallest order level that meets these conditions is at OL = 3. The corresponding order point is OP = 2.

Table 14.2 may also be used with the average monthly demand m = 2, the lead time L = .50 and the desired service level of SL = .95. The results show (OP,OL) = (2,4). The cause of the difference in results from the above calculation is that the service level shown in Table 14.1 is a rounded value not quite equal to SL = .95 but which rounds up to .95. In Table 14.2 the pair of (**OP** and **OL**) is searched until the calculated service level is precisely .95 or greater.

Example 14.3

Using the Poisson probability tables, verify the results found in Example 14.2.

Table 8.1 (where the average is denoted as **m**) lists the Poisson probabilities when the average lead time demand **d** is one. These figures are:

x	0	1	2	3	4	5	6
P_x	.368	.368	.184	.061	.015	.003	.001

When the order point and order level are (OP,OL) = (2,3), the expected demand over an order cycle is then:

$$(OL - OP) + d = (3 - 2) + 1 = 2$$

and the corresponding expected sales over the order cycle is:

$$(OL - OP) + s = (3 - 2) + s$$

s (the expected sales over the lead time) is now obtained in the following manner:

$$s = 0\,P_o + 1\,P_1 + 2\,P_2 + 2\,(P_3 + P_4 + P_5 + P_6) = .896$$

Therefore, using (OP,OL) = (2,3), the service level becomes:

$$SL = \frac{1 + .896}{2} = .948$$

which may round up to SL = .95.

Consider the situation when (OP,OL) = (2,4). Here the demand over the order cycle becomes $(4 - 2) + 1 = 3$. The expected sales over the lead time is again s = 0.896, so the average sales over the lead time is $(4 - 2) + .896 = 2.896$. Hence, the service level is:

$$SL = \frac{2.896}{3} = .965$$

which is larger than the desired service level of .95.

Example 14.4

Consider a clothing store that stocks a particular men's suit in 8 sizes. Assume the average demand for the suit is 40 per month and the lead time is 3 weeks. Suppose further that size 40-short receives 10 percent of the demand for this suit. What setting of the order point and order level is needed to maintain a service level of 90 percent?

Note first that the lead time is about .75 months, so the average lead time demand for the suit is $.75 \times 40 = 30$. Second, the average lead time demand for size 40-short is $d = .10 \times 30 = 3$. Table 14.1 is searched to find the smallest order level yielding a service level at least as large as SL = .90. This level is found when (OP,OL) = (4,5).

Table 14.2 could also have been used with an average monthly demand for size 40-short of $m = .10 \times 40 = 4$. Because L = .75 and SL = .90, the table thus shows (OP,OL) = (4,5), as above.

Table 14.1   Service Level by Average Lead Time Demand, Order Point and Order Level

d	OL 1 OP 0	2 0	2 1	3 0	3 1	3 2	4 0	4 1	4 2	4 3
.1	.91	.95	1.00	.97	1.00	1.00	.98	1.00	1.00	1.00
.2	.83	.91	.98	.94	.99	1.00	.95	.99	1.00	1.00
.3	.77	.87	.97	.91	.98	1.00	.93	.99	1.00	1.00
.4	.71	.83	.95	.88	.97	.99	.91	.98	1.00	1.00
.5	.67	.80	.93	.86	.96	.99	.89	.97	.99	1.00
.6	.63	.77	.91	.83	.94	.98	.87	.96	.99	1.00
.7	.59	.74	.88	.81	.93	.98	.85	.95	.98	1.00
.8	.56	.71	.86	.79	.91	.97	.83	.93	.98	.99
.9	.53	.69	.84	.77	.89	.96	.82	.92	.97	.99
1.0	.50	.67	.82	.75	.88	.95	.80	.91	.97	.99
1.1	.48	.65	.79	.73	.86	.94	.78	.89	.96	.98
1.2	.45	.63	.77	.71	.84	.93	.77	.88	.95	.98
1.3	.43	.61	.75	.70	.83	.91	.75	.87	.94	.98
1.4	.42	.59	.73	.68	.81	.90	.74	.85	.93	.97
1.5	.40	.57	.71	.67	.79	.89	.73	.84	.92	.96
1.6	.38	.56	.69	.65	.78	.87	.71	.83	.91	.96
1.7	.37	.54	.67	.64	.76	.86	.70	.81	.90	.95
1.8	.36	.53	.66	.63	.75	.85	.69	.80	.89	.94
1.9	.34	.51	.64	.61	.73	.83	.68	.79	.88	.94
2.0	.33	.50	.62	.60	.72	.82	.67	.77	.86	.93
2.1	.32	.49	.61	.59	.70	.81	.66	.76	.85	.92
2.2	.31	.48	.59	.58	.69	.79	.65	.75	.84	.91
2.3	.30	.47	.58	.57	.67	.78	.63	.74	.83	.90
2.4	.29	.45	.56	.56	.66	.76	.63	.72	.82	.89
2.5	.29	.44	.55	.55	.65	.75	.62	.71	.81	.88
2.6	.28	.43	.53	.54	.64	.74	.61	.70	.80	.87
2.7	.27	.43	.52	.53	.62	.73	.60	.69	.78	.86
2.8	.26	.42	.51	.52	.61	.71	.59	.68	.77	.85
2.9	.26	.41	.50	.51	.60	.70	.58	.67	.76	.84
3.0	.25	.40	.49	.50	.59	.69	.57	.66	.75	.83
3.1	.24	.39	.48	.49	.58	.68	.56	.65	.74	.82
3.2	.24	.38	.47	.48	.57	.66	.56	.64	.73	.81
3.3	.23	.38	.46	.48	.56	.65	.55	.63	.72	.80
3.4	.23	.37	.45	.47	.55	.64	.54	.62	.71	.79
3.5	.22	.36	.44	.46	.54	.63	.53	.61	.70	.78
3.6	.22	.36	.43	.45	.53	.62	.53	.60	.69	.77
3.7	.21	.35	.42	.45	.52	.61	.52	.59	.68	.76
3.8	.21	.34	.41	.44	.51	.60	.51	.58	.67	.75
3.9	.20	.34	.40	.43	.51	.59	.51	.58	.66	.74
4.0	.20	.33	.40	.43	.50	.58	.50	.57	.65	.73
4.1	.20	.33	.39	.42	.49	.57	.49	.56	.64	.72
4.2	.19	.32	.38	.42	.48	.56	.49	.55	.63	.71
4.3	.19	.32	.37	.41	.47	.55	.48	.55	.62	.70
4.4	.19	.31	.37	.41	.47	.54	.48	.54	.61	.69
4.5	.18	.31	.36	.40	.46	.53	.47	.53	.60	.68
4.6	.18	.30	.36	.39	.45	.52	.47	.52	.60	.67
4.7	.18	.30	.35	.39	.45	.52	.46	.52	.59	.66
4.8	.17	.29	.34	.38	.44	.51	.45	.51	.58	.66
4.9	.17	.29	.34	.38	.43	.50	.45	.51	.57	.65
5.0	.17	.29	.33	.38	.43	.49	.44	.50	.56	.64

d = Average Lead Time Demand

OL = Order Level

OP = Order Point

d	OL 5 OP 0	5 1	5 2	5 3	5 4	6 0	6 1	6 2	6 3	6 4	6 5
.1	.98	1.00	1.00	1.00	1.00	.98	1.00	1.00	1.00	1.00	1.00
.2	.96	1.00	1.00	1.00	1.00	.97	1.00	1.00	1.00	1.00	1.00
.3	.94	.99	1.00	1.00	1.00	.95	.99	1.00	1.00	1.00	1.00
.4	.93	.98	1.00	1.00	1.00	.94	.99	1.00	1.00	1.00	1.00
.5	.91	.98	1.00	1.00	1.00	.92	.98	1.00	1.00	1.00	1.00
.6	.89	.97	.99	1.00	1.00	.91	.97	.99	1.00	1.00	1.00
.7	.88	.96	.99	1.00	1.00	.90	.97	.99	1.00	1.00	1.00
.8	.86	.95	.98	1.00	1.00	.88	.96	.99	1.00	1.00	1.00
.9	.85	.94	.98	.99	1.00	.87	.95	.98	1.00	1.00	1.00
1.0	.83	.93	.97	.99	1.00	.86	.94	.98	.99	1.00	1.00
1.1	.82	.92	.97	.99	1.00	.85	.93	.97	.99	1.00	1.00
1.2	.81	.90	.96	.99	1.00	.83	.92	.97	.99	1.00	1.00
1.3	.79	.89	.95	.98	.99	.82	.91	.96	.99	1.00	1.00
1.4	.78	.88	.95	.98	.99	.81	.90	.96	.98	.99	1.00
1.5	.77	.87	.94	.97	.99	.80	.89	.95	.98	.99	1.00
1.6	.76	.86	.93	.97	.99	.79	.88	.94	.98	.99	1.00
1.7	.75	.85	.92	.96	.99	.78	.87	.93	.97	.99	1.00
1.8	.74	.83	.91	.96	.98	.77	.86	.93	.97	.99	1.00
1.9	.72	.82	.90	.95	.98	.76	.85	.92	.96	.98	.99
2.0	.71	.81	.89	.95	.97	.75	.84	.91	.96	.98	.99
2.1	.70	.80	.88	.94	.97	.74	.83	.90	.95	.98	.99
2.2	.69	.79	.87	.93	.97	.73	.82	.89	.94	.97	.99
2.3	.68	.78	.86	.92	.96	.72	.81	.88	.94	.97	.99
2.4	.68	.77	.85	.92	.96	.71	.80	.88	.93	.97	.98
2.5	.67	.76	.84	.91	.95	.71	.79	.87	.92	.96	.98
2.6	.66	.75	.83	.90	.95	.70	.78	.86	.92	.96	.98
2.7	.65	.74	.82	.89	.94	.69	.77	.85	.91	.95	.98
2.8	.64	.73	.81	.88	.93	.68	.76	.84	.90	.95	.97
2.9	.63	.72	.80	.87	.93	.67	.75	.83	.90	.94	.97
3.0	.63	.71	.79	.87	.92	.67	.74	.82	.89	.94	.97
3.1	.62	.70	.78	.86	.91	.66	.74	.81	.88	.93	.96
3.2	.61	.69	.77	.85	.91	.65	.73	.80	.87	.92	.96
3.3	.60	.68	.76	.84	.90	.65	.72	.80	.86	.92	.95
3.4	.60	.67	.75	.83	.89	.64	.71	.79	.86	.91	.95
3.5	.59	.66	.74	.82	.88	.63	.70	.78	.85	.90	.94
3.6	.58	.65	.73	.81	.88	.63	.69	.77	.84	.90	.94
3.7	.57	.65	.73	.80	.87	.62	.69	.76	.83	.89	.93
3.8	.57	.64	.72	.79	.86	.61	.68	.75	.82	.88	.93
3.9	.56	.63	.71	.78	.85	.61	.67	.74	.82	.88	.92
4.0	.56	.62	.70	.78	.84	.60	.66	.74	.81	.87	.92
4.1	.55	.62	.69	.77	.84	.59	.66	.73	.80	.86	.91
4.2	.54	.61	.68	.76	.83	.59	.65	.72	.79	.86	.91
4.3	.54	.60	.67	.75	.82	.58	.64	.71	.78	.85	.90
4.4	.53	.59	.67	.74	.81	.58	.64	.70	.78	.84	.89
4.5	.53	.59	.66	.73	.80	.57	.63	.70	.77	.83	.89
4.6	.52	.58	.65	.72	.79	.57	.62	.69	.76	.83	.88
4.7	.52	.57	.64	.71	.79	.56	.62	.68	.75	.82	.87
4.8	.51	.57	.63	.71	.78	.56	.61	.68	.74	.81	.87
4.9	.51	.56	.63	.70	.77	.55	.61	.67	.74	.80	.86
5.0	.50	.55	.62	.69	.76	.55	.60	.66	.73	.79	.85

d = Average
     Lead Time
     Demand

OL = Order
      Level

OP = Order
      Point

Table 14.2 Order Point and Order Level by Average Monthly Demand, Lead Time (in months) and Service Level

| | L .... .25 .... | | | | L .... .50 .... | | | |
m	SL .85 OP OL	.90 OP OL	.95 OP OL	.99 OP OL	.85 OP OL	.90 OP OL	.95 OP OL	.99 OP OL
.1	0 1	0 1	0 1	1 2	0 1	0 1	0 1	1 2
.2	0 1	0 1	0 1	1 2	0 1	0 1	0 2	1 2
.3	0 1	0 1	0 2	1 2	0 1	0 2	1 2	1 2
.4	0 1	0 1	0 2	1 2	0 2	0 2	1 2	1 3
.5	0 1	0 2	1 2	1 2	0 2	1 2	1 2	2 3
.6	0 1	0 2	1 2	1 2	0 2	1 2	1 2	2 3
.7	0 1	0 2	1 2	1 3	0 2	1 2	1 2	2 3
.8	0 2	0 2	1 2	1 3	1 2	1 2	1 3	2 3
.9	0 2	1 2	1 2	2 3	1 2	1 2	1 3	2 3
1.0	0 2	1 2	1 2	2 3	1 2	1 2	1 3	2 4
1.1	0 2	1 2	1 2	2 3	1 2	1 2	1 3	2 4
1.2	0 2	1 2	1 2	2 3	1 2	1 2	2 3	3 4
1.3	0 2	1 2	1 2	2 3	1 2	1 3	2 3	3 4
1.4	0 2	1 2	1 2	2 3	1 2	1 3	2 3	3 4
1.5	1 2	1 2	1 2	2 3	1 2	1 3	2 3	3 4
1.6	1 2	1 2	1 3	2 3	1 2	1 3	2 3	3 4
1.7	1 2	1 2	1 3	2 3	1 2	1 3	2 3	3 4
1.8	1 2	1 2	1 3	2 3	1 3	2 3	2 3	3 4
1.9	1 2	1 2	1 3	2 3	1 3	2 3	2 3	3 5
2.0	1 2	1 2	1 3	2 4	1 3	2 3	2 4	3 5
2.1	1 2	1 2	1 3	2 4	1 3	2 3	2 4	3 5
2.2	1 2	1 2	1 3	2 4	1 3	2 3	2 4	4 5
2.3	1 2	1 2	2 3	2 4	1 3	2 3	2 4	4 5
2.4	1 2	1 2	2 3	3 4	2 3	2 3	3 4	4 5
2.5	1 2	1 2	2 3	3 4	2 3	2 3	3 4	4 5
2.6	1 2	1 3	2 3	3 4	2 3	2 3	3 4	4 5
2.7	1 2	1 3	2 3	3 4	2 3	2 3	3 4	4 5
2.8	1 2	1 3	2 3	3 4	2 3	2 3	3 4	4 5
2.9	1 2	1 3	2 3	3 4	2 3	2 4	3 4	4 5
3.0	1 2	1 3	2 3	3 4	2 3	2 4	3 4	4 5
3.1	1 2	1 3	2 3	3 4	2 3	2 4	3 4	4 6
3.2	1 2	1 3	2 3	3 4	2 3	2 4	3 4	4 6
3.3	1 2	1 3	2 3	3 4	2 3	2 4	3 4	4 6
3.4	1 2	1 3	2 3	3 4	2 3	3 4	3 4	5 6
3.5	1 3	2 3	2 3	3 4	2 3	3 4	3 5	5 6
3.6	1 3	2 3	2 3	3 4	2 4	3 4	3 5	5 6
3.7	1 3	2 3	2 3	3 4	2 4	3 4	3 5	5 6
3.8	1 3	2 3	2 3	3 5	2 4	3 4	3 5	5 6
3.9	1 3	2 3	2 3	3 5	2 4	3 4	4 5	5 6
4.0	1 3	2 3	2 4	3 5	2 4	3 4	4 5	5 6
4.1	1 3	2 3	2 4	3 5	2 4	3 4	4 5	5 6
4.2	1 3	2 3	2 4	3 5	2 4	3 4	4 5	5 6
4.3	1 3	2 3	2 4	3 5	3 4	3 4	4 5	5 6
4.4	1 3	2 3	2 4	4 5	3 4	3 4	4 5	5 7
4.5	1 3	2 3	2 4	4 5	3 4	3 4	4 5	5 7
4.6	1 3	2 3	2 4	4 5	3 4	3 4	4 5	5 7
4.7	2 3	2 3	2 4	4 5	3 4	3 5	4 5	6 7
4.8	2 3	2 3	3 4	4 5	3 4	3 5	4 5	6 7
4.9	2 3	2 3	3 4	4 5	3 4	3 5	4 5	6 7
5.0	2 3	2 3	3 4	4 5	3 4	3 5	4 5	6 7

L = Lead Time (in months)

SL = Service Level = Sales/Demand

m = Average Monthly Demand

OP = Order Point

OL = Order Level

Table 14.2 Order Point and Order Level by Average Monthly Demand, Lead Time (in months) and Service Level (Continued)

	L = .75								L = 1.00							
	SL .85		.90		.95		.99		.85		.90		.95		.99	
m	OP	OL	OP	OL	OP	OL	OP	OL	OP	OL	OP	OL	OP	OL	OP	OL
.1	0	1	0	1	0	2	1	2	0	1	0	1	0	2	1	2
.2	0	1	0	2	1	2	1	2	0	2	0	2	1	2	1	3
.3	0	2	1	2	1	2	2	3	0	2	1	2	1	2	2	3
.4	0	2	1	2	1	2	2	3	1	2	1	2	1	3	2	3
.5	1	2	1	2	1	2	2	3	1	2	1	2	1	3	2	4
.6	1	2	1	2	1	3	2	3	1	2	1	2	2	3	3	4
.7	1	2	1	2	1	3	2	4	1	2	1	3	2	3	3	4
.8	1	2	1	2	2	3	3	4	1	2	1	3	2	3	3	4
.9	1	2	1	3	2	3	3	4	1	3	2	3	2	3	3	4
1.0	1	2	1	3	2	3	3	4	1	3	2	3	2	4	3	5
1.1	1	2	1	3	2	3	3	4	1	3	2	3	2	4	4	5
1.2	1	3	2	3	2	3	3	4	2	3	2	3	3	4	4	5
1.3	1	3	2	3	2	3	3	5	2	3	2	3	3	4	4	5
1.4	1	3	2	3	2	4	3	5	2	3	2	3	3	4	4	5
1.5	1	3	2	3	2	4	4	5	2	3	2	4	3	4	4	5
1.6	2	3	2	3	3	4	4	5	2	3	2	4	3	4	4	6
1.7	2	3	2	3	3	4	4	5	2	3	3	4	3	4	5	6
1.8	2	3	2	3	3	4	4	5	2	4	3	4	3	5	5	6
1.9	2	3	2	4	3	4	4	5	2	4	3	4	3	5	5	6
2.0	2	3	2	4	3	4	4	5	2	4	3	4	4	5	5	6
2.1	2	3	2	4	3	4	4	6	2	4	3	4	4	5	5	6
2.2	2	3	2	4	3	4	4	6	3	4	3	4	4	5	5	7
2.3	2	3	3	4	3	5	5	6	3	4	3	4	4	5	5	7
2.4	2	4	3	4	3	5	5	6	3	4	3	5	4	5	6	7
2.5	2	4	3	4	3	5	5	6	3	4	3	5	4	5	6	7
2.6	2	4	3	4	4	5	5	6	3	4	4	5	4	6	6	7
2.7	2	4	3	4	4	5	5	6	3	4	4	5	4	6	6	7
2.8	2	4	3	4	4	5	5	6	3	4	4	5	5	6	6	7
2.9	3	4	3	4	4	5	5	7	3	5	4	5	5	6	6	8
3.0	3	4	3	4	4	5	5	7	3	5	4	5	5	6	7	8
3.1	3	4	3	5	4	5	6	7	3	5	4	5	5	6	7	8
3.2	3	4	3	5	4	5	6	7	4	5	4	5	5	6	7	8
3.3	3	4	3	5	4	5	6	7	4	5	4	6	5	6	7	8
3.4	3	4	3	5	4	6	6	7	4	5	4	6	5	7	7	8
3.5	3	4	4	5	4	6	6	7	4	5	4	6	5	7	7	8
3.6	3	4	4	5	4	6	6	7	4	5	5	6	5	7	7	9
3.7	3	4	4	5	5	6	6	7	4	5	5	6	6	7	7	9
3.8	3	5	4	5	5	6	6	8	4	5	5	6	6	7	8	9
3.9	3	5	4	5	5	6	6	8	4	5	5	6	6	7	8	9
4.0	3	5	4	5	5	6	7	8	4	6	5	6	6	7	8	9
4.1	3	5	4	5	5	6	7	8	4	6	5	6	6	7	8	9
4.2	3	5	4	5	5	6	7	8	4	6	5	6	6	7	8	9
4.3	4	5	4	5	5	6	7	8	5	6	5	7	6	8	8	9
4.4	4	5	4	6	5	6	7	8	5	6	5	7	6	8	8	10
4.5	4	5	4	6	5	6	7	8	5	6	5	7	6	8	9	10
4.6	4	5	4	6	5	7	7	8	5	6	6	7	7	8	9	10
4.7	4	5	4	6	5	7	7	8	5	6	6	7	7	8	9	10
4.8	4	5	5	6	5	7	7	9	5	6	6	7	7	8	9	10
4.9	4	5	5	6	6	7	7	9	5	6	6	7	7	8	9	10
5.0	4	5	5	6	6	7	8	9	5	6	6	7	7	8	9	10

L = Lead Time (in months)

SL = Service Level = Sales/Demand

m = Average Monthly Demand

OP = Order Point

OL = Order Level

CHAPTER 15

Queueing Analysis For Reuseable Inventory Items With Backorders

Inventory is conventionally thought of as the stock that is held in a firm's facility until it is consumed by a demand in some manner, such as in the sale to a customer or in the manufacture of a higher level item. Once the demand for an inventory item occurs, the unit is taken out of the inventory and is no longer available to the firm. This kind of inventory is the primary concern of most firms and is the focus of the bulk of this book.

Consider, though, another form of inventory that is present in most firms but does not leave the firm's possession once a demand is fulfilled. This type of inventory demand takes place when a demand occurs for use of the item and, upon completion, the item remains to meet the next demand. Demands of this type may not directly relate to income received but are demands often indirectly needed in running the business. For purposes here, these items are labeled as *reuseable* inventory items. If all of the reuseable inventory items are occupied when a demand arrives and if the demand will wait, in essence the demand is in a backorder state. The results of this chapter are directly applicable to reuseable inventory items when backorders may occur. Chapters 16 and 18 also pertain to reuseable inventory items with backorders, and Chapter 17 is applicable for the lost sales counterpart situation.

Reuseable items with backorders may occur in a wide variety of forms. Examples in a manufacturing facility are the vast inventory of items held to carry out the processing, such as tools, fixtures, machines, pallets, molds, lift trucks and so forth. In a distribution center, examples are the storage racks, binding machines, lift trucks and order picking personnel. In a service repair facility reusable items are any that are loaned to the customers while the repair is taking place, as well as are the tools and fixtures needed in the repair. In an office, examples would be computer terminals, copy machines and printers. Finally, in a sales outlet facility or store, reuseable items may include the sales clerks, gas pumps (in a gas station), push carts (in a grocery store) or tables (in a restaurant).

In all of the above, the number of units to have available is the same as the number of facilities in a queueing system. The rate of demands on the item is the same as the rate of arrivals to the facility, and the time for which the item is in use is the same as the service time on the facility. Demands waiting to use the reuseable item are the same as units waiting in the queue to use one of the service facilities.

The results of Chapters 15 to 18 are developed from use of queueing theory (reference 1). This chapter concerns situations where one or more service facilities are available for units seeking service of some type. In a retail outlet customers arrive to checkout counters to purchase goods, in a distribution center sales slips arrive for the order pickers to fill orders, and in a manufacturing facility job orders arrive for use of particular molds, fixtures or machines. If all service facilities are busy when a new arrival joins the system, the arrival must wait in a line (called a queue) before being serviced. The waiting unit gradually moves forward in the queue and eventually enters the service facility. Upon completion of the service, the unit leaves the system.

The developments of this chapter are based on the assumption that the time between arrivals entering the system follows the exponential distribution shown in Figure 15.1. Also, the time to service a unit is assumed to follow an exponential distribution. The above assumptions imply that the number of arrivals in a unit of time follows a Poisson distribution. Further, the number of units serviced from a continuously busy service facility is also Poisson distributed.

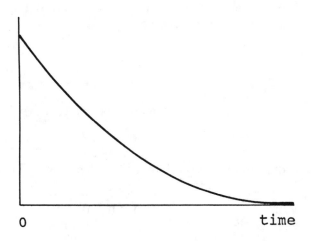

Figure 15.1. The exponential distribution

Data

The data used in this model are the following:

$$N = \text{number of service facilities}$$
$$t_a = \text{average time between arrivals}$$
$$t_s = \text{average time to service a unit}$$

The above average time measures must be in the same unit of time such as days, hours, minutes or seconds. Also, it is common in queueing theory literature to refer to the rate of arrivals and service. These are:

$\lambda = 1/t_a = $ average number of arrivals per unit of time

$\mu = 1/t_s = $ average number of units serviced on a continuously busy service facility in a unit of time

Again, λ and μ (Greek lambda and mu, respectively) are based on the same unit of time.

The utilization factor confronting the system is designated as ρ (Greek rho) and is measured by either of the following relations:

$$\rho = t_s/t_a$$

that is,

$$\rho = \lambda/\mu$$

In order for the model to be applicable, the utilization factor ρ must be less than the number of service facilities N. Otherwise, the units would be arriving to the system faster than they may be serviced, and thereby the system would never fall into an equilibrium state where average measures could be determined.

Model

Consider taking a snapshot of a facility system at an arbitrary moment in time. At such a time, let n designate the number of units in the system (the service facilities plus the queue); n must be an integer quantity of zero or larger. It is possible to determine the probability that the snapshot will find any one value of n. This probability is labeled as P_n.

When $n = 0$, the system is empty—the service facilities and queue have no units. The associated probability becomes:

$$P_o = \frac{1}{\sum\limits_{n=0}^{N-1} \rho^n/n! + \rho^N/[(N-1)!\,(N-\rho)]}$$

For n greater than zero, the probability is then found by the following relations:

$$P_n = P_o\,\rho^n/n! \qquad \text{when } n = 0 \text{ to } N-1$$
$$P_n = P_o\,\rho^n/N!N^{n-N} \qquad \text{when } n = N \text{ or larger}$$

With the probabilities associated with the system having been obtained, it is then possible to measure the average number of units in the queue, the service facility and the total system. These units are commonly denoted in queueing theory by L_q, L_s and L, respectively, and are calculated as:

$$L_q = \rho^{n+1}\,Po/(N-1)!(N-\rho)^2$$
$$L_s = \rho$$
$$L = L_q + L_s$$

Another common set of measures that are useful in queueing theory are measures of the average time a unit is in the queue, the service facility or the system in total. These measures are commonly labeled as w_q, w_s and w, respectively, and are obtained in the following manner:

$$w_q = L_q/\lambda$$
$$w_s = L_s/\lambda$$
$$w = L/\lambda$$

Note also that $w_s = t_s = 1/\mu$ and that $w = w_q + w_s$.

Recall from above that w_q represents the average amount of time a unit is in the queue. This average is based on all units whether or not they are delayed and wait in the queue in the first place. Any unit not waiting in the queue will have zero as its queue time. For those units that are delayed in the queue, the average time is designated as w_q'. This latter measure is determined by the following relation:

$$w_q' = w_q/P_{n \geq N}$$

where

$$P_{n \geq N} = \sum_{n=N}^{\infty} P_n$$

A final measure that may be of interest is here labeled as the service level **SL**. In this situation, the service level represents the percent of arriving units that find a service facility open and need not be delayed in the queue. This is obtained by the relation:

$$SL = \sum_{n=0}^{N-1} P_n$$

Tables

In Table 15.1 of this chapter, selected values of ρ, ranging from 0.10 to 45, are investigated. For each ρ, five representative values of **N** are selected. For each combination of ρ and **N**, the key measures listed above are calculated; however, in order to standardize the data, the value for the average time to service a unit is always set to one, $t_s = 1$. Its counterpart t_a is set relative to t_s. For example, if the average service time is really 10 minutes and the average time between arrivals is 5 minutes, then (in standardizing) $t_s = 1$ and $t_a = 0.5$ are used in their place. The only effect on the tables is that the average times are relative to standardized time averages of W_q, W_s, W and W_q', where $W_s = 1$. With these averages, the corresponding actual averages w_q, w_s, w and w_q' are obtained as illustrated here. Continuing with the example above, suppose the table entries yield $W_q = .7$, $W_s = 1$, $W = 1.7$ and $W_q' = 2.3$. Further, as the real average time to service a unit is 10 minutes, then $w = .7 \times 10 = 7$ minutes, $w_s = 1 \times 10 = 10$ minutes, $w = 1.7 \times 10 = 17$ minutes and $w_q' = 2.3 \times 10 = 23$ minutes.

Table 15.2 is directed more towards reuseable inventory items when backorders occur and gives the number of reuseable items (facilities) needed to achieve a desired service level for a particular utilization factor. The utilization factor ρ ranges from 0.10 to 700 and the desired service level entries are SL = .85, .90, .95 and .99.

Example 15.1

Consider a company whose computer system has two terminals. Suppose the need to use the terminals occurs on the average of 4 per hour ($t_a = 15$ minutes) and the average time the user is on the terminals is 12 minutes ($t_s = 12$ minutes). For this situation, find from the tables all of the queueing measures that are associated with this system.

First note that the utilization factor is $\rho = 12/15 = .8$ and that N = 2. For this situation, the tables show the following:

$P_o = $ .43 = the probability that both terminals are not in use

$L_q = $ .15 = the average number of employees waiting to use a terminal

$L_s = $ .80 = the average number of employees using the terminals

$L = $ .95 = the average number of employees either using the terminal or waiting to use a terminal

$$w_q = .19\,(12) = 2.28 \text{ minutes} = \text{the average time an employee is waiting to use a terminal}$$

$$w_s = 1.00\,(12) = 12 \text{ minutes} = \text{the average time an employee is using the terminal}$$

$$w = 1.19\,(12) = 14.28 \text{ minutes} = \text{the average time an employee is waiting for a terminal plus using a terminal}$$

$$w_q' = .83\,(12) = 9.96 \text{ minutes} = \text{the average time an employee must wait to use a terminal provided both terminals are busy when he/she seeks to use a terminal}$$

$$SL = .77 = \text{the probability an employee will find at least one of the terminals available when he/she desires to use a terminal.}$$

Example 15.2

A mold for a particular windshield is used in the manufacturing process. If the average demand for this windshield type is 8 per day and the average processing time per windshield is 4 hours, how many molds should be in stock to be at least 90 percent certain that the processing can begin as needed for the windshield type? Assume the process is open 8 hours per day.

Using one hour as the unit of time and noting that the process is open 8 hours a day, then $t_a = 1.0$ hour is the average time between demand arrivals and $t_s = 4$ hours is the average (process) service time. This gives $\rho = 4/1 = 4$. Table 15.1 is used to find that $N = 8$ molds are needed, as the associated service level is $SL = .94$. Note that when $N = 7$, the table yields $SL = .86$, which is not high enough to satisfy the goal.

Example 15.3

Consider the purse department in a retail store where customers arrive at an average rate of 6 per hour. If the average service time per customer is 5 minutes, how many sales clerks are needed so that a delayed customer does not have to wait more than 4 minutes on the average to gain service?

Using one minute as the unit of time, $t_a = 10$ minutes, $t_s = 5$ minutes and $\rho = 5/10 = 0.50$. Table 15.1 shows when $N = 1$, $w_q' = 2.00 \times t_s = 2.00 \times 5 = 10$ minutes. When $N = 2$, $w_q' = 0.67 \times 5 = 3.35$ minutes. Therefore, $N = 2$ sales clerks are required.

Example 15.4

A parts distribution center has 4 lift trucks to pick orders for large items. A truck is needed on the average 21 times per hour and the average time to fill the order is 10 minutes. Find the service level for the availability of a truck when it is needed. Also, how many trucks are necessary in order to raise the service level to 90 percent?

Using one hour as the unit of time, $t_a = 1/21$ hours and $t_s = 1/6$ hours; thus, $\rho = 21/6 = 3.5$. Table 15.1 is used to find that when $N = 4$, the service level is $SL = .26$. The table also shows that when $N = 7$, the service level rises to $SL = .92$.

Example 15.5

Consider a grocery store with 5 checkout counters where customers arrive at a rate of 45 per hour. The average time to process a customer is 6 minutes.

How long must the average customer wait in line before being serviced? Also, for a customer who waits, what is the average time that the customer must wait?

Using one minute as the unit of time, $t_a = 60/45 = 1.33$ minutes, $t_s = 6$ minutes and $\rho = 6/1.33 = 4.5$. Table 15.1 shows that when N = 5, the average time a customer must wait before being served is $w_q = 1.52 \times t_s = 1.52 \times 6 = 9.12$ minutes. Also, for a customer who must wait, the average waiting time becomes $w_q' = 2.00 \times 6 = 12$ minutes. Note also that the average customer is in the checkout line (waiting plus being served) an average of $2.52 \times 6 = 15.12$ minutes, which is the same as $w_q + w_s = 9.12 + 6.00 = 15.12$ minutes.

Example 15.6

In a warehouse receiving department, trucks arrive at a rate of 3 per hour and the average time required to unload a truck is 16 minutes. If one unloading crew is available, what is the average number of trucks waiting to be serviced? Also, what is the average time a truck must wait to be serviced?

Using one minute as the unit of time, then $t_a = 20$ minutes, $t_s = 16$ minutes and $\rho = 16/20 = 0.8$. Table 15.1 used with N = 1 gives $L_q = 3.20$ trucks waiting and $w_q = 4.00 \times t_s = 4.00 \times 16 = 64$ minutes average waiting time.

Example 15.7

Consider a jogging shoe manufacturer using a mold (called a "last") to produce a certain style shoe of a given size. Suppose the manufacturing orders for the style average 500 pair per 5 day week and, on the average, size small is called upon for 10 percent of the orders. If a last stays with the shoe for 2 days in the manufacturing stage, how many lasts for the style and size should be available to yield a 95 percent service level (the probability that a last is available when needed)?

The average weekly demand for the size shoe is 10 percent of 500, which is 50. This gives an average of 10 per day, so the average days between the demands for a size small last of the style is $t_a = 1/10 = 0.10$ days. As the average time a last is in use is $t_s = 2$ days, the utilization factor is $\rho = t_s/t_a = 2.0/0.1 = 20$. Table 15.2 is now scanned, with $\rho = 20$ and SL = .95 to yield N = 29. Hence, 29 lasts for the size small last should be available in the factory.

Example 15.8

Consider a distribution center where in a typical day 10,000 lines arrive for picking and the average picking time is 2 minutes. Suppose also that each order picker is available for 440 minutes per day. How many order pickers should be on hand to fill 85 percent of the lines as soon as the lines arrive?

The average number of lines that can be filled in a 440 minute day per order picker is $\mu = 440/2 = 220$. Because $\lambda = 10,000$ lines received per day, the utilization factor is $\rho = \lambda/\mu = 10,000/220 = 45.4$. Table 15.2 shows with $\rho = 45$ that 54 order pickers are needed to achieve a service level of .85.

Table 15.1 Queueing Statistics for Multi-Service Facilities

ρ	N	Po	Lq	Ls	L	Wq	Ws	W	Wq'	SL
.1	1	.90	.01	.10	.11	.11	1.00	1.11	1.11	.90
	2	.90	.00	.10	.10	.00	1.00	1.00	.53	1.00
	3	.90	.00	.10	.10	.00	1.00	1.00	.34	1.00
	4	.90	.00	.10	.10	.00	1.00	1.00	.26	1.00
	5	.90	.00	.10	.10	.00	1.00	1.00	.20	1.00
.2	1	.80	.05	.20	.25	.25	1.00	1.25	1.25	.80
	2	.82	.00	.20	.20	.01	1.00	1.01	.56	.98
	3	.82	.00	.20	.20	.00	1.00	1.00	.36	1.00
	4	.82	.00	.20	.20	.00	1.00	1.00	.26	1.00
	5	.82	.00	.20	.20	.00	1.00	1.00	.21	1.00
.3	1	.70	.13	.30	.43	.43	1.00	1.43	1.43	.70
	2	.74	.01	.30	.31	.02	1.00	1.02	.59	.96
	3	.74	.00	.30	.30	.00	1.00	1.00	.37	1.00
	4	.74	.00	.30	.30	.00	1.00	1.00	.27	1.00
	5	.74	.00	.30	.30	.00	1.00	1.00	.21	1.00
.4	1	.60	.27	.40	.67	.67	1.00	1.67	1.67	.60
	2	.67	.02	.40	.42	.04	1.00	1.04	.63	.93
	3	.67	.00	.40	.40	.00	1.00	1.00	.38	.99
	4	.67	.00	.40	.40	.00	1.00	1.00	.28	1.00
	5	.67	.00	.40	.40	.00	1.00	1.00	.22	1.00
.5	1	.50	.50	.50	1.00	1.00	1.00	2.00	2.00	.50
	2	.60	.03	.50	.53	.07	1.00	1.07	.67	.90
	3	.61	.00	.50	.50	.01	1.00	1.01	.40	.98
	4	.61	.00	.50	.50	.00	1.00	1.00	.29	1.00
	5	.61	.00	.50	.50	.00	1.00	1.00	.22	1.00

ρ = Average service time / Average time between arrivals

N   = Number of service facilities

Po = Probability of no units in the system

Lq = Average number of units in the queue

Ls = Average number of units in the service facilities

L   = Average number of units in the system

Wq = Standardized average time a unit is in the queue

Ws = Standardized average time a unit is in the service facility

W   = Standardized average time a unit is in the system

Wq' = Standardized average time a delayed unit is in the queue

SL = Service Level

Table 15.1 Queueing Statistics for Multi-Service Facilities (Continued)

ρ	N	Po	Lq	Ls	L	Wq	Ws	W	Wq'	SL
.6	1	.40	.90	.60	1.50	1.50	1.00	2.50	2.50	.40
	2	.54	.06	.60	.66	.10	1.00	1.10	.71	.86
	3	.55	.01	.60	.61	.01	1.00	1.01	.42	.98
	4	.55	.00	.60	.60	.00	1.00	1.00	.29	1.00
	5	.55	.00	.60	.60	.00	1.00	1.00	.23	1.00
.7	1	.30	1.63	.70	2.33	2.33	1.00	3.33	3.33	.30
	2	.48	.10	.70	.80	.14	1.00	1.14	.77	.82
	3	.50	.01	.70	.71	.02	1.00	1.02	.43	.96
	4	.50	.00	.70	.70	.00	1.00	1.00	.30	.99
	5	.50	.00	.70	.70	.00	1.00	1.00	.23	1.00
.8	1	.20	3.20	.80	4.00	4.00	1.00	5.00	5.00	.20
	2	.43	.15	.80	.95	.19	1.00	1.19	.83	.77
	3	.45	.02	.80	.82	.02	1.00	1.02	.45	.95
	4	.45	.00	.80	.80	.00	1.00	1.00	.31	.99
	5	.45	.00	.80	.80	.00	1.00	1.00	.24	1.00
.9	1	.10	8.10	.90	9.00	9.00	1.00	10.00	10.00	.10
	2	.38	.23	.90	1.13	.25	1.00	1.25	.91	.72
	3	.40	.03	.90	.93	.03	1.00	1.03	.48	.93
	4	.41	.00	.90	.90	.00	1.00	1.00	.32	.99
	5	.41	.00	.90	.90	.00	1.00	1.00	.24	1.00
1.0	2	.33	.33	1.00	1.33	.33	1.00	1.33	1.00	.67
	3	.36	.05	1.00	1.05	.05	1.00	1.05	.50	.91
	4	.37	.01	1.00	1.01	.01	1.00	1.01	.33	.98
	5	.37	.00	1.00	1.00	.00	1.00	1.00	.25	1.00
	6	.37	.00	1.00	1.00	.00	1.00	1.00	.20	1.00

ρ   = Average service time / Average time between arrivals
N   = Number of service facilities
Po = Probability of no units in the system
Lq = Average number of units in the queue
Ls = Average number of units in the service facilities
L   = Average number of units in the system
Wq = Standardized average time a unit is in the queue
Ws = Standardized average time a unit is in the service facility
W   = Standardized average time a unit is in the system
Wq' = Standardized average time a delayed unit is in the queue
SL = Service Level

Table 15.1   Queueing Statistics for Multi-Service Facilities   (Continued)

ρ	N	Po	Lq	Ls	L	Wq	Ws	W	Wq'	SL
1.2	2	.25	.68	1.20	1.88	.56	1.00	1.56	1.25	.55
	3	.29	.09	1.20	1.29	.08	1.00	1.08	.56	.86
	4	.30	.02	1.20	1.22	.01	1.00	1.01	.36	.96
	5	.30	.00	1.20	1.20	.00	1.00	1.00	.26	.99
	6	.30	.00	1.20	1.20	.00	1.00	1.00	.21	1.00
1.4	2	.18	1.35	1.40	2.75	.96	1.00	1.96	1.67	.42
	3	.24	.18	1.40	1.58	.13	1.00	1.13	.63	.80
	4	.24	.03	1.40	1.43	.02	1.00	1.02	.38	.94
	5	.25	.01	1.40	1.41	.00	1.00	1.00	.28	.98
	6	.25	.00	1.40	1.40	.00	1.00	1.00	.22	1.00
1.6	2	.11	2.84	1.60	4.44	1.78	1.00	2.78	2.50	.29
	3	.19	.31	1.60	1.91	.20	1.00	1.20	.71	.73
	4	.20	.06	1.60	1.66	.04	1.00	1.04	.42	.91
	5	.20	.01	1.60	1.61	.01	1.00	1.01	.29	.97
	6	.20	.00	1.60	1.60	.00	1.00	1.00	.23	.99
1.8	2	.05	7.67	1.80	9.47	4.26	1.00	5.26	5.00	.15
	3	.15	.53	1.80	2.33	.30	1.00	1.30	.83	.65
	4	.16	.11	1.80	1.91	.06	1.00	1.06	.45	.87
	5	.16	.02	1.80	1.82	.01	1.00	1.01	.31	.96
	6	.17	.00	1.80	1.80	.00	1.00	1.00	.24	.99
2.0	3	.11	.89	2.00	2.89	.44	1.00	1.44	1.00	.56
	4	.13	.17	2.00	2.17	.09	1.00	1.09	.50	.83
	5	.13	.04	2.00	2.04	.02	1.00	1.02	.33	.94
	6	.14	.01	2.00	2.01	.00	1.00	1.00	.25	.98
	7	.14	.00	2.00	2.00	.00	1.00	1.00	.20	1.00

ρ   = Average service time / Average time between arrivals
N   = Number of service facilities
Po = Probability of no units in the system
Lq = Average number of units in the queue
Ls = Average number of units in the service facilities
L   = Average number of units in the system
Wq = Standardized average time a unit is in the queue
Ws = Standardized average time a unit is in the service facility
W   = Standardized average time a unit is in the system
Wq' = Standardized average time a delayed unit is in the queue
SL = Service Level

Table 15.1   Queueing Statistics for Multi-Service Facilities   (Continued)

ρ	N	Po	Lq	Ls	L	Wq	Ws	W	Wq'	SL
2.2	3	.08	1.49	2.20	3.69	.68	1.00	1.68	1.25	.46
	4	.10	.28	2.20	2.48	.13	1.00	1.13	.56	.77
	5	.11	.07	2.20	2.27	.03	1.00	1.03	.36	.92
	6	.11	.02	2.20	2.22	.01	1.00	1.01	.26	.97
	7	.11	.00	2.20	2.20	.00	1.00	1.00	.21	.99
2.4	3	.06	2.59	2.40	4.99	1.08	1.00	2.08	1.67	.35
	4	.08	.43	2.40	2.83	.18	1.00	1.18	.63	.71
	5	.09	.10	2.40	2.50	.04	1.00	1.04	.38	.89
	6	.09	.03	2.40	2.43	.01	1.00	1.01	.28	.96
	7	.09	.01	2.40	2.41	.00	1.00	1.00	.22	.99
2.6	3	.03	4.93	2.60	7.53	1.90	1.00	2.90	2.50	.24
	4	.07	.66	2.60	3.26	.25	1.00	1.25	.71	.65
	5	.07	.16	2.60	2.76	.06	1.00	1.06	.42	.85
	6	.07	.04	2.60	2.64	.02	1.00	1.02	.29	.94
	7	.07	.01	2.60	2.61	.00	1.00	1.00	.23	.98
2.8	3	.02	12.27	2.80	15.07	4.38	1.00	5.38	5.00	.12
	4	.05	1.00	2.80	3.80	.36	1.00	1.36	.83	.57
	5	.06	.24	2.80	3.04	.09	1.00	1.09	.45	.81
	6	.06	.07	2.80	2.87	.02	1.00	1.02	.31	.92
	7	.06	.02	2.80	2.82	.01	1.00	1.01	.24	.97
3.0	4	.04	1.53	3.00	4.53	.51	1.00	1.51	1.00	.49
	5	.05	.35	3.00	3.35	.12	1.00	1.12	.50	.76
	6	.05	.10	3.00	3.10	.03	1.00	1.03	.33	.90
	7	.05	.03	3.00	3.03	.01	1.00	1.01	.25	.96
	8	.05	.01	3.00	3.01	.00	1.00	1.00	.20	.99

```
ρ   = Average service time / Average time between arrivals
N   = Number of service facilities
Po  = Probability of no units in the system
Lq  = Average number of units in the queue
Ls  = Average number of units in the service facilities
L   = Average number of units in the system
Wq  = Standardized average time a unit is in the queue
Ws  = Standardized average time a unit is in the service facility
W   = Standardized average time a unit is in the system
Wq' = Standardized average time a delayed unit is in the queue
SL  = Service Level
```

Table 15.1   Queueing Statistics for Multi-Service Facilities   (Continued)

ρ	N	Po	Lq	Ls	L	Wq	Ws	W	Wq'	SL
3.5	4	.01	5.17	3.50	8.67	1.48	1.00	2.48	2.00	.26
	5	.03	.88	3.50	4.38	.25	1.00	1.25	.67	.62
	6	.03	.25	3.50	3.75	.07	1.00	1.07	.40	.82
	7	.03	.08	3.50	3.58	.02	1.00	1.02	.29	.92
	8	.03	.02	3.50	3.52	.01	1.00	1.01	.22	.97
4.0	5	.01	2.22	4.00	6.22	.55	1.00	1.55	1.00	.45
	6	.02	.57	4.00	4.57	.14	1.00	1.14	.50	.72
	7	.02	.18	4.00	4.18	.05	1.00	1.05	.33	.86
	8	.02	.06	4.00	4.06	.01	1.00	1.01	.25	.94
	9	.02	.02	4.00	4.02	.00	1.00	1.00	.20	.98
4.5	5	.00	6.86	4.50	11.36	1.52	1.00	2.52	2.00	.24
	6	.01	1.26	4.50	5.76	.28	1.00	1.28	.67	.58
	7	.01	.39	4.50	4.89	.09	1.00	1.09	.40	.78
	8	.01	.13	4.50	4.63	.03	1.00	1.03	.29	.90
	9	.01	.05	4.50	4.55	.01	1.00	1.01	.22	.95
5.0	6	.00	2.94	5.00	7.94	.59	1.00	1.59	1.00	.41
	7	.01	.81	5.00	5.81	.16	1.00	1.16	.50	.68
	8	.01	.28	5.00	5.28	.06	1.00	1.06	.33	.83
	9	.01	.10	5.00	5.10	.02	1.00	1.02	.25	.92
	10	.01	.04	5.00	5.04	.01	1.00	1.01	.20	.96
5.5	6	.00	8.59	5.50	14.09	1.56	1.00	2.56	2.00	.22
	7	.00	1.67	5.50	7.17	.30	1.00	1.30	.67	.54
	8	.00	.55	5.50	6.05	.10	1.00	1.10	.40	.75
	9	.00	.20	5.50	5.70	.04	1.00	1.04	.29	.87
	10	.00	.08	5.50	5.58	.01	1.00	1.01	.22	.94

ρ = Average service time / Average time between arrivals
N = Number of service facilities
Po = Probability of no units in the system
Lq = Average number of units in the queue
Ls = Average number of units in the service facilities
L = Average number of units in the system
Wq = Standardized average time a unit is in the queue
Ws = Standardized average time a unit is in the service facility
W = Standardized average time a unit is in the system
Wq' = Standardized average time a delayed unit is in the queue
SL = Service Level

Table 15.1 Queueing Statistics for Multi-Service Facilities (Continued)

ρ	N	Po	Lq	Ls	L	Wq	Ws	W	Wq'	SL
6.0	7	.00	3.68	6.00	9.68	.61	1.00	1.61	1.00	.39
	9	.00	.39	6.00	6.39	.07	1.00	1.07	.33	.80
	11	.00	.06	6.00	6.06	.01	1.00	1.01	.20	.95
	13	.00	.01	6.00	6.01	.00	1.00	1.00	.14	.99
	15	.00	.00	6.00	6.00	.00	1.00	1.00	.11	1.00
7.0	8	.00	4.45	7.00	11.45	.64	1.00	1.64	1.00	.36
	10	.00	.52	7.00	7.52	.07	1.00	1.07	.33	.78
	12	.00	.09	7.00	7.09	.01	1.00	1.01	.20	.94
	14	.00	.01	7.00	7.01	.00	1.00	1.00	.14	.99
	16	.00	.00	7.00	7.00	.00	1.00	1.00	.11	1.00
8.0	9	.00	5.23	8.00	13.23	.65	1.00	1.65	1.00	.35
	11	.00	.65	8.00	8.65	.08	1.00	1.08	.33	.76
	13	.00	.12	8.00	8.12	.02	1.00	1.02	.20	.92
	15	.00	.02	8.00	8.02	.00	1.00	1.00	.14	.98
	17	.00	.00	8.00	8.00	.00	1.00	1.00	.11	1.00
9.0	10	.00	6.02	9.00	15.02	.67	1.00	1.67	1.00	.33
	12	.00	.80	9.00	9.80	.09	1.00	1.09	.33	.73
	14	.00	.16	9.00	9.16	.02	1.00	1.02	.20	.91
	16	.00	.03	9.00	9.03	.00	1.00	1.00	.14	.98
	18	.00	.01	9.00	9.01	.00	1.00	1.00	.11	.99
10.0	11	.00	6.82	10.00	16.82	.68	1.00	1.68	1.00	.32
	13	.00	.95	10.00	10.95	.10	1.00	1.10	.33	.71
	15	.00	.20	10.00	10.20	.02	1.00	1.02	.20	.90
	17	.00	.04	10.00	10.04	.00	1.00	1.00	.14	.97
	19	.00	.01	10.00	10.01	.00	1.00	1.00	.11	.99

ρ = Average service time / Average time between arrivals
N   = Number of service facilities
Po = Probability of no units in the system
Lq = Average number of units in the queue
Ls = Average number of units in the service facilities
L   = Average number of units in the system
Wq = Standardized average time a unit is in the queue
Ws = Standardized average time a unit is in the service facility
W   = Standardized average time a unit is in the system
Wq' = Standardized average time a delayed unit is in the queue
SL = Service Level

Table 15.1   Queueing Statistics for Multi-Service Facilities   (Continued)

ρ	N	Po	Lq	Ls	L	Wq	Ws	W	Wq'	SL
12.0	13	.00	8.45	12.00	20.45	.70	1.00	1.70	1.00	.30
	15	.00	1.28	12.00	13.28	.11	1.00	1.11	.33	.68
	17	.00	.30	12.00	12.30	.03	1.00	1.03	.20	.87
	19	.00	.07	12.00	12.07	.01	1.00	1.01	.14	.96
	21	.00	.02	12.00	12.02	.00	1.00	1.00	.11	.99
14.0	15	.00	10.11	14.00	24.11	.72	1.00	1.72	1.00	.28
	17	.00	1.63	14.00	15.63	.12	1.00	1.12	.33	.65
	19	.00	.42	14.00	14.42	.03	1.00	1.03	.20	.85
	21	.00	.11	14.00	14.11	.01	1.00	1.01	.14	.94
	23	.00	.03	14.00	14.03	.00	1.00	1.00	.11	.98
16.0	17	.00	11.79	16.00	27.79	.74	1.00	1.74	1.00	.26
	19	.00	1.99	16.00	17.99	.12	1.00	1.12	.33	.63
	21	.00	.55	16.00	16.55	.03	1.00	1.03	.20	.83
	23	.00	.16	16.00	16.16	.01	1.00	1.01	.14	.93
	25	.00	.05	16.00	16.05	.00	1.00	1.00	.11	.97
18.0	19	.00	13.50	18.00	31.50	.75	1.00	1.75	1.00	.25
	21	.00	2.38	18.00	20.38	.13	1.00	1.13	.33	.60
	23	.00	.69	18.00	18.69	.04	1.00	1.04	.20	.81
	25	.00	.21	18.00	18.21	.01	1.00	1.01	.14	.92
	27	.00	.07	18.00	18.07	.00	1.00	1.00	.11	.97
20.0	21	.00	15.21	20.00	35.21	.76	1.00	1.76	1.00	.24
	23	.00	2.77	20.00	22.77	.14	1.00	1.14	.33	.58
	25	.00	.84	20.00	20.84	.04	1.00	1.04	.20	.79
	27	.00	.27	20.00	20.27	.01	1.00	1.01	.14	.90
	29	.00	.09	20.00	20.09	.00	1.00	1.00	.11	.96

ρ = Average service time / Average time between arrivals
N = Number of service facilities
Po = Probability of no units in the system
Lq = Average number of units in the queue
Ls = Average number of units in the service facilities
L = Average number of units in the system
Wq = Standardized average time a unit is in the queue
Ws = Standardized average time a unit is in the service facility
W = Standardized average time a unit is in the system
Wq' = Standardized average time a delayed unit is in the queue
SL = Service Level

Table 15.1　Queueing Statistics for Multi-Service Facilities　(Continued)

ρ	N	Po	Lq	Ls	L	Wq	Ws	W	Wq'	SL
25.0	26	.00	19.56	25.00	44.56	.78	1.00	1.78	1.00	.22
	29	.00	2.13	25.00	27.13	.09	1.00	1.09	.25	.66
	32	.00	.45	25.00	25.45	.02	1.00	1.02	.14	.87
	35	.00	.10	25.00	25.10	.00	1.00	1.00	.10	.96
	38	.00	.02	25.00	25.02	.00	1.00	1.00	.08	.99
30.0	31	.00	23.97	30.00	53.97	.80	1.00	1.80	1.00	.20
	34	.00	2.82	30.00	32.82	.09	1.00	1.09	.25	.62
	37	.00	.67	30.00	30.67	.02	1.00	1.02	.14	.84
	40	.00	.17	30.00	30.17	.01	1.00	1.01	.10	.94
	43	.00	.04	30.00	30.04	.00	1.00	1.00	.08	.98
35.0	36	.00	28.42	35.00	63.42	.81	1.00	1.81	1.00	.19
	39	.00	3.55	35.00	38.55	.10	1.00	1.10	.25	.59
	42	.00	.91	35.00	35.91	.03	1.00	1.03	.14	.82
	45	.00	.25	35.00	35.25	.01	1.00	1.01	.10	.93
	48	.00	.07	35.00	35.07	.00	1.00	1.00	.08	.98
40.0	41	.00	32.92	40.00	72.92	.82	1.00	1.82	1.00	.18
	44	.00	4.32	40.00	44.32	.11	1.00	1.11	.25	.57
	47	.00	1.17	40.00	41.17	.03	1.00	1.03	.14	.80
	50	.00	.35	40.00	40.35	.01	1.00	1.01	.10	.91
	53	.00	.10	40.00	40.10	.00	1.00	1.00	.08	.97
45.0	46	.00	37.44	45.00	82.44	.83	1.00	1.83	1.00	.17
	49	.00	5.11	45.00	50.11	.11	1.00	1.11	.25	.55
	52	.00	1.46	45.00	46.46	.03	1.00	1.03	.14	.77
	55	.00	.46	45.00	45.46	.01	1.00	1.01	.10	.90
	58	.00	.14	45.00	45.14	.00	1.00	1.00	.08	.96

ρ　= Average service time / Average time between arrivals

N　= Number of service facilities

Po　= Probability of no units in the system

Lq　= Average number of units in the queue

Ls　= Average number of units in the service facilities

L　= Average number of units in the system

Wq　= Standardized average time a unit is in the queue

Ws　= Standardized average time a unit is in the service facility

W　= Standardized average time a unit is in the system

Wq'　= Standardized average time a delayed unit is in the queue

SL　= Service Level

Table 15.2 Minimum Units Needed to Maintain a Desired Service Level for a Reusable Inventory System with Backorders

ρ	SL 85	SL 90	SL 95	SL 99	ρ	SL 85	SL 90	SL 95	SL 99
	N					N			
.1	2	2	2	2	55	65	67	69	74
.2	2	2	2	3	60	70	72	75	80
.3	2	2	2	3	65	76	78	80	86
.4	2	2	3	3	70	81	83	86	92
.5	2	2	3	4	75	86	88	91	97
.6	2	3	3	4	80	92	94	97	103
.7	3	3	3	4	85	97	99	102	109
.8	3	3	4	4	90	102	105	108	114
.9	3	3	4	5	95	108	110	113	120
1.0	3	3	4	5	100	113	115	119	125
1.2	3	4	4	5	110	124	126	129	137
1.4	4	4	5	6	120	134	137	140	148
1.6	4	4	5	6	130	145	147	151	159
1.8	4	5	5	7	140	155	158	162	170
2.0	5	5	6	7	150	166	168	173	181
2.5	5	6	6	8	160	176	179	183	192
3.0	6	6	7	9	170	187	190	194	203
3.5	7	7	8	10	180	197	200	205	214
4.0	7	8	9	10	190	208	211	215	224
4.5	8	9	9	11	200	218	221	226	235
5	9	9	10	12	210	229	232	236	246
10	15	16	17	19	220	239	242	247	257
15	21	22	23	26	230	249	253	258	268
20	26	27	29	32	240	260	263	268	278
25	32	33	35	39	250	270	274	279	289
30	38	39	41	45	260	281	284	289	300
35	43	44	47	51	270	291	294	300	311
40	49	50	52	57	280	301	305	310	321
45	54	56	58	63	290	312	315	321	332
50	60	61	64	66	300	322	326	331	343

N = minimum number of reuseable units
ρ = utilization factor (average service time / average time between arrivals)
SL = service level

Table 15.2 Minimum Units Needed to Maintain a Desired Service Level for a Reusable Inventory System with Backorders (Continued)

ρ	SL 85	90	95	99	ρ	SL 85	90	95	99
	N					N			
310	332	336	342	354	510	538	543	551	565
320	343	346	352	364	520	549	553	561	576
330	353	357	363	375	530	559	564	571	586
340	363	367	373	386	540	569	574	582	597
350	374	378	384	396	550	579	584	592	607
360	384	388	394	407	560	590	595	602	618
370	394	398	405	417	570	600	605	613	628
380	405	409	415	428	580	610	615	623	639
390	415	419	426	439	590	620	626	634	649
400	425	429	436	449	600	631	636	644	660
410	436	440	446	460	610	641	646	654	670
420	446	450	457	470	620	651	656	665	681
430	456	461	467	481	630	661	667	675	691
440	466	471	478	492	640	672	677	685	702
450	477	481	488	502	650	682	687	696	712
460	487	492	499	513	660	692	698	706	723
470	497	502	509	523	670	702	708	716	733
480	508	512	519	534	680	713	718	727	744
490	518	523	530	544	690	723	728	737	754
500	528	533	540	555	700	733	739	747	765

N = minimum number of reuseable units
ρ = utilization factor (average service time / average time between arrivals)
SL = service level

CHAPTER 16

Queueing Analysis For A One Unit Reuseable Inventory Item With Backorders

This chapter is an extension of reuseable inventory items with backorders as was described in Chapter 15, but two exceptions are considered here. First, the results pertain when only one reuseable inventory item is stocked in inventory. Second, in this chapter, the service times are allowed to follow any probablility distribution and are not confined only to the exponential distribution as in Chapter 15. The table results are especially useful in comparing the sensitivity of the queueing measures when different service time distributions are assumed. Examples of situations where only one reuseable unit is in stock may typically be more expensive inventory items. For example, only one tractor may be stocked in a rental agency, just one diagnostic system may be available in an auto service station, and only one package binding machine may be in service at a distribution center.

The results of this chapter are developed from the methods of queueing theory where only one service facility is available (reference 1). The service facility is available to meet oncoming demands on the system, and the time between arrival of demands must have a known average and must follow an exponential distribution (as in Chapter 15). The service times may follow any probability distribution as long as the average and standard deviation are known. One last requirement is that the average of the service times be smaller than the average of the arrival times. If a new arrival is delayed because the service facility is occupied, it will wait in the queue until the service facility is available. In an inventory environment, the service facility represents a reuseable inventory item, the arrivals represent demands and the system is one where backorders may occur.

Data

The input data required to use the model are the following:

$$t_a = \text{average time between arrivals}$$
$$t_s = \text{average time to service a unit}$$
$$\sigma = \text{standard deviation of the service time}$$

If t_a and t_s are set with the same unit of time, their counterpart rates $\lambda = 1/t_a$ and $\mu = 1/t_s$ are then the same, as described in Chapter 15. Further, the utilization factor ρ for the system becomes:

$$\rho = t_s/t_a = \lambda/\mu$$

In order to achieve an equilibrium status, the value of ρ must be less than one, and thus the model of this chapter is applicable only under these circumstances.

Model

Using the same notation as in Chapter 15, the system measures are determined as listed:

$$P_o = 1 - \rho$$
$$L_q = [(\lambda \sigma)^2 + \rho^2]/2\,(1 - \rho)$$
$$L_s = \rho$$
$$L = L_q + L_s$$
$$w_q = L_q/\lambda$$
$$w_s = t_s$$
$$w = w_q + w_s$$
$$w_q' = w_q/(1 - P_o)$$
$$SL = P_o$$

Tables

In the development of the tables of this chapter, certain standardization of the input data are followed. The first standardization concerns the service time statistics, where t_s and σ are combined to yield the coefficient of variation **cov**:

$$\text{cov} = \sigma/t_s$$

The adjoining tables list results with selected values of **cov** ranging from 0 to 2. Note that cov = 0 occurs when the service time is a fixed value that never changes and thereby $\sigma = 0$. When the service time is shaped like a normal distribution, the coefficient of variation must be ⅓ or less, because the service times are positive values where t_s must be at least three times larger than 0 to follow the shape of the normal distribution. When the service time is shaped like an exponential distribution (as in Chapter 15), then $\sigma = t_s$ or cov = 1.

The tables are also developed using a standard service time average of one, and as was the case in Chapter 15, the only table entries that become standardized are those associated with time. The table entries of W_q, W_s, W and W_q' are standardized values based on $W_s = 1$. The actual counterpart time measures are obtained by the following relations:

$$w_q = W_q\,t_s$$
$$w_s = W_s\,t_s$$
$$w = W\,t_s$$
$$w_q' = W_q'\,t_s$$

Example 16.1

Suppose a warehouse clerk fills one order at a time as the orders arrive to his/her input bin and the orders arrive at an average rate of 12 per hour. Suppose also the time to fill an order is shaped like a normal distribution with a mean of 4 minutes and a standard deviation of 1.2 minutes. Find the queueing measures associated with this clerk.

First, the unit of time may be set in a common unit such as minutes, whereby the average time between orders becomes $t_a = 5$ minutes. Since $t_s = 4$ minutes and $\sigma = 1.2$ minutes, then cov = 1.2/4 = 0.30. Also $\rho = t_s/t_a = 4/5 = 0.80$. The results for this situation are obtained by interpolation of Table 16.1, using the halfway entries of cov = .2 and .4. The results are described below.

$P_o = 0.20$ is the probability that the clerk is idle and has no unfilled orders in his/her bin. $L_q = 1.76$ states that the average number of unfilled orders waiting in the bin is 1.76. $L_s = .80$ implies that on the average 0.80 orders are in the process of being filled. $L = 2.56$ shows that, on the average, 2.56 orders are waiting to be filled or are in the process of being filled by the clerk.

$W_q = 2.20$ shows that the average waiting time for an unfilled order is $w_q = 2.20 \times 4 = 8.8$ minutes. $W_s = 1.00$ states that the average time to fill an order is $w_s = 1.00 \times 4 = 4$ minutes. Now $W = 3.20$ implies that the average time an order is in the system is $w = 3.20 \times 4 = 12.8$ minutes. Finally, $W_q' = 2.75$ pertains to those orders that must wait in the clerk's bin before being filled. The average waiting time for these orders becomes $w_q' = 2.75 \times 4 = 11$ minutes.

$SL = .20$ gives the service level for newly arrived orders and states that 20 percent of new orders will be serviced immediately without waiting.

Example 16.2

Consider a distribution center where the items that are set for customer delivery are placed in boxes and processed through a mechanical sealing and binding machine. The sealing process time is constant and always takes 40.5 seconds. The boxes arrive to this process at an average rate of 80 per hour. How long is such a box in the total system before it is sealed and ready for delivery?

The unit of time for this situation may be set to seconds—where $t_a = 1/80$ hours $= 60/80$ minutes $= 3600/80 = 45$ seconds. Because $t_s = 40.5$ seconds and $\sigma = 0$, $cov = 0$ and $\rho = 40.5/45 = 0.9$. The table shows $W = 5.50$; hence the average unit is in the system for a length of time $w = 5.50 \times 40.5 = 222.75$ seconds or $222.75/60 = 3.71$ minutes.

Example 16.3

Customers arrive to a retail counter at a rate of 24 per hour with items to purchase. The current processing time of the item requires an average of 2 minutes with a standard deviation of 1.6 minutes. A new system is being considered where the average is still 2 minutes but the standard deviation will be reduced to 0.80 minutes. Show the waiting time effects that the new system will have on the customers.

In this situation, let the unit of time be set at 1 minute, whereby $t_a = 60/24 = 2.5$ minutes and $t_s = 2$ minutes; hence, $\rho = 2/2.5 = 0.8$. In the current system, where $cov = 1.6/2.0 = 0.8$,

$$w_q = 3.28\,(2) = 6.56 \text{ minutes}$$
$$w_q' = 4.10\,(2) = 8.20 \text{ minutes}$$

With the proposed system where $cov = 0.8/2 = 0.40$, then:

$$w_q = 2.32\,(2) = 4.64 \text{ minutes}$$
$$w_q' = 2.90\,(2) = 5.80 \text{ minutes}$$

Table 16.1 Queueing Statistics for One Service Facility and Arbitrary Service Times

ρ	COV	Po	Lq	Ls	L	Wq	Ws	W	Wq'	SL
.1	.0	.90	.01	.10	.11	.06	1.00	1.06	.56	.90
	.2	.90	.01	.10	.11	.06	1.00	1.06	.58	.90
	.4	.90	.01	.10	.11	.06	1.00	1.06	.64	.90
	.6	.90	.01	.10	.11	.08	1.00	1.08	.76	.90
	.8	.90	.01	.10	.11	.09	1.00	1.09	.91	.90
	1.0	.90	.01	.10	.11	.11	1.00	1.11	1.11	.90
	1.5	.90	.02	.10	.12	.18	1.00	1.18	1.81	.90
	2.0	.90	.03	.10	.13	.28	1.00	1.28	2.78	.90
.2	.0	.80	.02	.20	.23	.12	1.00	1.13	.63	.80
	.2	.80	.03	.20	.23	.13	1.00	1.13	.65	.80
	.4	.80	.03	.20	.23	.15	1.00	1.15	.73	.80
	.6	.80	.03	.20	.23	.17	1.00	1.17	.85	.80
	.8	.80	.04	.20	.24	.21	1.00	1.21	1.03	.80
	1.0	.80	.05	.20	.25	.25	1.00	1.25	1.25	.80
	1.5	.80	.08	.20	.28	.41	1.00	1.41	2.03	.80
	2.0	.80	.13	.20	.33	.63	1.00	1.63	3.13	.80
.3	.0	.70	.06	.30	.36	.21	1.00	1.21	.71	.70
	.2	.70	.07	.30	.37	.22	1.00	1.22	.74	.70
	.4	.70	.07	.30	.37	.25	1.00	1.25	.83	.70
	.6	.70	.09	.30	.39	.29	1.00	1.29	.97	.70
	.8	.70	.11	.30	.41	.35	1.00	1.35	1.17	.70
	1.0	.70	.13	.30	.43	.43	1.00	1.43	1.43	.70
	1.5	.70	.21	.30	.51	.70	1.00	1.70	2.32	.70
	2.0	.70	.32	.30	.62	1.07	1.00	2.07	3.57	.70

ρ = Average service time / Average time between arrivals
COV = Coefficient of variation for service times
Po = Probability of no units in the system
Lq = Average number of units in the queue
Ls = Average number of units in the service facility
L = Average number of units in the system
Wq = Standardized average time a unit is in the queue
Ws = Standardized average time a unit is in the service facility
W = Standardized average time a unit is in the system
Wq' = Standardized average time a delayed unit is in the queue
SL = Service Level

ρ	COV	Po	Lq	Ls	L	Wq	Ws	W	Wq'	SL
.4	.0	.60	.13	.40	.53	.33	1.00	1.33	.83	.60
	.2	.60	.14	.40	.54	.35	1.00	1.35	.87	.60
	.4	.60	.15	.40	.55	.39	1.00	1.39	.97	.60
	.6	.60	.18	.40	.58	.45	1.00	1.45	1.13	.60
	.8	.60	.22	.40	.62	.55	1.00	1.55	1.37	.60
	1.0	.60	.27	.40	.67	.67	1.00	1.67	1.67	.60
	1.5	.60	.43	.40	.83	1.08	1.00	2.08	2.71	.60
	2.0	.60	.67	.40	1.07	1.67	1.00	2.67	4.17	.60
.5	.0	.50	.25	.50	.75	.50	1.00	1.50	1.00	.50
	.2	.50	.26	.50	.76	.52	1.00	1.52	1.04	.50
	.4	.50	.29	.50	.79	.58	1.00	1.58	1.16	.50
	.6	.50	.34	.50	.84	.68	1.00	1.68	1.36	.50
	.8	.50	.41	.50	.91	.82	1.00	1.82	1.64	.50
	1.0	.50	.50	.50	1.00	1.00	1.00	2.00	2.00	.50
	1.5	.50	.81	.50	1.31	1.63	1.00	2.63	3.25	.50
	2.0	.50	1.25	.50	1.75	2.50	1.00	3.50	5.00	.50
.6	.0	.40	.45	.60	1.05	.75	1.00	1.75	1.25	.40
	.2	.40	.47	.60	1.07	.78	1.00	1.78	1.30	.40
	.4	.40	.52	.60	1.12	.87	1.00	1.87	1.45	.40
	.6	.40	.61	.60	1.21	1.02	1.00	2.02	1.70	.40
	.8	.40	.74	.60	1.34	1.23	1.00	2.23	2.05	.40
	1.0	.40	.90	.60	1.50	1.50	1.00	2.50	2.50	.40
	1.5	.40	1.46	.60	2.06	2.44	1.00	3.44	4.06	.40
	2.0	.40	2.25	.60	2.85	3.75	1.00	4.75	6.25	.40

```
ρ    = Average service time / Average time between arrivals
COV  = Coefficient of variation for service times
Po   = Probability of no units in the system
Lq   = Average number of units in the queue
Ls   = Average number of units in the service facility
L    = Average number of units in the system
Wq   = Standardized average time a unit is in the queue
Ws   = Standardized average time a unit is in the service facility
W    = Standardized average time a unit is in the system
Wq'  = Standardized average time a delayed unit is in the queue
SL   = Service Level
```

Table 16.1 Queueing Statistics for One Service Facility and Arbitrary Service Times (Continued)

ρ	COV	Po	Lq	Ls	L	Wq	Ws	W	Wq'	SL
.7	.0	.30	.82	.70	1.52	1.17	1.00	2.17	1.67	.30
	.2	.30	.85	.70	1.55	1.21	1.00	2.21	1.73	.30
	.4	.30	.95	.70	1.65	1.35	1.00	2.35	1.93	.30
	.6	.30	1.11	.70	1.81	1.59	1.00	2.59	2.27	.30
	.8	.30	1.34	.70	2.04	1.91	1.00	2.91	2.73	.30
	1.0	.30	1.63	.70	2.33	2.33	1.00	3.33	3.33	.30
	1.5	.30	2.65	.70	3.35	3.79	1.00	4.79	5.42	.30
	2.0	.30	4.08	.70	4.78	5.83	1.00	6.83	8.33	.30
.8	.0	.20	1.60	.80	2.40	2.00	1.00	3.00	2.50	.20
	.2	.20	1.66	.80	2.46	2.08	1.00	3.08	2.60	.20
	.4	.20	1.86	.80	2.66	2.32	1.00	3.32	2.90	.20
	.6	.20	2.18	.80	2.98	2.72	1.00	3.72	3.40	.20
	.8	.20	2.62	.80	3.42	3.28	1.00	4.28	4.10	.20
	1.0	.20	3.20	.80	4.00	4.00	1.00	5.00	5.00	.20
	1.5	.20	5.20	.80	6.00	6.50	1.00	7.50	8.13	.20
	2.0	.20	8.00	.80	8.80	10.00	1.00	11.00	12.50	.20
.9	.0	.10	4.05	.90	4.95	4.50	1.00	5.50	5.00	.10
	.2	.10	4.21	.90	5.11	4.68	1.00	5.68	5.20	.10
	.4	.10	4.70	.90	5.60	5.22	1.00	6.22	5.80	.10
	.6	.10	5.51	.90	6.41	6.12	1.00	7.12	6.80	.10
	.8	.10	6.64	.90	7.54	7.38	1.00	8.38	8.20	.10
	1.0	.10	8.10	.90	9.00	9.00	1.00	10.00	10.00	.10
	1.5	.10	13.16	.90	14.06	14.62	1.00	15.62	16.25	.10
	2.0	.10	20.25	.90	21.15	22.50	1.00	23.50	25.00	.10

ρ	= Average service time / Average time between arrivals
COV	= Coefficient of variation for service times
Po	= Probability of no units in the system
Lq	= Average number of units in the queue
Ls	= Average number of units in the service facility
L	= Average number of units in the system
Wq	= Standardized average time a unit is in the queue
Ws	= Standardized average time a unit is in the service facility
W	= Standardized average time a unit is in the system
Wq'	= Standardized average time a delayed unit is in the queue
SL	= Service Level

CHAPTER 17

Queueing Analysis For Reuseable Inventory Items With Lost Sales

Chapter 15 introduced the notion of a *reuseable inventory*, an item that is used only temporarily to service an oncoming demand. Upon completion of the service, the item remains in the possession of the firm and is available to service yet another demand. The results of Chapter 15 apply when the demand waits in a backorder state if all the reuseable inventory items are occupied. This chapter describes the lost sales case—where the demands will *not* wait for service when all reuseable inventory items are busy.

These situations frequently occur in a sales outlet facility, a store or a rental agency, where potential customers will seek another outlet if no reuseable items are available. In a gas station, if all pumps are busy, the potential customer may merely drive on to the next gas station. In a restaurant, if all tables are filled, the party may move on to another restaurant rather than wait. In a rental agency, if all units of an item are leased out, the potential customer may seek another rental agency for the item. Also, potential customers may seek another firm if all phone lines are busy when they call to place an order or inquire about a product.

As in Chapter 15, the average time between demands is the same as the average time between arrivals to a queueing system. The average usage time of the reuseable item is the same as the average service time of the queueing facility, and the number of reuseable inventory items is the same as the number of facilities.

The results of this chapter are developed from the methods of queueing theory (reference 1). In particular, a finite number of service facilities are available to serve arriving units and no queue exists for any arriving units when all service facilities are occupied. With no queue available for these units, the units cannot then wait for a service facility to open, and thereby they are assumed as lost to the system. An example may be an office phone system that has five lines. Any calls attempted to the office when all five lines are busy are rejected.

The results obtained in this chapter assume that the time between arrival of units is exponentially distributed and the time required to service a unit is also exponentially distributed. As in Chapter 15, the above assumptions also imply that the number of arrivals in a unit of time is Poisson distributed.

A Perpetual Provision Inventory System

The model of this chapter also applies in an inventory system when the provision (on-hand plus on-order or OH + OO) size of the inventory is set with the purpose of maintaining a fixed inventory level called an order level (OL). If stock is available to satisfy an oncoming demand, then the unit is sold and a new unit is immediately ordered for replenishment. In this way the OH + OO is always equal to the order level **OL**. Further, the order point **OP** becomes OP = OL − 1. Stock must be available when a customer seeks to purchase—or the sale is lost.

The average time between arrival of demands is used as before, and the average procurement lead time is the same as the average service time. Also, the size of the order level (**OL**) is the same as the number of facilities in the queueing system.

Data

The data required to apply the model are the following:

$$N = \text{number of service facilities}$$
$$t_a = \text{average time between arrivals}$$
$$t_s = \text{average time to service a unit}$$

in this model there is no restriction on the relation between t_a, t_s and N. Any combination is possible.

As in Chapters 15 and 16, a common unit of time is selected to carry out the analysis. Also, for conformance in the queueing literature, it is common to use the reciprocal of t_a and t_s as before, i.e.:

$$\lambda = 1/t_a = \text{average number of arrivals per unit of time}$$
$$\mu = 1/t_s = \text{average number of units serviced on a continuously busy service facility in a unit of time}$$

The utilization factor for the system is identified as ρ where:

$$\rho = t_s/t_a$$

that is,

$$\rho = \lambda/\mu$$

Model

Again consider taking a snapshot of a facility system at an arbitrary moment in time. The number of units that will be found in the system will be identified as **n**, which may range within any integer from 0 to **N**. The probability that n = 0 is denoted as P_o and is calculated:

$$P_o = \cfrac{1}{\sum\limits_{n=0}^{N} \rho^n/n!}$$

The probability that **n** units are in the system becomes P_n where:

$$P_n = P_o \, \rho^n / n!$$

Another measure of interest is the average number of units in the system at an arbitrary moment in time. This measure is designated as **L**:

$$L = \sum\limits_{n=0}^{N} n \, P_n$$

A further measure that can be determined is the probability that a new arrival will not be able to enter the system because all **N** service facilities are occupied. This measure is denoted as **P(loss)** and is calculated by:

$$P(\text{loss}) = P_0 \, \rho^N / N!$$

The above probability is commonly called the *Erlang loss probability*. This useful measurement yields the probability that a potential arrival is lost because the system capacity is not adequate. Note finally that the service level **SL** in this situation may be defined as the complement of the Erlang loss probability, whereby:

$$SL = 1 - P(\text{loss})$$

Tables

Table 17.1 is arranged by values of the utilization factor ρ and the number of service facilities **N**. Selected values of ρ ranging from 0.10 to 80 are used. For each ρ, a set of **N** values is chosen in a way to give reasonably small values for **P**(loss). For each combination of ρ and **N**, the tables list the associated values of P_0, **L** and **P**(loss).

Table 17.2 is directed more towards the reuseable inventory item when lost sales occur, although the results are also applicable for the queueing model of this chapter as well as for the perpetual provision inventory system described. The table lists the number of units to stock for the reuseable item (facilities) to achieve a given service level **SL** for a particular utilization factor ρ. The service level is the probability that an arriving demand will find a unit of the reuseable item available for use. This calculation becomes $SL = 1 - P(\text{loss})$. The table entries give values of the utilization factor ρ ranging from 0.10 to 700, and the service level entries investigated are SL = .85, .90, .95 and .99.

Example 17.1

A firm with a 30 line telephone system finds that the average length of a phone conversation is 6 minutes, and on the average the number of lines in use is 28.0. The firm does not know how many potential phone calls are placed on the firm because some are lost due to busy signals. The firm president, suspecting several calls are lost due to busy signals, wishes to determine the average number of such lost calls per hour.

Table 17.1 is used with $N = 30$ to search for a value of **L** (the average number of units in the service facilities) that is close to 28.0. This value occurs when $\rho = 40$, whereby L = 28.028. With $N = 30$ and $\rho = 40$, then $P(\text{loss}) = .299$. Now as $t_s = 6$ minutes is the average service time and since:

$$\rho = t_s / t_a$$

reversing the above relation gives $t_a = t_s / \rho = 6/40 = 0.15$ minutes (the estimated average time between potential calls). With $t_a = 0.15$ minutes, the average calls per minute is then $1/0.15 = 6.67$ and the average calls per hour is $6.67 \times 60 = 400$. Finally, the average number of lost calls in an hour is determined by:

$$\lambda \, P(\text{loss}) = 400 \times .299 = 119.6$$

Example 17.2

Considering the firm in Example 17.1, how many lines should be installed to reduce the number of lost calls per hour from the current level of 119.6 to 10 or less?

The following table shows the number of lost calls when the number of lines is increased from $N = 30$ to 60. The results are obtained in the same way as in Example 17.1, i.e., the number of lost calls is $400 \times P(\text{loss})$ using $\rho = 40$.

N	lost calls
30	119.6
35	80.0
40	46.4
45	21.6
50	7.6
55	1.6
60	0.4

The results indicate that when the number of lines is increased to 50, the average number of lost calls in an hour will be less than 10. Therefore, the number of lines to install is 50.

Example 17.3

A rental agency open seven days a week has small cargo trailers for rent. The average number of requests is 10 per week and the average rental time is 2 days. Customers who request a trailer when all are rented out will not wait and will find another source. How many trailers should the rental agency have in order to limit the probability of a loss of a request to 5 percent or less?

For this situation, if the unit of time is set at one day, the average time between requests is $t_a = 7/10 = 0.70$ days and the average service time is $t_s = 2$ days. The utilization factor becomes:

$$\rho = 2/0.7 = 2.86 \text{ (or about 2.8)}$$

Table 17.1 is scanned with $\rho = 2.8$ to seek the value of N which gives $P(\text{loss})$ of 0.05 or smaller. This value first occurs when $N = 6$ where $P(\text{loss}) = .042$. The rental agency should therefore have 6 trailers available for rent.

Example 17.4

An auto dealer has 7 loaner cars for customers who request them in order to bring in their cars for service. The request for such loaners occurs at an average rate of 4 per day, and the average time a car is on loan is one and one half days. Suppose the customers who do not obtain a loaner will take their cars elsewhere for service. What is the average number of customers who are lost because a loaner is not available?

Letting the unit of time be a day, the average time between requests is $t_a = 1/4 = 0.25$ days, and the average loan time is $t_s = 1.5$ days; hence, $\rho = 1.5/0.25 = 6$. Table 17.1 shows that when $\rho = 6$ and $N = 7$, the probability of a lost customer is $P(\text{loss}) = .185$, and thus the average number of lost customers in a day is $\lambda P(\text{loss}) = 4 \times 0.185 = 0.74$.

Example 17.5

Suppose a restaurant estimates that during the lunch hour customers arrive in parties that require an average of 200 tables per hour. If a table is available upon arrival, the party dines in and occupies the table for 30 minutes on the average. If a table is not available, the party leaves for another restaurant. How many tables should the restaurant have to service 95 percent of its potential parties?

The average time between arrival of potential parties is $t_a = 1/200 = .005$ hours, and the average service time is $t_s = 30/60 = 0.5$ hours; therefore, the utilization factor is $\rho = t_s/t_a = .50/.005 = 100$. Table 17.2 is now used with $\rho = 100$ and $SL = .95$ to find $N = 105$. Thus, 105 tables are needed.

Example 17.6

A bicycle dealer wishes to maintain a system of continuous availability for each model bike where, as soon as a bike is sold, another is ordered from the supplier. If the bike is not in stock when a customer demand arrives, the sale is lost. For a particular model, suppose the average demand is 2 units per week and the average procurement lead time is 2 weeks. How large should the order level be for this model in order to attain a 99 percent service level?

The time between customer demands is $t_a = 1/2 = 0.5$ weeks and the lead time $t_s = 2$ weeks. The utilization factor is $\rho = t_s/t_a = 2.0/0.5 = 4$. Table 17.2 shows that, to achieve a service level SL = .99 with $\rho = 4$, 10 bikes is the order level required.

Table 17.1 Queueing Statistics for Multi-Service Facilities with No Queue

ρ	N	Po	L	P(loss)	ρ	N	Po	L	P(loss)
.1	1	.909	.091	.091	.2	1	.833	.167	.167
	2	.905	.100	.005		2	.820	.197	.016
	3	.905	.100	.000		3	.819	.200	.001
	4	.905	.100	.000		4	.819	.200	.000
	5	.905	.100	.000		5	.819	.200	.000
.3	1	.769	.231	.231	.4	1	.714	.286	.286
	2	.743	.290	.033		2	.676	.378	.054
	3	.741	.299	.003		3	.671	.397	.007
	4	.741	.300	.000		4	.670	.400	.001
	5	.741	.300	.000		5	.670	.400	.000
.5	1	.667	.333	.333	.6	1	.625	.375	.375
	2	.615	.462	.077		2	.562	.539	.101
	3	.608	.494	.013		3	.551	.588	.020
	4	.607	.499	.002		4	.549	.598	.003
	5	.607	.500	.000		5	.549	.600	.000
.7	1	.588	.412	.412	.8	1	.556	.444	.444
	2	.514	.612	.126		2	.472	.679	.151
	3	.499	.680	.029		3	.453	.769	.039
	4	.497	.697	.005		4	.450	.794	.008
	5	.497	.700	.001		5	.449	.799	.001
.9	1	.526	.474	.474	1	2	.400	.800	.200
	2	.434	.742	.176		3	.375	.938	.063
	3	.412	.855	.050		4	.369	.985	.015
	4	.408	.890	.011		5	.368	.997	.003
	5	.407	.898	.002		6	.368	.999	.001
1.2	2	.342	.904	.247	1.4	2	.296	.994	.290
	3	.312	1.092	.090		3	.261	1.233	.119
	4	.304	1.169	.026		4	.250	1.344	.040
	5	.302	1.192	.006		5	.247	1.384	.011
	6	.301	1.199	.001		6	.247	1.396	.003
	7	.301	1.200	.000		7	.247	1.399	.001
	8	.301	1.200	.000		8	.247	1.400	.000

ρ = Average service time / Average time between arrivals
N = Number of service facilities
Po = Probability of no units in the system
L = Average number of units in the system
P(loss) = Probability an arrival is rejected because the system is full

Table 17.1 Queueing Statistics for Multi-Service Facilities with No Queue (Continued)

ρ	N	Po	L	P(loss)	ρ	N	Po	L	P(loss)
1.6	2	.258	1.072	.330	1.8	2	.226	1.140	.367
	3	.219	1.361	.150		3	.185	1.476	.180
	4	.207	1.510	.056		4	.172	1.665	.075
	5	.203	1.572	.018		5	.167	1.753	.026
	6	.202	1.592	.005		6	.166	1.786	.008
	7	.202	1.598	.001		7	.165	1.796	.002
	8	.202	1.600	.000		8	.165	1.799	.000
2.0	2	.200	1.200	.400	2.2	3	.135	1.672	.240
	3	.158	1.579	.211		4	.119	1.943	.117
	4	.143	1.810	.095		5	.114	2.093	.049
	5	.138	1.927	.037		6	.112	2.161	.018
	6	.136	1.976	.012		7	.111	2.188	.005
	7	.135	1.993	.003		8	.111	2.197	.002
	8	.135	1.998	.001		9	.111	2.199	.000
2.4	3	.116	1.756	.268	2.6	3	.101	1.831	.296
	4	.100	2.067	.139		4	.085	2.181	.161
	5	.094	2.250	.062		5	.078	2.399	.077
	6	.092	2.342	.024		6	.076	2.516	.032
	7	.091	2.380	.008		7	.075	2.569	.012
	8	.091	2.394	.002		8	.074	2.590	.004
	9	.091	2.398	.001		9	.074	2.597	.001
2.8	3	.088	1.900	.322	3.0	3	.077	1.962	.346
	4	.072	2.286	.184		4	.061	2.382	.206
	5	.065	2.539	.093		5	.054	2.670	.110
	6	.062	2.683	.042		6	.052	2.844	.052
	7	.061	2.754	.016		7	.050	2.934	.022
	8	.061	2.784	.006		8	.050	2.976	.008
	9	.061	2.795	.002		9	.050	2.992	.003
4	3	.042	2.197	.451	5	4	.015	3.008	.398
	4	.029	2.757	.311		5	.011	3.576	.285
	5	.023	3.204	.199		6	.009	4.041	.192
	6	.021	3.531	.117		7	.008	4.397	.121
	7	.019	3.749	.063		8	.007	4.650	.070
	8	.019	3.878	.030		9	.007	4.813	.037
	9	.018	3.947	.013		10	.007	4.908	.018
	10	.018	3.979	.005		11	.007	4.959	.008
	11	.018	3.992	.002		12	.007	4.983	.003

ρ   = Average service time / Average time between arrivals
N   = Number of service facilities
Po   = Probability of no units in the system
L   = Average number of units in the system
P(loss) = Probability an arrival is rejected because the system is full

Table 17.1 Queueing Statistics for Multi-Service Facilities with No Queue (Continued)

ρ	N	Po	L	P(loss)	ρ	N	Po	L	P(loss)
6	5	.006	3.838	.360	7	6	.002	4.681	.331
	6	.004	4.410	.265		7	.002	5.258	.249
	7	.003	4.890	.185		8	.001	5.748	.179
	8	.003	5.269	.122		9	.001	6.145	.122
	9	.003	5.549	.075		10	.001	6.449	.079
	10	.003	5.741	.043		11	.001	6.666	.048
	11	.003	5.862	.023		12	.001	6.810	.027
	12	.003	5.932	.011		13	.001	6.899	.014
	13	.002	5.969	.005		14	.001	6.950	.007
8	7	.001	5.535	.308	9	8	.000	6.398	.289
	8	.001	6.115	.236		9	.000	6.981	.224
	9	.000	6.615	.173		10	.000	7.488	.168
	10	.000	7.027	.122		11	.000	7.913	.121
	11	.000	7.350	.081		12	.000	8.252	.083
	12	.000	7.589	.051		13	.000	8.510	.054
	13	.000	7.755	.031		14	.000	8.696	.034
	14	.000	7.862	.017		15	.000	8.821	.020
	15	.000	7.927	.009		16	.000	8.901	.011
10	9	.000	7.268	.273	15	14	.000	11.700	.220
	10	.000	7.854	.215		15	.000	12.295	.180
	11	.000	8.368	.163		16	.000	12.831	.145
	12	.000	8.803	.120		17	.000	13.303	.113
	13	.000	9.157	.084		18	.000	13.707	.086
	14	.000	9.432	.057		19	.000	14.045	.064
	15	.000	9.635	.036		20	.000	14.316	.046
	16	.000	9.777	.022		21	.000	14.527	.032
	17	.000	9.871	.013		22	.000	14.684	.021
20	19	.000	16.222	.189	25	24	.000	20.800	.168
	20	.000	16.822	.159		25	.000	21.404	.144
	21	.000	17.371	.131		26	.000	21.963	.121
	22	.000	17.865	.107		27	.000	22.472	.101
	23	.000	18.301	.085		28	.000	22.930	.083
	24	.000	18.678	.066		29	.000	23.334	.067
	25	.000	18.996	.050		30	.000	23.685	.053
	26	.000	19.256	.037		31	.000	23.983	.041
	27	.000	19.464	.027		32	.000	24.230	.031

ρ = Average service time / Average time between arrivals

N = Number of service facilities

Po = Probability of no units in the system

L = Average number of units in the system

P(loss) = Probability an arrival is rejected because the system is full

Table 17.1 Queueing Statistics for Multi-Service Facilities with No Queue (Continued)

ρ	N	Po	L	P(loss)	ρ	N	Po	L	P(loss)
30	10	.000	9.560	.681	35	15	.000	14.351	.590
	15	.000	14.183	.527		20	.000	18.935	.459
	20	.000	18.597	.380		25	.000	23.305	.334
	25	.000	22.640	.245		30	.000	27.305	.220
	30	.000	26.026	.132		35	.000	30.678	.123
	35	.000	28.387	.054		40	.000	33.101	.054
	40	.000	29.568	.014		45	.000	34.414	.017
	45	.000	29.930	.002		50	.000	34.883	.003
	50	.000	29.993	.000		55	.000	34.985	.000
40	20	.000	19.148	.521	45	25	.000	23.950	.468
	25	.000	23.698	.408		30	.000	28.469	.367
	30	.000	28.028	.299		35	.000	32.763	.272
	35	.000	31.991	.200		40	.000	36.695	.185
	40	.000	35.354	.116		45	.000	40.049	.110
	45	.000	37.828	.054		50	.000	42.565	.054
	50	.000	39.252	.019		55	.000	44.086	.020
	55	.000	39.825	.004		60	.000	44.755	.005
	60	.000	39.973	.001		65	.000	44.955	.001
50	30	.000	28.758	.425	55	35	.000	33.571	.390
	35	.000	33.248	.335		40	.000	38.033	.308
	40	.000	37.510	.250		45	.000	42.267	.232
	45	.000	41.414	.172		50	.000	46.146	.161
	50	.000	44.761	.105		55	.000	49.486	.100
	55	.000	47.313	.054		60	.000	52.069	.053
	60	.000	48.917	.022		65	.000	53.746	.023
	65	.000	49.678	.006		70	.000	54.592	.007
	70	.000	49.932	.001		75	.000	54.903	.002
60	40	.000	38.388	.360	65	45	.000	43.209	.335
	45	.000	42.825	.286		50	.000	47.623	.267
	50	.000	47.033	.216		55	.000	51.806	.203
	55	.000	50.890	.152		60	.000	55.643	.144
	60	.000	54.224	.096		65	.000	58.972	.093
	65	.000	56.833	.053		70	.000	61.605	.052
	70	.000	58.575	.024		75	.000	63.405	.025
	75	.000	59.500	.008		80	.000	64.404	.009
	80	.000	59.868	.002		85	.000	64.828	.003
70	50	.000	48.034	.314	80	60	.000	57.694	.279
	55	.000	52.426	.251		65	.000	62.046	.224
	60	.000	56.587	.192		70	.000	66.167	.173
	65	.000	60.406	.137		75	.000	69.954	.126
	70	.000	63.730	.090		80	.000	73.271	.084
	75	.000	66.384	.052		85	.000	75.960	.050
	80	.000	68.236	.025		90	.000	77.901	.026
	85	.000	69.302	.010		95	.000	79.090	.011
	90	.000	69.784	.003		100	.000	79.681	.004

Table 17.2 Minimum Units Needed to Maintain a Desired Service Level for a Reuseable Inventory System with Lost Sales

ρ	85	90	95	99	ρ	85	90	95	99
.1	2	2	2	2	55	51	56	61	69
.2	2	2	2	3	60	56	60	66	75
.3	2	2	2	3	65	60	65	71	80
.4	2	2	3	3	70	64	69	76	85
.5	2	2	3	4	75	69	74	81	91
.6	2	3	3	4	80	73	78	86	96
.7	2	3	3	4	85	77	83	90	101
.8	3	3	3	4	90	81	88	95	107
.9	3	3	4	5	95	86	92	100	112
1.0	3	3	4	5	100	90	97	105	117
1.2	3	3	4	5	110	99	106	115	128
1.4	3	4	4	6	120	107	115	125	138
1.6	3	4	5	6	130	116	124	134	149
1.8	4	4	5	6	140	124	133	144	159
2.0	4	4	5	7	150	133	142	154	170
2.5	4	5	6	7	160	141	151	163	180
3.0	5	6	7	8	170	150	160	173	190
3.5	6	6	7	9	180	158	169	183	201
4.0	6	7	8	10	190	167	178	192	211
4.5	7	7	8	11	200	175	188	202	221
5	7	8	9	11	210	184	197	212	232
10	12	13	15	18	220	192	206	221	242
15	16	18	20	24	230	201	215	231	252
20	21	23	26	30	240	209	224	240	263
25	25	28	31	36	250	218	233	250	273
30	30	32	36	42	260	227	242	260	283
35	34	37	41	47	270	235	251	269	293
40	38	42	46	53	280	244	260	279	303
45	43	46	51	58	290	252	269	288	314
50	47	51	56	64	300	261	278	298	324

N = minimum number of reuseable units
ρ = utilization factor (average service time / average time between arrivals)
SL = service level

	--------- SL --------						--------- SL ---------			
ρ	85	90	95	99	ρ	85	90	95	99
	--------- N ----------						--------- N ----------			
310	269	287	308	334	510	439	467	499	537
320	278	296	317	344	520	448	476	508	547
330	286	305	327	354	530	456	485	518	557
340	295	314	336	365	540	465	494	527	567
350	303	323	346	375	550	473	503	537	577
360	312	332	355	385	560	482	512	547	587
370	320	341	365	395	570	490	521	556	597
380	329	350	375	405	580	499	530	566	607
390	337	359	384	415	590	507	539	575	618
400	346	368	394	426	600	516	549	585	628
410	354	377	403	436	610	524	558	594	638
420	363	386	413	446	620	533	567	604	648
430	371	395	422	456	630	541	576	613	658
440	380	404	432	466	640	550	585	623	668
450	388	413	442	476	650	558	594	632	678
460	397	422	451	486	660	567	603	642	688
470	405	431	461	496	670	575	612	651	698
480	414	440	470	507	680	584	621	661	708
490	422	449	480	517	690	592	630	671	718
500	431	458	489	527	700	601	639	680	728

N = minimum number of reuseable units
ρ = utilization factor (average service time / average time between arrivals)
SL = service level

CHAPTER 18

Queueing Analysis For Reuseable Inventory Items With Backorders And With A Limited Number Of Customers

This chapter is an extension of Chapter 15, which pertains to the use of reuseable inventory items with backorders. The exception herein is that only a limited (or finite) number of customers are the possible users of the reuseable items. For example, in a purchasing department of a firm, five terminals are available for use by fifteen buyers. In this situation, the terminals—the reuseable inventory items—are available for use only by the fifteen buyers in the department.

The results of this chapter are developed by the methods of queueing theory (reference 1). In particular, consider a system where **M** machines are operating and, when the machines are running without failure, they are not included in a repair queueing system. However, once a machine fails and is in need of repair, the machine then enters the repair queueing system. Further the model assumes **R** repairmen are available to service the machines but only one repairman at a time works on a machine. A failed machine will be serviced immediately as long as a repairman is available to service it; otherwise, the machine must wait in a repair queue for a repairman to become free.

The model assumes that the operative time for a machine between its need for a repair is exponentially distributed. The time to service each machine is also assumed to follow an exponential distribution.

Data
The data used in this model are the following (note that t_a is different from Chapter 15):

M = number of machines
R = number of repairmen
t_a = average operating time between failures for a machine
t_s = average repair time for a machine

As is necessary in queueing practice, the values for t_a and t_s must be set in a common unit of time. In addition, the above average times are often placed in the corresponding rate of occurrences as below:

$$\lambda = 1/t_a$$
$$\mu = 1/t_s$$

Now the utilization factor ρ for a machine becomes:

$$\rho = t_s/t_a$$

that is,

$$\rho = \lambda/\mu$$

Note that the above utilization factor corresponds to an individual machine and not the total system.

Model

Let **n** designate the number of machines in the repair queueing system. These are machines that have failed and are currently in need of repair. Since **M** is the total of all machines, **n** can range from 0 to **M**.

When n = 0, then no machines are in need of repair, and the probability of this occurrence is represented by P_0, where:

$$P_0 = \cfrac{1}{\displaystyle\sum_{n=0}^{R} M!\rho^n/[(M-n)!n!] + \sum_{n=R+1}^{M} M!\rho^n/[(M-n)!R^{n-R}R!]}$$

To determine the probability of **n** machines in need of repair P_n:

$$P_n = P_0 M!\rho^n/[(M-n)!n!] \qquad \text{when } n = 0 \text{ to } R$$

$$P_n = P_0 M!\rho^n/[(M-n)!R^{n-R}R!] \qquad \text{when } n = R+1 \text{ to } M$$

The average number of machines currently being serviced by the repairmen is denoted as L_s:

$$L_s = \sum_{n=0}^{R} nP_n + \sum_{n=R+1}^{M} R P_n$$

The average number of machines in the queue waiting to be repaired is:

$$L_q = \sum_{n=R+1}^{M} (n-R) P_n$$

And the total number of machines in need of repair is:

$$L = L_q + L_s$$

Finally, the service level for this system (here denoted as **SL**) may be defined as the probability that a newly-failed machine will be serviced without waiting in the queue:

$$SL = \sum_{n=0}^{R-1} P_n$$

Tables

The tables of this chapter include three input parameters, ρ, **M** and **R**. The values of ρ that are included are .01, .05, .10, .15, and .20. Selected values of **M** are taken from 1 to 150. With each value of **M**, selected values of **R** are investigated; these are chosen to show the sensitivity of ρ, **M** and **R**.

Example 18.1

A firm has 8 drill machines and 1 repairman to service all of the machines. Each machine is operative on the average 5 hours before it is in need of repair, and the average repair time is 1 hour. Find the queueing implications associated with this situation.

Letting the unit of time be 1 hour, $t_a = 5$ hours and $t_s = 1$ hour. Thus, the utilization factor is $\rho = 1/5 = 0.20$. Using $M = 8$ and $R = 1$ in Table 18.1, the following is then found.

$P_o = .07$ is the probability that no drill machine is in need of a repair. This also is the probability that all 8 drill machines are in operation and is also the probability that the repairman is idle.

$L_q = 2.42$ is the average number of drill machines in a queue waiting for repair. $L_s = .93$ is the average number of machines that are being repaired, and $L = 3.35 = (2.42 + .93)$ is the average number of machines in need of repair.

$SL = .07$ is the service level that gives the probability that a newly-failed drill machine will find the repairman available to service the machine.

Example 18.2

A computer repair firm services 20 computers. Each computer runs on the average 10 days before some type of service is needed. The average service time is 1 day. How many servicemen should the repair firm have in order to be able to provide immediate service on 95 percent of the requests?

Using 1 day as the unit of time, $t_a = 10$, $t_s = 1$ and $\rho = 1/10 = 0.10$. Table 18.1 is used with $M = 20$ to seek the smallest value of R that yields SL greater or larger than 95 percent. This point occurs when $R = 5$; thus, the repair firm should have 5 repairmen available for call.

Example 18.3

A warehouse has 80 lift trucks, each running 100 hours before it needs repair. The average service time per truck is 5 hours. Find the minimum number of repairmen needed so that the average number of operating trucks is larger than 75.

Since $t_a = 100$ hours and $t_s = 5$ hours, $\rho = 5/100 = .05$. Table 18.1 shows, when $M = 80$ and $R = 5$, that $L = 4.85$ trucks are in the repair stage. The average number of trucks operating without repair becomes $(80 - L) = (80 - 4.85) = 75.15$, which exceeds 75. Consequently, 5 repairmen are sufficient for this purpose.

Example 18.4

A copy machine will run on the average 20 hours before it requires some type of repair. One repairman is available to service the copy machines, and the average service time is 4 hours. Find the number of copy machines to have available so that the average number of operative copy machines is 4 or larger.

Using 1 hour as the unit of time, $t_a = 20$, $t_s = 4$ and $\rho = 4/20 = 0.20$. Also, using $R = 1$, Table 18.1 is searched to find the smallest value of M where $(M - L)$ is larger than 4. The table below is used to help analyze the findings:

M	L	M − L
4	.99	3.01
5	1.42	3.58
6	1.96	4.04

The table shows that when 6 copy machines are available, the average number of machines in proper operating form will be 4.04. Thus, 6 copy machines are needed.

Example 18.5

Assume the same conditions as Example 18.4, but now suppose the average running time increases when M = 5 and 6, as the copy machines are not as heavily used as when M = 4. At M = 5, the machines are used only $4/5 = .8$ as much time as before and thus $t_a = 20/.8 = 25$ hours. When M = 6, the machines are used $4/6 = .67$ as much time as before and therefore $t_a = 20/.67 = 30$ hours. When M = 5, $\rho = 4/25 = .16$, and with interpolation of the results in Table 18.1, L = 1.11 and M − L = 3.89. When M = 6, $\rho = 4/30 = .13$ and (again with interpolation) the findings yield L = 1.18 and M − L = 4.82. So, as in the earlier example, 6 machines are needed to assure at least 4 machines on the average are in operating condition.

Example 18.6

A company has a computer system with 15 printers; the average running time of a printer before it needs repairs is 200 hours, and the average repair time for a printer is 10 hours. If 1 repairman is available, how many printers on the average are in need of repair?

Since $t_a = 200$ hours and $t_s = 10$ hours, $\rho = 10/200 = .05$. Table 18.1 is used with M = 15 and R = 1 to find L = 1.60. The result indicates that on the average 1.60 printers are down and in need of repair.

Table 18.1   Queueing Statistics for a Finite Number of Machines and Repairmen

ρ	M	R	Po	Lq	Ls	L	SL
.01	1	1	.99	.00	.01	.01	.99
.05	1	1	.95	.00	.05	.05	.95
.10	1	1	.91	.00	.09	.09	.91
.15	1	1	.87	.00	.13	.13	.87
.20	1	1	.83	.00	.17	.17	.83
.01	2	1	.98	.00	.02	.02	.98
.01	2	2	.98	.00	.02	.02	1.00
.05	2	1	.90	.00	.10	.10	.90
.05	2	2	.91	.00	.10	.10	1.00
.10	2	1	.82	.02	.18	.20	.82
.10	2	2	.83	.00	.18	.18	.99
.15	2	1	.74	.03	.26	.29	.74
.15	2	2	.76	.00	.26	.26	.98
.20	2	1	.68	.05	.32	.38	.68
.20	2	2	.69	.00	.33	.33	.97
.01	3	1	.97	.00	.03	.03	.97
.01	3	2	.97	.00	.03	.03	1.00
.01	3	3	.97	.00	.03	.03	1.00
.05	3	1	.86	.01	.14	.16	.86
.05	3	2	.86	.00	.14	.14	.99
.05	3	3	.86	.00	.14	.14	1.00
.10	3	1	.73	.05	.27	.32	.73
.10	3	2	.75	.00	.27	.27	.98
.10	3	3	.75	.00	.27	.27	1.00
.15	3	1	.62	.11	.38	.49	.62
.15	3	2	.66	.00	.39	.39	.95
.15	3	3	.66	.00	.39	.39	1.00
.20	3	1	.53	.18	.47	.65	.53
.20	3	2	.58	.01	.50	.51	.92
.20	3	3	.58	.00	.50	.50	1.00

ρ = Average time to repair a machine / Average time between failures for a machine
M = Number of machines
R = Number of repairmen
Po = Probability of no defective machines in the system
Lq = Average number of defective machines in the repair queue
Ls = Average number of defective machines being repaired
L = Average number of defective machines in the system
SL = Service Level (probability a defective machine does not wait for repair)

ρ	M	R	Po	Lq	Ls	L	SL
.01	4	1	.96	.00	.04	.04	.96
.01	4	2	.96	.00	.04	.04	1.00
.01	4	3	.96	.00	.04	.04	1.00
.05	4	1	.81	.03	.19	.22	.81
.05	4	2	.82	.00	.19	.19	.99
.05	4	3	.82	.00	.19	.19	1.00
.10	4	1	.65	.11	.35	.47	.65
.10	4	2	.68	.00	.36	.37	.95
.10	4	3	.68	.00	.36	.36	1.00
.15	4	1	.51	.24	.49	.73	.51
.15	4	2	.57	.01	.52	.53	.91
.15	4	3	.57	.00	.52	.52	.99
.20	4	1	.40	.39	.60	.99	.40
.20	4	2	.48	.03	.66	.69	.86
.20	4	3	.48	.00	.67	.67	.98
.01	5	1	.95	.00	.05	.05	.95
.01	5	2	.95	.00	.05	.05	1.00
.01	5	3	.95	.00	.05	.05	1.00
.05	5	1	.76	.05	.24	.29	.76
.05	5	2	.78	.00	.24	.24	.98
.05	5	3	.78	.00	.24	.24	1.00
.10	5	1	.56	.20	.44	.64	.56
.10	5	2	.62	.01	.45	.46	.93
.10	5	3	.62	.00	.45	.45	.99
.15	5	1	.40	.43	.60	1.03	.40
.15	5	2	.49	.03	.65	.68	.86
.15	5	3	.50	.00	.65	.65	.98
.20	5	1	.28	.71	.72	1.42	.28
.20	5	2	.39	.07	.82	.89	.79
.20	5	3	.40	.00	.83	.84	.96

ρ = Average time to repair a machine / Average time between failures for a machine

M = Number of machines

R = Number of repairmen

Po = Probability of no defective machines in the system

Lq = Average number of defective machines in the repair queue

Ls = Average number of defective machines being repaired

L = Average number of defective machines in the system

SL = Service Level (probability a defective machine does not wait for repair)

ρ	M	R	Po	Lq	Ls	L	SL
.01	6	1	.94	.00	.06	.06	.94
.01	6	2	.94	.00	.06	.06	1.00
.01	6	3	.94	.00	.06	.06	1.00
.01	6	4	.94	.00	.06	.06	1.00
.05	6	1	.72	.08	.28	.36	.72
.05	6	2	.75	.00	.29	.29	.97
.05	6	3	.75	.00	.29	.29	1.00
.05	6	4	.75	.00	.29	.29	1.00
.10	6	1	.48	.33	.52	.85	.48
.10	6	2	.56	.02	.54	.57	.90
.10	6	3	.56	.00	.55	.55	.99
.10	6	4	.56	.00	.55	.55	1.00
.15	6	1	.31	.71	.69	1.40	.31
.15	6	2	.42	.07	.77	.84	.80
.15	6	3	.43	.01	.78	.79	.97
.15	6	4	.43	.00	.78	.78	1.00
.20	6	1	.19	1.15	.81	1.96	.19
.20	6	2	.32	.14	.98	1.12	.70
.20	6	3	.33	.01	1.00	1.01	.93
.20	6	4	.33	.00	1.00	1.00	.99
.01	7	1	.93	.00	.07	.07	.93
.01	7	2	.93	.00	.07	.07	1.00
.01	7	3	.93	.00	.07	.07	1.00
.01	7	4	.93	.00	.07	.07	1.00
.05	7	1	.67	.12	.33	.45	.67
.05	7	2	.71	.01	.33	.34	.96
.05	7	3	.71	.00	.33	.33	1.00
.05	7	4	.71	.00	.33	.33	1.00
.10	7	1	.41	.50	.59	1.09	.41
.10	7	2	.51	.04	.63	.67	.86
.10	7	3	.51	.00	.64	.64	.98
.10	7	4	.51	.00	.64	.64	1.00
.15	7	1	.23	1.08	.77	1.85	.23
.15	7	2	.36	.12	.90	1.02	.74
.15	7	3	.37	.01	.91	.92	.95
.15	7	4	.38	.00	.91	.91	.99
.20	7	1	.12	1.72	.88	2.60	.12
.20	7	2	.26	.24	1.13	1.37	.62
.20	7	3	.28	.03	1.16	1.19	.90
.20	7	4	.28	.00	1.17	1.17	.98

ρ = Average time to repair a machine / Average time between failures for a machine

M = Number of machines

R = Number of repairmen

Po = Probability of no defective machines in the system

Lq = Average number of defective machines in the repair queue

Ls = Average number of defective machines being repaired

L = Average number of defective machines in the system

SL = Service Level (probability a defective machine does not wait for repair)

Table 18.1 Queueing Statistics for a Finite Number of Machines and Repairmen (Continued)

ρ	M	R	Po	Lq	Ls	L	SL
.01	8	1	.92	.01	.08	.08	.92
.01	8	2	.92	.00	.08	.08	1.00
.01	8	3	.92	.00	.08	.08	1.00
.01	8	4	.92	.00	.08	.08	1.00
.05	8	1	.63	.17	.37	.54	.63
.05	8	2	.67	.01	.38	.39	.94
.05	8	3	.68	.00	.38	.38	.99
.05	8	4	.68	.00	.38	.38	1.00
.10	8	1	.34	.72	.66	1.38	.34
.10	8	2	.46	.06	.72	.79	.82
.10	8	3	.47	.01	.73	.73	.97
.10	8	4	.47	.00	.73	.73	1.00
.15	8	1	.16	1.56	.84	2.40	.16
.15	8	2	.31	.19	1.02	1.21	.67
.15	8	3	.32	.02	1.04	1.06	.92
.15	8	4	.33	.00	1.04	1.05	.99
.20	8	1	.07	2.42	.93	3.35	.07
.20	8	2	.20	.40	1.27	1.66	.53
.20	8	3	.23	.06	1.32	1.38	.85
.20	8	4	.23	.01	1.33	1.34	.97
.01	9	1	.91	.01	.09	.10	.91
.01	9	2	.91	.00	.09	.09	1.00
.01	9	3	.91	.00	.09	.09	1.00
.01	9	4	.91	.00	.09	.09	1.00
.05	9	1	.58	.23	.42	.64	.58
.05	9	2	.64	.01	.43	.44	.93
.05	9	3	.64	.00	.43	.43	.99
.05	9	4	.64	.00	.43	.43	1.00
.10	9	1	.27	1.01	.73	1.73	.27
.10	9	2	.41	.10	.81	.91	.78
.10	9	3	.42	.01	.82	.83	.96
.10	9	4	.42	.00	.82	.82	.99
.15	9	1	.11	2.14	.89	3.04	.11
.15	9	2	.26	.29	1.14	1.43	.61
.15	9	3	.28	.04	1.17	1.21	.89
.15	9	4	.28	.00	1.17	1.18	.98
.20	9	1	.04	3.22	.96	4.19	.04
.20	9	2	.16	.61	1.40	2.01	.44
.20	9	3	.19	.10	1.48	1.59	.80
.20	9	4	.19	.01	1.50	1.51	.95

ρ = Average time to repair a machine / Average time between failures for a machine
M = Number of machines
R = Number of repairmen
Po = Probability of no defective machines in the system
Lq = Average number of defective machines in the repair queue
Ls = Average number of defective machines being repaired
L = Average number of defective machines in the system
SL = Service Level (probability a defective machine does not wait for repair)

Table 18.1 Queueing Statistics for a Finite Number of Machines and Repairmen (Continued)

ρ	M	R	Po	Lq	Ls	L	SL
.01	10	1	.90	.01	.10	.11	.90
.01	10	2	.91	.00	.10	.10	1.00
.01	10	3	.91	.00	.10	.10	1.00
.01	10	4	.91	.00	.10	.10	1.00
.05	10	1	.54	.30	.46	.76	.54
.05	10	2	.61	.02	.48	.50	.91
.05	10	3	.61	.00	.48	.48	.99
.05	10	4	.61	.00	.48	.48	1.00
.10	10	1	.21	1.36	.79	2.15	.21
.10	10	2	.37	.14	.90	1.04	.74
.10	10	3	.38	.02	.91	.92	.94
.10	10	4	.39	.00	.91	.91	.99
.15	10	2	.21	.43	1.25	1.68	.54
.15	10	3	.24	.07	1.30	1.36	.85
.15	10	4	.25	.01	1.30	1.31	.97
.15	10	5	.25	.00	1.30	1.31	.99
.20	10	3	.15	.17	1.64	1.80	.74
.20	10	4	.16	.03	1.66	1.69	.92
.20	10	5	.16	.00	1.67	1.67	.98
.20	10	6	.16	.00	1.67	1.67	1.00
.01	15	1	.85	.02	.15	.17	.85
.01	15	2	.86	.00	.15	.15	.99
.01	15	3	.86	.00	.15	.15	1.00
.01	15	4	.86	.00	.15	.15	1.00
.05	15	1	.33	.93	.67	1.60	.33
.05	15	2	.47	.08	.71	.79	.82
.05	15	3	.48	.01	.71	.72	.97
.05	15	4	.48	.00	.71	.71	1.00
.10	15	1	.04	4.40	.96	5.36	.04
.10	15	2	.20	.61	1.31	1.92	.49
.10	15	3	.23	.10	1.35	1.45	.83
.10	15	4	.24	.02	1.36	1.38	.96
.15	15	2	.07	1.86	1.71	3.58	.22
.15	15	3	.11	.39	1.91	2.30	.62
.15	15	4	.12	.08	1.95	2.03	.86
.15	15	5	.12	.02	1.95	1.97	.96
.20	15	3	.05	.97	2.34	3.31	.41
.20	15	4	.06	.24	2.46	2.70	.73
.20	15	5	.06	.06	2.49	2.55	.90
.20	15	6	.06	.01	2.50	2.51	.97

ρ = Average time to repair a machine / Average time between failures for a machine

M = Number of machines

R = Number of repairmen

Po = Probability of no defective machines in the system

Lq = Average number of defective machines in the repair queue

Ls = Average number of defective machines being repaired

L = Average number of defective machines in the system

SL = Service Level (probability a defective machine does not wait for repair)

ρ	M	R	Po	Lq	Ls	L	SL
.01	20	1	.80	.04	.20	.24	.80
.01	20	2	.82	.00	.20	.20	.98
.01	20	3	.82	.00	.20	.20	1.00
.01	20	4	.82	.00	.20	.20	1.00
.05	20	2	.35	.21	.94	1.15	.71
.05	20	3	.37	.03	.95	.98	.93
.05	20	4	.38	.00	.95	.96	.99
.05	20	5	.38	.00	.95	.95	1.00
.10	20	3	.14	.34	1.79	2.13	.67
.10	20	4	.15	.07	1.81	1.88	.88
.10	20	5	.15	.01	1.82	1.83	.97
.10	20	6	.15	.00	1.82	1.82	.99
.15	20	4	.06	.35	2.56	2.91	.69
.15	20	5	.06	.09	2.60	2.68	.88
.15	20	6	.06	.02	2.61	2.63	.96
.15	20	7	.06	.00	2.61	2.61	.99
.20	20	6	.03	.08	3.32	3.40	.89
.20	20	7	.03	.02	3.33	3.35	.96
.20	20	8	.03	.00	3.33	3.34	.99
.20	20	9	.03	.00	3.33	3.33	1.00
.01	30	1	.70	.12	.30	.41	.70
.01	30	2	.74	.01	.30	.30	.96
.01	30	3	.74	.00	.30	.30	1.00
.01	30	4	.74	.00	.30	.30	1.00
.05	30	2	.18	.94	1.38	2.32	.44
.05	30	3	.22	.15	1.42	1.57	.80
.05	30	4	.23	.03	1.43	1.45	.94
.05	30	5	.23	.00	1.43	1.43	.99
.10	30	3	.03	2.07	2.54	4.61	.29
.10	30	4	.05	.52	2.68	3.20	.64
.10	30	5	.06	.13	2.72	2.85	.85
.10	30	6	.06	.03	2.72	2.76	.94
.15	30	4	.01	2.61	3.57	6.19	.24
.15	30	5	.01	.85	3.80	4.65	.55
.15	30	6	.01	.27	3.88	4.15	.77
.15	30	7	.01	.08	3.90	3.99	.90
.20	30	6	.00	1.04	4.83	5.87	.51
.20	30	7	.00	.38	4.94	5.32	.73
.20	30	8	.00	.13	4.98	5.11	.87
.20	30	9	.00	.04	4.99	5.04	.94

ρ   = Average time to repair a machine / Average time between failures for a machine

M   = Number of machines

R   = Number of repairmen

Po = Probability of no defective machines in the system

Lq = Average number of defective machines in the repair queue

Ls = Average number of defective machines being repaired

L   = Average number of defective machines in the system

SL = Service Level (probability a defective machine does not wait for repair)

ρ	M	R	Po	Lq	Ls	L	SL
.01	40	1	.61	.24	.39	.63	.61
.01	40	2	.67	.01	.40	.41	.94
.01	40	3	.67	.00	.40	.40	.99
.01	40	4	.67	.00	.40	.40	1.00
.05	40	2	.06	3.18	1.75	4.93	.18
.05	40	3	.13	.51	1.88	2.39	.62
.05	40	4	.14	.11	1.90	2.01	.86
.05	40	5	.14	.02	1.90	1.93	.96
.10	40	4	.01	2.26	3.43	5.69	.31
.10	40	5	.02	.67	3.58	4.24	.62
.10	40	6	.02	.21	3.62	3.82	.82
.10	40	7	.02	.06	3.63	3.69	.92
.15	40	5	.00	4.11	4.68	8.79	.17
.15	40	6	.00	1.56	5.01	6.57	.44
.15	40	7	.00	.58	5.14	5.72	.67
.15	40	8	.00	.21	5.19	5.40	.83
.20	40	7	.00	2.41	6.26	8.68	.33
.20	40	8	.00	1.03	6.49	7.53	.56
.20	40	9	.00	.43	6.60	7.02	.74
.20	40	10	.00	.17	6.64	6.81	.86
.01	50	1	.51	.44	.49	.93	.51
.01	50	2	.60	.03	.49	.52	.90
.01	50	3	.61	.00	.50	.50	.99
.01	50	4	.61	.00	.50	.50	1.00
.05	50	3	.06	1.45	2.31	3.77	.41
.05	50	4	.08	.32	2.37	2.69	.73
.05	50	5	.09	.08	2.38	2.46	.90
.05	50	6	.09	.02	2.38	2.40	.97
.10	50	5	.01	2.40	4.33	6.73	.33
.10	50	6	.01	.80	4.47	5.27	.61
.10	50	7	.01	.27	4.52	4.80	.80
.10	50	8	.01	.09	4.54	4.63	.91
.15	50	6	.00	5.80	5.77	11.56	.12
.15	50	7	.00	2.48	6.20	8.68	.34
.15	50	8	.00	1.02	6.39	7.41	.58
.15	50	9	.00	.42	6.47	6.88	.76
.20	50	8	.00	4.50	7.58	12.09	.19
.20	50	9	.00	2.17	7.97	10.14	.39
.20	50	10	.00	1.01	8.17	9.17	.60
.20	50	11	.00	.45	8.26	8.71	.76

ρ = Average time to repair a machine / Average time between failures for a machine

M = Number of machines

R = Number of repairmen

Po = Probability of no defective machines in the system

Lq = Average number of defective machines in the repair queue

Ls = Average number of defective machines being repaired

L = Average number of defective machines in the system

SL = Service Level (probability a defective machine does not wait for repair)

Table 18.1 Queueing Statistics for a Finite Number of Machines and Repairmen (Continued)

ρ	M	R	Po	Lq	Ls	L	SL
.01	60	1	.41	.76	.59	1.35	.41
.01	60	2	.54	.05	.59	.65	.87
.01	60	3	.55	.01	.59	.60	.98
.01	60	4	.55	.00	.59	.59	1.00
.05	60	3	.02	3.75	2.68	6.43	.20
.05	60	4	.05	.81	2.82	3.63	.57
.05	60	5	.05	.21	2.85	3.06	.81
.05	60	6	.05	.06	2.85	2.91	.93
.10	60	6	.00	2.51	5.23	7.74	.35
.10	60	7	.00	.92	5.37	6.29	.60
.10	60	8	.00	.34	5.42	5.77	.78
.10	60	9	.00	.13	5.44	5.57	.89
.15	60	8	.00	3.59	7.36	10.95	.27
.15	60	9	.00	1.61	7.62	9.22	.49
.15	60	10	.00	.71	7.73	8.44	.68
.15	60	11	.00	.31	7.79	8.09	.82
.20	60	11	.00	1.98	9.67	11.65	.45
.20	60	12	.00	.97	9.84	10.81	.63
.20	60	13	.00	.46	9.92	10.39	.77
.20	60	14	.00	.22	9.96	10.18	.87
.01	70	1	.32	1.29	.68	1.97	.32
.01	70	2	.48	.09	.69	.78	.82
.01	70	3	.50	.01	.69	.70	.97
.01	70	4	.50	.00	.69	.69	.99
.05	70	4	.02	1.89	3.24	5.13	.39
.05	70	5	.03	.50	3.31	3.81	.69
.05	70	6	.03	.15	3.33	3.47	.86
.05	70	7	.03	.04	3.33	3.37	.94
.10	70	7	.00	2.60	6.13	8.72	.36
.10	70	8	.00	1.02	6.27	7.29	.60
.10	70	9	.00	.41	6.33	6.73	.77
.10	70	10	.00	.16	6.35	6.51	.88
.15	70	9	.00	4.90	8.49	13.39	.21
.15	70	10	.00	2.34	8.82	11.17	.41
.15	70	11	.00	1.10	8.99	10.09	.61
.15	70	12	.00	.51	9.06	9.57	.76
.20	70	12	.00	3.44	11.09	14.53	.32
.20	70	13	.00	1.81	11.36	13.18	.50
.20	70	14	.00	.93	11.51	12.44	.66
.20	70	15	.00	.47	11.59	12.06	.78

ρ = Average time to repair a machine / Average time between failures for a machine
M = Number of machines
R = Number of repairmen
Po = Probability of no defective machines in the system
Lq = Average number of defective machines in the repair queue
Ls = Average number of defective machines being repaired
L = Average number of defective machines in the system
SL = Service Level (probability a defective machine does not wait for repair)

ρ	M	R	Po	Lq	Ls	L	SL
.01	80	1	.23	2.18	.77	2.95	.23
.01	80	2	.43	.14	.79	.93	.78
.01	80	3	.45	.02	.79	.81	.95
.01	80	4	.45	.00	.79	.79	.99
.05	80	4	.01	4.19	3.61	7.80	.21
.05	80	5	.02	1.09	3.76	4.85	.55
.05	80	6	.02	.33	3.79	4.12	.77
.05	80	7	.02	.10	3.80	3.91	.90
.10	80	8	.00	2.66	7.03	9.69	.38
.10	80	9	.00	1.11	7.17	8.28	.60
.10	80	10	.00	.47	7.23	7.70	.76
.10	80	11	.00	.19	7.26	7.45	.87
.15	80	11	.00	3.24	10.01	13.25	.34
.15	80	12	.00	1.60	10.23	11.83	.54
.15	80	13	.00	.78	10.33	11.11	.70
.15	80	14	.00	.38	10.39	10.76	.81
.20	80	15	.00	1.67	13.05	14.73	.54
.20	80	16	.00	.89	13.18	14.08	.68
.20	80	17	.00	.46	13.26	13.72	.79
.20	80	18	.00	.24	13.29	13.53	.87
.01	90	1	.15	3.76	.85	4.61	.15
.01	90	2	.38	.21	.89	1.10	.73
.01	90	3	.41	.03	.89	.92	.93
.01	90	4	.41	.00	.89	.89	.99
.05	90	6	.01	.68	4.25	4.94	.66
.05	90	7	.01	.23	4.27	4.50	.83
.05	90	8	.01	.08	4.28	4.36	.92
.05	90	9	.01	.02	4.28	4.31	.97
.10	90	10	.00	1.18	8.07	9.26	.60
.10	90	11	.00	.52	8.13	8.66	.76
.10	90	12	.00	.23	8.16	8.39	.86
.10	90	13	.00	.10	8.17	8.27	.93
.15	90	13	.00	2.22	11.45	13.67	.47
.15	90	14	.00	1.13	11.59	12.72	.63
.15	90	15	.00	.57	11.66	12.23	.76
.15	90	16	.00	.28	11.70	11.98	.85
.20	90	17	.00	1.55	14.74	16.29	.58
.20	90	18	.00	.85	14.86	15.71	.71
.20	90	19	.00	.46	14.92	15.38	.81
.20	90	20	.00	.24	14.96	15.20	.88

ρ = Average time to repair a machine / Average time between failures for a machine

M = Number of machines

R = Number of repairmen

Po = Probability of no defective machines in the system

Lq = Average number of defective machines in the repair queue

Ls = Average number of defective machines being repaired

L = Average number of defective machines in the system

SL = Service Level (probability a defective machine does not wait for repair)

Table 18.1 Queueing Statistics for a Finite Number
of Machines and Repairmen (Continued)

ρ	M	R	Po	Lq	Ls	L	SL
.01	100	1	.08	6.65	.92	7.57	.08
.01	100	2	.34	.30	.99	1.29	.68
.01	100	3	.37	.04	.99	1.03	.91
.01	100	4	.37	.01	.99	1.00	.98
.05	100	5	.00	4.55	4.55	9.09	.23
.05	100	6	.01	1.34	4.70	6.04	.53
.05	100	7	.01	.45	4.74	5.19	.75
.05	100	8	.01	.16	4.75	4.91	.88
.10	100	10	.00	2.76	8.84	11.60	.40
.10	100	11	.00	1.25	8.98	10.23	.60
.10	100	12	.00	.57	9.04	9.61	.75
.10	100	13	.00	.26	9.07	9.33	.85
.15	100	14	.00	2.96	12.66	15.62	.41
.15	100	15	.00	1.57	12.84	14.41	.57
.15	100	16	.00	.82	12.94	13.76	.71
.15	100	17	.00	.42	12.99	13.41	.81
.20	100	19	.00	1.44	16.43	17.86	.61
.20	100	20	.00	.81	16.53	17.34	.73
.20	100	21	.00	.45	16.59	17.04	.82
.20	100	22	.00	.24	16.63	16.87	.88
.01	150	1	.00	49.00	1.00	50.00	.00
.01	150	2	.15	1.57	1.47	3.04	.38
.01	150	3	.21	.21	1.48	1.70	.77
.01	150	4	.22	.04	1.48	1.53	.93
.05	150	10	.00	.49	7.12	7.61	.77
.05	150	11	.00	.20	7.13	7.34	.87
.05	150	12	.00	.08	7.14	7.22	.94
.05	150	13	.00	.03	7.14	7.17	.97
.10	150	15	.00	2.88	13.37	16.25	.45
.10	150	16	.00	1.50	13.50	15.00	.61
.10	150	17	.00	.79	13.56	14.35	.74
.10	150	18	.00	.41	13.60	14.01	.83
.15	150	19	.00	8.67	18.43	27.11	.17
.15	150	20	.00	5.30	18.87	24.17	.30
.15	150	21	.00	3.17	19.15	22.32	.45
.15	150	22	.00	1.88	19.32	21.20	.58
.20	150	24	.00	9.33	23.44	32.78	.16
.20	150	25	.00	6.24	23.96	30.20	.27
.20	150	26	.00	4.07	24.32	28.39	.39
.20	150	27	.00	2.60	24.57	27.17	.52

ρ = Average time to repair a machine / Average time between failures for a machine
M = Number of machines
R = Number of repairmen
Po = Probability of no defective machines in the system
Lq = Average number of defective machines in the repair queue
Ls = Average number of defective machines being repaired
L = Average number of defective machines in the system
SL = Service Level (probability a defective machine does not wait for repair)

CHAPTER 19

Customer Service When Variable Lead Times

Chapter 9 illustrates how to determine the size of the safety stock that will yield a service level consistent with the goal set by inventory management. In carrying out the process, an order point is also found where a new replenishment order is called upon each time the on-hand plus on-order inventory reaches the order point. In order to determine the size of the safety stock and the order point, certain data from the inventory are needed. These are the forecast of demands, the standard error of the forecast, the size of the order quantity and the procurement lead time. A difficulty that often arises is that the procurement lead time duration is *not* a constant but instead is a variable. This situation may occur because the supplier sometimes delivers the items early and sometimes late, with the stated lead time representing an average. The goal of this chapter is to show how sensitive certain customer service measures are when this variation in lead time takes place.

In this analysis, the lead time is assumed to be normally distributed (as described in Chapter 7) with a particular mean and standard deviation. These parameters define the range wherein the actual lead time may lie. In addition, three different measures of customer service are defined. The first measure is the service level that is the same as described above. A second measure of customer service is the probability of an out of stock condition over an order cycle. This probability merely states the percent of order cycles when the item will be out of stock and does not give the number of units out of stock. (Recall that an order cycle is the time elapsing between two replenishments of stock for the item.) The third measure of customer service is the average time for which a unit is in the backorder condition. Again recall that a backorder occurs when a demand cannot be filled from stock and the customer waits until the next replenishment arrives.

Data

The following data and parameters are needed to carry out the analysis in this chapter.

$$F = \text{forecast of monthly demands}$$
$$\sigma = \text{standard deviation of the forecast}$$
$$SL = \text{desired service level}$$
$$Q = \text{order quantity}$$
$$L = \text{average of the lead time}$$
$$s = \text{standard deviation of the lead time}$$

Constant Lead Time Model

Recall (from Chapter 9) that when the desired service level **SL** is specified, the safety stock is obtained in the following manner. First the standard deviation of the forecast σ and the lead time L are combined to determine the standard error of the lead time forecast by the relation:

$$\sigma_L = \sqrt{L}\,\sigma$$

By using the order quantity Q and the service level SL, the relation below obtains $E(k)$, the partial expectation:

$$E(k) = \frac{(1 - SL)\,Q}{\sigma_L}$$

With the value of $E(k)$ calculated, Table 7.2 is used to find the corresponding size of the safety factor k. The safety stock SS is then found by the relation:

$$SS = k\,\sigma_L$$

It was noted in Chapter 9 that only positive values of k are used, and when $k < 0$, k is set to zero to avoid using a negative safety stock. Doing so yields a higher value of service level than the desired service level.

In order to find the order point, it is necessary to determine the lead time forecast F_L by the relation:

$$F_L = L \times F$$

Thus the order point OP becomes:

$$OP = F_L + SS$$

If the on-hand plus on-order inventory is less or equal to the order point, a replenishment of size Q is ordered from the supplier. This order will be received a lead time later. The expected service level under these conditions is the same as the desired service level (SL), the exception being when k is set to zero to avoid a negative safety stock.

Variable Lead Time Model

Consider the situation where the safety stock SS and order point OP are obtained as shown above using the lead time L as though it were a constant value. Assume further that L is the average value of the lead time, and the true lead time varies as a normal distribution with standard deviation of the lead time s. Under these circumstances the goal now is to determine the expected service level $E(SL)$, which in essence is an *effective* service level. In addition, the corresponding probability of an out of stock condition during an order cycle $P(out)$ will also be found. Further when a backorder does occur during an order cycle, then the average time a demand is in backorder τ_{BO} will be found.

- *Customer service when the lead time is L'*

In the following analysis it is assumed that the safety stock is determined using the lead time L as given above. For a particular order cycle, let L' designate the actual lead time that occurs and also let x represent the demand for this lead time period. Note that the mean and standard deviation of x become:

$$F_L' = L' \times F$$

and

$$\sigma_L' = \sqrt{L'}\,\sigma$$

So now the effective safety factor is determined from:

$$k' = (OP - F_{L'}) / \sigma_{L'}$$

Information from Table 7.1 yields the associated values of the effective partial expectation $E(k')$ and the effective probability of not being out of stock $F(k')$. With the effective partial expectation, the corresponding service level is then obtained from:

$$SL' = 1 - E(k')\,\sigma_{L'} / Q$$

Further, the probability of an out of stock condition becomes:

$$P(out)' = 1 - F(k')$$

- *Expected time per backorder when the lead time is L' and a backorder occurs in the order cycle*

Consider now an order cycle when a backorder occurs and the actual lead time is L'. Here the expected number of backorders, denoted as BO', is obtained by:

$$BO' = E(k')\,\sigma_{L'} / P(out)'$$

Thus for this order cycle the expected demand incurred from when the order point is reached until the new replenishment is received [denoted as $E(x')$] becomes:

$$E(x') = OP + BO'$$

Starting from when the new replenishment is ordered, let t_{op} represent the average length of time until the order point stock is consumed—at which time the item first becomes out of stock. Also note that L' is the time to reach $E(x')$. Using L' and t_{op}, the average time for which the item is in a backorder condition is determined by:

$$\tau' = L' - t_{op}$$

Relating the ratio of time and quantity that begins when the order point is reached and ends when the replenishment is received, then:

$$\frac{\tau'}{L'} = \frac{BO'}{OP + BO'}$$

therefore,

$$\tau' = L'\,\frac{BO'}{OP + BO'}$$

and so the average time a backorder demand is in the backorder condition becomes:

$$\tau'_{BO} = \tau'/2$$

- *Customer service*

Recall that the customer service measures just obtained, SL', $P(out)'$ and τ'_{BO}, are under conditions when the lead time is a particular value L'. Also, recall that L' is a variable following the normal distribution with mean L, standard deviation of the lead time s and probability density $f(L')$. Under these circumstances the expected values of the customer service can be determined as follows:

$$E(SL) = \int SL' f(L') \, dL'$$
$$P(out) = \int P(out)' f(L') \, dL'$$
$$\tau_{BO} = \int \tau'_{BO} f(L') \, dL'$$

Tables

The tables of this chapter are generated using standardized data. The average monthly forecast F and the corresponding standard deviation or the forecast σ are combined to yield the coefficient of variation:

$$cov = \sigma / F$$

Also, the lead time average L and the associated standard deviation of the lead time s are combined to give:

$$cov\,(L) = s / L$$

Finally, the order quantity Q and the average monthly forecast F are used to find the number of months M associated with the order quantity:

$$M = Q / F$$

The tables of this chapter present results when the desired service levels SL are set at .90, .95 and .97. The coefficient of variation for monthly demand **cov** are for values of 0.30 and 0.50. The coefficient of variation for the lead time **cov(L)** are 0.00 and 0.10. Note, when cov(L) = 0.00, the lead time is then a constant value without any variation. For each table, results are given where the lead time L varies from .25 (of a month) to 6 months and where the month's supply in the order quantity M ranges from .25 to 6 months.

The tables of this chapter list the effective (or expected) values of the customer service—$E(SL)$ for the service level, $P(out)$ for the probability of an out of stock condition, and τ_{BO} for the average time a demand in backorder is in the backorder condition.

The tables are arranged in the following manner:

Table	SL	cov	cov(L)
19.1	.90	.30	.00
19.2	.90	.30	.10
19.3	.90	.50	.00
19.4	.90	.50	.10
19.5	.95	.30	.00
19.6	.95	.30	.10
19.7	.95	.50	.00
19.8	.95	.50	.10
19.9	.97	.30	.00
19.10	.97	.30	.10
19.11	.97	.50	.00
19.12	.97	.50	.10

Example 19.1

Suppose that a gear stocked in a service center has an average monthly demand of 100 units with a standard deviation of 30 units. The gear is replenished in sizes of 200 units and the lead time is 4 months. Assume further that the desired service level is set at .95. Find the customer service measures for this item assuming no variation in the lead time.

Note $F = 100$ is the average monthly demand and $\sigma = 30$ is the standard deviation of the forecast. The corresponding coefficient of variation becomes cov $= \sigma/F = 30/100 = .30$. The average lead time is $L = 4$ months and the corresponding standard deviation of the lead time is $s = 0$, so the coefficient of variation cov$(L) = s/L = 0/4 = 0$. Because the order quantity is $Q = 200$, the months M associated with Q becomes $M = Q/F = 200/100 = 2$ (months). Finally, the desired service level is $SL = .95$.

With $SL = .95$, cov $= .30$ and cov$(L) = 0$, Table 19.5 is used along with $L = 4$ and $M = 2$. The table entries show that the expected service level (also called the effective service level) is $E(SL) = .95$, and the probability that the stock will run out during an order cycle is $P(out) = .27$. Also, for an order cycle with a backorder, the average backorder time is $\tau_{BO} = .16$ of a month. Note that the average time a gear is in a backorder condition is $2 \times .16 = .32$ months.

Example 19.2

Assume the same conditions as Example 19.1, with the exception that the lead time is subject to variation with a standard deviation of $s = .40$ months. Find the associated measures of the customer service.

Note that the coefficient of variation for the lead time is cov$(L) = s/L = .4/4 = .10$. Recall also that cov $= .30$, $SL = .95$, $L = 4$ and $M = 2$. Table 19.6 is now used to yield the following results:

$$E(SL) = .93$$
$$P(out) = .30$$
$$\tau_{BO} = .17$$

Example 19.3

Assume the same conditions as Example 19.2, where the desired service level is $SL = .95$, but because of the variation in lead time the expected service level becomes $E(SL) = .93$. Suppose management chooses to increase the desired service level to $SL = .97$ in hopes of bringing the associated expected service level closer to the desired .95 value. Find the customer service measures that are obtained.

With $SL = .97$, cov $= .30$ and cov$(L) = .10$, Table 19.10 will be used. Recalling that $L = 4$ months and $M = 2$ months, the table values thus yield the following results:

$$E(SL) = .95$$
$$P(out) = .22$$
$$\tau_{BO} = .14$$

Table 19.1 Effective Service Level, Probability of Out of Stock and Backorder Time

SL   = .90 (desired service level)
cov   = .30 (coefficient of variation for one month forecast)
cov(L) = .00 (coefficient of variation for lead time)

Effective Service Level

L \ M	.25	.50	.75	1	2	3	4	5	6
.25	.90	.90	.92	.94	.97	.98	.99	.99	.99
.50	.90	.90	.90	.92	.96	.97	.98	.98	.99
.75	.90	.90	.90	.90	.95	.97	.97	.98	.98
1	.90	.90	.90	.90	.94	.96	.97	.98	.98
2	.90	.90	.90	.90	.92	.94	.96	.97	.97
3	.90	.90	.90	.90	.90	.93	.95	.96	.97
4	.90	.90	.90	.90	.90	.92	.94	.95	.96
5	.90	.90	.90	.90	.90	.91	.93	.95	.96
6	.90	.90	.90	.90	.90	.90	.93	.94	.95

Probability of an Out of Stock Condition in an Order Cycle

L \ M	.25	.50	.75	1	2	3	4	5	6
.25	.27	.44	.50	.50	.50	.50	.50	.50	.50
.50	.21	.35	.46	.50	.50	.50	.50	.50	.50
.75	.18	.30	.40	.49	.50	.50	.50	.50	.50
1	.16	.27	.36	.44	.50	.50	.50	.50	.50
2	.12	.21	.28	.35	.50	.50	.50	.50	.50
3	.10	.18	.24	.30	.49	.50	.50	.50	.50
4	.09	.16	.22	.27	.44	.50	.50	.50	.50
5	.08	.15	.20	.25	.41	.50	.50	.50	.50
6	.08	.14	.19	.23	.39	.50	.50	.50	.50

Average Time per Backorder

L \ M	.25	.50	.75	1	2	3	4	5	6
.25	.03	.04	.04	.04	.04	.04	.04	.04	.04
.50	.04	.05	.06	.06	.06	.06	.06	.06	.06
.75	.05	.06	.07	.08	.08	.08	.08	.08	.08
1	.05	.07	.08	.09	.10	.10	.10	.10	.10
2	.08	.09	.11	.12	.14	.14	.14	.14	.14
3	.09	.11	.13	.14	.18	.18	.18	.18	.18
4	.11	.13	.14	.16	.20	.21	.21	.21	.21
5	.12	.14	.16	.17	.22	.24	.24	.24	.24
6	.13	.15	.17	.18	.23	.27	.27	.27	.27

L = average lead time in months
M = order quantity (in months of forecast)

Table 19.2 Effective Service Level, Probability of Out of Stock and Backorder Time

SL   = .90 (desired service level)
cov   = .30 (coefficient of variation for one month forecast)
cov(L) = .10 (coefficient of variation for lead time)

Effective Service Level

M L	.25	.50	.75	1	2	3	4	5	6
.25	.90	.90	.92	.94	.97	.98	.98	.99	.99
.50	.89	.90	.90	.91	.96	.97	.98	.98	.99
.75	.89	.89	.89	.90	.95	.96	.97	.98	.98
1	.88	.89	.89	.89	.94	.96	.97	.97	.98
2	.85	.87	.88	.88	.91	.94	.95	.96	.97
3	.83	.85	.86	.87	.88	.92	.94	.95	.96
4	.80	.83	.85	.86	.88	.90	.93	.94	.95
5	.78	.81	.83	.84	.87	.89	.92	.93	.94
6	.77	.80	.81	.83	.86	.87	.91	.92	.94

Probability of an Out of Stock Condition in an Order Cycle

M L	.25	.50	.75	1	2	3	4	5	6
.25	.27	.44	.50	.50	.50	.50	.50	.50	.50
.50	.21	.35	.46	.50	.50	.50	.50	.50	.50
.75	.19	.31	.40	.48	.49	.49	.49	.49	.49
1	.17	.28	.37	.44	.49	.49	.49	.49	.49
2	.14	.23	.30	.36	.49	.49	.49	.49	.49
3	.14	.21	.27	.32	.48	.49	.49	.49	.49
4	.13	.20	.25	.30	.45	.49	.49	.49	.49
5	.13	.20	.25	.29	.42	.49	.49	.49	.49
6	.13	.20	.24	.28	.41	.49	.49	.49	.49

Average Time per Backorder

M L	.25	.50	.75	1	2	3	4	5	6
.25	.03	.04	.04	.04	.04	.04	.04	.04	.04
.50	.04	.05	.06	.06	.06	.06	.06	.06	.06
.75	.05	.06	.07	.08	.08	.08	.08	.08	.08
1	.06	.07	.08	.09	.10	.10	.10	.10	.10
2	.08	.10	.11	.12	.15	.15	.15	.15	.15
3	.10	.12	.13	.15	.19	.19	.19	.19	.19
4	.11	.14	.15	.17	.21	.23	.23	.23	.23
5	.13	.15	.17	.19	.23	.26	.26	.26	.26
6	.14	.17	.19	.20	.25	.29	.29	.29	.29

L = average lead time in months
M = order quantity (in months of forecast)

Table 19.3 Effective Service Level, Probability of Out of Stock and Backorder Time

```
SL    = .90  (desired service level)
cov   = .50  (coefficient of variation for one month forecast)
cov(L) = .00  (coefficient of variation for lead time)
```

Effective Service Level

M \ L	.25	.50	.75	1	2	3	4	5	6
.25	.90	.90	.90	.90	.95	.97	.98	.98	.98
.50	.90	.90	.90	.90	.93	.95	.96	.97	.98
.75	.90	.90	.90	.90	.91	.94	.96	.97	.97
1	.90	.90	.90	.90	.90	.93	.95	.96	.97
2	.90	.90	.90	.90	.90	.91	.93	.94	.95
3	.90	.90	.90	.90	.90	.90	.91	.93	.94
4	.90	.90	.90	.90	.90	.90	.90	.92	.93
5	.90	.90	.90	.90	.90	.90	.90	.91	.93
6	.90	.90	.90	.90	.90	.90	.90	.90	.92

Probability of an Out of Stock Condition in an Order Cycle

M \ L	.25	.50	.75	1	2	3	4	5	6
.25	.18	.31	.41	.50	.50	.50	.50	.50	.50
.50	.14	.24	.32	.40	.50	.50	.50	.50	.50
.75	.12	.21	.28	.34	.50	.50	.50	.50	.50
1	.10	.18	.25	.31	.50	.50	.50	.50	.50
2	.08	.14	.19	.24	.40	.50	.50	.50	.50
3	.07	.12	.16	.21	.34	.46	.50	.50	.50
4	.06	.10	.15	.18	.31	.41	.50	.50	.50
5	.05	.10	.13	.17	.29	.38	.47	.50	.50
6	.05	.09	.12	.16	.27	.36	.44	.50	.50

Average Time per Backorder

M \ L	.25	.50	.75	1	2	3	4	5	6
.25	.03	.04	.05	.06	.06	.06	.06	.06	.06
.50	.04	.05	.06	.07	.09	.09	.09	.09	.09
.75	.05	.07	.08	.09	.12	.12	.12	.12	.12
1	.06	.08	.09	.10	.14	.14	.14	.14	.14
2	.10	.11	.13	.14	.19	.22	.22	.22	.22
3	.12	.14	.16	.17	.22	.26	.28	.28	.28
4	.14	.17	.18	.20	.25	.29	.33	.33	.33
5	.16	.19	.21	.22	.28	.32	.36	.38	.38
6	.18	.21	.23	.24	.30	.34	.39	.42	.42

```
L   = average lead time in months
M   = order quantity (in months of forecast)
```

Table 19.4 Effective Service Level, Probability of Out of Stock and Backorder Time

SL   = .90 (desired service level)
cov   = .50 (coefficient of variation for one month forecast)
cov(L) = .10 (coefficient of variation for lead time)

Effective Service Level

M / L	.25	.50	.75	1	2	3	4	5	6
.25	.90	.90	.90	.90	.95	.97	.97	.98	.98
.50	.89	.90	.90	.90	.93	.95	.96	.97	.98
.75	.89	.89	.90	.90	.91	.94	.96	.96	.97
1	.89	.89	.89	.90	.90	.93	.95	.96	.97
2	.88	.88	.89	.89	.89	.90	.93	.94	.95
3	.86	.87	.88	.88	.89	.89	.91	.93	.94
4	.85	.86	.87	.87	.89	.89	.89	.91	.93
5	.84	.85	.86	.87	.88	.89	.89	.90	.92
6	.82	.84	.85	.86	.87	.88	.89	.89	.91

Probability of an Out of Stock Condition in an Order Cycle

M / L	.25	.50	.75	1	2	3	4	5	6
.25	.18	.31	.41	.50	.50	.50	.50	.50	.50
.50	.14	.24	.32	.40	.50	.50	.50	.50	.50
.75	.12	.21	.28	.34	.50	.50	.50	.50	.50
1	.11	.19	.25	.31	.50	.50	.50	.50	.50
2	.09	.15	.20	.25	.40	.49	.49	.49	.49
3	.08	.13	.18	.22	.35	.45	.49	.49	.49
4	.07	.12	.16	.20	.32	.41	.49	.49	.49
5	.07	.12	.16	.19	.30	.39	.46	.49	.49
6	.07	.11	.15	.18	.28	.37	.44	.49	.49

Average Time per Backorder

M / L	.25	.50	.75	1	2	3	4	5	6
.25	.03	.04	.05	.06	.06	.06	.06	.06	.06
.50	.04	.05	.07	.08	.09	.09	.09	.09	.09
.75	.05	.07	.08	.09	.12	.12	.12	.12	.12
1	.06	.08	.09	.10	.14	.14	.14	.14	.14
2	.10	.12	.13	.15	.19	.22	.22	.22	.22
3	.13	.15	.16	.18	.23	.27	.29	.29	.29
4	.15	.17	.19	.21	.26	.30	.34	.34	.34
5	.17	.20	.22	.23	.29	.33	.37	.39	.39
6	.18	.21	.24	.26	.31	.36	.40	.44	.44

L   = average lead time in months
M   = order quantity (in months of forecast)

Table 19.5 Effective Service Level, Probability of Out of Stock and Backorder Time

SL   = .95 (desired service level)
cov   = .30 (coefficient of variation for one month forecast)
cov(L) = .00 (coefficient of variation for lead time)

Effective Service Level

L \ M	.25	.50	.75	1	2	3	4	5	6
.25	.95	.95	.95	.95	.97	.98	.99	.99	.99
.50	.95	.95	.95	.95	.96	.97	.98	.98	.99
.75	.95	.95	.95	.95	.95	.97	.97	.98	.98
1	.95	.95	.95	.95	.95	.96	.97	.98	.98
2	.95	.95	.95	.95	.95	.95	.96	.97	.97
3	.95	.95	.95	.95	.95	.95	.95	.96	.97
4	.95	.95	.95	.95	.95	.95	.95	.95	.96
5	.95	.95	.95	.95	.95	.95	.95	.95	.96
6	.95	.95	.95	.95	.95	.95	.95	.95	.95

Probability of an Out of Stock Condition in an Order Cycle

L \ M	.25	.50	.75	1	2	3	4	5	6
.25	.16	.27	.36	.44	.50	.50	.50	.50	.50
.50	.12	.21	.28	.35	.50	.50	.50	.50	.50
.75	.10	.18	.24	.30	.49	.50	.50	.50	.50
1	.09	.16	.22	.27	.44	.50	.50	.50	.50
2	.07	.12	.17	.21	.35	.46	.50	.50	.50
3	.06	.10	.14	.18	.30	.40	.49	.50	.50
4	.05	.09	.13	.16	.27	.36	.44	.50	.50
5	.04	.08	.12	.15	.25	.34	.41	.48	.50
6	.04	.08	.11	.14	.23	.32	.39	.45	.50

Average Time per Backorder

L \ M	.25	.50	.75	1	2	3	4	5	6
.25	.02	.03	.03	.04	.04	.04	.04	.04	.04
.50	.03	.04	.04	.05	.06	.06	.06	.06	.06
.75	.04	.05	.05	.06	.08	.08	.08	.08	.08
1	.05	.05	.06	.07	.09	.10	.10	.10	.10
2	.07	.08	.09	.09	.12	.14	.14	.14	.14
3	.08	.09	.10	.11	.14	.16	.18	.18	.18
4	.10	.11	.12	.13	.16	.18	.20	.21	.21
5	.11	.12	.13	.14	.17	.19	.22	.24	.24
6	.12	.13	.14	.15	.18	.21	.23	.25	.27

L = average lead time in months
M = order quantity (in months of forecast)

Table 19.6   Effective Service Level, Probability of Out of Stock and Backorder Time

SL   = .95 (desired service level)
cov   = .30 (coefficient of variation for one month forecast)
cov(L) = .10 (coefficient of variation for lead time)

Effective Service Level

L \ M	.25	.50	.75	1	2	3	4	5	6
.25	.95	.95	.95	.95	.97	.98	.98	.99	.99
.50	.94	.95	.95	.95	.96	.97	.98	.98	.99
.75	.94	.94	.94	.95	.95	.96	.97	.98	.98
1	.93	.94	.94	.94	.95	.96	.97	.97	.98
2	.92	.93	.93	.94	.94	.94	.95	.96	.97
3	.90	.91	.92	.93	.94	.94	.94	.95	.96
4	.88	.90	.91	.92	.93	.93	.94	.94	.95
5	.86	.88	.90	.90	.92	.93	.93	.94	.94
6	.84	.87	.88	.89	.91	.92	.93	.93	.94

Probability of an Out of Stock Condition in an Order Cycle

L \ M	.25	.50	.75	1	2	3	4	5	6
.25	.16	.27	.36	.44	.50	.50	.50	.50	.50
.50	.13	.21	.29	.35	.50	.50	.50	.50	.50
.75	.11	.19	.25	.31	.48	.49	.49	.49	.49
1	.10	.17	.23	.28	.44	.49	.49	.49	.49
2	.09	.14	.19	.23	.36	.46	.49	.49	.49
3	.09	.14	.18	.21	.32	.41	.48	.49	.49
4	.09	.13	.17	.20	.30	.38	.45	.49	.49
5	.09	.13	.17	.20	.29	.36	.42	.47	.49
6	.09	.13	.17	.20	.28	.35	.41	.45	.49

Average Time per Backorder

L \ M	.25	.50	.75	1	2	3	4	5	6
.25	.02	.03	.03	.04	.04	.04	.04	.04	.04
.50	.03	.04	.04	.05	.06	.06	.06	.06	.06
.75	.04	.05	.05	.06	.08	.08	.08	.08	.08
1	.05	.06	.06	.07	.09	.10	.10	.10	.10
2	.07	.08	.09	.10	.12	.14	.15	.15	.15
3	.08	.10	.11	.12	.15	.17	.19	.19	.19
4	.10	.11	.13	.14	.17	.19	.21	.23	.23
5	.11	.13	.14	.15	.19	.21	.23	.26	.26
6	.11	.14	.15	.17	.20	.23	.25	.28	.29

L = average lead time in months
M = order quantity (in months of forecast)

Table 19.7   Effective Service Level, Probability of Out of Stock and Backorder Time

SL   = .95   (desired service level)

cov   = .50   (coefficient of variation for one month forecast)

cov(L) = .00   (coefficient of variation for lead time)

Effective Service Level

M \ L	.25	.50	.75	1	2	3	4	5	6
.25	.95	.95	.95	.95	.95	.97	.98	.98	.98
.50	.95	.95	.95	.95	.95	.95	.96	.97	.98
.75	.95	.95	.95	.95	.95	.95	.96	.97	.97
1	.95	.95	.95	.95	.95	.95	.95	.96	.97
2	.95	.95	.95	.95	.95	.95	.95	.95	.95
3	.95	.95	.95	.95	.95	.95	.95	.95	.95
4	.95	.95	.95	.95	.95	.95	.95	.95	.95
5	.95	.95	.95	.95	.95	.95	.95	.95	.95
6	.95	.95	.95	.95	.95	.95	.95	.95	.95

Probability of an Out of Stock Condition in an Order Cycle

M \ L	.25	.50	.75	1	2	3	4	5	6
.25	.10	.18	.25	.31	.50	.50	.50	.50	.50
.50	.08	.14	.19	.24	.40	.50	.50	.50	.50
.75	.07	.12	.16	.21	.34	.46	.50	.50	.50
1	.06	.10	.15	.18	.31	.41	.50	.50	.50
2	.04	.08	.11	.14	.24	.32	.40	.46	.50
3	.04	.07	.09	.12	.21	.28	.34	.40	.46
4	.03	.06	.08	.10	.18	.25	.31	.36	.41
5	.03	.05	.07	.10	.17	.23	.29	.34	.38
6	.03	.05	.07	.09	.16	.21	.27	.32	.36

Average Time per Backorder

M \ L	.25	.50	.75	1	2	3	4	5	6
.25	.02	.03	.03	.04	.06	.06	.06	.06	.06
.50	.03	.04	.05	.05	.07	.09	.09	.09	.09
.75	.04	.05	.06	.07	.09	.11	.12	.12	.12
1	.05	.06	.07	.08	.10	.12	.14	.14	.14
2	.08	.10	.11	.11	.14	.17	.19	.21	.22
3	.11	.12	.13	.14	.17	.20	.22	.24	.26
4	.13	.14	.16	.17	.20	.23	.25	.27	.29
5	.15	.16	.18	.19	.22	.25	.28	.30	.32
6	.17	.18	.19	.21	.24	.27	.30	.32	.34

L   = average lead time in months

M   = order quantity (in months of forecast)

Table 19.8   Effective Service Level, Probability of Out of Stock and Backorder Time

```
SL     = .95  (desired service level)
cov    = .50  (coefficient of variation for one month forecast)
cov(L) = .10  (coefficient of variation for lead time)
```

Effective Service Level

M\L	.25	.50	.75	1	2	3	4	5	6
.25	.95	.95	.95	.95	.95	.97	.97	.98	.98
.50	.95	.95	.95	.95	.95	.95	.96	.97	.98
.75	.94	.95	.95	.95	.95	.95	.96	.96	.97
1	.94	.94	.95	.95	.95	.95	.95	.96	.97
2	.93	.94	.94	.94	.94	.95	.95	.95	.95
3	.93	.93	.93	.94	.94	.94	.94	.95	.95
4	.92	.92	.93	.93	.94	.94	.94	.94	.94
5	.91	.92	.92	.93	.93	.94	.94	.94	.94
6	.90	.91	.92	.92	.93	.93	.94	.94	.94

Probability of an Out of Stock Condition in an Order Cycle

M\L	.25	.50	.75	1	2	3	4	5	6
.25	.11	.18	.25	.31	.50	.50	.50	.50	.50
.50	.08	.14	.19	.24	.40	.50	.50	.50	.50
.75	.07	.12	.17	.21	.34	.45	.50	.50	.50
1	.06	.11	.15	.19	.31	.41	.50	.50	.50
2	.05	.09	.12	.15	.25	.33	.40	.46	.49
3	.05	.08	.11	.13	.22	.29	.35	.40	.45
4	.04	.07	.10	.12	.20	.26	.32	.37	.41
5	.04	.07	.10	.12	.19	.25	.30	.34	.39
6	.04	.07	.09	.11	.18	.24	.28	.33	.37

Average Time per Backorder

M\L	.25	.50	.75	1	2	3	4	5	6
.25	.02	.03	.03	.04	.06	.06	.06	.06	.06
.50	.03	.04	.05	.05	.08	.09	.09	.09	.09
.75	.05	.05	.06	.07	.09	.11	.12	.12	.12
1	.05	.06	.07	.08	.10	.12	.14	.14	.14
2	.08	.10	.11	.12	.15	.17	.19	.21	.22
3	.11	.13	.14	.15	.18	.20	.23	.25	.27
4	.12	.15	.16	.17	.21	.23	.26	.28	.30
5	.14	.17	.18	.20	.23	.26	.29	.31	.33
6	.15	.18	.20	.21	.26	.29	.31	.34	.36

```
L = average lead time in months
M = order quantity (in months of forecast)
```

Table 19.9   Effective Service Level, Probability of Out of Stock and Backorder Time

SL   = .97 (desired service level)

cov   = .30 (coefficient of variation for one month forecast)

cov(L) = .00 (coefficient of variation for lead time)

Effective Service Level

M	.25	.50	.75	1	2	3	4	5	6
L									
.25	.97	.97	.97	.97	.97	.98	.99	.99	.99
.50	.97	.97	.97	.97	.97	.97	.98	.98	.99
.75	.97	.97	.97	.97	.97	.97	.97	.98	.98
1	.97	.97	.97	.97	.97	.97	.97	.98	.98
2	.97	.97	.97	.97	.97	.97	.97	.97	.97
3	.97	.97	.97	.97	.97	.97	.97	.97	.97
4	.97	.97	.97	.97	.97	.97	.97	.97	.97
5	.97	.97	.97	.97	.97	.97	.97	.97	.97
6	.97	.97	.97	.97	.97	.97	.97	.97	.97

Probability of an Out of Stock Condition in an Order Cycle

M	.25	.50	.75	1	2	3	4	5	6
L									
.25	.10	.18	.25	.31	.50	.50	.50	.50	.50
.50	.08	.14	.19	.24	.40	.50	.50	.50	.50
.75	.07	.12	.16	.21	.34	.46	.50	.50	.50
1	.06	.10	.15	.18	.31	.41	.50	.50	.50
2	.04	.08	.11	.14	.24	.32	.40	.46	.50
3	.04	.07	.09	.12	.21	.28	.34	.40	.46
4	.03	.06	.08	.10	.18	.25	.31	.36	.41
5	.03	.05	.07	.10	.17	.23	.29	.34	.38
6	.03	.05	.07	.09	.16	.21	.27	.32	.36

Average Time per Backorder

M	.25	.50	.75	1	2	3	4	5	6
L									
.25	.02	.02	.03	.03	.04	.04	.04	.04	.04
.50	.03	.03	.04	.04	.05	.06	.06	.06	.06
.75	.03	.04	.05	.05	.06	.08	.08	.08	.08
1	.04	.05	.05	.06	.07	.08	.10	.10	.10
2	.06	.07	.07	.08	.10	.11	.13	.14	.14
3	.08	.09	.09	.10	.12	.13	.15	.16	.17
4	.09	.10	.11	.11	.13	.15	.17	.18	.19
5	.10	.11	.12	.13	.15	.17	.18	.19	.21
6	.11	.12	.13	.14	.16	.18	.20	.21	.22

L   = average lead time in months

M   = order quantity (in months of forecast)

Table 19.10 Effective Service Level, Probability of Out of Stock and Backorder Time

```
SL     = .97  (desired service level)
cov    = .30  (coefficient of variation for one month forecast)
cov(L) = .10  (coefficient of variation for lead time)
```

Effective Service Level

M / L	.25	.50	.75	1	2	3	4	5	6
.25	.97	.97	.97	.97	.97	.98	.98	.99	.99
.50	.96	.97	.97	.97	.97	.97	.98	.98	.99
.75	.96	.96	.97	.97	.97	.97	.97	.98	.98
1	.96	.96	.96	.96	.97	.97	.97	.97	.98
2	.95	.95	.96	.96	.96	.96	.97	.97	.97
3	.93	.94	.95	.95	.96	.96	.96	.96	.96
4	.92	.93	.94	.94	.95	.96	.96	.96	.96
5	.90	.92	.93	.93	.95	.95	.95	.96	.96
6	.89	.91	.92	.92	.94	.95	.95	.95	.96

Probability of an Out of Stock Condition in an Order Cycle

M / L	.25	.50	.75	1	2	3	4	5	6
.25	.11	.19	.25	.31	.50	.50	.50	.50	.50
.50	.09	.15	.20	.24	.40	.50	.50	.50	.50
.75	.08	.13	.17	.21	.35	.45	.49	.49	.49
1	.07	.12	.16	.19	.32	.41	.49	.49	.49
2	.06	.10	.13	.16	.26	.33	.40	.46	.49
3	.06	.10	.13	.15	.23	.30	.36	.41	.45
4	.06	.10	.12	.15	.22	.28	.33	.38	.42
5	.07	.10	.12	.15	.22	.27	.32	.36	.40
6	.07	.10	.13	.15	.21	.27	.31	.35	.38

Average Time per Backorder

M / L	.25	.50	.75	1	2	3	4	5	6
.25	.02	.02	.03	.03	.04	.04	.04	.04	.04
.50	.03	.03	.04	.04	.05	.06	.06	.06	.06
.75	.03	.04	.05	.05	.06	.08	.08	.08	.08
1	.04	.05	.05	.06	.07	.09	.10	.10	.10
2	.06	.07	.08	.08	.10	.12	.13	.14	.15
3	.07	.09	.10	.10	.12	.14	.16	.17	.18
4	.08	.10	.11	.12	.14	.16	.18	.19	.20
5	.09	.11	.12	.13	.16	.18	.20	.21	.23
6	.10	.12	.14	.15	.18	.20	.21	.23	.24

```
L = average lead time in months
M = order quantity (in months of forecast)
```

Table 19.11 Effective Service Level, Probability of Out of Stock and Backorder Time

```
SL      = .97  (desired service level)
cov     = .50  (coefficient of variation for one month forecast)
cov(L)  = .00  (coefficient of variation for lead time)
```

Effective Service Level

M \ L	.25	.50	.75	1	2	3	4	5	6
.25	.97	.97	.97	.97	.97	.97	.98	.98	.98
.50	.97	.97	.97	.97	.97	.97	.97	.97	.98
.75	.97	.97	.97	.97	.97	.97	.97	.97	.97
1	.97	.97	.97	.97	.97	.97	.97	.97	.97
2	.97	.97	.97	.97	.97	.97	.97	.97	.97
3	.97	.97	.97	.97	.97	.97	.97	.97	.97
4	.97	.97	.97	.97	.97	.97	.97	.97	.97
5	.97	.97	.97	.97	.97	.97	.97	.97	.97
6	.97	.97	.97	.97	.97	.97	.97	.97	.97

Probability of an Out of Stock Condition in an Order Cycle

M \ L	.25	.50	.75	1	2	3	4	5	6
.25	.07	.12	.17	.21	.35	.47	.50	.50	.50
.50	.05	.09	.13	.16	.28	.37	.45	.50	.50
.75	.04	.08	.11	.14	.24	.32	.39	.46	.50
1	.04	.07	.10	.12	.21	.29	.35	.41	.47
2	.03	.05	.07	.09	.16	.22	.28	.32	.37
3	.02	.04	.06	.08	.14	.19	.24	.28	.32
4	.02	.04	.05	.07	.12	.17	.21	.25	.29
5	.02	.03	.05	.06	.11	.15	.19	.23	.26
6	.02	.03	.04	.06	.10	.14	.18	.21	.25

Average Time per Backorder

M \ L	.25	.50	.75	1	2	3	4	5	6
.25	.02	.02	.03	.03	.04	.05	.06	.06	.06
.50	.03	.04	.04	.04	.06	.07	.08	.09	.09
.75	.04	.05	.05	.06	.07	.09	.10	.11	.12
1	.05	.06	.06	.07	.08	.10	.11	.12	.13
2	.08	.09	.09	.10	.12	.14	.15	.17	.18
3	.10	.11	.12	.13	.15	.17	.18	.20	.21
4	.12	.13	.14	.15	.17	.19	.21	.23	.24
5	.14	.15	.16	.17	.20	.22	.23	.25	.27
6	.15	.17	.18	.19	.21	.24	.26	.27	.29

```
L   = average lead time in months
M   = order quantity (in months of forecast)
```

Table 19.12 Effective Service Level, Probability of Out of Stock and Backorder Time

```
SL     = .97  (desired service level)
cov    = .50  (coefficient of variation for one month forecast)
cov(L) = .10  (coefficient of variation for lead time)
```

Effective Service Level

M \ L	.25	.50	.75	1	2	3	4	5	6
.25	.97	.97	.97	.97	.97	.97	.97	.98	.98
.50	.97	.97	.97	.97	.97	.97	.97	.97	.98
.75	.97	.97	.97	.97	.97	.97	.97	.97	.97
1	.96	.97	.97	.97	.97	.97	.97	.97	.97
2	.96	.96	.96	.96	.97	.97	.97	.97	.97
3	.95	.96	.96	.96	.96	.96	.97	.97	.97
4	.95	.95	.95	.96	.96	.96	.96	.96	.97
5	.94	.95	.95	.95	.96	.96	.96	.96	.96
6	.93	.94	.94	.95	.95	.96	.96	.96	.96

Probability of an Out of Stock Condition in an Order Cycle

M \ L	.25	.50	.75	1	2	3	4	5	6
.25	.07	.12	.17	.21	.35	.47	.50	.50	.50
.50	.05	.09	.13	.16	.28	.37	.45	.50	.50
.75	.05	.08	.11	.14	.24	.32	.39	.45	.50
1	.04	.07	.10	.13	.21	.29	.35	.41	.46
2	.03	.06	.08	.10	.17	.23	.28	.33	.37
3	.03	.05	.07	.09	.15	.20	.25	.29	.32
4	.03	.05	.07	.08	.14	.19	.23	.26	.30
5	.03	.05	.07	.08	.13	.18	.21	.25	.28
6	.03	.05	.07	.08	.13	.17	.20	.24	.27

Average Time per Backorder

M \ L	.25	.50	.75	1	2	3	4	5	6
.25	.02	.02	.03	.03	.04	.05	.06	.06	.06
.50	.03	.04	.04	.05	.06	.07	.08	.09	.09
.75	.04	.05	.05	.06	.07	.09	.10	.11	.12
1	.05	.06	.06	.07	.09	.10	.11	.12	.14
2	.07	.09	.10	.10	.12	.14	.16	.17	.18
3	.09	.11	.12	.13	.15	.17	.19	.20	.22
4	.11	.13	.14	.15	.18	.20	.22	.23	.25
5	.12	.15	.16	.17	.20	.23	.24	.26	.28
6	.13	.16	.18	.19	.22	.25	.27	.29	.30

```
L = average lead time in months
M = order quantity (in months of forecast)
```

CHAPTER 20

Optimal Order Quantity For Dated Items

In the retail industry, many inventory items become obsolete for one reason or another, after a particular amount of time elapses or after a particular date is reached. For purposes of this chapter, these items are called *dated items* and the time during which the item may be sold prior to obsolescence is called the *shelf life*. Some of these dated items, such as beer, soft drinks and cereals, have a long shelf life and stand little chance of not being sold before the critical date is reached. These items, although dated, generally do not require special attention in the control of the inventory.

Other dated items have a relatively short shelf life, and the control of the inventory is deeply dependent on the length of that shelf life. Well known examples are milk, yogurt and other dairy products. These types of items must be sold prior to the expiration of the shelf life or else face being scrapped or returned to the supplier. Bakery, fruit and vegetable items have an even shorter shelf life and must be sold soon after being placed in stock in order to avoid spoilage. Other dated items are those stocked for particular holidays, such as Christmas, Easter and Valentine day. If these items are not sold before the holiday, the retailer may then need to reduce the price to clear the inventory.

The goal of this chapter is to determine how the optimal order quantity may be obtained for dated inventory items. To begin, the actual amount of demand for the item over the shelf life is not exactly known. A forecast gives an estimate of the average demand over the shelf life, and the standard deviation of the forecast is used to determine the range of the actual demand in relation to the shelf life. Further, the item is procured at a particular cost—and if sold during the shelf life—yields its normal selling price. If the item is not sold during the shelf life, the retailer may receive a price relatively lower than the normal selling price, if he receives any compensation at all. If the retailer runs short of the item and is out of stock when a customer demand occurs, the retailer is faced with a goodwill loss due to the customer's dissatisfaction. In seeking the optimal order quantity, all of the above factors are taken into consideration.

Data

The data needed to find the optimal order quantity are the following:

μ = average demand over the shelf life
σ = standard deviation of the shelf life demand
C = procurement cost per unit
$P1$ = selling price per unit if sold during the shelf life
$P2$ = return price per unit if sold after the shelf life
$P3$ = goodwill loss per unit if the item is out of stock when a customer demand occurs

For purposes of this chapter, it is assumed that the demand for the item over the shelf life is normally distributed with a mean μ and standard deviation σ as stated above.

Model

Let **Q** designate the quantity of stock available at the start of the order cycle, representing the shelf life for the item. Suppose further that **x** represents the actual demand over the shelf life, where **x** has a probability density of **f(x)**. If **x** is less or equal to **Q**, all **x** sold items will sell for **P1** each, and for those (Q − x) items not sold, the return price will be **P2** each. If **x** is larger than **Q**, the price will be **P1** for each of the **Q** units in stock, and the goodwill loss will be **P3** for each of the (x − Q) demands that are unfilled. The total cost for the lot is C × Q. With the information stated above, the effective profit (**EP**) can be determined for a particular value of **x**. Of more use is the *expected* value of the effective profit, here labeled as **E(EP)**. This value is obtained by the expression:

$$E(EP) = P1 \int_{x \le Q} x f(x) dx + P2 \int_{x \le Q} (Q - x) f(x) dx$$

$$+ P1 \int_{x > Q} Q\, f(x) dx - P3 \int_{x > Q} (x - Q)\, f(x) dx - (C \times Q)$$

Note that the realized profit (**RP**) is the same as the above when the goodwill loss is excluded from the expression. This result represents the actual amount of profit that the retailer receives. The expected value of **RP** is denoted as **E(RP)** and is obtained by using only the first three integral terms above, minus the cost of the lot (C × Q).

Recall that **x** (the actual demand over the shelf life) is assumed in this chapter to follow the normal probability distribution and has a mean of μ and a standard deviation of σ. With this distribution of **x**, no closed form solution on the optimal value of **Q** is presented. Instead, the optimal value of **Q** is obtained by quantitative methods; that is, the value of **Q** is found which yields the maximum value of the expected effective profit **E(EP)**. Also note that for the optimal value of **Q** the corresponding value of the expected realized profit, **E(RP)**, may be determined as well.

Tables

The tables of this chapter are presented using standardized input data. The ratios associated with the selling price, return price and goodwill loss are the following:

R1 = P1/C = selling price / unit cost
R2 = P2/C = return price / unit cost
R3 = P3/C = goodwill cost / unit cost

Further, the mean and standard deviation of shelf life demand is expressed in terms of the coefficient of variation **cov** as shown below:

cov = σ/μ = standard deviation/mean

The tables of this chapter give results when **R1** ranges from 1.1 to 3.0, **R2** ranges from 0 to 1.0, and **R3** at values of 0, .25, .50 and 1.00. Further, the results are shown with **cov** values of 0.10 and 0.20. The tables are arranged as follows:

Table	cov	R3
20.1	.1	.00
20.2	.1	.25
20.3	.1	.50
20.4	.1	1.00
20.5	.2	.00
20.6	.2	.25
20.7	.2	.50
20.8	.2	1.00

The tables report the optimal order quantity in standardized form, denoted as **q**, by taking the ratio of the order quantity **Q** over the mean value μ. This is:

$$q = Q / \mu$$

The tables also list the corresponding expected realized profit per unit in standardized form, labeled as **r**. This result is derived by taking **E(RP)** over the lot cost $C \times Q$ as shown below:

$$r = E(RP) / C \times Q$$

Example 20.1

Consider a grocery store that stocks gallons of 2% milk with a shelf life of 10 days. Assume the average demand over the shelf life is 1000 units with a standard deviation of 100 units. Suppose further the procurement cost per gallon is $C = \$1.10$ and the selling price is $P1 = \$1.76$. Also assume the return price (of those gallons not sold during the shelf life) is $P2 = 0$, and the goodwill loss is $P3 = \$0.55$ for each demand occurring when the milk is out of stock. Determine the optimal order quantity to stock and the corresponding realized profit per gallon.

Note the coefficient of variation is cov $= \sigma / \mu = 100/1000 = 0.10$. Also the normalized price ratios are $R1 = P1/C = 1.76/1.10 = 1.60$, $R2 = P2/C = 0/1.10 = 0$ and $R3 = P3/C = 0.55/1.10 = 0.50$. Because cov $= 0.10$ and $R3 = .50$, Table 20.3 yields the standardized order quantity $q = 1.01$ and the expected profit ratio $r = 0.53$. Thus, the optimal order quantity is $Q = q \times \mu = 1.01 \times 1,000 = 1,010$ gallons and the expected profit per gallon is $r \times C = 0.53 \times 1.10 = \$0.583$.

Example 20.2

Consider a fruit market selling peaches with a 7 day shelf life. The manager estimates the average demand over this period is 20 bushels with a standard deviation of 2 bushels. The procurement cost per bushel is $2.00, and the retailer reports the ratio of the selling price over the procurement cost is $R1 = 2.60$. Further, the ratio of the return price over the procurement cost is $R2 = 0.70$ and the goodwill cost is zero or $R3 = 0$. Find the optimal order quantity for the peaches and the corresponding expected total profit from this purchase.

Note the coefficient of variation is cov $= \sigma/\mu = 2/20 = 0.10$. With cov $= .10$ and $R3 = 0$, Table 20.1 entries show that the standardized order quantity and expected profit ratio are $q = 1.10$ and $r = 1.41$, respectively. Thus the order quantity **Q** becomes $q \times \mu = 1.10 \times 20 = 22$ bushels. Also, the expected total profit from this purchase is obtained by:

$$Q \times r \times C = 22 \times 1.41 \times 2.00 = \$62.04.$$

Example 20.3

Consider a drug store that stocks sets of tree lights for the Christmas season. The store manager reports that the forecast of sales over this season is 2000 sets with a standard deviation of 400 sets. The procurement cost per set is $0.80; the selling price is $P1 = \$2.40$. If any sets are not sold during the holiday season, they are later sold at a discount price of $P2 = \$0.80$. If the store is out of stock, the goodwill loss per demand is assumed at $P3 = \$0.20$. Find the number of sets to have available at the start of the selling season and the corresponding total expected profit.

Note that the coefficient of variation becomes $cov = \sigma / \mu = 400/2000 = 0.20$. The price ratios are $R1 = P1/C = 2.40/0.80 = 3.00$ for the selling price, $R2 = P2/C = 0.80/0.80 = 1.00$ for the return price, and $R3 = P3/C = 0.20/0.80 = 0.25$ for the goodwill cost. With $cov = .20$ and $R3 = .25$, Table 20.6 yields the standardized results $q = 1.60$ and $r = 1.25$. The number of sets to have available over for the Christmas season is therefore $Q = q \times \mu = 1.60 \times 2,000 = 3,200$. The expected total profit is the following:

$$Q \times r \times C = 3,200 \times 1.25 \times 0.80 = \$3,200$$

Table 20.1　Optimal Order Quantity and Profit Ratio for Dated Items

```
cov     = .10  (coefficient of variation of demand)
R1      =  selling price / cost per unit
R2      =  return price / cost per unit
R3      = .00  (goodwill loss / cost per unit)
```

Optimal Order Quantity / Average Demand

R1 \ R2	.0	.1	.2	.3	.4	.5	.6	.7	.8	.9	1
1.1	.87	.87	.88	.89	.89	.90	.92	.93	.96	1.00	1.30
1.2	.90	.91	.92	.92	.93	.94	.96	.97	1.00	1.04	1.30
1.3	.93	.93	.94	.95	.96	.97	.98	1.00	1.03	1.07	1.30
1.4	.94	.95	.96	.97	.97	.99	1.00	1.02	1.04	1.08	1.30
1.5	.96	.96	.97	.98	.99	1.00	1.01	1.03	1.06	1.10	1.30
1.6	.97	.97	.98	.99	1.00	1.01	1.03	1.04	1.07	1.11	1.30
1.7	.98	.98	.99	1.00	1.01	1.02	1.03	1.05	1.08	1.11	1.30
1.8	.99	.99	1.00	1.01	1.02	1.03	1.04	1.06	1.08	1.12	1.30
1.9	.99	1.00	1.01	1.02	1.03	1.04	1.05	1.07	1.09	1.13	1.30
2.0	1.00	1.01	1.01	1.02	1.03	1.04	1.06	1.07	1.10	1.13	1.30
2.2	1.01	1.02	1.03	1.03	1.04	1.05	1.07	1.08	1.11	1.14	1.30
2.4	1.02	1.03	1.03	1.04	1.05	1.06	1.08	1.09	1.11	1.15	1.30
2.6	1.03	1.04	1.04	1.05	1.06	1.07	1.08	1.10	1.12	1.16	1.30
2.8	1.04	1.04	1.05	1.06	1.07	1.08	1.09	1.11	1.13	1.16	1.30
3.0	1.04	1.05	1.06	1.06	1.07	1.08	1.10	1.11	1.13	1.17	1.30

Profit / Cost per Unit

R1 \ R2	.0	.1	.2	.3	.4	.5	.6	.7	.8	.9	1
1.1	.09	.09	.09	.09	.09	.09	.09	.09	.09	.09	.08
1.2	.19	.19	.19	.19	.19	.19	.19	.19	.18	.18	.15
1.3	.28	.28	.28	.28	.28	.28	.28	.28	.27	.27	.23
1.4	.37	.37	.37	.37	.37	.37	.37	.37	.36	.36	.31
1.5	.46	.47	.46	.46	.46	.46	.46	.46	.45	.44	.38
1.6	.56	.56	.56	.55	.55	.55	.54	.55	.54	.53	.46
1.7	.65	.65	.65	.64	.64	.64	.64	.63	.62	.62	.54
1.8	.74	.74	.74	.73	.73	.73	.73	.72	.71	.70	.62
1.9	.83	.83	.82	.82	.82	.82	.81	.81	.80	.78	.69
2.0	.92	.92	.92	.92	.91	.91	.90	.90	.88	.87	.77
2.2	1.10	1.10	1.09	1.10	1.09	1.09	1.07	1.07	1.05	1.04	.92
2.4	1.28	1.27	1.28	1.27	1.27	1.26	1.25	1.24	1.23	1.20	1.08
2.6	1.46	1.45	1.45	1.45	1.44	1.43	1.43	1.41	1.40	1.36	1.23
2.8	1.63	1.64	1.63	1.62	1.61	1.60	1.60	1.58	1.56	1.53	1.38
3.0	1.82	1.81	1.80	1.80	1.80	1.79	1.76	1.76	1.74	1.69	1.54

Table 20.2 Optimal Order Quantity and Profit Ratio for Dated Items

```
cov    = .10   (coefficient of variation of demand)
R1     = selling price / cost per unit
R2     = return price / cost per unit
R3     = .25   (goodwill loss / cost per unit)
```

Optimal Order Quantity / Average Demand

R2\R1	.0	.1	.2	.3	.4	.5	.6	.7	.8	.9	1
1.1	.94	.94	.95	.96	.97	.98	.99	1.01	1.03	1.08	1.30
1.2	.95	.96	.96	.97	.98	.99	1.01	1.03	1.05	1.09	1.30
1.3	.96	.97	.98	.98	.99	1.01	1.02	1.04	1.06	1.10	1.30
1.4	.97	.98	.99	1.00	1.01	1.02	1.03	1.05	1.07	1.11	1.30
1.5	.98	.99	1.00	1.00	1.01	1.03	1.04	1.06	1.08	1.12	1.30
1.6	.99	1.00	1.00	1.01	1.02	1.03	1.05	1.06	1.09	1.12	1.30
1.7	1.00	1.00	1.01	1.02	1.03	1.04	1.05	1.07	1.09	1.13	1.30
1.8	1.00	1.01	1.02	1.03	1.03	1.05	1.06	1.08	1.10	1.14	1.30
1.9	1.01	1.02	1.02	1.03	1.04	1.05	1.07	1.08	1.10	1.14	1.30
2.0	1.01	1.02	1.03	1.04	1.05	1.06	1.07	1.09	1.11	1.14	1.30
2.2	1.02	1.03	1.04	1.05	1.05	1.07	1.08	1.10	1.12	1.15	1.30
2.4	1.03	1.04	1.04	1.05	1.06	1.07	1.09	1.10	1.12	1.16	1.30
2.6	1.04	1.04	1.05	1.06	1.07	1.08	1.09	1.11	1.13	1.16	1.30
2.8	1.04	1.05	1.06	1.07	1.08	1.09	1.10	1.11	1.13	1.17	1.30
3.0	1.05	1.06	1.06	1.07	1.08	1.09	1.10	1.12	1.14	1.17	1.30

Profit / Cost per Unit

R2\R1	.0	.1	.2	.3	.4	.5	.6	.7	.8	.9	1
1.1	.08	.08	.08	.08	.08	.08	.08	.08	.08	.08	.08
1.2	.18	.17	.18	.18	.17	.18	.17	.17	.17	.17	.15
1.3	.27	.27	.27	.27	.27	.26	.27	.26	.26	.26	.23
1.4	.36	.36	.36	.36	.36	.36	.36	.35	.35	.35	.31
1.5	.45	.45	.45	.45	.45	.44	.45	.44	.44	.43	.38
1.6	.54	.54	.54	.54	.54	.54	.53	.53	.53	.52	.46
1.7	.63	.64	.63	.63	.63	.63	.63	.62	.62	.60	.54
1.8	.73	.72	.72	.72	.72	.71	.71	.71	.70	.69	.62
1.9	.82	.81	.82	.81	.81	.81	.80	.80	.79	.77	.69
2.0	.91	.91	.90	.90	.89	.89	.89	.88	.87	.86	.77
2.2	1.09	1.08	1.08	1.07	1.08	1.07	1.06	1.05	1.04	1.03	.92
2.4	1.27	1.26	1.27	1.26	1.25	1.25	1.23	1.23	1.22	1.19	1.08
2.6	1.44	1.45	1.44	1.43	1.43	1.42	1.42	1.40	1.39	1.36	1.23
2.8	1.63	1.62	1.61	1.60	1.60	1.59	1.58	1.58	1.56	1.52	1.38
3.0	1.80	1.79	1.80	1.79	1.78	1.77	1.76	1.74	1.72	1.69	1.54

Table 20.3   Optimal Order Quantity and Profit Ratio for Dated Items

```
cov  = .10  (coefficient of variation of demand)
R1   =  selling price / cost per unit
R2   =  return price / cost per unit
R3   = .50  (goodwill loss / cost per unit)
```

Optimal Order Quantity / Average Demand

R2 / R1	.0	.1	.2	.3	.4	.5	.6	.7	.8	.9	1
1.1	.97	.97	.98	.99	1.00	1.01	1.03	1.04	1.07	1.11	1.30
1.2	.98	.98	.99	1.00	1.01	1.02	1.03	1.05	1.08	1.11	1.30
1.3	.99	.99	1.00	1.01	1.02	1.03	1.04	1.06	1.08	1.12	1.30
1.4	.99	1.00	1.01	1.02	1.03	1.04	1.05	1.07	1.09	1.13	1.30
1.5	1.00	1.01	1.01	1.02	1.03	1.04	1.06	1.07	1.10	1.13	1.30
1.6	1.01	1.01	1.02	1.03	1.04	1.05	1.06	1.08	1.10	1.14	1.30
1.7	1.01	1.02	1.03	1.03	1.04	1.05	1.07	1.08	1.11	1.14	1.30
1.8	1.02	1.02	1.03	1.04	1.05	1.06	1.07	1.09	1.11	1.15	1.30
1.9	1.02	1.03	1.03	1.04	1.05	1.06	1.08	1.09	1.11	1.15	1.30
2.0	1.03	1.03	1.04	1.05	1.06	1.07	1.08	1.10	1.12	1.15	1.30
2.2	1.03	1.04	1.05	1.05	1.06	1.08	1.09	1.10	1.12	1.16	1.30
2.4	1.04	1.05	1.05	1.06	1.07	1.08	1.09	1.11	1.13	1.16	1.30
2.6	1.05	1.05	1.06	1.07	1.08	1.09	1.10	1.11	1.14	1.17	1.30
2.8	1.05	1.06	1.07	1.07	1.08	1.09	1.10	1.12	1.14	1.17	1.30
3.0	1.06	1.06	1.07	1.08	1.09	1.10	1.11	1.12	1.14	1.18	1.30

Profit / Cost per Unit

R2 / R1	.0	.1	.2	.3	.4	.5	.6	.7	.8	.9	1
1.1	.07	.07	.07	.07	.07	.07	.07	.08	.08	.08	.08
1.2	.16	.17	.16	.16	.16	.17	.17	.17	.17	.17	.15
1.3	.25	.26	.26	.26	.26	.26	.26	.26	.26	.26	.23
1.4	.35	.35	.35	.35	.34	.35	.35	.34	.34	.34	.31
1.5	.44	.44	.44	.44	.44	.44	.43	.44	.43	.43	.38
1.6	.53	.53	.53	.53	.53	.53	.53	.52	.52	.51	.46
1.7	.62	.62	.62	.62	.62	.62	.61	.61	.61	.60	.54
1.8	.71	.72	.71	.71	.71	.71	.71	.70	.69	.68	.62
1.9	.81	.80	.81	.80	.80	.80	.79	.79	.78	.77	.69
2.0	.89	.90	.89	.89	.88	.88	.88	.87	.87	.85	.77
2.2	1.08	1.07	1.07	1.07	1.07	1.06	1.05	1.05	1.04	1.02	.92
2.4	1.25	1.25	1.25	1.25	1.24	1.24	1.23	1.22	1.21	1.19	1.08
2.6	1.43	1.43	1.43	1.42	1.41	1.41	1.40	1.40	1.37	1.35	1.23
2.8	1.61	1.60	1.60	1.60	1.60	1.59	1.58	1.56	1.55	1.52	1.38
3.0	1.78	1.79	1.78	1.77	1.76	1.75	1.75	1.74	1.72	1.68	1.54

Table 20.4   Optimal Order Quantity and Profit Ratio for Dated Items

cov = .10 (coefficient of variation of demand)
R1 = selling price / cost per unit
R2 = return price / cost per unit
R3 =1.00 (goodwill loss / cost per unit)

Optimal Order Quantity / Average Demand

R2 R1	.0	.1	.2	.3	.4	.5	.6	.7	.8	.9	1
1.1	1.01	1.01	1.02	1.03	1.04	1.05	1.06	1.08	1.10	1.14	1.30
1.2	1.01	1.02	1.03	1.03	1.04	1.05	1.07	1.08	1.11	1.14	1.30
1.3	1.02	1.02	1.03	1.04	1.05	1.06	1.07	1.09	1.11	1.15	1.30
1.4	1.02	1.03	1.03	1.04	1.05	1.06	1.08	1.09	1.11	1.15	1.30
1.5	1.03	1.03	1.04	1.05	1.06	1.07	1.08	1.10	1.12	1.15	1.30
1.6	1.03	1.04	1.04	1.05	1.06	1.07	1.08	1.10	1.12	1.16	1.30
1.7	1.03	1.04	1.05	1.05	1.06	1.08	1.09	1.10	1.12	1.16	1.30
1.8	1.04	1.04	1.05	1.06	1.07	1.08	1.09	1.11	1.13	1.16	1.30
1.9	1.04	1.05	1.05	1.06	1.07	1.08	1.09	1.11	1.13	1.16	1.30
2.0	1.04	1.05	1.06	1.06	1.07	1.08	1.10	1.11	1.13	1.17	1.30
2.2	1.05	1.06	1.06	1.07	1.08	1.09	1.10	1.12	1.14	1.17	1.30
2.4	1.05	1.06	1.07	1.08	1.08	1.09	1.11	1.12	1.14	1.17	1.30
2.6	1.06	1.07	1.07	1.08	1.09	1.10	1.11	1.13	1.15	1.18	1.30
2.8	1.06	1.07	1.08	1.08	1.09	1.10	1.11	1.13	1.15	1.18	1.30
3.0	1.07	1.07	1.08	1.09	1.10	1.11	1.12	1.13	1.15	1.18	1.30

Profit / Cost per Unit

R2 R1	.0	.1	.2	.3	.4	.5	.6	.7	.8	.9	1
1.1	.05	.06	.06	.06	.06	.06	.06	.07	.07	.07	.08
1.2	.15	.15	.14	.15	.15	.15	.15	.16	.16	.16	.15
1.3	.24	.24	.24	.24	.24	.24	.24	.24	.25	.25	.23
1.4	.33	.33	.33	.33	.33	.33	.33	.34	.34	.33	.31
1.5	.42	.42	.42	.42	.42	.42	.42	.42	.42	.42	.38
1.6	.51	.51	.52	.51	.51	.51	.51	.51	.51	.50	.46
1.7	.61	.60	.60	.61	.61	.60	.60	.60	.60	.59	.54
1.8	.69	.70	.69	.69	.69	.69	.69	.68	.68	.67	.62
1.9	.78	.78	.79	.78	.78	.78	.78	.77	.77	.76	.69
2.0	.88	.87	.87	.88	.87	.87	.86	.86	.86	.84	.77
2.2	1.05	1.05	1.05	1.05	1.05	1.04	1.04	1.03	1.02	1.01	.92
2.4	1.24	1.23	1.23	1.22	1.23	1.23	1.21	1.21	1.20	1.18	1.08
2.6	1.41	1.40	1.41	1.40	1.40	1.39	1.39	1.37	1.36	1.34	1.23
2.8	1.60	1.59	1.58	1.59	1.58	1.57	1.57	1.55	1.53	1.51	1.38
3.0	1.76	1.77	1.76	1.75	1.74	1.74	1.73	1.73	1.71	1.68	1.54

Table 20.5 Optimal Order Quantity and Profit Ratio for Dated Items

```
cov  = .20  (coefficient of variation of demand)
R1   = selling price / cost per unit
R2   = return price / cost per unit
R3   = .00  (goodwill loss / cost per unit)
```

Optimal Order Quantity / Average Demand

R1＼R2	.0	.1	.2	.3	.4	.5	.6	.7	.8	.9	1
1.1	.74	.74	.76	.78	.78	.80	.84	.86	.92	1.00	1.60
1.2	.80	.82	.84	.84	.86	.88	.92	.94	1.00	1.08	1.60
1.3	.86	.86	.88	.90	.92	.94	.96	1.00	1.06	1.14	1.60
1.4	.88	.90	.92	.94	.94	.98	1.00	1.04	1.08	1.16	1.60
1.5	.92	.92	.94	.96	.98	1.00	1.02	1.06	1.12	1.20	1.60
1.6	.94	.94	.96	.98	1.00	1.02	1.06	1.08	1.14	1.22	1.60
1.7	.96	.96	.98	1.00	1.02	1.04	1.06	1.10	1.16	1.22	1.60
1.8	.98	.98	1.00	1.02	1.04	1.06	1.08	1.12	1.16	1.24	1.60
1.9	.98	1.00	1.02	1.04	1.06	1.08	1.10	1.14	1.18	1.26	1.60
2.0	1.00	1.02	1.02	1.04	1.06	1.08	1.12	1.14	1.20	1.26	1.60
2.2	1.02	1.04	1.06	1.06	1.08	1.10	1.14	1.16	1.22	1.28	1.60
2.4	1.04	1.06	1.06	1.08	1.10	1.12	1.16	1.18	1.22	1.30	1.60
2.6	1.06	1.08	1.08	1.10	1.12	1.14	1.16	1.20	1.24	1.32	1.60
2.8	1.08	1.08	1.10	1.12	1.14	1.16	1.18	1.22	1.26	1.32	1.60
3.0	1.08	1.10	1.12	1.12	1.14	1.16	1.20	1.22	1.26	1.34	1.60

Profit / Cost per Unit

R1＼R2	.0	.1	.2	.3	.4	.5	.6	.7	.8	.9	1
1.1	.09	.09	.09	.09	.09	.09	.09	.09	.08	.08	.06
1.2	.18	.17	.17	.17	.17	.17	.17	.17	.17	.16	.13
1.3	.26	.26	.26	.26	.25	.25	.26	.25	.25	.24	.19
1.4	.35	.34	.34	.34	.34	.34	.34	.33	.33	.32	.25
1.5	.42	.43	.43	.42	.42	.42	.42	.41	.40	.39	.31
1.6	.51	.51	.51	.51	.50	.50	.49	.49	.48	.47	.38
1.7	.59	.60	.59	.59	.59	.58	.58	.57	.56	.55	.44
1.8	.67	.68	.67	.67	.66	.66	.66	.65	.64	.62	.50
1.9	.76	.76	.75	.74	.74	.74	.74	.72	.71	.69	.56
2.0	.84	.83	.84	.83	.83	.82	.81	.81	.78	.77	.63
2.2	1.01	1.00	.99	1.00	.99	.98	.96	.96	.93	.91	.75
2.4	1.17	1.15	1.16	1.15	1.15	1.14	1.11	1.11	1.09	1.05	.88
2.6	1.32	1.31	1.32	1.31	1.30	1.29	1.28	1.26	1.24	1.18	1.00
2.8	1.47	1.48	1.47	1.46	1.45	1.44	1.43	1.40	1.37	1.33	1.13
3.0	1.65	1.63	1.62	1.63	1.62	1.60	1.57	1.56	1.53	1.46	1.25

Table 20.6   Optimal Order Quantity and Profit Ratio for Dated Items

```
cov   = .20  (coefficient of variation of demand)
R1    = selling price / cost per unit
R2    = return price / cost per unit
R3    = .25  (goodwill loss / cost per unit)
```

Optimal Order Quantity / Average Demand

R2 \ R1	.0	.1	.2	.3	.4	.5	.6	.7	.8	.9	1
1.1	.88	.88	.90	.92	.94	.96	.98	1.02	1.06	1.16	1.60
1.2	.90	.92	.92	.94	.96	.98	1.02	1.06	1.10	1.18	1.60
1.3	.92	.94	.96	.96	.98	1.02	1.04	1.08	1.12	1.20	1.60
1.4	.94	.96	.98	1.00	1.02	1.04	1.06	1.10	1.14	1.22	1.60
1.5	.96	.98	1.00	1.00	1.02	1.06	1.08	1.12	1.16	1.24	1.60
1.6	.98	1.00	1.00	1.02	1.04	1.06	1.10	1.12	1.18	1.24	1.60
1.7	1.00	1.00	1.02	1.04	1.06	1.08	1.10	1.14	1.18	1.26	1.60
1.8	1.00	1.02	1.04	1.06	1.06	1.10	1.12	1.16	1.20	1.28	1.60
1.9	1.02	1.04	1.04	1.06	1.08	1.10	1.14	1.16	1.20	1.28	1.60
2.0	1.02	1.04	1.06	1.08	1.10	1.12	1.14	1.18	1.22	1.28	1.60
2.2	1.04	1.06	1.08	1.10	1.10	1.14	1.16	1.20	1.24	1.30	1.60
2.4	1.06	1.08	1.08	1.10	1.12	1.14	1.18	1.20	1.24	1.32	1.60
2.6	1.08	1.08	1.10	1.12	1.14	1.16	1.18	1.22	1.26	1.32	1.60
2.8	1.08	1.10	1.12	1.14	1.16	1.18	1.20	1.22	1.26	1.34	1.60
3.0	1.10	1.12	1.12	1.14	1.16	1.18	1.20	1.24	1.28	1.34	1.60

Profit / Cost per Unit

R2 \ R1	.0	.1	.2	.3	.4	.5	.6	.7	.8	.9	1
1.1	.06	.06	.06	.06	.06	.06	.06	.06	.07	.07	.06
1.2	.15	.14	.15	.15	.15	.15	.15	.15	.15	.15	.13
1.3	.23	.23	.23	.24	.24	.23	.23	.23	.23	.23	.19
1.4	.32	.32	.31	.31	.31	.31	.31	.31	.31	.30	.25
1.5	.40	.40	.40	.40	.40	.39	.39	.39	.39	.38	.31
1.6	.49	.48	.49	.49	.48	.48	.47	.48	.46	.46	.38
1.7	.56	.57	.57	.56	.56	.56	.56	.55	.55	.53	.44
1.8	.66	.65	.64	.64	.65	.64	.64	.63	.62	.60	.50
1.9	.73	.72	.73	.73	.72	.72	.71	.71	.70	.68	.56
2.0	.82	.81	.81	.80	.80	.79	.79	.78	.77	.75	.63
2.2	.99	.98	.97	.96	.97	.95	.95	.93	.92	.89	.75
2.4	1.14	1.13	1.14	1.13	1.13	1.12	1.09	1.09	1.08	1.03	.88
2.6	1.30	1.31	1.30	1.28	1.27	1.27	1.26	1.24	1.22	1.18	1.00
2.8	1.47	1.46	1.44	1.43	1.42	1.41	1.40	1.40	1.37	1.31	1.13
3.0	1.62	1.60	1.62	1.60	1.59	1.58	1.57	1.53	1.51	1.46	1.25

Table 20.7 Optimal Order Quantity and Profit Ratio for Dated Items

```
cov   = .20  (coefficient of variation of demand)
R1    =  selling price / cost per unit
R2    =  return price / cost per unit
R3    = .50  (goodwill loss / cost per unit)
```

Optimal Order Quantity / Average Demand

R1 \ R2	.0	.1	.2	.3	.4	.5	.6	.7	.8	.9	1
1.1	.94	.94	.96	.98	1.00	1.02	1.06	1.08	1.14	1.22	1.60
1.2	.96	.96	.98	1.00	1.02	1.04	1.06	1.10	1.16	1.22	1.60
1.3	.98	.98	1.00	1.02	1.04	1.06	1.08	1.12	1.16	1.24	1.60
1.4	.98	1.00	1.02	1.04	1.06	1.08	1.10	1.14	1.18	1.26	1.60
1.5	1.00	1.02	1.02	1.04	1.06	1.08	1.12	1.14	1.20	1.26	1.60
1.6	1.02	1.02	1.04	1.06	1.08	1.10	1.12	1.16	1.20	1.28	1.60
1.7	1.02	1.04	1.06	1.06	1.08	1.10	1.14	1.16	1.22	1.28	1.60
1.8	1.04	1.04	1.06	1.08	1.10	1.12	1.14	1.18	1.22	1.30	1.60
1.9	1.04	1.06	1.06	1.08	1.10	1.12	1.16	1.18	1.22	1.30	1.60
2.0	1.06	1.06	1.08	1.10	1.12	1.14	1.16	1.20	1.24	1.30	1.60
2.2	1.06	1.08	1.10	1.10	1.12	1.16	1.18	1.20	1.24	1.32	1.60
2.4	1.08	1.10	1.10	1.12	1.14	1.16	1.18	1.22	1.26	1.32	1.60
2.6	1.10	1.10	1.12	1.14	1.16	1.18	1.20	1.22	1.28	1.34	1.60
2.8	1.10	1.12	1.14	1.14	1.16	1.18	1.20	1.24	1.28	1.34	1.60
3.0	1.12	1.12	1.14	1.16	1.18	1.20	1.22	1.24	1.28	1.36	1.60

Profit / Cost per Unit

R1 \ R2	.0	.1	.2	.3	.4	.5	.6	.7	.8	.9	1
1.1	.04	.04	.04	.04	.04	.05	.05	.05	.06	.06	.06
1.2	.12	.13	.13	.13	.13	.13	.14	.14	.14	.14	.13
1.3	.21	.21	.21	.21	.21	.21	.22	.22	.22	.22	.19
1.4	.30	.30	.29	.29	.29	.29	.30	.30	.30	.29	.25
1.5	.38	.38	.39	.38	.38	.38	.38	.38	.37	.37	.31
1.6	.46	.47	.46	.46	.46	.46	.46	.46	.46	.44	.38
1.7	.55	.54	.54	.55	.55	.55	.54	.54	.53	.52	.44
1.8	.62	.63	.63	.62	.62	.62	.62	.61	.61	.59	.50
1.9	.71	.71	.72	.71	.71	.71	.69	.70	.69	.66	.56
2.0	.79	.80	.79	.78	.78	.78	.78	.77	.76	.74	.63
2.2	.96	.95	.95	.96	.95	.93	.93	.93	.92	.88	.75
2.4	1.12	1.11	1.12	1.11	1.10	1.10	1.09	1.07	1.06	1.03	.88
2.6	1.27	1.28	1.27	1.26	1.25	1.24	1.24	1.24	1.20	1.16	1.00
2.8	1.44	1.43	1.42	1.43	1.42	1.41	1.40	1.37	1.35	1.31	1.13
3.0	1.59	1.60	1.59	1.57	1.56	1.55	1.54	1.53	1.51	1.44	1.25

Table 20.8 Optimal Order Quantity and Profit Ratio for Dated Items

```
cov    = .20  (coefficient of variation of demand)
R1     =  selling price / cost per unit
R2     =  return price / cost per unit
R3     =1.00  (goodwill loss / cost per unit)
```

Optimal Order Quantity / Average Demand

R1＼R2	.0	.1	.2	.3	.4	.5	.6	.7	.8	.9	1
1.1	1.02	1.02	1.04	1.06	1.08	1.10	1.12	1.16	1.20	1.28	1.60
1.2	1.02	1.04	1.06	1.06	1.08	1.10	1.14	1.16	1.22	1.28	1.60
1.3	1.04	1.04	1.06	1.08	1.10	1.12	1.14	1.18	1.22	1.30	1.60
1.4	1.04	1.06	1.06	1.08	1.10	1.12	1.16	1.18	1.22	1.30	1.60
1.5	1.06	1.06	1.08	1.10	1.12	1.14	1.16	1.20	1.24	1.30	1.60
1.6	1.06	1.08	1.08	1.10	1.12	1.14	1.16	1.20	1.24	1.32	1.60
1.7	1.06	1.08	1.10	1.10	1.12	1.16	1.18	1.20	1.24	1.32	1.60
1.8	1.08	1.08	1.10	1.12	1.14	1.16	1.18	1.22	1.26	1.32	1.60
1.9	1.08	1.10	1.10	1.12	1.14	1.16	1.18	1.22	1.26	1.32	1.60
2.0	1.08	1.10	1.12	1.12	1.14	1.16	1.20	1.22	1.26	1.34	1.60
2.2	1.10	1.12	1.12	1.14	1.16	1.18	1.20	1.24	1.28	1.34	1.60
2.4	1.10	1.12	1.14	1.16	1.16	1.18	1.22	1.24	1.28	1.34	1.60
2.6	1.12	1.14	1.14	1.16	1.18	1.20	1.22	1.26	1.30	1.36	1.60
2.8	1.12	1.14	1.16	1.16	1.18	1.20	1.22	1.26	1.30	1.36	1.60
3.0	1.14	1.14	1.16	1.18	1.20	1.22	1.24	1.26	1.30	1.36	1.60

Profit / Cost per Unit

R1＼R2	.0	.1	.2	.3	.4	.5	.6	.7	.8	.9	1
1.1	.00	.01	.01	.01	.02	.02	.03	.04	.05	.06	.06
1.2	.09	.09	.09	.10	.11	.11	.11	.12	.12	.13	.13
1.3	.17	.18	.18	.18	.19	.19	.20	.20	.20	.21	.19
1.4	.26	.26	.27	.27	.27	.28	.27	.28	.29	.28	.25
1.5	.34	.35	.35	.35	.35	.35	.36	.36	.36	.36	.31
1.6	.43	.42	.44	.44	.44	.44	.44	.44	.44	.43	.38
1.7	.52	.51	.51	.52	.52	.51	.51	.52	.52	.50	.44
1.8	.59	.60	.60	.59	.59	.59	.60	.59	.59	.58	.50
1.9	.68	.67	.68	.68	.68	.68	.68	.67	.67	.65	.56
2.0	.77	.76	.75	.77	.76	.76	.75	.75	.74	.72	.63
2.2	.92	.91	.93	.92	.91	.91	.91	.90	.89	.87	.75
2.4	1.10	1.08	1.07	1.07	1.08	1.08	1.06	1.06	1.04	1.02	.88
2.6	1.24	1.23	1.25	1.24	1.23	1.22	1.22	1.19	1.18	1.15	1.00
2.8	1.42	1.40	1.39	1.40	1.39	1.38	1.38	1.35	1.33	1.29	1.13
3.0	1.56	1.57	1.56	1.54	1.53	1.52	1.51	1.51	1.48	1.44	1.25

CHAPTER 21

Learning Curves

When an operator begins a new task of some type, the first unit worked on takes longer than the second unit, the second unit takes longer than the third and so forth. In general, the amount of time required to complete a given task will be less with each repetition of the task. This reduction in time follows a pattern that is called a learning curve. One of the most widely accepted formulations of learning curves is based upon the power function where the task time per unit decreases with additional repetitions by a constant percentage every time the number of units is doubled. This theory is used in a wide variety of applications where work tasks are repeated such as in order picking, assembly and manufacturing.

Data

In order to apply the model, the following input data are used:

$$a \;=\; \text{time to complete the first task unit}$$
$$R \;=\; \text{the learning rate } (.5 < R < 1)$$

If **r** represents the number of repetitions of a task and **t(r)** is the time to complete the *rth* unit, then **t(2r)** is the time needed to complete the task when **r** is doubled. The relation between **t(r)** and **t(2r)** is:

$$R = \frac{t(2r)}{t(r)}$$

and so **R** represents the rate by which the task length varies each time the number of repetitions is doubled. In the model of this chapter, the only valid values of **R** are when $.5 < R < 1.0$.

Because the time to complete the first task is $t(1) = a$, the time for the second task is $t(2) = R\,t(1)$. For the fourth task, the time is $t(4) = R\,t(2)$. The general relationship is the following:

$$t(1) = a$$
$$t(2) = R\,t(1) = Ra$$
$$t(4) = R\,t(2) = R^2 a$$
$$t(8) = R\,t(4) = R^3 a$$
$$t(16) = R\,t(8) = R^4 a$$

and so forth. Because **R** is smaller than one, the improvement of task times are dropping in a consistent pattern. This concept was first described by T.P. Wright in 1936, where he notes that the manufacturing costs per unit of aircraft decreases with additional production by a constant percentage every time the number of units is doubed. This relationship has been upheld through the years with a great variety of applications and reports in the literature (references 1, 2 and 3).

Model

The time to complete the rth unit is represented by the relation:

$$t(r) = a\ r^b$$

where $r = 1,2,3,\ \ldots$ Since 100R represents the percentage change in **t(r)** every time **r** is doubled, then:

$$\frac{t(2r)}{t(r)} = R = 2^b$$

For a particular value of **R**, the coefficient **b** is determined by:

$$b = \frac{\log R}{\log 2}$$

where **b** is a negative constant. Note the values of **b** below for selected values of **R**:

R	b
.975	−.037
.95	−.074
.925	−.112
.90	−.152
.85	−.234
.80	−.322
.75	−.415
.70	−.515
.65	−.621
.60	−.737
.55	−.862

The total time **T(r)** to complete the first **r** tasks is approximated by:

$$T(r) = \sum_{x=1}^{r} t(x) \approx \int_{0}^{r} a\ x^b\ dx = a\ r^{b+1} / (b + 1)$$

This approximation is weakest at the smaller values of **r**, but improves as **r** increases and is valid only for $b > -1$ or $.5 < R < 1.0$.

The average time **a(r)** to complete a unit from the first **r** units is determined by:

$$a(r) = T(r) / r = a\ r^b / (b + 1)$$

Again, the above average time becomes smaller as **r** increases.

The parameter **a** is generally some multiple of the work content time of the unit. That is, suppose **t** represents the true standard time required to complete one unit and is based on standard measured time. The time to process the first unit is then larger than **t** by a multiple **k**, whereby:

$$a = k\ t$$

and $k > 1$ is a constant. For example, if (typically) the first unit worked on takes twice as long as the standard time, then $k = 2$.

Tables

The tables of this chapter gives results on **t(r)**, **T(r)** and **a(r)** for selected values of the learning rate **R** ranging from .60 to .975. The number of repetitions listed are chosen to range from 1 to 100,000. In order to give standardized results, the value of the first unit is set at a = 1. In this way, the table entries may be multiplied by the true values of **a** (the time to complete the first unit) to yield results for particular applications.

Example 21.1

Suppose the assembly time for the first unit of a new product requires 100 minutes and the learning rate is estimated as R = 90 percent. Find the assembly time for units 2, 4 and 8. Also find the corresponding total times and the average times per unit.

Table 21.1, used because R = .90, yields the following results when a = 100:

r	t(r)	T(r)	a(r)
1	100	100	100
2	90	190	95
4	81	360	88.91
8	72.9	660	82.17

Note that t(2) = .9 t(1), t(4) = .9 t(2) and t(8) = .9 t(4).

Example 21.2

Suppose an order for 5,000 units arrives and the units are to be produced on a facility that experiences a learning rate of R = .95. If the labor cost of the first unit is $40, what is the estimated labor cost for the lot of 5,000 units?

Using Table 21.1 with R = .95 and r = 5,000, then T(5000) = 2875.0 is found. Since the labor cost for unit one is $40, the estimated labor cost for 5,000 units becomes:

$$40 \times 2875.0 = \$115,000.$$

Example 21.3

Assume an order for 10,000 units arrives at a facility with a learning rate of R = .90. Further suppose the facility is open on one shift of 40 hours a week and the first unit requires 20 minutes to complete. Estimate the number of weeks that will be required to complete the entire lot of 10,000 units.

Table 21.1 is used with R = .90 and r = 10,000 to give T(10,000) = 2908. Using a = 1/3 of an hour, the total hours estimated to complete the lot is:

$$1/3 \times 2908 = 969.33 \text{ hours.}$$

With a 40 hour week, the elapsed time to complete the task becomes:

$$969.33 / 40 = 24.2 \text{ weeks.}$$

Example 21.4

Suppose Example 21.3 again and assume the management considers the elapsed number of 24.2 weeks too long and wishes to investigate 2, 3 or 4 facilities that are run in parallel. With two facilities, each facility is charged with completing 5,000 units each, three facilities with 3,333 and four facilities with 2,500. Show the results obtained using the above four options.

Table 21.1 is used with R = .90. Because r = 3,333 and r = 2,500 are not listed, interpolation results are given below.

Facilities	1	2	3	4
Units	10,000	5,000	3,333	2,500
$T(r)$	2,908	1,615	1,144	894
$T(r)$ hours	969	538	381	298
$a(r)$ hours	.0969	.1076	.1143	.1192
Elapsed weeks	24.2	13.5	9.5	7.5
Total weeks	24.2	27.0	28.5	30.0

The above entry labeled total weeks gives the value of $T(r)$ in weeks (called elapsed weeks) multiplied by the number of facilities used. Even though increasing the number of facilities will shorten the elapsed time to complete the lot, the total work time increases due to a loss in learning time because the workload is spread among more than one facility.

Example 21.5

Consider a warehouse where a new order picker requires 10 minutes to pick his first order. Assume after the first 40 hours of picking orders that the picker has completed 600 orders. Estimate the learning rate for this picker.

As the first order requires 10 minutes, the number of 10 minute intervals in a 40 hour week is:

$$\frac{40\,(60)}{10} = 240$$

The adjoining tables of this chapter should be searched to seek a value of **R** where $T(600) = 240$, because the tables are developed using the parameter $a = 1$ and the completion of 600 units requires 240 ten minute intervals.

The results yield the following:

R	.95	.90	.85
$T(600)$	403.6	267.6	174.9

which indicate that the learning rate falls somewhere between R = .90 and .85. Using interpolation,

$$\frac{267.6 - 240}{267.6 - 174.9} = .30$$

shows that 240 is about 30 percent of this distance from $T(600)$ at R = .90 to $T(600)$ at R = .85. Thus the estimate of **R** becomes:

$$R = .90 - .30\,(.05) = .885$$

Table 21.1 Learning Curves

r	R ---------- 97.5 ---------- t(r)	T(r)	a(r)	---------- 95 ---------- t(r)	T(r)	a(r)
1	1.0000	1.0	1.0000	1.0000	1.0	1.0000
2	.9750	2.0	.9875	.9500	2.0	.9750
3	.9607	2.9	.9786	.9219	2.9	.9573
4	.9506	3.9	.9716	.9025	3.8	.9436
5	.9429	4.8	.9658	.8877	4.7	.9324
6	.9367	5.8	.9610	.8758	5.5	.9230
7	.9314	6.7	.9567	.8659	6.4	.9148
8	.9269	7.6	.9530	.8574	7.3	.9077
9	.9229	8.5	.9497	.8499	8.1	.9012
10	.9193	9.5	.9466	.8433	9.0	.8954
20	.8964	18.5	.9260	.8012	17.1	.8565
30	.8832	27.4	.9135	.7775	25.0	.8334
40	.8739	36.2	.9046	.7611	32.7	.8171
50	.8668	44.9	.8977	.7486	40.2	.8045
60	.8611	53.5	.8920	.7386	47.7	.7942
70	.8563	62.1	.8872	.7302	55.0	.7856
80	.8521	70.6	.8830	.7231	62.3	.7782
90	.8484	79.1	.8794	.7168	69.4	.7717
100	.8452	87.6	.8761	.7112	76.6	.7659
200	.8240	171.1	.8553	.6757	145.9	.7296
300	.8119	252.8	.8427	.6557	212.4	.7081
400	.8034	333.6	.8339	.6419	277.3	.6932
500	.7969	413.6	.8271	.6314	340.9	.6818
600	.7916	493.0	.8216	.6229	403.6	.6727
700	.7872	571.9	.8170	.6158	465.5	.6650
800	.7834	650.4	.8131	.6098	526.8	.6585
900	.7800	728.6	.8096	.6045	587.5	.6528
1,000	.7770	806.5	.8065	.5998	647.7	.6477
2,000	.7576	1,572.6	.7863	.5698	1,230.7	.6153
3,000	.7464	2,324.2	.7747	.5530	1,791.4	.5971
4,000	.7386	3,066.6	.7666	.5413	2,338.3	.5846
5,000	.7326	3,802.1	.7604	.5324	2,875.0	.5750
6,000	.7278	4,532.2	.7554	.5253	3,403.7	.5673
7,000	.7237	5,257.9	.7511	.5194	3,926.0	.5609
8,000	.7202	5,979.8	.7475	.5142	4,442.7	.5553
9,000	.7171	6,698.4	.7443	.5098	4,954.7	.5505
10,000	.7143	7,414.1	.7414	.5058	5,462.4	.5462
20,000	.6965	14,457.4	.7229	.4805	10,378.6	.5189
30,000	.6862	21,367.3	.7122	.4663	15,107.8	.5036
40,000	.6791	28,192.0	.7048	.4565	19,719.4	.4930
50,000	.6735	34,953.9	.6991	.4490	24,245.6	.4849
60,000	.6691	41,666.3	.6944	.4430	28,704.8	.4784
70,000	.6653	48,337.7	.6905	.4380	33,109.1	.4730
80,000	.6621	54,974.4	.6872	.4337	37,466.9	.4683
90,000	.6592	61,580.7	.6842	.4299	41,784.5	.4643
100,000	.6567	68,160.1	.6816	.4266	46,066.6	.4607

R   = learning rate (% of [process time for unit 2r / process time for unit r])

r   = repetition number

t(r) = unit process time for repetition r

T(r) = cumulative unit process time for first r repetitions

a(r) = average unit process time per unit from the first r repetitions

Table 21.1   Learning Curves (Continued)

r	R ———— 92.5 ———— t(r)	T(r)	a(r)	———— 90 ———— t(r)	T(r)	a(r)
1	1.0000	1.0	1.0000	1.0000	1.0	1.0000
2	.9250	1.9	.9625	.9000	1.9	.9500
3	.8838	2.8	.9363	.8462	2.7	.9154
4	.8556	3.7	.9161	.8100	3.6	.8891
5	.8344	4.5	.8998	.7830	4.3	.8678
6	.8175	5.3	.8860	.7616	5.1	.8501
7	.8034	6.1	.8742	.7439	5.8	.8350
8	.7915	6.9	.8639	.7290	6.6	.8217
9	.7810	7.7	.8547	.7161	7.3	.8100
10	.7718	8.5	.8464	.7047	8.0	.7994
20	.7139	15.8	.7914	.6342	14.6	.7304
30	.6821	22.8	.7593	.5963	20.7	.6909
40	.6604	29.5	.7369	.5708	26.5	.6636
50	.6440	36.0	.7197	.5518	32.1	.6428
60	.6310	42.4	.7059	.5367	37.6	.6262
70	.6201	48.6	.6943	.5243	42.9	.6124
80	.6109	54.8	.6844	.5137	48.1	.6007
90	.6028	60.8	.6757	.5046	53.1	.5904
100	.5957	66.8	.6680	.4966	58.1	.5814
200	.5511	124.2	.6209	.4469	105.4	.5270
300	.5265	178.0	.5932	.4202	148.7	.4955
400	.5097	229.7	.5743	.4022	189.7	.4743
500	.4971	280.0	.5601	.3888	229.3	.4585
600	.4870	329.2	.5487	.3782	267.6	.4460
700	.4786	377.5	.5393	.3694	305.0	.4357
800	.4715	425.0	.5312	.3620	341.5	.4269
900	.4653	471.8	.5243	.3556	377.4	.4193
1,000	.4598	518.1	.5181	.3499	412.7	.4127
2,000	.4253	958.4	.4792	.3149	742.8	.3714
3,000	.4064	1,373.6	.4579	.2961	1,047.6	.3492
4,000	.3934	1,773.1	.4433	.2834	1,337.0	.3343
5,000	.3837	2,161.5	.4323	.2740	1,615.6	.3231
6,000	.3759	2,541.1	.4235	.2665	1,885.7	.3143
7,000	.3694	2,913.7	.4162	.2603	2,149.0	.3070
8,000	.3639	3,280.3	.4100	.2551	2,406.7	.3008
9,000	.3591	3,641.7	.4046	.2506	2,659.4	.2955
10,000	.3549	3,998.7	.3999	.2466	2,908.0	.2908
20,000	.3283	7,397.6	.3699	.2219	5,234.4	.2617
30,000	.3136	10,601.7	.3534	.2087	7,382.3	.2461
40,000	.3037	13,685.6	.3421	.1997	9,421.9	.2355
50,000	.2961	16,683.0	.3337	.1931	11,384.6	.2277
60,000	.2901	19,613.2	.3269	.1878	13,288.1	.2215
70,000	.2851	22,488.8	.3213	.1835	15,143.7	.2163
80,000	.2809	25,318.4	.3165	.1798	16,959.4	.2120
90,000	.2772	28,108.3	.3123	.1766	18,740.8	.2082
100,000	.2739	30,863.5	.3086	.1738	20,492.3	.2049

R   = learning rate (% of [process time for unit 2r / process time for unit r])

r   = repetition number

t(r) = unit process time for repetition r

T(r) = cumulative unit process time for first r repetitions

a(r) = average unit process time per unit from the first r repetitions

Table 21.1 Learning Curves (Continued)

r	R ---------- 85 ---------- t(r)	T(r)	a(r)	---------- 80 ---------- t(r)	T(r)	a(r)
1	1.0000	1.0	1.0000	1.0000	1.0	1.0000
2	.8500	1.9	.9250	.8000	1.8	.9000
3	.7729	2.6	.8743	.7021	2.5	.8340
4	.7225	3.3	.8364	.6400	3.1	.7855
5	.6857	4.0	.8062	.5956	3.7	.7475
6	.6570	4.7	.7813	.5617	4.3	.7166
7	.6337	5.3	.7602	.5345	4.8	.6906
8	.6141	5.9	.7420	.5120	5.3	.6682
9	.5974	6.5	.7259	.4929	5.8	.6488
10	.5828	7.1	.7116	.4765	6.3	.6315
20	.4954	12.4	.6201	.3812	10.5	.5242
30	.4505	17.1	.5697	.3346	14.0	.4673
40	.4211	21.4	.5356	.3050	17.2	.4298
50	.3996	25.5	.5103	.2838	20.1	.4024
60	.3829	29.4	.4902	.2676	22.9	.3811
70	.3693	33.2	.4738	.2547	25.5	.3639
80	.3579	36.8	.4599	.2440	28.0	.3495
90	.3482	40.3	.4480	.2349	30.3	.3372
100	.3397	43.8	.4375	.2271	32.7	.3265
200	.2887	75.4	.3772	.1816	53.6	.2679
300	.2625	102.9	.3430	.1594	70.5	.2351
400	.2454	128.2	.3206	.1453	85.7	.2143
500	.2329	152.1	.3042	.1352	99.7	.1995
600	.2232	174.9	.2915	.1275	112.9	.1881
700	.2152	196.8	.2812	.1214	125.3	.1790
800	.2086	218.0	.2725	.1163	137.2	.1715
900	.2029	238.6	.2651	.1119	148.6	.1651
1,000	.1980	258.6	.2586	.1082	159.6	.1596
2,000	.1683	439.6	.2198	.0866	255.3	.1277
3,000	.1530	599.6	.1999	.0760	336.1	.1120
4,000	.1430	747.4	.1868	.0692	408.5	.1021
5,000	.1357	886.6	.1773	.0644	475.2	.0950
6,000	.1301	1,019.4	.1699	.0608	537.8	.0896
7,000	.1254	1,147.1	.1639	.0578	597.0	.0853
8,000	.1216	1,270.5	.1588	.0554	653.6	.0817
9,000	.1183	1,390.4	.1545	.0533	707.9	.0787
10,000	.1154	1,507.2	.1507	.0516	760.3	.0760
20,000	.0981	2,562.3	.1281	.0412	1,216.6	.0608
30,000	.0892	3,494.8	.1165	.0362	1,601.5	.0534
40,000	.0834	4,355.8	.1089	.0330	1,946.5	.0487
50,000	.0791	5,167.3	.1033	.0307	2,264.5	.0453
60,000	.0758	5,941.2	.0990	.0290	2,562.4	.0427
70,000	.0731	6,685.4	.0955	.0276	2,844.8	.0406
80,000	.0709	7,404.9	.0926	.0264	3,114.4	.0389
90,000	.0689	8,103.6	.0900	.0254	3,373.3	.0375
100,000	.0672	8,784.3	.0878	.0246	3,623.1	.0362

R = learning rate (% of [process time for unit 2r / process time for unit r])

r = repetition number

t(r) = unit process time for repetition r

T(r) = cumulative unit process time for first r repetitions

a(r) = average unit process time per unit from the first r repetitions

Table 21.1   Learning Curves   (Continued)

r	R ---------- 75 ---------- t(r)	T(r)	a(r)	---------- 70 ---------- t(r)	T(r)	a(r)
1	1.0000	1.0	1.0000	1.0000	1.0	1.0000
2	.7500	1.8	.8750	.7000	1.7	.8500
3	.6338	2.4	.7946	.5682	2.3	.7561
4	.5625	2.9	.7366	.4900	2.8	.6895
5	.5127	3.5	.6918	.4368	3.2	.6390
6	.4754	3.9	.6557	.3977	3.6	.5988
7	.4459	4.4	.6258	.3674	4.0	.5657
8	.4219	4.8	.6003	.3430	4.3	.5379
9	.4017	5.2	.5782	.3228	4.6	.5140
10	.3846	5.6	.5589	.3058	4.9	.4932
20	.2884	8.8	.4414	.2141	7.4	.3703
30	.2437	11.4	.3815	.1737	9.3	.3102
40	.2163	13.7	.3431	.1498	10.9	.2726
50	.1972	15.8	.3155	.1336	12.3	.2461
60	.1828	17.7	.2944	.1216	13.6	.2262
70	.1715	19.4	.2776	.1123	14.7	.2105
80	.1622	21.1	.2637	.1049	15.8	.1977
90	.1545	22.7	.2519	.0987	16.8	.1870
100	.1479	24.2	.2418	.0935	17.8	.1779
200	.1109	37.9	.1896	.0655	27.0	.1348
300	.0937	48.1	.1602	.0531	32.8	.1095
400	.0832	56.9	.1422	.0458	37.8	.0944
500	.0758	64.8	.1296	.0408	42.1	.0842
600	.0703	72.1	.1202	.0372	46.0	.0766
700	.0659	78.9	.1127	.0344	49.5	.0708
800	.0624	85.3	.1067	.0321	52.9	.0661
900	.0594	91.4	.1016	.0302	56.0	.0622
1,000	.0569	97.2	.0972	.0286	58.9	.0589
2,000	.0427	145.8	.0729	.0200	82.5	.0412
3,000	.0360	184.9	.0616	.0162	100.4	.0335
4,000	.0320	218.7	.0547	.0140	115.5	.0289
5,000	.0292	249.2	.0498	.0125	128.7	.0257
6,000	.0270	277.3	.0462	.0114	140.6	.0234
7,000	.0254	303.5	.0434	.0105	151.5	.0216
8,000	.0240	328.1	.0410	.0098	161.6	.0202
9,000	.0228	351.5	.0391	.0092	171.1	.0190
10,000	.0219	373.9	.0374	.0087	180.1	.0180
20,000	.0164	560.8	.0280	.0061	252.2	.0126
30,000	.0139	710.9	.0237	.0050	307.0	.0102
40,000	.0123	841.2	.0210	.0043	353.1	.0088
50,000	.0112	958.5	.0192	.0038	393.4	.0079
60,000	.0104	1,066.4	.0178	.0035	429.9	.0072
70,000	.0098	1,167.0	.0167	.0032	463.3	.0066
80,000	.0092	1,261.8	.0158	.0030	494.3	.0062
90,000	.0088	1,351.8	.0150	.0028	523.4	.0058
100,000	.0084	1,437.8	.0144	.0027	550.8	.0055

R   = learning rate (% of [process time for unit 2r / process time for unit r])

r   = repetition number

t(r) = unit process time for repetition r

T(r) = cumulative unit process time for first r repetitions

a(r) = average unit process time per unit from the first r repetitions

Table 21.1   Learning Curves   (Continued)

r	R ---------- 65 ---------- t(r)	T(r)	a(r)	---------- 60 ---------- t(r)	T(r)	a(r)
1	1.0000	1.0	1.0000	1.0000	1.0	1.0000
2	.6500	1.6	.8250	.6000	1.6	.8000
3	.5052	2.2	.7184	.4450	2.0	.6817
4	.4225	2.6	.6444	.3600	2.4	.6013
5	.3678	2.9	.5891	.3054	2.7	.5421
6	.3284	3.3	.5456	.2670	3.0	.4962
7	.2984	3.6	.5103	.2383	3.2	.4594
8	.2746	3.8	.4809	.2160	3.4	.4290
9	.2552	4.1	.4558	.1980	3.6	.4033
10	.2391	4.3	.4341	.1832	3.8	.3813
20	.1554	6.2	.3097	.1099	5.2	.2585
30	.1208	7.5	.2513	.0815	6.1	.2032
40	.1010	8.6	.2158	.0660	6.8	.1705
50	.0879	9.6	.1913	.0560	7.4	.1484
60	.0785	10.4	.1732	.0489	7.9	.1324
70	.0713	11.1	.1591	.0437	8.4	.1200
80	.0657	11.8	.1477	.0396	8.8	.1102
90	.0610	12.4	.1383	.0363	9.2	.1021
100	.0572	13.0	.1303	.0336	9.5	.0954
200	.0371	19.6	.0981	.0201	15.3	.0766
300	.0289	22.9	.0763	.0149	17.0	.0568
400	.0241	25.5	.0638	.0121	18.4	.0460
500	.0210	27.8	.0555	.0103	19.5	.0390
600	.0188	29.7	.0496	.0090	20.5	.0341
700	.0171	31.5	.0451	.0080	21.3	.0304
800	.0157	33.2	.0415	.0073	22.1	.0276
900	.0146	34.7	.0385	.0067	22.8	.0253
1,000	.0137	36.1	.0361	.0062	23.4	.0234
2,000	.0089	46.9	.0235	.0037	28.1	.0140
3,000	.0069	54.7	.0182	.0027	31.2	.0104
4,000	.0058	61.0	.0153	.0022	33.7	.0084
5,000	.0050	66.4	.0133	.0019	35.7	.0071
6,000	.0045	71.1	.0119	.0016	37.5	.0062
7,000	.0041	75.4	.0108	.0015	39.0	.0056
8,000	.0038	79.3	.0099	.0013	40.4	.0051
9,000	.0035	82.9	.0092	.0012	41.7	.0046
10,000	.0033	86.3	.0086	.0011	42.9	.0043
20,000	.0021	112.2	.0056	.0007	51.4	.0026
30,000	.0017	130.8	.0044	.0005	57.2	.0019
40,000	.0014	145.8	.0036	.0004	61.7	.0015
50,000	.0012	158.7	.0032	.0003	65.5	.0013
60,000	.0011	170.0	.0028	.0003	68.7	.0011
70,000	.0010	180.2	.0026	.0003	71.5	.0010
80,000	.0009	189.6	.0024	.0002	74.1	.0009
90,000	.0008	198.2	.0022	.0002	76.4	.0008
100,000	.0008	206.3	.0021	.0002	78.6	.0008

R   = learning rate (% of [process time for unit 2r / process time for unit r])

r   = repetition number

t(r) = unit process time for repetition r

T(r) = cumulative unit process time for first r repetitions

a(r) = average unit process time per unit from the first r repetitions

CHAPTER 22

Calendar Days

The Gregorian calendar is satisfactory for most everyday purposes but may be awkward to use in various inventory and production applications, since the number of days are not the same for all months and the number of days are different between non-leap and leap years. In addition, holidays may occur at irregular dates across the year. Because of the above difficulties, a number of specially designed scheduling procedures have been devised with planned shutdown days, to meet individual company purposes. The goal of this chapter is merely to list the cumulative number of days associated with a particular calendar day of the year, thus allowing a handy tool to count the number of days elapsing between two specific calendar days.

Tables

Table 22.1 lists a calendar for a non-leap year, arranged by month and date of the month. The entries give the cumulative day of the year starting with 1 on January 1 and ending with 365 on December 31. Table 22.2 gives the corresponding dates for a leap year.

Example 22.1

In a non-leap year an order is placed with a supplier on June 17, and the promise date is September 13 of the same year. What is the procurement lead time for the order?

Table 22.1 shows the following days of the year:

June 17 is day 168
September 13 is day 256

Since the difference is 88 days, then from and including June 17 to September 13, the number of days is 88 + 1 = 89 days.

Example 22.2

An order placed on November 4 of a non-leap year order is due to arrive on March 23 of the next year (which is a leap year). How many days does this procurement lead time span?

Tables 22.1 and 22.2 show the following days of the year:

November 4 is day 308 for a non-leap year
December 31 is day 365 for a non-leap year
March 23 is day 83 for a leap year

Hence, the lead time spans:

$$(365 - 308 + 1) + 83 = 141 \text{ days.}$$

Table 22.1   Days of the Year for a Non-Leap Year

					Month							
Date	Jan	Feb	Mar	Apr	May	Jun	Jul	Aug	Sep	Oct	Nov	Dec
1	1	32	60	91	121	152	182	213	244	274	305	335
2	2	33	61	92	122	153	183	214	245	275	306	336
3	3	34	62	93	123	154	184	215	246	276	307	337
4	4	35	63	94	124	155	185	216	247	277	308	338
5	5	36	64	95	125	156	186	217	248	278	309	339
6	6	37	65	96	126	157	187	218	249	279	310	340
7	7	38	66	97	127	158	188	219	250	280	311	341
8	8	39	67	98	128	159	189	220	251	281	312	342
9	9	40	68	99	129	160	190	221	252	282	313	343
10	10	41	69	100	130	161	191	222	253	283	314	344
11	11	42	70	101	131	162	192	223	254	284	315	345
12	12	43	71	102	132	163	193	224	255	285	316	346
13	13	44	72	103	133	164	194	225	256	286	317	347
14	14	45	73	104	134	165	195	226	257	287	318	348
15	15	46	74	105	135	166	196	227	258	288	319	349
16	16	47	75	106	136	167	197	228	259	289	320	350
17	17	48	76	107	137	168	198	229	260	290	321	351
18	18	49	77	108	138	169	199	230	261	291	322	352
19	19	50	78	109	139	170	200	231	262	292	323	353
20	20	51	79	110	140	171	201	232	263	293	324	354
21	21	52	80	111	141	172	202	233	264	294	325	355
22	22	53	81	112	142	173	203	234	265	295	326	356
23	23	54	82	113	143	174	204	235	266	296	327	357
24	24	55	83	114	144	175	205	236	267	297	328	358
25	25	56	84	115	145	176	206	237	268	298	329	359
26	26	57	85	116	146	177	207	238	269	299	330	360
27	27	58	86	117	147	178	208	239	270	300	331	361
28	28	59	87	118	148	179	209	240	271	301	332	362
29	29		88	119	149	180	210	241	272	302	333	363
30	30		89	120	150	181	211	242	273	303	334	364
31	31		90		151		212	243		304		365

Table 22.2   Days of the Year for a Leap Year

Date	Jan	Feb	Mar	Apr	May	Jun	Jul	Aug	Sep	Oct	Nov	Dec
1	1	32	61	92	122	153	183	214	245	275	306	336
2	2	33	62	93	123	154	184	215	246	276	307	337
3	3	34	63	94	124	155	185	216	247	277	308	338
4	4	35	64	95	125	156	186	217	248	278	309	339
5	5	36	65	96	126	157	187	218	249	279	310	340
6	6	37	66	97	127	158	188	219	250	280	311	341
7	7	38	67	98	128	159	189	220	251	281	312	342
8	8	39	68	99	129	160	190	221	252	282	313	343
9	9	40	69	100	130	161	191	222	253	283	314	344
10	10	41	70	101	131	162	192	223	254	284	315	345
11	11	42	71	102	132	163	193	224	255	285	316	346
12	12	43	72	103	133	164	194	225	256	286	317	347
13	13	44	73	104	134	165	195	226	257	287	318	348
14	14	45	74	105	135	166	196	227	258	288	319	349
15	15	46	75	106	136	167	197	228	259	289	320	350
16	16	47	76	107	137	168	198	229	260	290	321	351
17	17	48	77	108	138	169	199	230	261	291	322	352
18	18	49	78	109	139	170	200	231	262	292	323	353
19	19	50	79	110	140	171	201	232	263	293	324	354
20	20	51	80	111	141	172	202	233	264	294	325	355
21	21	52	81	112	142	173	203	234	265	295	326	356
22	22	53	82	113	143	174	204	235	266	296	327	357
23	23	54	83	114	144	175	205	236	267	297	328	358
24	24	55	84	115	145	176	206	237	268	298	329	359
25	25	56	85	116	146	177	207	238	269	299	330	360
26	26	57	86	117	147	178	208	239	270	300	331	361
27	27	58	87	118	148	179	209	240	271	301	332	362
28	28	59	88	119	149	180	210	241	272	302	333	363
29	29	60	89	120	150	181	211	242	273	303	334	364
30	30		90	121	151	182	212	243	274	304	335	365
31	31		91		152		213	244		305		366

CHAPTER 23

Loan Payments

A wide variety of interest formulas are used in the daily operation between lending institutions and their customers (reference 1). The purpose of the tables adjoining this chapter is to focus on just one of these formulas. Here, a lending institution gives a loan of a certain amount to a customer who will pay back the amount plus interest in equal monthly installments over a fixed time period with a constant interest rate to cover the unpaid portion of the loan. This type of loan, the most preferred by the customer, is the most common method and is most likely to be encountered by a firm seeking a loan for such purposes as equipment acquisition, building remodeling and so forth.

Data

In order to apply the formulas of this chapter, the following data are used:

P = mortgage amount (the loan amount)
Y = number of years to repay the loan in equal monthly installments
R = annual interest rate on the unpaid balance

From the above, the number of months N corresponding to the loan is determined by the relation:

$$N = 12\,Y$$

Also, the interest charge per month on the unpaid balance is calculated as:

$$i = R/12$$

Model

The above data is used for a loan of size P, borrowed for Y years (or N months) with an interest rate of R per year on the unpaid balance. The equal monthly repayment A by the customer becomes:

$$A = \frac{P\,i\,(1 + i)^N}{(1 + i)^N - 1}$$

and the total amount (denoted as T) paid by the customer over N months becomes:

$$T = A \times N$$

Finally, the total interest costs (here denoted as I) paid by the customer over the course of the loan is:

$$I = T - P$$

Tables

The tables adjoining this chapter give payment quantities based on an annual interest rate and the number of years to pay off a loan. The interest rates span from 5 percent to 20 percent and the years to pay range from one half of a year to 30 years. The tables are formulated on a basic loan value of $1,000.

The tables list the equal payment amounts, the total payments over the course of the loan, and the total interest costs over the course of the loan.

Example 23.1

A small firm seeking a loan to purchase a warehouse space applies for a loan of $100,000. A lending institution agrees to lend the amount at an annual interest rate of 12 percent for 10 years of equal monthly payments. Find the monthly payments, the total amount paid and the total interest payment costs.

Table 23.1 used with a 12 percent interest rate and 10 years to pay yields the following:

$$\text{Monthly payments} = 100\,(14.35) = \$1435.00$$
$$\text{Total payments} = 100\,(1{,}721.65) = \$172{,}165.00$$
$$\text{Total interest} = 100\,(721.65) = \$72{,}165.00$$

Note in the above that because the loan ($100,000) is 100 times as large as the $1000 from which the tables are based, the multiplier of 100 is used.

Example 23.2

A company, with intent to purchase a computer system, has the options of a $40,000 loan at 12 percent payable in 5 years of equal monthly payments or at 11 percent in 4 years. Show the difference in total payments from these two options.

Option	5 years at 12%	4 years at 11%
Monthly payments	$ 889.60	$ 1,034.00
Total payments	$53,386.80	$49,623.20
Total interest	$13,386.80	$ 9,623.20

Example 23.3

A firm wishes to take out a $10,000 loan to purchase a new lift truck for the warehouse. The lending institution agrees to give a loan for equal monthly payments of $330.00 over 3 years. Find the approximate interest rate for this loan.

The adjoining tables are searched to find the interest rate that gives the nearest monthly payment for 3 years at $330/10 = $33. The divisor of 10 is used since the loan of $10,000 is 10 times larger than the $1000 upon which the tables are based.

A search of the tables show that the interest rate is approximately 11.55 percent, since 11 percent gives $32.74 and 12 percent gives $33.21. Interpolation of the table entries yields the 11.55 percent result.

Table 23.1   Mortgage Payments Tables

(Based on $1,000 Mortgage and Equal Monthly Payments)

Annual Interest Rates

		.05			.06	
Years to Pay	Monthly Payments	Total Payments	Total Interest	Monthly Payments	Total Payments	Total Interest
½	169.10	1,014.61	14.61	169.59	1,017.57	17.57
1	85.61	1,027.27	27.27	86.07	1,032.80	32.80
1½	57.78	1,040.03	40.03	58.23	1,048.17	48.17
2	43.87	1,052.89	52.89	44.32	1,063.69	63.69
2½	35.53	1,065.86	65.86	35.98	1,079.37	79.37
3	29.97	1,078.93	78.93	30.42	1,095.19	95.19
3½	26.00	1,092.11	92.11	26.46	1,111.16	111.16
4	23.03	1,105.39	105.39	23.49	1,127.28	127.28
4½	20.72	1,118.77	118.77	21.18	1,143.55	143.55
5	18.87	1,132.25	132.25	19.33	1,159.97	159.97
6	16.10	1,159.54	159.54	16.57	1,193.25	193.25
7	14.13	1,187.23	187.23	14.61	1,227.12	227.12
8	12.66	1,215.33	215.33	13.14	1,261.58	261.58
9	11.52	1,243.85	243.85	12.01	1,296.62	296.62
10	10.61	1,272.77	272.77	11.10	1,332.25	332.25
11	9.86	1,302.09	302.09	10.37	1,368.45	368.45
12	9.25	1,331.82	331.82	9.76	1,405.22	405.22
13	8.73	1,361.95	361.95	9.25	1,442.57	442.57
14	8.29	1,392.48	392.48	8.81	1,480.48	480.48
15	7.91	1,423.41	423.41	8.44	1,518.94	518.94
16	7.58	1,454.73	454.73	8.11	1,557.96	557.96
17	7.29	1,486.44	486.44	7.83	1,597.52	597.52
18	7.03	1,518.53	518.53	7.58	1,637.63	637.63
19	6.80	1,551.02	551.02	7.36	1,678.27	678.27
20	6.60	1,583.88	583.88	7.16	1,719.43	719.43
21	6.42	1,617.11	617.11	6.99	1,761.12	761.12
22	6.25	1,650.72	650.72	6.83	1,803.32	803.32
23	6.10	1,684.70	684.70	6.69	1,846.02	846.02
24	5.97	1,719.05	719.05	6.56	1,889.22	889.22
25	5.85	1,753.75	753.75	6.44	1,932.90	932.90
26	5.73	1,788.82	788.82	6.34	1,977.07	977.07
27	5.63	1,824.23	824.23	6.24	2,021.71	1,021.71
28	5.54	1,859.99	859.99	6.15	2,066.82	1,066.82
29	5.45	1,896.10	896.10	6.07	2,112.38	1,112.38
30	5.37	1,932.54	932.54	6.00	2,158.38	1,158.38

Table 23.1   Mortgage Payments Tables   (Continued)

(Based on $1,000 Mortgage and Equal Monthly Payments)

Annual Interest Rates

-------------- .07 --------------   -------------- .08 --------------

Years to Pay	Monthly Payments	Total Payments	Total Interest	Monthly Payments	Total Payments	Total Interest
½	170.09	1,020.51	20.51	170.58	1,023.46	23.46
1	86.53	1,038.32	38.32	86.99	1,043.86	43.86
1½	58.68	1,056.33	56.33	59.14	1,064.52	64.52
2	44.77	1,074.54	74.54	45.23	1,085.45	85.45
2½	36.43	1,092.95	92.95	36.89	1,106.65	106.65
3	30.88	1,111.57	111.57	31.34	1,128.11	128.11
3½	26.91	1,130.39	130.39	27.38	1,149.83	149.83
4	23.95	1,149.42	149.42	24.41	1,171.82	171.82
4½	21.64	1,168.64	168.64	22.11	1,194.07	194.07
5	19.80	1,188.07	188.07	20.28	1,216.58	216.58
6	17.05	1,227.53	227.53	17.53	1,262.39	262.39
7	15.09	1,267.78	267.78	15.59	1,309.24	309.24
8	13.63	1,308.83	308.83	14.14	1,357.12	357.12
9	12.51	1,350.68	350.68	13.02	1,406.02	406.02
10	11.61	1,393.30	393.30	12.13	1,455.93	455.93
11	10.88	1,436.70	436.70	11.42	1,506.84	506.84
12	10.28	1,480.87	480.87	10.82	1,558.73	558.73
13	9.78	1,525.79	525.79	10.33	1,611.59	611.59
14	9.35	1,571.47	571.47	9.91	1,665.41	665.41
15	8.99	1,617.89	617.89	9.56	1,720.17	720.17
16	8.67	1,665.04	665.04	9.25	1,775.86	775.86
17	8.40	1,712.91	712.91	8.98	1,832.44	832.44
18	8.16	1,761.48	761.48	8.75	1,889.92	889.92
19	7.94	1,810.76	810.76	8.55	1,948.26	948.26
20	7.75	1,860.71	860.71	8.36	2,007.46	1,007.46
21	7.58	1,911.35	911.35	8.20	2,067.48	1,067.48
22	7.43	1,962.64	962.64	8.06	2,128.31	1,128.31
23	7.30	2,014.57	1,014.57	7.93	2,189.93	1,189.93
24	7.18	2,067.15	1,067.15	7.82	2,252.32	1,252.32
25	7.07	2,120.34	1,120.34	7.72	2,315.45	1,315.45
26	6.97	2,174.13	1,174.13	7.63	2,379.31	1,379.31
27	6.88	2,228.52	1,228.52	7.54	2,443.87	1,443.87
28	6.80	2,283.48	1,283.48	7.47	2,509.11	1,509.11
29	6.72	2,339.01	1,339.01	7.40	2,575.01	1,575.01
30	6.65	2,395.09	1,395.09	7.34	2,641.55	1,641.55

Table 23.1   Mortgage Payments Tables   (Continued)

(Based on $1,000 Mortgage and Equal Monthly Payments)

Annual Interest Rates

-------------- .09 --------------   -------------- .10 --------------

Years to Pay	Monthly Payments	Total Payments	Total Interest	Monthly Payments	Total Payments	Total Interest
½	171.07	1,026.40	26.40	171.56	1,029.37	29.37
1	87.45	1,049.41	49.41	87.92	1,054.99	54.99
1½	59.60	1,072.75	72.75	60.06	1,081.03	81.03
2	45.68	1,096.42	96.42	46.15	1,107.48	107.48
2½	37.35	1,120.43	120.43	37.81	1,134.35	134.35
3	31.80	1,144.78	144.78	32.27	1,161.62	161.62
3½	27.84	1,169.46	169.46	28.32	1,189.31	189.31
4	24.88	1,194.47	194.47	25.36	1,217.41	217.41
4½	22.59	1,219.82	219.82	23.07	1,245.91	245.91
5	20.76	1,245.49	245.49	21.25	1,274.83	274.83
6	18.03	1,297.83	297.83	18.53	1,333.86	333.86
7	16.09	1,351.47	351.47	16.60	1,394.50	394.50
8	14.65	1,406.41	406.41	15.17	1,456.72	456.72
9	13.54	1,462.63	462.63	14.08	1,520.50	520.50
10	12.67	1,520.10	520.10	13.22	1,585.81	585.81
11	11.96	1,578.82	578.82	12.52	1,652.63	652.63
12	11.38	1,638.76	638.76	11.95	1,720.92	720.92
13	10.90	1,699.89	699.89	11.48	1,790.65	790.65
14	10.49	1,762.21	762.21	11.08	1,861.78	861.78
15	10.14	1,825.67	825.67	10.75	1,934.29	934.29
16	9.85	1,890.26	890.26	10.46	2,008.14	1,008.14
17	9.59	1,955.95	955.95	10.21	2,083.27	1,083.27
18	9.36	2,022.71	1,022.71	10.00	2,159.67	1,159.67
19	9.17	2,090.52	1,090.52	9.81	2,237.27	1,237.27
20	9.00	2,159.34	1,159.34	9.65	2,316.06	1,316.06
21	8.85	2,229.14	1,229.14	9.51	2,395.97	1,395.97
22	8.71	2,299.89	1,299.89	9.38	2,476.97	1,476.97
23	8.59	2,371.57	1,371.57	9.27	2,559.02	1,559.02
24	8.49	2,444.15	1,444.15	9.17	2,642.08	1,642.08
25	8.39	2,517.58	1,517.58	9.09	2,726.11	1,726.11
26	8.31	2,591.85	1,591.85	9.01	2,811.05	1,811.05
27	8.23	2,666.92	1,666.92	8.94	2,896.88	1,896.88
28	8.16	2,742.76	1,742.76	8.88	2,983.55	1,983.55
29	8.10	2,819.34	1,819.34	8.82	3,071.02	2,071.02
30	8.05	2,896.64	1,896.64	8.78	3,159.26	2,159.26

Table 23.1   Mortgage Payments Tables (Continued)

(Based on $1,000 Mortgage and Equal Monthly Payments)

Annual Interest Rates

-------------- .11 --------------   -------------- .12 --------------

Years to Pay	Monthly Payments	Total Payments	Total Interest	Monthly Payments	Total Payments	Total Interest
½	172.05	1,032.32	32.32	172.55	1,035.29	35.29
1	88.38	1,060.58	60.58	88.85	1,066.19	66.19
1½	60.52	1,089.33	89.33	60.98	1,097.68	97.68
2	46.61	1,118.58	118.58	47.07	1,129.76	129.76
2½	38.28	1,148.34	148.34	38.75	1,162.44	162.44
3	32.74	1,178.59	178.59	33.21	1,195.72	195.72
3½	28.79	1,209.34	209.34	29.28	1,229.58	229.58
4	25.85	1,240.58	240.58	26.33	1,264.02	264.02
4½	23.56	1,272.32	272.32	24.06	1,299.06	299.06
5	21.74	1,304.54	304.54	22.24	1,334.67	334.67
6	19.03	1,370.45	370.45	19.55	1,407.61	407.61
7	17.12	1,438.28	438.28	17.65	1,482.83	482.83
8	15.71	1,508.00	508.00	16.25	1,560.27	560.27
9	14.63	1,579.59	579.59	15.18	1,639.90	639.90
10	13.77	1,653.00	653.00	14.35	1,721.65	721.65
11	13.09	1,728.19	728.19	13.68	1,805.48	805.48
12	12.54	1,805.12	805.12	13.13	1,891.32	891.32
13	12.08	1,883.74	883.74	12.69	1,979.12	979.12
14	11.69	1,964.01	964.01	12.31	2,068.80	1,068.80
15	11.37	2,045.87	1,045.87	12.00	2,160.30	1,160.30
16	11.09	2,129.28	1,129.28	11.74	2,253.55	1,253.55
17	10.85	2,214.17	1,214.17	11.51	2,348.48	1,348.48
18	10.65	2,300.50	1,300.50	11.32	2,445.01	1,445.01
19	10.47	2,388.21	1,388.21	11.15	2,543.08	1,543.08
20	10.32	2,477.25	1,477.25	11.01	2,642.61	1,642.61
21	10.19	2,567.55	1,567.55	10.89	2,743.52	1,743.52
22	10.07	2,659.07	1,659.07	10.78	2,845.76	1,845.76
23	9.97	2,751.74	1,751.74	10.69	2,949.24	1,949.24
24	9.88	2,845.51	1,845.51	10.60	3,053.90	2,053.90
25	9.80	2,940.34	1,940.34	10.53	3,159.67	2,159.67
26	9.73	3,036.15	2,036.15	10.47	3,266.49	2,266.49
27	9.67	3,132.92	2,132.92	10.41	3,374.29	2,374.29
28	9.61	3,230.57	2,230.57	10.37	3,483.02	2,483.02
29	9.57	3,329.07	2,329.07	10.32	3,592.61	2,592.61
30	9.52	3,428.36	2,428.36	10.29	3,703.01	2,703.01

Table 23.1   Mortgage Payments Tables (Continued)

(Based on $1,000 Mortgage and Equal Monthly Payments)

Annual Interest Rates

	.13			.14		
Years to Pay	Monthly Payments	Total Payments	Total Interest	Monthly Payments	Total Payments	Total Interest
½	173.04	1,038.26	38.26	173.54	1,041.23	41.23
1	89.32	1,071.81	71.81	89.79	1,077.45	77.45
1½	61.45	1,106.05	106.05	61.92	1,114.47	114.47
2	47.54	1,141.00	141.00	48.01	1,152.31	152.31
2½	39.22	1,176.64	176.64	39.70	1,190.95	190.95
3	33.69	1,212.98	212.98	34.18	1,230.40	230.40
3½	29.76	1,250.01	250.01	30.25	1,270.64	270.64
4	26.83	1,287.72	287.72	27.33	1,311.67	311.67
4½	24.56	1,326.11	326.11	25.06	1,353.49	353.49
5	22.75	1,365.18	365.18	23.27	1,396.10	396.10
6	20.07	1,445.33	445.33	20.61	1,483.62	483.62
7	18.19	1,528.12	528.12	18.74	1,574.16	574.16
8	16.81	1,613.49	613.49	17.37	1,667.67	667.67
9	15.75	1,701.39	701.39	16.33	1,764.04	764.04
10	14.93	1,791.73	791.73	15.53	1,863.20	863.20
11	14.28	1,884.44	884.44	14.89	1,965.04	965.04
12	13.75	1,979.46	979.46	14.37	2,069.46	1,069.46
13	13.31	2,076.69	1,076.69	13.95	2,176.36	1,176.36
14	12.95	2,176.04	1,176.04	13.60	2,285.62	1,285.62
15	12.65	2,277.43	1,277.43	13.32	2,397.14	1,397.14
16	12.40	2,380.77	1,380.77	13.08	2,510.78	1,510.78
17	12.19	2,485.97	1,485.97	12.87	2,626.45	1,626.45
18	12.00	2,592.93	1,592.93	12.70	2,744.03	1,744.03
19	11.85	2,701.57	1,701.57	12.56	2,863.40	1,863.40
20	11.72	2,811.78	1,811.78	12.44	2,984.45	1,984.45
21	11.60	2,923.49	1,923.49	12.33	3,107.08	2,107.08
22	11.50	3,036.60	2,036.60	12.24	3,231.17	2,231.17
23	11.42	3,151.02	2,151.02	12.16	3,356.64	2,356.64
24	11.34	3,266.69	2,266.69	12.10	3,483.37	2,483.37
25	11.28	3,383.50	2,383.50	12.04	3,611.28	2,611.28
26	11.22	3,501.40	2,501.40	11.99	3,740.28	2,740.28
27	11.17	3,620.30	2,620.30	11.95	3,870.29	2,870.29
28	11.13	3,740.13	2,740.13	11.91	4,001.21	3,001.21
29	11.09	3,860.82	2,860.82	11.88	4,132.99	3,132.99
30	11.06	3,982.32	2,982.32	11.85	4,265.54	3,265.54

Table 23.1   Mortgage Payments Tables   (Continued)

(Based on $1,000 Mortgage and Equal Monthly Payments)

Annual Interest Rates

------------- .15 ---------------   -------------- .16 -------------

Years to Pay	Monthly Payments	Total Payments	Total Interest	Monthly Payments	Total Payments	Total Interest
½	174.03	1,044.20	44.20	174.53	1,047.18	47.18
1	90.26	1,083.09	83.09	90.73	1,088.77	88.77
1½	62.38	1,122.92	122.92	62.86	1,131.42	131.42
2	48.49	1,163.67	163.67	48.96	1,175.12	175.12
2½	40.18	1,205.35	205.35	40.66	1,219.87	219.87
3	34.67	1,247.95	247.95	35.16	1,265.66	265.66
3½	30.75	1,291.46	291.46	31.25	1,312.48	312.48
4	27.83	1,335.87	335.87	28.34	1,360.34	360.34
4½	25.58	1,381.19	381.19	26.10	1,409.21	409.21
5	23.79	1,427.39	427.39	24.32	1,459.09	459.09
6	21.14	1,522.44	522.44	21.69	1,561.82	561.82
7	19.30	1,620.92	620.92	19.86	1,668.42	668.42
8	17.95	1,722.75	722.75	18.53	1,778.77	778.77
9	16.92	1,827.82	827.82	17.53	1,892.73	892.73
10	16.13	1,936.01	936.01	16.75	2,010.16	1,010.16
11	15.51	2,047.20	1,047.20	16.14	2,130.90	1,130.90
12	15.01	2,161.26	1,161.26	15.66	2,254.79	1,254.79
13	14.60	2,278.04	1,278.04	15.27	2,381.66	1,381.66
14	14.27	2,397.42	1,397.42	14.95	2,511.34	1,511.34
15	14.00	2,519.25	1,519.25	14.69	2,643.66	1,643.66
16	13.77	2,643.39	1,643.39	14.47	2,778.45	1,778.45
17	13.58	2,769.71	1,769.71	14.29	2,915.55	1,915.55
18	13.42	2,898.05	1,898.05	14.14	3,054.78	2,054.77
19	13.28	3,028.29	2,028.29	14.02	3,195.98	2,195.98
20	13.17	3,160.29	2,160.29	13.91	3,339.02	2,339.02
21	13.07	3,293.93	2,293.93	13.82	3,483.73	2,483.73
22	12.99	3,429.09	2,429.09	13.75	3,629.97	2,629.97
23	12.92	3,565.64	2,565.64	13.69	3,777.63	2,777.63
24	12.86	3,703.47	2,703.47	13.63	3,926.57	2,926.57
25	12.81	3,842.49	2,842.49	13.59	4,076.67	3,076.67
26	12.76	3,982.59	2,982.59	13.55	4,227.83	3,227.83
27	12.73	4,123.67	3,123.67	13.52	4,379.94	3,379.94
28	12.70	4,265.65	3,265.65	13.49	4,532.92	3,532.92
29	12.67	4,408.45	3,408.45	13.47	4,686.67	3,686.67
30	12.64	4,552.00	3,552.00	13.45	4,841.13	3,841.13

Table 23.1   Mortgage Payments Tables   (Continued)

(Based on $1,000 Mortgage and Equal Monthly Payments)

Annual Interest Rates

------------ .17 ------------   ------------ .18 ------------

Years to Pay	Monthly Payments	Total Payments	Total Interest	Monthly Payments	Total Payments	Total Interest
½	175.03	1,050.16	50.16	175.53	1,053.16	53.16
1	91.20	1,094.45	94.45	91.68	1,100.16	100.16
1½	63.33	1,139.94	139.94	63.81	1,148.51	148.51
2	49.44	1,186.61	186.61	49.92	1,198.18	198.18
2½	41.15	1,234.46	234.46	41.64	1,249.18	249.18
3	35.65	1,283.49	283.49	36.15	1,301.49	301.49
3½	31.75	1,333.69	333.69	32.26	1,355.10	355.10
4	28.85	1,385.04	385.04	29.38	1,410.00	410.00
4½	26.62	1,437.53	437.53	27.15	1,466.18	466.18
5	24.85	1,491.15	491.15	25.39	1,523.61	523.61
6	22.25	1,601.72	601.72	22.81	1,642.16	642.16
7	20.44	1,716.60	716.60	21.02	1,765.50	765.50
8	19.12	1,835.66	835.66	19.72	1,893.43	893.43
9	18.14	1,958.70	958.70	18.76	2,025.75	1,025.75
10	17.38	2,085.57	1,085.57	18.02	2,162.22	1,162.22
11	16.79	2,216.05	1,216.05	17.44	2,302.63	1,302.63
12	16.32	2,349.97	1,349.97	16.99	2,446.73	1,446.73
13	15.94	2,487.10	1,487.10	16.63	2,594.28	1,594.28
14	15.64	2,627.25	1,627.25	16.34	2,745.04	1,745.04
15	15.39	2,770.20	1,770.20	16.10	2,898.76	1,898.76
16	15.19	2,915.77	1,915.77	15.91	3,055.21	2,055.21
17	15.02	3,063.76	2,063.76	15.76	3,214.17	2,214.17
18	14.88	3,213.96	2,213.96	15.63	3,375.42	2,375.42
19	14.76	3,366.21	2,366.21	15.52	3,538.74	2,538.74
20	14.67	3,520.32	2,520.32	15.43	3,703.95	2,703.95
21	14.59	3,676.13	2,676.13	15.36	3,870.86	2,870.86
22	14.52	3,833.48	2,833.48	15.30	4,039.30	3,039.30
23	14.46	3,992.23	2,992.23	15.25	4,209.11	3,209.11
24	14.42	4,152.24	3,152.24	15.21	4,380.16	3,380.16
25	14.38	4,313.39	3,313.39	15.17	4,552.29	3,552.29
26	14.34	4,475.56	3,475.56	15.15	4,725.40	3,725.40
27	14.32	4,638.64	3,638.64	15.12	4,899.37	3,899.37
28	14.29	4,802.53	3,802.53	15.10	5,074.10	4,074.10
29	14.27	4,967.16	3,967.16	15.08	5,249.51	4,249.51
30	14.26	5,132.43	4,132.43	15.07	5,425.51	4,425.51

Table 23.1   Mortgage Payments Tables (Continued)

(Based on $1,000 Mortgage and Equal Monthly Payments)

Annual Interest Rates

-------------- .19 --------------   -------------- .20 --------------

Years to Pay	Monthly Payments	Total Payments	Total Interest	Monthly Payments	Total Payments	Total Interest
½	176.02	1,056.14	56.14	176.52	1,059.14	59.14
1	92.16	1,105.88	105.88	92.63	1,111.62	111.62
1½	64.28	1,157.10	157.10	64.76	1,165.74	165.74
2	50.41	1,209.80	209.80	50.90	1,221.50	221.50
2½	42.13	1,263.98	263.98	42.63	1,278.89	278.89
3	36.66	1,319.61	319.61	37.16	1,337.89	337.89
3½	32.78	1,376.69	376.69	33.30	1,398.49	398.49
4	29.90	1,435.20	435.20	30.43	1,460.66	460.66
4½	27.69	1,495.12	495.12	28.23	1,524.38	524.38
5	25.94	1,556.43	556.43	26.49	1,589.63	589.63
6	23.38	1,683.12	683.12	23.95	1,724.60	724.60
7	21.61	1,815.07	815.07	22.21	1,865.32	865.32
8	20.33	1,952.05	952.05	20.95	2,011.51	1,011.51
9	19.39	2,093.80	1,093.80	20.03	2,162.86	1,162.86
10	18.67	2,240.07	1,240.07	19.33	2,319.07	1,319.07
11	18.11	2,390.56	1,390.56	18.79	2,479.80	1,479.80
12	17.67	2,545.00	1,545.00	18.37	2,644.72	1,644.72
13	17.33	2,703.11	1,703.11	18.04	2,813.50	1,813.50
14	17.05	2,864.59	1,864.59	17.77	2,985.81	1,985.81
15	16.83	3,029.18	2,029.18	17.56	3,161.33	2,161.33
16	16.65	3,196.59	2,196.59	17.39	3,339.78	2,339.78
17	16.50	3,366.58	2,366.58	17.26	3,520.84	2,520.84
18	16.38	3,538.91	2,538.91	17.15	3,704.26	2,704.26
19	16.29	3,713.33	2,713.33	17.06	3,889.79	2,889.79
20	16.21	3,889.64	2,889.64	16.99	4,077.18	3,077.18
21	16.14	4,067.64	3,067.64	16.93	4,266.23	3,266.23
22	16.09	4,247.14	3,247.14	16.88	4,456.74	3,456.74
23	16.04	4,427.97	3,427.97	16.84	4,648.53	3,648.53
24	16.01	4,609.98	3,609.98	16.81	4,841.45	3,841.45
25	15.98	4,793.04	3,793.04	16.78	5,035.36	4,035.36
26	15.95	4,977.01	3,977.01	16.76	5,230.12	4,230.12
27	15.93	5,161.79	4,161.79	16.75	5,425.62	4,425.62
28	15.91	5,347.28	4,347.28	16.73	5,621.77	4,621.77
29	15.90	5,533.38	4,533.38	16.72	5,818.48	4,818.48
30	15.89	5,720.01	4,720.01	16.71	6,015.67	5,015.67

CHAPTER 24

Measures

In various business transactions—including the control of inventory—a firm may encounter differences in measurements. There are two major systems for measurements, the *customary* system and the *metric* system. The customary system, also called the English system since it was started in England in the 1200's, is widely used in the United States and Canada. Most other countries around the world use the metric system, created by a group of French scientists in the 1790's and officially called the International System of Units. Once learned, the metric system is far more simple to use than the customary system. The metric system is also more preferred by scientists in their applications. In 1975, a U.S. law called for the conversion from the customary to the metric system.

Various types of measurements are taken of objects, including measures of length or distance, area, volume or capacity, and weight. This chapter describes various measurements in both the customary and metric system and gives the conversion method from one system to the other (reference 1).

Length and Distance

Length (or distance) gives the measurement from one point to another. For the customary system, common units are inches, feet, yards and miles. For the metric system, the common units are the millimeter, centimeter, decimeter, meter and kilometer.

Area

Area is a measure of how many square units can be fit into a plane surface of any shape. For the customary system, common units are the square inch, square foot, square yard, and acre. For the metric system, common units are the square centimeter, square meter and so forth.

Volume and Capacity

Volume of an object is a measure of the total size of the space that it occupies. For the customary system, common measures are the cubic inch, cubic foot and cubic yard. For the metric system, common measures are the cubic centimeter, the cubic meter and so on.

Capacity is a measure of how much material can be included in an object, such as milk in a carton. Capacity measures are different depending on whether the material is a liquid (e.g., oil or paint) or a dry substance (e.g., powder or grain). For the customary system, common measures are the pint, quart and gallon; for the metric system the common measure is the liter.

Weight

Weight is the measure of the heaviness of an object. The customary system has three separate systems of weight measures—apothecary, troy and avoirdupois. These three systems can be confusing because some of their units have the same names but are measures of different weights. The apothecary system is primarily used to measure drugs, and the troy system is used to measure various types of gems. In this chapter only the avoirdupois system is described; the avoirdupois system is mostly used in the United States, and the common measure is the pound. For the metric system, the most common measure is the gram.

Tables

The tables of this chapter are arranged in the following manner:

Table	Measure
24.1	Length and Distance
24.2	Area
24.3	Volume
24.4	Capacity
24.5	Weight

Example 24.1

A part manufacturing company has the need for 500 linear feet of a raw material that comes in individual rolls of one dekameter each. How many such rolls should be purchased?

Table 24.1 shows the following relations:

$$1 \text{ foot} = 0.3048 \text{ meters}$$
$$1 \text{ dekameter} = 10 \text{ meters}$$

As:

$$500 \text{ feet} = 0.3048 \,(500) = 152 \text{ meters}$$

therefore:

$$152 \text{ meters} = 152/10 = 15.2 \text{ dekameters}$$

Thus, 16 rolls should be purchased to cover all the needs.

Example 24.2

A European manufacturer sells fabric that comes in units of 33 square decimeters. Find the equivalent area in square inches.

Table 24.2 is used with the relations listed below:

$$1 \text{ square meter} = 100 \text{ square decimeters}$$
$$1 \text{ square meter} = 10.757 \text{ square feet}$$
$$1 \text{ square foot} = 144 \text{ square inches}$$

Using the above relations:

$$1 \text{ square decimeter} = 0.01 \text{ square meters}$$
$$33 \text{ square decimeters} = 0.33 \text{ square meters}$$
$$0.33 \text{ square meters} = .33\,(10.757) = 3.54981 \text{ square feet}$$

Finally, the area for the fabric becomes:

$$3.54981 \text{ square feet} = 144\,(3.54981) = 511.2 \text{ square inches}$$

Example 24.3

A company receives an order for 100 kiloliters of grain from a foreign firm. How many bushels of grain should be shipped?

Table 24.4 with Customary Dry Capacity and the relation listed below is used:

$$1 \text{ kiloliter} = 28.38 \text{ bushels}$$

Therefore, 100 kiloliters of grain becomes 100×28.38 or

$$100 \text{ kiloliters} = 2838 \text{ bushels}$$

Example 24.4

A buyer for a paint manufacturer gets a quote from an Asian distributor to purchase a coloring powder at $400 per metric ton. Find the equivalent cost per pound.

Table 24.5 gives the relations below:

$$1 \text{ metric ton} = 1000 \text{ kilograms}$$
$$1 \text{ kilogram} = 2.20462 \text{ pounds}$$

So,

$$1 \text{ metric ton} = 2.20462 \, (1000) = 2204.62 \text{ pounds}$$

whereby the cost per pound becomes:

$$400/2204.62 = \$0.1814$$

Table 24.1   Length and Distance

Customary

1 inch (in)	=	2.54 centimeters (cm)
1 foot (ft)	=	12 inches (in)
1 yard (yd)	=	3 ft
1 rod (rd)	=	5.50 yd
1 furlong (fur)	=	40 rd
1 statute mile (mi)	=	5280 ft
1 league (statute)	=	3 mi

Metric

1 millimeter (mm)	=	0.03937 in
1 centimeter (cm)	=	10 mm
1 decimeter (dm)	=	10 cm
1 meter (m)	=	10 dm
1 dekameter (dkm)	=	10 m
1 hectometer (hm)	=	10 dkm
1 kilometer (km)	=	10 hm

Conversion Customary to Metric

1 in	=	2.54 cm
1 ft	=	0.3048 m
1 yd	=	0.9144 m
1 mi	=	1.6093 km

Conversion Metric to Customary

1 cm	=	0.3937 in
1 m	=	3.281 ft
1 m	=	1.0936 yd
1 km	=	0.62137 mi

Table 24.2   Area

Customary

1 square in (sq in)	=	6.4516 square centimeters (cm^2)
1 square foot (sq ft)	=	144 sq in
1 square yard (sq yd)	=	9 sq ft
1 square yard (sq yd)	=	30.25 sq yd
1 acre (A)	=	160 sq rd
1 square mile (sq mi)	=	640 A

Metric

1 square millimeter (mm^2)	=	0.002 sq in
1 square centimeter (cm^2)	=	100 mm^2
1 square decimeter (dm^2)	=	100 cm^2
1 square meter (m^2)	=	100 dm^2
1 square dekameter (dkm^2)	=	100 m^2
1 square hectometer (hm^2)	=	100 dkm^2
1 square kilometer (km^2)	=	100 hm^2

Conversion Customary to Metric

1 sq in	=	6.4516 cm^2
1 sq ft	=	0.0920 m^2
1 sq yd	=	0.8361 m^2
1 sq mi	=	2.590 km^2

Conversion Metric to Customary

1 cm^2	=	0.1549 sq in
1 m^2	=	10.757 sq ft
1 m^2	=	1.1960 sq yd
1 km^2	=	0.3861 sq mi

Table 24.3   Volume

Customary

1 cubic inch (cu in)	=	16.387 cm^3
1 cubic foot (cu ft)	=	1728 cu in
1 cubic yard (cu yd)	=	27 cu ft

Metric Volume

1 cubic millimeter (mm^3)	=	0.00006 cu in
1 cubic centimeter (cm^3)	=	1000 mm^3
1 cubic decimeter (dm^3)	=	1000 cm^3
1 cubic meter (m^3)	=	1000 dm^3
1 cubic dekameter (dkm^3)	=	1000 m^3
1 cubic hectometer (hm^3)	=	1000 dkm^3

Conversion Customary to Metric

1 cubic foot	=	0.0283 m^3

Conversion Metric to Customary

1 m^3	=	35.315 cu ft

Table 24.4   Capacity

Metric Capacity

1 milliliter (ml)	=	0.0610 cubic inches
1 centiliter (cl)	=	10 ml
1 deciliter (dl)	=	10 cl
1 liter (l)	=	10 dl
1 dekaliter (dkl)	=	10 l
1 hectoliter (hl)	=	10 dkl
1 kiloliter (kl)	=	10 hl

Customary Liquid Capacity
Customary

1 gill (gi)	=	7.219 cubic inches
1 pint (pt)	=	4 gi
1 quart (qt)	=	2 pt
1 gallon (gal)	=	4 qt
1 barrel (liquid) (bbl)	=	31.5 gal
1 barrel (petroleum) (bbl)	=	42 gal

Imperial

1 imperial quart	=	1.2009 US qt
1 imperial gallon	=	1.2009 US gal

Customary Dry Capacity
Customary

1 pint (pt)	=	33.6 cubic inches
1 quart (qt)	=	2 pt
1 peck (pk)	=	8 qt
1 bushel (bu)	=	4 pk
1 barrel (bbl)	=	4.08 cubic feet

Imperial

1 imperial dry quart	=	1.032 US qt
1 imperial bushel	=	1.032 US bu

Table 24.4 Capacity (continued)

Conversion Metric Capacity to Customary Liquid Capacity

1 liter	=	1.057 liquid quart
1 kiloliter	=	264.178 gallons

Conversion Customary Liquid Capacity to Metric Capacity

1 gallon	=	3.7853 liters
1 barrel	=	119.24 liters

Conversion Metric Capacity to Customary Dry Capacity

1 liter	=	0.908 dry quarts
1 kiloliter	=	28.38 bushels

Conversion Customer Dry Capacity to Metric Volume

1 quart	=	1101.21 cm^3
1 bushel	=	0.035239 m^3
1 barrel	=	0.115627 m^3

Conversion Metric Capacity to Customary Volume

1 liter	=	61.025 cubic inches
1 kiloliter	=	35.315 cubic feet

Table 24.5   Weight

Avoirdupois Weight

1 grain (gr)	=	0.0648 gram (g)
1 dram (dr)	=	27.34375 gr
1 ounce (oz)	=	16 dr
1 pound (lb)	=	16 oz
1 hundredweight (cwt)	=	100 lb
1 short ton (st)	=	2000 lb

Special British Units

1 stone (st)	=	14 lb
1 hundredweight (cwt)	=	112 lb
1 long ton (lt)	=	2240 lb

Metric

1 milligram (mg)	=	0.0154 gr
1 centigram (cg)	=	10 mg
1 decigram (dg)	=	10 cg
1 gram (g)	=	10 dg
1 dekagram (dkg)	=	10 g
1 hectogram (hg)	=	10 dkg
1 kilogram (kg)	=	10 hg
1 quintal (q)	=	100 kg
1 metric ton (MT)	=	10 q or 1000 kg

Conversion Avoirdupois to Metric

1 ounce	=	28349.5 mg
1 ounce	=	28.350 g
1 pound	=	453.59 g
1 pound	=	0.4536 kg

Conversion Metric to Avoirdupois

1 milligram	=	0.000035 oz
1 gram	=	0.035274 oz or 0.002204 lb
1 kilogram	=	2.20462 lb

Bibliographical References

Chapter 1

1. Makridakis, S. and S.W. Wheelwright. *Forecasting, Methods and Applications.* New York: John Wiley and Sons, 1978.
2. Montgomery, D.C. and L.A. Johnson. *Forecasting and Time Series Analysis.* New York: McGraw-Hill, 1979.
3. Thomopoulos, N.T. *Applied Forecasting Methods.* Englewood Cliffs, N.J.: Prentice-Hall, Inc., 1980.
4. Brown, R.G. *Statistical Forecasting for Inventory Control.* New York: McGraw-Hill, 1959.
5. Holt, C.C. "Forecasting Seasonal and Trends by Exponentially Weighted Moving Averages." Carnegie Institute of Technology: Pittsburg, Pa., 1957.
6. Winters, P.R. "Forecasting Sales by Exponentially Weighted Moving Averages." *Management Science.* April 1960, pp. 324-342.

Chapter 2

1. Hadley, G. and T.M. Whitin. *Analysis of Inventory Systems.* Englewood Cliffs, N.J.: Prentice-Hall, Inc., 1963.
2. Fetter, R.B. and W.C. Dalleck. *Decision Models for Inventory Management.* New York: John Wiley and Sons, 1959.

Chapter 3

1. Hadley, G. and T.M. Whitin. *Analysis of Inventory Systems.* Englewood Cliffs, N.J.: Prentice-Hall, Inc., 1963.

Chapter 4

1. Fetter, R.B. and W.C. Dalleck. *Decision Models for Inventory Management.* New York: John Wiley and Sons, 1959.
2. Hadley, G. and T.M. Whitin. *Analysis of Inventory Systems.* Englewood Cliffs, N.J.: Prentice-Hall, Inc., 1963.
3. Sasieni, M., A. Yaspan and L. Friedman. *Operations Research, Methods and Problems.* New York: John Wiley and Sons, 1959.

Chapter 5

1. Hadley, G. and T.M. Whitin. *Analysis of Inventory Systems.* Englewood Cliffs, N.J.: Prentice-Hall, Inc., 1963.

Chapter 6

1. Beyer, W.H. *Handbook of Tables for Probability and Statistics.* Cleveland: The Chemical Rubber Co., 1966.
2. Brown, R.G. *Forecasting and Prediction of Discrete Time Series.* Englewood Cliffs, N.J.: Prentice-Hall, Inc., 1962.
3. Thomopoulos, N.T. *Applied Forecasting Methods.* Englewood Cliffs, N.J.: Prentice-Hall, Inc., 1980.

Chapter 8

1. Beyer, W.H. *Handbook of Tables for Probability and Statistics.* Cleveland: The Chemical Rubber Co., 1966.

Chapter 9

1. Brown, R.G. *Forecasting and Prediction of Discrete Time Series.* Englewood Cliffs, N.J.: Prentice-Hall, Inc., 1962.
2. Brown, R.G. *Decision Rules for Inventory Management.* New York: Holt, Rinehart and Winston, Inc., 1967.
3. Thomopoulos, N.T. *Applied Forecasting Methods.* Englewood Cliffs, N.J.: Prentice-Hall, Inc., 1980.

Chapter 11

1. Hadley, G. and T.M. Whitin. *Analysis of Inventory Systems.* Englewood Cliffs, N.J.: Prentice-Hall, Inc., 1963.
2. Brown, R.G. *Forecasting and Prediction of Discrete Time Series.* Englewood Cliffs, N.J.: Prentice-Hall, Inc., 1962.
3. Thomopoulos, N.T. *Applied Forecasting Methods.* Englewood Cliffs, N.J.: Prentice-Hall, Inc., 1980.

Chapter 12

1. Brown, R.G. *Forecasting and Prediction of Discrete Time Series.* Englewood Cliffs, N.J.: Prentice-Hall, Inc., 1962.

Chapter 13

1. Brown, R.G. *Forecasting and Prediction of Discrete Time Series.* Englewood Cliffs, N.J.: Prentice-Hall, Inc., 1962.

Chapter 15

1. Saaty, T.L. *Elements of Queueing Theory with Applications.* New York: McGraw-Hill, 1961.

Chapter 16

1. Saaty, T.L. *Elements of Queueing Theory with Applications.* New York: McGraw-Hill, 1961.

Chapter 17

1. Saaty, T.L. *Elements of Queueing Theory with Applications.* New York: McGraw-Hill, 1961.

Chapter 18

1. Saaty, T.L. *Elements of Queueing Theory with Applications.* New York: McGraw-Hill, 1961.

Chapter 21

1. Prenting, T.O. and N.T. Thomopoulos. *Humanism and Technology in Assembly Line Systems.* Rochelle Park, N.J.: Hayden Book Co., 1974.
2. Stair, R.M. and B. Render. *Production and Operations Management.* Boston: Allyn and Bacon, 1980.
3. Wright, T.P. "Factors Affecting the Cost of Airplanes." *Journal of Aeronautical Sciences.* February, 1936.

Chapter 23

1. Arya, J.C. and R.W. Lardner. *Mathematical Analysis for Business, Economics, and the Life and Social Sciences, 3rd ed.,* Englewood Cliffs, N.J.: Prentice-Hall, Inc., 1989.

Chapter 24

1. *The World Book Dictionary.* Chicago: Doubleday and Company, 1981.

Glossary

Add-on cost — Any increase in the cost per unit (for an item) incurred due to stocking the unit. These costs include the direct and indirect expenses such as holding, ordering and shortages.

All-time requirement — A forecast of the demand for an item covering all future time periods. For service parts, this forecast may include only the future years covering the service obligation for the part, i.e., future years wherein the original equipment manufacturer is obligated to carry the part in stock.

Allocation — The assignment to stocking locations (in number of units) of a lot quantity for an item. Usually the lot is available for receipt from a source and the stocking locations share the quantity to be received.

Amortization — The liquidation of a debt by periodic payments (usually every month) to the creditor.

Annual cost — The cost incurred per year for stocking an item, including costs associated with holding, ordering and shortages.

Annual demand — The demand for an item over a one year duration.

Annual holding cost — The cost incurred per year attributed to holding (carrying) an item in stock. Costs associated with the bin space, warehouse overhead, theft, deterioration, obsolescence, insurance, taxes and potential revenue lost from other investment opportunities are those costs included.

Annual holding rate — The percent of the cost per unit that is attributed to holding a unit of the item in stock for one year. This is the ratio of (the annual holding cost) over (the cost per unit).

Assemble-to-order — The term used when a product is built by a manufacturer using first-level subassemblies and components to produce finished products that are configured to order (as in Just-in-Time), thus reducing the need for finished product inventory.

Attribute type data — In statistical process control, the two main methods of describing the quality of output from a process are by means of attribute type data and variable type data. Data of attribute type are encountered when the units of output are judged as either conforming or nonconforming (i.e., acceptable or nonacceptable with respect to the standards).

Availability — A measure of customer service that gives the portion (or percent) of occasions where the stock is sufficient to cover all demands that occur over the time span of an order cycle.

Available-to-promise — A byproduct of the master production schedule, available-to-promise establishes the future dates (with accompanying quantities) that newly received orders can be fulfilled, based on the current inventory and future schedules as well as the unfilled orders to date. This information is used by the sales staff to inform (new) customers on anticipated deliveries of their orders.

Average on-hand inventory — A measure of the expected on-hand inventory in the stocking facility over time. When stock is replenished, the on-hand inventory is at a high level; just prior to receiving a shipment of stock from the supplier, on-hand inventory is usually at a low level. For inventory planning purposes, the average on-hand inventory is used as a basis of measurement.

Backorder — A customer demand (or order) waiting to be filled as soon as possible because the stocking facility is out of stock for an item. The customer is willing to wait until the stocking facility receives a shipment to fulfill the demand.

Basic goods — Product that has been transformed from raw material into a state where it can be used in the manufacture of a higher level product such as a part, component or finished good. Examples are sheet metal, rubber compounds and lumber.

Capability — In statistical process control, a measure of the proportion of output that will be within the product specification limits (or tolerances).

Capacity — The highest sustainable output rate that can be achieved with the current product specifications, product mix, work force, plant and equipment.

Center line — In statistical process control, the average, i.e., the average of the measurement of the data used to describe the output from a process.

Coefficient of variation — A relative way to describe the variation associated with a variable. Often denoted as **cov** and computed as the ratio of (the standard deviation) over (the average) of the variable.

Components — Items that either have undergone some inhouse processing or have been received ready for use as discrete components. Components are lower level parts used in the makeup of a higher level product.

Conforming unit — In statistical process control, a process output unit that is deemed as acceptable for use (e.g., nondefective).

Consumer — A user of goods and services.

Control limits — In statistical process control, a process that produces an output of some kind is analyzed to determine the natural variation of the quality of the subgroups (samples) from the process. The average from all subgroups is called the center line, and the averages from the subgroups range between lower and upper limits computed to define the statistical variation of the output. These ranges are called control limits and become the lower control limit and the upper control limit of the process. If any future average from a subgroup of the process falls outside of these control limits, the process is then called out of control and is halted until the cause is found and remedied (see statistical control).

Cost function — Used in developing inventory models to determine the costs associated with ordering different sizes of stock. The costs are typically associated with the expenditures of holding, ordering and shortages incurred for the item.

Cost per backorder — The cost to the stocking facility that is incurred with each unit of demand in backorder.

Cost per order — The cost (for an item) to the stocking facility for each occasion when an order is placed with the supplier. The cost may include the expenses incurred with processing the order, plant setup, receiving the stock, binning the stock and transportation.

Cost per shortage — The cost (for an item) to the stocking facility for each unit of demand that is not filled because on-hand inventory is currently out of stock.

Cost per unit — The cost (for an item) to procure one unit of stock at the stocking facility. A unit purchased from a supplier is the procurement cost, and when received from the plant is the plant standard cost.

Customer — One who purchases goods or services from another, either for the purpose of resale to another customer or for use as a consumer.

Cycle stock — The portion of on-hand inventory that is sufficient to fill the forecast of demands for an item. This amount does not include the safety stock portion of the on-hand inventory. The cycle stock is at a high point just after a replenishment and at a low point just prior to a replenishment. The average of the cycle stock is generally used as a reference measure. The (average) cycle stock is computed as one-half of the order quantity.

Dated items — Items stocked in the inventory that are generally salable for fixed time periods only. Examples are many grocery items (such as milk and fruits) and holiday items (such as Christmas cards).

Demand — Represents the number of item units that are requested when an order is received at the stocking facility or when a customer wishes to purchase. For example, if a customer needs six spark plugs, the demand for the spark plug is six units.

Demand pattern — The shape of the demands per month as they vary over time. Generally three demand patterns occur, the horizontal (no trend or seasonal influence), the trend (no seasonal influence, but a gradual upward or gradual downward movement), and the trend-seasonal (with both trend and seasonal influence over the span of a year).

Desired service level — The service level that represents the goal from management in controlling the customer service for an item or a group of items. Service level is the ratio of (the demand filled immediately from the stock) over (the total demand).

Distributors — Facilities that serve as a link between manufacturers and retailers. They buy large quantities of stock from manufacturers and sell to retailers.

Economic order quantity — The order quantity (for an item) that has been computed from a mathematical relationship to yield the minimum stocking cost. The stocking cost includes those costs that pertain to the item and the stocking facility, such as holding, ordering and shortage costs. Not necessarily the same as order quantity.

Effective cost — In the calculation of an order quantity for an item, an add-on cost (called the stocking cost) is incurred due to stocking the item. The average stocking cost per unit is added to the cost per unit to yield the effective cost per unit for the item.

Effective service level — The service level that is expected to result for an item and which may be different from the desired service level for various reasons. One typical reason (for this difference) is that the actual lead time may differ from the planned procurement lead time.

Equilibrium state — In queueing theory, this point occurs when the average and spread of the number of units in a system are level, i.e., not increasing or decreasing over time.

Expected demand — A statistical term to indicate the average demand (for an item) that is anticipated to occur over a particular future time period, such as a month. Often the expected demand is the same as the forecast and is computed using a forecast model and the history of demands over past time periods.

Expected sales — A statistical term to indicate the average sales (for an item) anticipated to occur over a particular future time period. In a lost sales case, the expected sales may be less than the expected demand because the item may be out of stock when a demand occurs and the sale is thereby lost.

Finished goods — Products that are available for delivery; complete units and assemblies carried in stock and ready for sale to the customers, retailers and distributors or for transfer to other plants.

Firm schedule — Orders to be received from a source (or supplier) that have been committed for receipt to a stocking facility. The firm schedule consists of the dates and associated quantities that are committed and consists of all such orders up to the lead time period. The sum of all quantities from the firm schedule becomes the on-order inventory. (Compare to planning schedule.)

Horizontal demand pattern — In forecasting, when the average demand per month is the same for all of the months, the demand follows a horizontal pattern. There is no trend or seasonal influence on the average demand.

Initial quantity — An order of stock for a new item that has no previous history of demands on which to base a forecast. Typically, these orders are for service parts associated with either a new finished goods model or with an engineering change of a current model.

Just-in-Time — A philosophy of production based on the concept of adding value and eliminating waste. Value is added only by work performed on the product and waste is anything, other than a minimal amount of necessary resources like material, manpower and the capital equipment required for production, that does not add value to the product.

Kanban — The Japanese word for "card" or "ticket" and which gives the name to a system of material management and production control. The goal of this system is to have each operation produce only the necessary quantity of goods at the necessary time (as in Just-in-Time).

Lead time — The time interval that begins with the placement (with the supplier) of an order for new stock and ends when the stock is received and binned. Also referred as the procurement lead time.

Learning curve — A method to measure the amount of time to complete a task when tasks follow a successive repetition. The relationship that expresses how the task times vary by repetition follows a pattern called a learning curve.

Level — In forecasting, the expected demand for a particular time period (usually a month) is called the level of demand for that time period. In the horizontal demand pattern the level is the same for all time periods, in a trend demand pattern the level is constantly shifting upwards or shifting downwards, and in a trend-seasonal demand pattern the level is a cyclic shape over the time periods of a year.

Line balancing — The procedure of assigning work to assembly operators in such a manner as to apportion the assembly work among the operators as evenly as possible without violating any sequential or precedence restrictions in the assembly process.

Lost sale — When a customer seeks to purchase an item but does not do so because the stocking facility is out of stock. This situation is contrary to the event of a backorder where the customer is willing to wait until the demand can be filled when a new shipment of stock arrives.

Make-to-order — The term used when a product is built by a manufacturer to meet the specifications of the customer. Government products are often of this type. Make-to-order usually necessitates carrying or making inventory of subassemblies and components.

Make-to-stock — The term used when a product is built by the manufacturer as a finished good and stocked as an "off the shelf" item prior to receiving a customer order. Make-to-stock necessitates carrying and making finished goods inventory as well as (probably) subassemblies and components.

Manufacturing progress function — Same as a learning curve: the relation between the time required to complete a task and the cumulative repetitions of the task.

Measures — Units and standards for expressing the amount of some quantity such as the length, distance, area, volume, capacity and weight. The two major systems of measuring objects are the customary and the metric systems.

Nonconforming unit — In statistical process control, any process output unit that is not acceptable with respect to the specification standards is called a nonconforming unit. Those units that are acceptable are called conforming units.

Order cycle — The time span (for an item) that lies between two successive replenishments of stock.

Order level — One way to control the inventory status for an item is to monitor the on-hand plus on-order inventory (OH + OO) so that this quantity always falls within two limits, the order point and the order level. When the (OH + OO) reaches the order point or below, a replenishment of stock brings the (OH + OO) up to the order level. The order level for an item is simply computed by adding the order quantity to the order point.

Order point — In controlling the inventory status for an item, the on-hand plus on-order inventory (OH + OO) is monitored so that when the (OH + OO) falls to the order point or below, a replenishment order is sent to the supply source. The order point (often also called the reorder point) is computed as the sum of the lead time forecast plus the safety stock.

Order quantity — The amount of stock (for an item) that is ordered from the supplier, such as a new order or a replenishment order. Not necessarily the same as economic order quantity.

Packager — A contracted firm or an operation of a manufacturer that places the units produced from the manufacturer into containers suitable for sale, storage or delivery. The resulting packages identify the product within and are consistent with the manufacturer's specifications.

Planning schedule — The orders (by date and quantity) to a supplier or source that are beyond the lead time period and thereby not yet committed. These orders are used by the supplier to plan procurement of materials, labor and equipment for the future time periods. (Compare to firm schedule.)

Queueing theory — A discipline in mathematics that uses probability to study a waiting line system. The system consists of one or more service facilities and a queue. Units requesting use of the service facilities arrive to the system and are serviced when a service facility is unoccupied. The arrival times and service times are probabilistic. Units that seek service when all the service facilities are busy must wait in the queue until a service facility is available.

Reorder point — Same as the order point (see above).

Replenishment order — An order placed by a stocking facility to a supplier for the purpose of replenishing the supply of an item in stock.

Reuseable item — An item, used to service a demand, that can be reused when it has completed its service need. In queueing theory, the reuseable items are the service facilities and the demands for these items are the arrival of units into the system. Examples of reuseable items are any of the items in a rental agency, the bins, order pickers and lift trucks in a distribution center, the molds, tools and machines in a production facility and the sales clerks, gas pumps and grocery carts in a retail facility.

Safety stock — The amount of stock held for precautionary purposes (for an item) to fill customer demands for those possible occasions when demands may rise above the forecast quantity. Safety stock is needed in retail stores and distributions centers because demands for the items are not precisely known in advance and forecasts of the demands are used as a basis in inventory planning. This situation also holds for certain items in manufacturing facilities, where safety stock is needed to yield the desired service level requested by the management. In most manufacturing operations there is no need for safety stock, as orders for the products are known in advance and the production schedules are generated from these orders.

Service facilities — In queueing theory, the location or device where the customers receive service to fulfill their needs. In reusable inventory systems, the reusable item is the same as the service facility.

Service level — A measure of customer service. For an item, service level is the ratio of (the number of units of demand that are filled from the stock available) over (the total demand). The notation for the service level is SL where, in the backorder case, SL = demand filled/total demand, and in the lost sales case, SL = sales/total demand. For reuseable inventory items where queueing theory is used, SL = service facility available for use upon arrival of a new demand/total demand.

Service obligation — Often associated with service parts to designate the latest future time period (usually a future year) where the original equipment manufacturer is obliged to carry a part in stock.

Service part — A part or component used in the repair or maintenance of a finished good.

Source — The location (usually a work center in the firm or an outside supplier) where the supply of stock for an item is obtained upon placing an order.

Specification limits — In statistical process control, lower and upper limits of a measure from the output of a product are often set to designate when the product is acceptable for use. These limits are usually specified by engineering and are sometimes called the specification tolerances.

Standard cost — In a distribution stocking facility, the cost to procure one unit of the item from the supplier.

Statistical control — In statistical process control, the state when a process produces output units that are homogeneous in quality. The measurements from the output have an average called the center line, and the variations of output are randomly scattered above and below this average. Statistical control implies that no trends or cyclical patterns or occasional extreme variations of the output are present (see control limits).

Statistical process control — Statistical process control (often denoted as SPC) uses statistical techniques such as control charts to analyze, monitor and control the quality of output from a process. When the output is found out of control or nonacceptable, action is taken to bring the process into statistical control and to improve the process capability. A process is a combination of people, equipment, materials, methods and environment that produces output of a given product or service.

Stocking cost — The cost associated with storing an item in the stocking facility. The costs include expenditures other than the procurement costs, such as those attributed to holding, ordering and shortages.

Stocking rate — The ratio of (the stocking cost per unit) over (the cost per unit). The cost per unit is the procurement cost or the standard cost, whichever pertains.

Stockkeeping unit — Represents a particular item that is stocked separately in a facility and where the stock status and requirements are monitored. A stockkeeping unit (SKU) could be an individual item itself if the item is stocked in only one location and if it has no variations. An item stocked in N locations then becomes N SKU's and an item with K variations (such as in size or color) then becomes K SKU's. Each variation of the product is itself an **SKU**.

Supplier — Usually a vendor or plant that provides the supply of stock for an item upon placement of an order.

Total stock — The average on-hand inventory held in stock over time. The total stock consists of the average cycle stock plus the safety stock.

Trend demand pattern — In forecasting, when the average demand per month is steadily changing over the time horizon (either continually moving upwards or continually moving downwards).

Trend seasonal demand pattern — In forecasting, when the average demand per month is changing over the time horizon with two influences, trend and seasonal. The trend influence causes a continual upward movement or a continual downward movement, and the seasonal influence causes a cyclic movement over certain months of a year.

Turnover — Often referred to as the turnover ratio. A measure of the frequency in a year that the inventory is replaced because of the sale of the units. The turnover ratio is usually measured as the ratio of (the annual sales) over (the average on-hand inventory).

Utilization factor — A queueing theory term to represent the rate at which the demands occur for the service facilities. The utilization factor is the ratio of (the average service time to complete serving a unit of demand) over (the average time between which units of demand arrive for service). The utilization factor can also be expressed as the ratio of (the average rate in which units arrive for service) over (the average rate in which units can be serviced by a service facility), where both of the rates are set with equal units of time, such as a minute, hour or day.

Variable type data — Used in statistical process control in describing the type of information attained in measuring the output from a process. The measure is from some characteristic of a unit of output, such as the strength, length or weight. Examples are the elasticity of a rubber compound, the ounces in a can of soup and the hardness of a steel rod.

Work-in-process — Consists of material that is either undergoing processing or is temporarily being held between operations.

Index